Elementary
Linear Algebra
Second Edition

W. Keith Nicholson
University of Calgary

**McGraw-Hill
Ryerson**

Toronto   Montréal   New York   Burr Ridge   Bangkok   Beijing   Bogotá   Caracas   Dubuque
Kuala Lumpur   Lisbon   London   Madison   Madrid   Mexico City   Milan   New Delhi
San Francisco   Santiago   St. Louis   Seoul   Singapore   Sydney   Taipei

McGraw-Hill Ryerson

Elementary Linear Algebra,
Second Edition

ISBN: 0-07-071980-2

1 2 3 4 5 6 7 8 9 10 TCP 0 9 8 7 6 5 4

Printed and bound in Canada

Care has been taken to trace ownership of copyright material contained in this text; however, the publisher will welcome any information that enables them to rectify any reference or credit for subsequent editions.

Vice President, Editorial and Media Technology: Patrick Ferrier
Senior Sponsoring Editor: Catherine Koop
Developmental Editors: Su Mei Ku and Darren Hick
Marketing Manager: David Groth
Supervising Editor: Anne Macdonald
Copy Editor: Edie Franks
Production Coordinator: Jennifer Wilkie
Cover Design: Dianna Little
Cover Image Credit: © Hideki Kuwajima/Photonica
Composition: Pronk&Associates
Printer: Transcontinental Printing Group

National Library of Canada Cataloguing in Publication

Nicholson, W. Keith
    Elementary linear algebra / W. Keith Nicholson. -- 2nd ed.

Includes index.
ISBN 0-07-091142-8

    1. Algebras, Linear. I. Title.

QA184.N52 2003   512'.5   C2002-904210-0

"Nicholson writes in a very clear and understandable way that enables readers to understand the material easily. It is possible to enter the text at a random point and still understand what he is writing."
- *P.W. Aitchison, University of Manitoba*

"One of the best features of the book is the early introduction of the concept of diagonalization of matrices. This is an important topic, and motivates the discussion of eigenvectors and eigenvalues. It is one of the topics that brings everything together for the students."
- *Murray Bremner, University of Saskatchewan*

"I think the text is well written, and I am very much impressed with the layout of material [...] The organization of this text should make it easy to cover some topics in different orders."
- *James Lewis, University of Alberta*

"Nicholson covers what is *supposed* to be covered in an elementary linear algebra text."
- *David Kaminski; University of Lethbridge*

"I think this [the early introduction of eigenvalues and diagonalization, using only determinants and matrix inverses and not requiring notions like dimension and independence] is excellent; one of the really great features of the text. In particular, most of the interesting applications of linear algebra use eigenvalues, and this allows one to start doing these applications in tandem with the more theoretical aspects."
- *Deirdre Haskell, McMaster University*

"The exposition [in Nicholson's text] is presented with clarity and rigor. There are good mathematical applications to suit all tastes."
- *Stanley Kochman, York University*

To Kathleen, Jason, and Mark

Contents

Chapter Dependencies

This diagram suggests how the material in each chapter depends on earlier chapters. The dependence of Chapter 4 on Chapter 3 is primarily for motivation and examples. A dotted line in the diagram indicates a minor dependency.

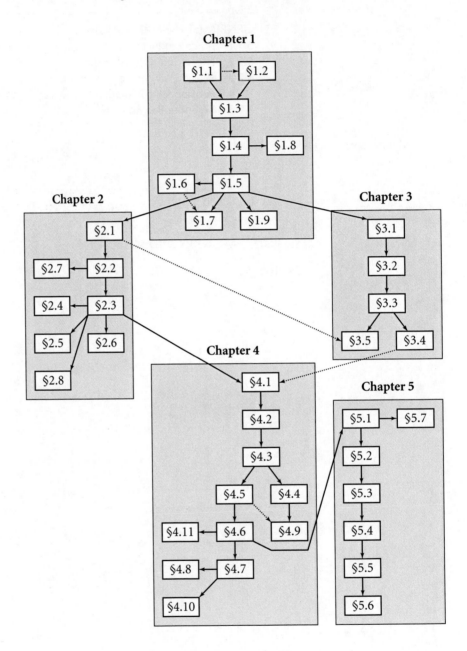

Visit the text website at www.mcgrawhill.ca/college/nicholson.

Preface

This book springs from three sources: The needs of the users of linear algebra as a service course, the trend away from the abstract view of the subject toward a more matrix approach, and the desire to incorporate the optional use of technology to help with instruction and computation. Let me explain.

In the late 1990s discussions with Engineering and Science faculty members revealed a desire for early introduction of diagonalization and for more emphasis on linear transformations. Consequently, eigenvalues and diagonalization are introduced in Chapter 2 (using only determinants and matrix algebra), motivated by examples of dynamical systems that the students can relate to. Linear transformations of the plane are discussed in Chapter 3, providing a solid introduction to the treatment in Chapter 4 of $\mathbb{R}^n$ and giving geometrical interpretations of multiplication, determinants, and inverses of 2×2 matrices.

The desire for a more matrix-oriented linear algebra course expressed by the engineers and scientists echos a more general trend in the subject away from the abstract approach. The second half of the book (Chapters 4 and 5) continues this evolution. Every teacher of linear algebra knows that the students "hit the wall" when the notion of an abstract vector space is introduced. One reason for this is that they are coping simultaneously with *two* new ideas: the concept of an abstract structure, and mastering difficult notions like spanning, independence, and linear transformations. This double jeopardy is difficult to deal with for students, even the most talented ones. Consequently, in Chapter 4 topics like independence are discussed first in the context of $\mathbb{R}^n$, so the students can deal with them without having to cope with the abstract baggage of an n-dimensional space. Then the general setup is introduced in Chapter 5, with $\mathbb{R}^n$ as the principal motivating example. This has been tested in the classroom, and it works very well pedagogically.

The third theme is to involve technology in a way that is more than merely a "book-in-the-computer," and is more accessible than a computational package. This has been achieved in the creation of LILA (Lyryx—Interactive Linear Algebra). This is an (optional) Internet-based computer tutorial that provides audio-enhanced lessons covering the entire text, interactive explorations allowing the student to "play" with the central concepts or perform the more difficult computations, and self-assessment in the form of labs with feedback to help the student discover where and why an error was made. The system has been class tested, and is available (at a nominal price) to users of this book.[1]

On the other hand, this book serves as a stand-alone text for the traditional linear algebra syllabus (see the Table of Contents). It can be used for a two-semester course for beginners with a working knowledge of high school algebra, or for a single-semester course for more advanced students. For students in many application areas, Chapters 1 through 4 may be all the linear algebra they need. While the text is designed with Science and

---

[1] More information about LILA can be found on pages xiv–xv.

Engineering students in mind, it will also serve the needs of students in Management and the Social Sciences. Calculus is not a prerequisite; the few places where it is needed are clearly marked and can be omitted with no loss of continuity.

Wherever possible, concepts are introduced with real-world examples that are meaningful to the students, and theorems are stated simply with short proofs often preceded by an example. (Longer or more difficult proofs are deferred to the end of the section and can be omitted.) Nearly 350 solved examples are included to aid understanding, introduce techniques, illustrate algorithms, and motivate theorems. These examples are reinforced by the exercises (about 800 in all) at the end of each section, many with answers or solutions at the end of the book.

Features

- **Early eigenvalues**. Eigenvalues and diagonalization are introduced in Chapter 2 using only determinants and matrix inverses, and not requiring notions like dimension and independence. This allows a number of applications (for example, dynamical systems) that are seen as relevant by the students.

- **Early introduction of linear transformations**. In response to a request from scientists and engineers, rotations, reflections, shears, etc. in $\mathbb{R}^2$ are described using matrix multiplication in Section 3.4. The idea of a linear transformation is introduced in this context, and its relation to matrix multiplication is made explicit. This leads to geometrical interpretations of matrix multiplication, inverses, and determinants, and it provides a basis for the study of linear transformations in $\mathbb{R}^n$ in Chapter 4.

- **Matrix approach**. In keeping with a trend over the past few years, more emphasis is placed on matrix computations. For example, the following topics are discussed: Positive definite matrices, LU-factorization, QR-factorization, Triangular form, Complex matrices, and Singular value decomposition. This has the effect of reducing the overall level of abstraction in the book.

- **Vector space concepts introduced first in $\mathbb{R}^n$**. Independence, spanning, subspaces, and dimension are introduced first in $\mathbb{R}^n$ (in Chapter 4) before the student has to cope with abstract vector spaces. The general notions then come easily in the abstract context (Chapter 5), thus allowing the student to focus on the new conceptual framework.

- **Applications**. These occur both as separate subsections or as examples in the text. Examples: Markov chains, systems of differential equations, directed graphs, linear dynamical systems, computer graphics, statistical principal component analysis, and constrained optimization.

- **Motivating examples**. Wherever possible, concepts are introduced with examples that are not only understandable to the students but are seen as relevant to the real world. A good illustration is the motivation (in Section 2.3) of diagonalization by looking at the possible extinction of a species of birds.

- **Solved examples**. Nearly 350 solved examples are given to help the student to understand the techniques of the subject and to motivate theorems and proofs.

- **Exercises**. Almost 800 exercises are included, which are keyed to the examples. They start with routine, computational problems and progress to more theoretical exercises. Answers or solutions are provided at the end of the book to all even-numbered

The elementary properties of symmetric matrices come from Theorem 4. Here is an example of how they are used.

Example 17 If A and B are symmetric, show that $A + B$ is also symmetric.

SOLUTION We are given that $A^T = A$ and $B^T = B$. Hence Theorem 4 gives
$$(A + B)^T = A^T + B^T = A + B.$$
This shows that $A + B$ is symmetric.

■ Exercises 1.1

1. A store sells road bikes and mountain bikes. The manager has the following two data tables available, the first giving sales volumes of each kind for each quarter of 1998, and the second for each quarter of 1999:

1998	Road Bikes	Mountain Bikes
1st Quarter	32	27
2nd Quarter	65	78
3rd Quarter	53	74
4th Quarter	35	46

1999	Road Bikes	Mountain Bikes
1st Quarter	38	43
2nd Quarter	72	97
3rd Quarter	76	102
4th Quarter	43	65

a) Express each of the tables as a matrix.

b) Find a matrix operation that will produce the total sales volumes for these two years combined, and perform the calculations.

c) The data for 1997 was given in a slightly different format as follows:

1997	1st Quarter	2nd Quarter	3rd Quarter	4th Quarter
Road Bikes	24	29	32	21
Mountain Bikes	23	31	37	29

Express this data also as a matrix, find a matrix operation that will produce the total sales volumes for these three years combined, and perform the calculations.

d) A second store sold exactly three times as many of each kind of bike as the first store for each quarter in 1997, exactly twice as many for 1998, and exactly four times as many for 1999. Find a matrix operation that will produce the total sales volumes for this second store for these three years combined, and perform the calculations.

2. a) If A is an $m \times n$ matrix, what do the m and n represent?
   b) What are the requirements needed to add two matrices A and B?

3. How could matrix addition, scalar multiplication, and transposition be helpful in practice?

4. Compute the following:

a) $3\left(\begin{bmatrix} 1 & -3 & 2 \\ 0 & 4 & -9 \\ 2 & -3 & 1 \end{bmatrix} - 21 \begin{bmatrix} 2 & 0 & 12 \\ -15 & -3 & 2 \\ 12 & -8 & -32 \end{bmatrix} \right) + 5 \begin{bmatrix} 1 & -5 & -43 \\ 0 & 7 & 0 \\ 21 & 45 & -34 \end{bmatrix}^T$

b) $\begin{bmatrix} 21 & 20 & -21 \\ 56 & 11 & 34 \\ 45 & 83 & -34 \end{bmatrix} - 9 \left(2 \begin{bmatrix} 90 & -45 & 20 \\ -23 & 32 & 72 \\ 65 & 23 & 89 \end{bmatrix} - 13 \begin{bmatrix} 19 & -25 & 87 \\ 47 & 40 & 81 \\ 85 & 35 & 24 \end{bmatrix}^T \right)$

5. a) Describe when a matrix is the same as its transpose. Such matrices are called *symmetric* matrices.
   b) Describe when a matrix is equal to the negative of its transpose. Such matrices are called *skew-symmetric* matrices.

6. In each case show either that the statement is true or that it is false by giving an example. Assume throughout that A, B, and C denote matrices.
   a) If $A + B = A + C$, then B and C have the same size.
   b) If $A + B = 0$, then $B = 0$.
   c) If the $(2, 3)$-entry of A is 7, then the $(3, 2)$-entry of A^T is -7.
   d) If $A = -A$, then $A = 0$.
   e) A and A^T have the same main diagonal for every matrix A.

7. Find a, b, c, and d if:
   a) $\begin{bmatrix} a & b \\ c & d \end{bmatrix} = \begin{bmatrix} b-c & c \\ d & 1 \end{bmatrix}$.
   b) $3 \begin{bmatrix} a \\ b \end{bmatrix} - 2 \begin{bmatrix} b \\ 0 \end{bmatrix} = \begin{bmatrix} 1 \\ 4 \end{bmatrix}$.

8. In each case find the matrix A:
   a) $2A - \begin{bmatrix} 1 & 0 & -2 \\ 4 & 7 & 3 \end{bmatrix}^T = \begin{bmatrix} 2 & 0 \\ -3 & 4 \\ 0 & 8 \end{bmatrix}$.
   b) $\left(3A^T - 2 \begin{bmatrix} 0 & 2 \\ -5 & 2 \\ 1 & 3 \end{bmatrix} \right)^T = \begin{bmatrix} 7 & 0 & -1 \\ 2 & 1 & 5 \end{bmatrix}$.

9. **a)** Simplify $3(5A - 3B) + 6(B - 4A) + 3(2A + B)$.

   b) Simplify $2(3A - 5B) + 4(B - 2A) + 2(3B - A)$.

10. A matrix A is called *diagonal* if it is square and every entry off the main diagonal is zero. If A and B are both diagonal, show that each of the following matrices is diagonal:

   a) $A + B$.   **b)** cA for any scalar c.   **c)** A^T.

11. **a)** If A is any matrix, show that $(c + d)A = cA + dA$ for all scalars c and d. [Part (2) of Theorem 2]

   b) If A is any matrix, show that $(cd)A = c(dA)$ for all scalars c and d. [Part (3) of Theorem 2]

1.2   LINEAR EQUATIONS

One of the historical motivations for the development of mathematics has been to find a way to analyze and solve practical problems. Apart from calculus, the most common method has been to reduce a problem to the solution of a set of linear equations. This has proved to be effective in science, engineering, and social science. Here is a simple example.

1.2.1   Linear Equations

Example 1   A charity wishes to endow a fund that will provide $50 000 per year for cancer research. The charity has $480 000 and, to reduce risk, wants to invest in two banks paying 10% and 11% respectively. How much should be invested in each bank?

SOLUTION   If x dollars are invested at 10% and y dollars are invested at 11%, then $x + y = 480\,000$ and the yearly interest is $\frac{10}{100}x + \frac{11}{100}y$. Hence x and y must satisfy the equations

$$x + \quad y = 480\,000$$
$$\tfrac{10}{100}x + \tfrac{11}{100}y = 50\,000$$

If the first equation is multiplied by 10, and the second by 100, the resulting equations are

$$10x + 10y = 4\,800\,000$$
$$10x + 11y = 5\,000\,000$$

Subtracting the first equation from the second gives $y = 200\,000$, whence $x = 280\,000$. In other words, the charity should invest $280 000 at 10% and $200 000 at 11%.

An equation of the form $ax + by = c$ is called a linear equation[5] in the variables x and y. If more than two variables are present, they will usually be denoted by $x_1, x_2, \cdots, x_n$. Then an equation of the form

$$a_1x_1 + a_2x_2 + \cdots + a_nx_n = b \qquad (*)$$

is called a **linear equation** in the **variables** $x_1, x_2, \cdots, x_n$. Here $a_1, a_2, \cdots, a_n$ denote real numbers, called the **coefficients** of the variables $x_1, x_2, \cdots, x_n$, and the number b is called the **constant term** of the equation. The column matrix

$$X = \begin{bmatrix} x_1 \\ x_2 \\ \vdots \\ x_n \end{bmatrix} = \begin{bmatrix} x_1 & x_2 & \cdots & x_n \end{bmatrix}^T$$

---

[5] The graph of the equation $ax + by = c$ is a straight line if a and b are not both zero; hence the name.

is called the **matrix of variables**. A set of numbers $s_1, s_2, \cdots, s_n$ is called a **solution** to the linear equation (∗) if

$$a_1 s_1 + a_2 s_2 + \cdots + a_n s_n = b,$$

that is, if the equation is satisfied when the substitutions $x_1 = s_1, x_2 = s_2, \cdots, x_n = s_n$ are made. We express this by saying that $X = [s_1 \ \ s_2 \ \ \cdots \ \ s_n]^T$ is a solution[6] to equation (∗).

Example 2   Show that $X = [1 \ \ -2]^T$ is a solution to the equation $2x_1 - 3x_2 = 8$, but that $Y = [1 \ \ 1]^T$ is not a solution.

SOLUTION $[1 \ \ -2]^T$ is a solution because $x_1 = 1$ and $x_2 = -2$ satisfy the equation: $2(1) - 3(-2) = 8$. But $x_1 = 1$ and $x_2 = 1$ do not satisfy the equation since $2(1) - 3(1) \neq 8$, so $[1 \ \ 1]^T$ is not a solution.

1.2.2   Systems of Linear Equations

A finite collection of linear equations is called a **system of linear equations**, or simply a **system**. A solution to *every* equation in the system is called a **solution to the system**. The heart of linear algebra is a routine procedure for finding all solutions to any system of linear equations. But first some examples.

Example 3   In Example 1, the system of two linear equations

$$
\begin{aligned}
x + y &= 480\ 000 \\
\tfrac{10}{100}x + \tfrac{11}{100}y &= 50\ 000
\end{aligned}
\quad \text{has solution } X = \begin{bmatrix} x \\ y \end{bmatrix} = \begin{bmatrix} 280\ 000 \\ 200\ 000 \end{bmatrix}.
$$

Note that this system has a *unique* solution.

Example 4   A system of equations need not have a solution. For example, the system

$$
\begin{aligned}
x + y \phantom{{}-z} &= 1 \\
x \phantom{{}+y} - z &= 2 \\
y + z &= 1
\end{aligned}
$$

has *no* solution. Indeed adding the last two equations gives $x + y = 3$, contrary to the first equation.

A system of linear equations is called **inconsistent** if it has no solutions, and the system is called **consistent** if it has one or more solutions.

Example 5   Verify that $X = [1 + t - s \ \ \ 2 + t + s \ \ \ s \ \ \ t]^T$ is a solution to the system

$$
\begin{aligned}
x_1 - 2x_2 + 3x_3 + x_4 &= -3 \\
2x_1 - x_2 + 3x_3 - x_4 &= 0
\end{aligned}
$$

for all values of the numbers s and t, called **parameters** in this context.

SOLUTION   Simply substitute $x_1 = 1 + t - s$, $x_2 = 2 + t + s$, $x_3 = s$ and $x_4 = t$ into each equation:

$$
\begin{aligned}
x_1 - 2x_2 + 3x_3 + x_4 &= (1 + t - s) - 2(2 + t + s) + 3s + t = -3 \\
2x_1 - x_2 + 3x_3 - x_4 &= 2(1 + t - s) - (2 + t + s) + 3s - t = 0
\end{aligned}
$$

---

[6] The reason for writing solutions (or variables) as *columns* will be clear later. We will frequently use the transpose notation $[s_1 \ \ s_2 \ \ \cdots \ \ s_n]^T$ to simplify printing.

Because both equations are satisfied, X is a solution for all s and t. Note that this system has *infinitely many* solutions since there are infinitely many choices for the parameters s and t.

In fact, *every* solution of the system in Example 5 arises as shown for some parameters s and t. To see why this is so, and to see how one arrives at sets of solutions like those in Example 5, we develop a general procedure for finding solutions in this form. To simplify the computations we introduce a matrix notation for describing systems of linear equations. Given the system

$$x_1 - 2x_2 + 3x_3 + x_4 = -3$$
$$2x_1 - x_2 + 3x_3 - x_4 = 0$$

of 2 equations in 4 variables, the coefficients of the variables form a 2×4 matrix

$$\begin{bmatrix} 1 & -2 & 3 & 1 \\ 2 & -1 & 3 & -1 \end{bmatrix}$$

called the **coefficient matrix** for the system. The 2×5 matrix

$$\begin{bmatrix} 1 & -2 & 3 & 1 & -3 \\ 2 & -1 & 3 & -1 & 0 \end{bmatrix}$$

is called the **augmented matrix** for the system (it is just the coefficient matrix *augmented* by the column of constants). It is evident that the system is completely described by the augmented matrix,[7] so it is not surprising that by manipulating this matrix we can find all solutions to the system.

To see how this is done, it is convenient to call two systems of linear equations **equivalent** if they have the same set of solutions. Starting with a given system of linear equations, we solve it by writing a series of systems, one after the other, each of which is equivalent to the previous one. Since all these systems have the same solutions, the aim is to find one that is easy to solve. Surprisingly enough, there is a simple, routine method for doing this. The following example provides an illustration.

Example 6   Find all solutions to the system in Example 5:

$$\begin{cases} x_1 - 2x_2 + 3x_3 + x_4 = -3 \\ 2x_1 - x_2 + 3x_3 - x_4 = 0 \end{cases}$$

SOLUTION   The system is written below together with its augmented matrix:

$$\begin{array}{ll} x_1 - 2x_2 + 3x_3 + x_4 = -3 & \begin{bmatrix} 1 & -2 & 3 & 1 & -3 \\ 2 & -1 & 3 & -1 & 0 \end{bmatrix} \\ 2x_1 - x_2 + 3x_3 - x_4 = 0 & \end{array}$$

We first eliminate x_1 from equation 2 by subtracting twice the first equation from the second. The result is the following system (with its augmented matrix).

$$\begin{array}{ll} x_1 - 2x_2 + 3x_3 + x_4 = -3 & \begin{bmatrix} 1 & -2 & 3 & 1 & -3 \\ 0 & 3 & -3 & -3 & 6 \end{bmatrix} \\ 3x_2 - 3x_3 - 3x_4 = 6 & \end{array}$$

This new system is equivalent to the original system (see Theorem 1 below). Note that the new augmented matrix can be obtained directly from the original one by subtracting twice the first row from the second row.

We now multiply the second equation by $\frac{1}{3}$ to obtain another equivalent system

$$\begin{array}{ll} x_1 - 2x_2 + 3x_3 + x_4 = -3 & \begin{bmatrix} 1 & -2 & 3 & 1 & -3 \\ 0 & 1 & -1 & -1 & 2 \end{bmatrix} \\ x_2 - x_3 - x_4 = 2 & \end{array}$$

---

[7] When the system is solved in a computer, it is the augmented matrix that is used.

Again the new augmented matrix comes from the preceding one by multiplying the second row by $\frac{1}{3}$.

Finally, we eliminate x_2 from equation 1 by adding twice the second equation to the first. The result is the (equivalent) system

$$\begin{array}{ll} x_1 \quad\;\; + x_3 - x_4 = 1 \\ \quad\;\; x_2 - x_3 - x_4 = 2 \end{array} \qquad \begin{bmatrix} 1 & 0 & 1 & -1 & 1 \\ 0 & 1 & -1 & -1 & 2 \end{bmatrix}$$

This system is *easy* to solve. Indeed, if the numbers x_3 and x_4 are chosen arbitrarily, then x_1 and x_2 can be found so that the equations are satisfied. More precisely, if we set $x_3 = s$ and $x_4 = t$ where s and t are arbitrary parameters, the equations become $x_1 + s - t = 1$ and $x_2 - s - t = 2$, whence

$$x_1 = 1 + t - s \quad \text{and} \quad x_2 = 2 + t + s$$

This gives the solutions exhibited in Example 5 and, because all the systems in the series are equivalent (as will be proved in Theorem 1), we have obtained *all* the solutions to the original system.

Observe that at each stage in the above procedure a certain operation is performed on the system (and thus on the augmented matrix) to produce an equivalent system. The following operations, called **elementary operations**, can routinely be performed on systems to produce equivalent systems:

I   *Interchange two equations.*
II   *Multiply an equation by a nonzero number.*
III *Add a multiple of one equation to a different equation.*

We only needed operations of type II and III in the computation in Example 6, but type I operations are sometimes useful as well. The next theorem is crucial for the method we are developing.

THEOREM ①   If an elementary operation is performed on a system of linear equations, the resulting system is equivalent to the original system.

PROOF   We prove it for type III operations; similar arguments work for operations of type I or II.

Suppose we modify the original system by replacing equation p by a new equation, formed by adding a multiple of a different equation q to equation p. Then any solution to the original system will satisfy this new equation (it satisfies both equations p and q), and so will be a solution to the new system. On the other hand, the new system contains equation q (because p and q are *different* equations). This means that the new system can be transformed *back* to the original system by *subtracting* the same multiple of equation q from the new equation. Hence the same argument shows that every solution to the new system is a solution to the original system. Thus the two systems have the same set of solutions, so operations of type III produce equivalent systems.

Theorem 1 has profound consequences for linear algebra. In particular it allows us to use the procedure in Example 6 on *any* system of linear equations. The idea is to apply a series of elementary operations to the system with the goal of finding a system that is easy to solve. Since all the systems created in this way are equivalent (by Theorem 1), the solutions to the easy system are the solutions to the original system.

As in Example 6, elementary operations performed on a system of equations produce corresponding manipulations of the *rows* of the augmented matrix (regarded as row matrices). In hand calculations (and in computer programs) it is easier to manipulate rows than equations. For this reason we restate these elementary operations for rows:

I   *Interchange two rows.*
II   *Multiply a row by a nonzero number.*
III   *Add a multiple of one row to a different row.*

These are called **elementary row operations.** Here is another example of our method where the entire calculation is carried out by manipulating the augmented matrix.

Example 7   Find all solutions to the following system of linear equations:

$$\begin{aligned} x_1 + x_2 - 3x_3 &= 3 \\ -2x_1 - x_2 &= -4 \\ 4x_1 + 2x_2 + 3x_3 &= 7 \end{aligned}$$

PROOF   The augmented matrix of the original system is

$$\begin{bmatrix} 1 & 1 & -3 & 3 \\ -2 & -1 & 0 & -4 \\ 4 & 2 & 3 & 7 \end{bmatrix}.$$

We begin by using the 1 in the upper left corner to "clean up" column 1; that is, to obtain zeros in the other locations (this corresponds to eliminating x_1 from equations 2 and 3). More precisely, we add twice row 1 to row 2, and we subtract 4 times row 1 from row 3. The result is

$$\begin{bmatrix} 1 & 1 & -3 & 3 \\ 0 & 1 & -6 & 2 \\ 0 & -2 & 15 & -5 \end{bmatrix}.$$

This completes the work on column 1.

We now use the 1 in the second position of row 2 to clean up column 2; that is, to obtain zeros in the top and bottom positions (this corresponds to eliminating x_2 from equations 1 and 3). We do this by subtracting row 2 from row 1 and adding twice row 2 to row 3. This gives

$$\begin{bmatrix} 1 & 0 & 3 & 1 \\ 0 & 1 & -6 & 2 \\ 0 & 0 & 3 & -1 \end{bmatrix}.$$

Note that these row operations have not disturbed column 1 because the first entry of row 2 is a *zero.*

We next divide row 3 by 3 to obtain a 1 in the third position:

$$\begin{bmatrix} 1 & 0 & 3 & 1 \\ 0 & 1 & -6 & 2 \\ 0 & 0 & 1 & -\frac{1}{3} \end{bmatrix}.$$

Finally, we clean up column 3 by subtracting 3 times row 3 from row 1, and adding 6 times row 3 to row 2:

$$\begin{bmatrix} 1 & 0 & 0 & 2 \\ 0 & 1 & 0 & 0 \\ 0 & 0 & 1 & -\frac{1}{3} \end{bmatrix}.$$

The corresponding system of equations is

$$
\begin{aligned}
x_1 &&&= 2 \\
&& x_2 && = 0 \\
&&&& x_3 = -\tfrac{1}{3}
\end{aligned}
$$

and the (unique) solution $X = \begin{bmatrix} 2 & 0 & -\tfrac{1}{3} \end{bmatrix}^T$ is apparent. Since this system of equations is equivalent to the original system, this is the solution to the original system.

1.2.3 Gaussian[8] Elimination

In the computations in Examples 6 and 7, elementary row operations (on the augmented matrix) led to matrices of the form

$$
\begin{bmatrix} 1 & 0 & * & * & * \\ 0 & 1 & * & * & * \end{bmatrix} \quad \text{and} \quad \begin{bmatrix} 1 & 0 & 0 & * \\ 0 & 1 & 0 & * \\ 0 & 0 & 1 & * \end{bmatrix}
$$

respectively, where each $*$ indicates a number. In both cases the solution was easily obtained from the corresponding system of equations. The matrices that arise in general are described as follows.

A matrix is said to be in **row-echelon form** (and will be called a **row-echelon matrix**) if the following conditions are satisfied:

1. All zero rows are at the bottom.
2. The first nonzero entry from the left in each nonzero row is a 1, called the **leading 1** for that row.
3. Each leading 1 is to the right of all leading 1's in the rows above it.

A row-echelon matrix is said to be in **reduced row-echelon form** if, in addition, it satisfies

4. Each leading 1 is the only nonzero entry in its column.

Thus the row-echelon matrices have a "staircase" form as indicated below (as before, the asterisks indicate arbitrary numbers):

$$
\begin{bmatrix} 0 & 1 & * & * & * & * & * \\ 0 & 0 & 0 & 1 & * & * & * \\ 0 & 0 & 0 & 0 & 1 & * & * \\ 0 & 0 & 0 & 0 & 0 & 0 & 1 \\ 0 & 0 & 0 & 0 & 0 & 0 & 0 \end{bmatrix}.
$$

The leading 1's proceed down and to the right through the matrix, and every entry below and to the left of a leading 1 is a zero. In a *reduced* row-echelon matrix the additional requirement is that all entries *above* each leading 1 must also be zero. Any row-echelon matrix can be carried to reduced form using a few more row operations (clean up above the leading 1's one after the other).

Example 8   The first matrix below is in row-echelon form, and the second matrix is the reduced row-echelon matrix to which it can be carried by row operations:

---

[8] Carl Friedrich Gauss (1777–1855) was one of the greatest mathematicians of all time. He made ground-breaking discoveries in every part of mathematics, and made important contributions to astronomy and physics.

$$\begin{bmatrix} 1 & * & * & * & * \\ 0 & 0 & 1 & * & * \\ 0 & 0 & 0 & 0 & 1 \end{bmatrix} \rightarrow \begin{bmatrix} 1 & * & 0 & * & 0 \\ 0 & 0 & 1 & * & 0 \\ 0 & 0 & 0 & 0 & 1 \end{bmatrix}$$

In general we use an arrow $\rightarrow$ to indicate that row operations have been performed.

Here is a procedure by which any matrix can be carried to row-echelon form (and hence to reduced form if desired) using nothing but elementary row operations.

GAUSSIAN ALGORITHM[9]   Every matrix can be carried to row-echelon form as follows:

Step 1.   If the matrix consists entirely of zeros, stop: it is already in row-echelon form.

Step 2.   Otherwise, find the first column from the left containing a nonzero entry k, and move the row containing that entry to the top of the matrix.

Step 3.   Multiply the top row by $\frac{1}{k}$ to create the first leading 1.

Step 4.   Make each entry below the leading 1 zero by subtracting multiples of its row from lower rows.

This completes the first row; all further row operations are carried out on the remaining rows.

Step 5.   Repeat steps 1–4 on the matrix consisting of the remaining rows.

Note that the Gaussian algorithm is recursive in the sense that, after the first leading 1 has been created, the whole procedure is repeated on the remaining rows. This makes it easy to use on a computer. Note further that at step 4 we can also make every entry *above* the leading 1 zero. Then the algorithm carries the matrix to *reduced* row-echelon form (as in Examples 6 and 7). The reason for distinguishing two row-echelon forms will be discussed later.

The Gaussian algorithm certainly proves the following important theorem.

THEOREM 2   Every matrix can be carried to row-echelon form (reduced, if desired) by a sequence of elementary row operations.

Example 9   Find all solutions to the following system of linear equations:

$$\begin{aligned} x_1 - 2x_2 - x_3 + 3x_4 &= 1 \\ 2x_1 - 4x_2 + x_3 \phantom{{}+3x_4} &= 5 \\ x_1 - 2x_2 + 2x_3 - 3x_4 &= 4 \end{aligned}$$

SOLUTION   The augmented matrix is given below. The first leading 1 is in place so we clean up column 1:

$$\begin{bmatrix} 1 & -2 & -1 & 3 & 1 \\ 2 & -4 & 1 & 0 & 5 \\ 1 & -2 & 2 & -3 & 4 \end{bmatrix} \rightarrow \begin{bmatrix} 1 & -2 & -1 & 3 & 1 \\ 0 & 0 & 3 & -6 & 3 \\ 0 & 0 & 3 & -6 & 3 \end{bmatrix}$$

Now subtract the second row from the third, and then[10] multiply the second row by $\frac{1}{3}$, to get the matrix below (now in row-echelon form):

---

[9] While Gauss did use this procedure, the method has been attributed to the Chinese several centuries earlier.

[10] These steps are not strictly in the order specified by the algorithm. However, the point is to carry the matrix to reduced form using *some* sequence of row operations. The sequence in the algorithm will always work, but it may not be the most efficient.

$$\rightarrow \begin{bmatrix} 1 & -2 & -1 & 3 & 1 \\ 0 & 0 & 1 & -2 & 1 \\ 0 & 0 & 0 & 0 & 0 \end{bmatrix}$$

Next use the second leading 1 (in column 3) to clean up column 3 and so achieve reduced row-echelon form:

$$\rightarrow \begin{bmatrix} 1 & -2 & 0 & 1 & 2 \\ 0 & 0 & 1 & -2 & 1 \\ 0 & 0 & 0 & 0 & 0 \end{bmatrix}$$

This is as far as the Gaussian algorithm will take us. The corresponding system of equations is

$$x_1 - 2x_2 \qquad + \ x_4 = 2$$
$$x_3 - 2x_4 = 1$$
$$0 = 0$$

The leading 1's are in columns 1 and 3 here, and the corresponding variables x_1 and x_3 are called the leading variables. To solve the system the nonleading variables are assigned arbitrary values (called parameters), and then the two equations are used to determine the leading variables in terms of the parameters. More precisely, we set $x_2 = s$, and $x_4 = t$ where s and t are arbitrary parameters, so the equations become $x_1 - 2s + t = 2$ and $x_3 - 2t = 1$. Solving these gives $x_1 = 2 + 2s - t$ and $x_3 = 1 + 2t$. Hence the solutions are given by

$$X = [2 + 2s - t \ \ s \ \ 1 + 2t \ \ t]^T = \begin{bmatrix} 2+2s-t \\ s \\ 1+2t \\ t \end{bmatrix}.$$

The solution $X = [2 + 2s - t \ \ s \ \ 1 + 2t \ \ t]^T$ in Example 9 is called the **general solution** of the system because *every* solution has this form for some values of the parameters s and t.

When the augmented matrix of a linear system has been carried to reduced row-echelon form, the variables corresponding to the leading 1's are called the **leading variables**. Then the method of solution in Example 9 provides a way of writing down the solutions of any linear system (assuming that there are solutions).

Gaussian Elimination   Assume that a system of linear equations has at least one solution. Then the general solution can be found in parametric form as follows:

Step 1. Carry the augmented matrix of the system to reduced row-echelon form.
Step 2. Assign the nonleading variables as parameters.
Step 3. Use the equations corresponding to the reduced row-echelon form to solve for the leading variables in terms of the parameters.

This procedure solves any system of linear equations which *has* a solution. The following example shows how the method reveals that a system has *no* solution.

Example 10   In Example 4 it was shown directly that the system

$$x + y \qquad = 1$$
$$x \qquad - z = 2$$
$$y + z = 1$$

has no solution. The reduction of the augmented matrix to row-echelon form is as follows:

$$\begin{bmatrix} 1 & 1 & 0 & 1 \\ 1 & 0 & -1 & 2 \\ 0 & 1 & 1 & 1 \end{bmatrix} \rightarrow \begin{bmatrix} 1 & 1 & 0 & 1 \\ 0 & -1 & -1 & 1 \\ 0 & 1 & 1 & 1 \end{bmatrix}$$

$$\rightarrow \begin{bmatrix} 1 & 1 & 0 & 1 \\ 0 & 1 & 1 & -1 \\ 0 & 0 & 0 & 2 \end{bmatrix}$$

$$\rightarrow \begin{bmatrix} 1 & 1 & 0 & 1 \\ 0 & 1 & 1 & -1 \\ 0 & 0 & 0 & 1 \end{bmatrix}$$

This last matrix corresponds to a system in which the last equation is

$$0x + 0y + 0z = 1.$$

It is clear that *no* choice of x, y and z will satisfy *this* equation, so this last system (and hence the original system) has no solution. This is typical of what happens when there is no solution.

When using Gaussian elimination to solve a large system it is more efficient to carry the augmented matrix only to row-echelon form,[11] assign parameters to the nonleading variables, and then solve for the leading variables using **back-substitution**: Use the last equation to find the last leading variable in terms of the parameters, then substitute that value in the second last equation to solve for the second last leading variable, and so on. This method is more efficient than carrying the matrix directly to reduced row-echelon form, and follows from an operations count (see most numerical analysis books).

1.2.4   Rank of a Matrix

It will be proved in Section 1.6 (Theorem 4) that:

The reduced row-echelon form of a matrix A is uniquely determined by A.

That is, no matter which series of row operations is used to carry A to a reduced row-echelon matrix, the result will always be the same. By contrast, the same matrix can be taken to *different* row-echelon matrices. For example, if $A = \begin{bmatrix} 1 & 3 & 4 \\ 2 & 7 & 9 \end{bmatrix}$, then

$$A \rightarrow \begin{bmatrix} 1 & 3 & 4 \\ 0 & 1 & 1 \end{bmatrix} \text{ and } A \rightarrow \begin{bmatrix} 1 & 3 & 4 \\ 0 & 1 & 1 \end{bmatrix} \rightarrow \begin{bmatrix} 1 & 2 & 3 \\ 0 & 1 & 1 \end{bmatrix}.$$

Hence A can be carried to two different row-echelon matrices $\begin{bmatrix} 1 & 3 & 4 \\ 0 & 1 & 1 \end{bmatrix}$ and $\begin{bmatrix} 1 & 2 & 3 \\ 0 & 1 & 1 \end{bmatrix}$. However, we will show in Section 4.4 that:

The number of leading 1's must be the same no matter how A is carried to row-echelon form.

This number of leading 1's is called the **rank** of the matrix A and is denoted *rankA*.

Example 11   Compute the rank of $A = \begin{bmatrix} 1 & 2 & -1 & 3 \\ 2 & 1 & 1 & 5 \\ -1 & 4 & -5 & -1 \end{bmatrix}$.

SOLUTION   The matrix A is carried to row-echelon form as follows:

---

[11] This is often referred to as the Gaussian algorithm, particularly in numerical analysis.

$$A = \begin{bmatrix} 1 & 2 & -1 & 3 \\ 2 & 1 & 1 & 5 \\ -1 & 4 & -5 & -1 \end{bmatrix} \rightarrow \begin{bmatrix} 1 & 2 & -1 & 3 \\ 0 & -3 & 3 & -1 \\ 0 & 6 & -6 & 2 \end{bmatrix} \rightarrow \begin{bmatrix} 1 & 2 & -1 & 3 \\ 0 & 1 & -1 & \frac{1}{3} \\ 0 & 0 & 0 & 0 \end{bmatrix}$$

Because there are two leading 1's, we have $rank A = 2$.

The relationship between rank and systems of equations is given in the following theorem.

THEOREM 3   Suppose a system of m equations in n variables has at least one solution. If the rank of the augmented matrix is r, the set of solutions has exactly $(n - r)$ parameters.

PROOF   Carry the augmented matrix to a reduced row-echelon matrix R. Then R has r leading 1's (since the rank is r), so there are exactly r leading variables. Hence there are $(n - r)$ nonleading variables, and each of these is assigned a parameter.

Theorem 3 has a surprising number of consequences and will be referred to several times below. We have seen examples of systems with no solution, one solution, or infinitely many solutions; the first application of Theorem 3 is to show that these are the only possibilities.

THEOREM 4   For any system of linear equations there are exactly three possibilities:
   (1) No solution.
   (2) A unique solution.
   (3) Infinitely many solutions.

PROOF   If there is a solution, then either every variable is a leading variable (unique solution) or there is at least one nonleading variable (infinitely many solutions because a parameter is involved).

A system of linear equations is called **consistent** if it has at least one solution, and the system is called **inconsistent** if it has no solution. Thus a consistent system has either a unique solution or infinitely many solutions; it cannot have (say) exactly two solutions.

The truth of Theorem 4 can be seen graphically for a system of two equations in two variables x and y. Recall that the graph of an equation $ax + by = c$ is a straight line if a and b are not both zero, and that $\begin{bmatrix} s \\ t \end{bmatrix}$ is a solution of the equation exactly when the point $P(s, t)$ with coordinates (s, t) lies on the line. Now consider a system

$$\begin{aligned} a_1 x + b_1 y &= c_1 \\ a_2 x + b_2 y &= c_2 \end{aligned} \qquad (**)$$

The graphs of these equations are two straight lines, L_1 and L_2 assuming that a_1 and b_1 are not both zero, and that a_2 and b_2 are not both zero. Geometrically there are three possibilities for these two lines (illustrated in Figure 1.1):

(1) Lines are parallel and distinct   System (**) has no solution because there is no point on both lines

(2) Lines are not parallel   System (**) has a unique solution corresponding to the point of intersection of the lines

(3) Lines are identical   System (**) has infinitely many solutions, one for each point on the (common) line

Clearly these three possibilities correspond to those in Theorem 4.

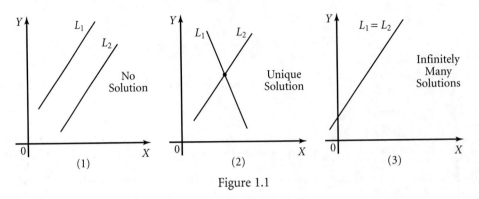

Figure 1.1

The graph of an equation $ax + by + cz = d$ is a plane in space if a, b, and c are not all zero (this is discussed in detail in Section 3.3). Thus a system of 2 equations in 3 variables must either have no solutions (the planes are parallel) or have infinitely many solutions (the planes coincide or intersect in a line). A unique solution is not possible here. This illustrates Theorem 3 since there are $n = 3$ variables and the augmented matrix has rank $r \leq 2$ (because there are 2 equations) so $n - r \geq 3 - 2 = 1$ and these are parameters.

A similar graphical argument can be given that a system of 3 equations in 3 variables must have zero, one, or infinitely many solutions as in Theorem 4. However, this geometrical argument fails for systems with more than three variables, and we must rely on Theorem 4.

Exercises 1.2

1. In each case show that the column matrix X is a solution to the given system of linear equations; if it involves parameters s and t, show that X is a solution for all possible values of these parameters.

a) $x_1 - 2x_2 + 3x_3 + x_4 = -3$
$2x_1 - x_2 + 3x_3 - x_4 = 0$
$X = [1\ \ 2\ \ 0\ \ 0]^T$
$X = [1\ \ 4\ \ 1\ \ 1]^T$
$X = [-s + t + 1\ \ \ s + t + 2\ \ \ s\ \ \ t]^T$

b) $x_1 - 2x_2 + 3x_3 - 3x_4 = 2$
$2x_1 - x_2 + 3x_3 \qquad\quad = 1$
$-x_1 - 4x_2 + 3x_3 - 9x_4 = 4$
$2x_1 - 7x_2 + 9x_3 - 12x_4 = 7$
$X = [-2\ \ -2\ \ 1\ \ 1]^T$
$X = [-3\ \ -1\ \ 2\ \ 1]^T$
$X = [-s - t\ \ \ -1 + s - 2t\ \ \ s\ \ \ t]^T$

2. Describe each of the following in your own words: A linear equation, a solution to a linear equation, a system of linear equations, and a solution to a system of linear equations.

3. In each case carry the given matrix to reduced row-echelon form. For a methodical approach, follow the Gaussian algorithm.

a) $\begin{bmatrix} 3 & -1 & 2 & 1 & 2 & 1 \\ -4 & 1 & -2 & 2 & 7 & 2 \\ 2 & -2 & 4 & 3 & 7 & 1 \\ 0 & 3 & -6 & 1 & 6 & 4 \end{bmatrix}$
b) $\begin{bmatrix} 1 & -1 & 3 & 1 & 3 & 2 & 1 \\ -1 & -2 & 6 & 1 & -5 & 0 & -1 \\ 2 & 3 & -9 & 2 & 4 & 1 & -1 \\ 1 & 1 & -3 & -1 & 3 & 0 & 1 \end{bmatrix}$

4. For each of the following systems of linear equations, form the augmented matrix, perform elementary row operations to transform it to reduced row-echelon form, and solve the given system this way. For a methodical approach to reducing to row-echelon form, follow the Gaussian algorithm.

a) $3x_1 - x_2 = 4$
$2x_1 - \frac{1}{2}x_2 = 1$

b) $2x_1 - 3x_2 = 4$
$x_1 - 3x_2 = 1$

c) $x_1 + x_2 - x_3 = 1$
$3x_1 - x_2 + x_3 = 0$
$x_1 - 3x_2 + 3x_3 = -2$

d) $2x_1 + 2x_2 - 3x_3 = 1$
$x_1 \qquad\ + x_3 = 5$
$3x_1 + 4x_2 - 7x_3 = -3$

e) $x_1 - 2x_2 + 2x_3 = 4$
$-2x_1 + x_2 + x_3 = 1$
$x_1 - 5x_2 + 7x_3 = -1$

f) $4x_1 + x_2 - 8x_3 = 1$
$3x_1 - 2x_2 + 3x_3 = 5$
$-x_1 + 8x_2 - 25x_3 = -3$

g)
$$x_1 - 3x_2 + x_3 + x_4 - x_5 = 8$$
$$-2x_1 + 6x_2 + x_3 - 2x_4 - 4x_5 = -1$$
$$3x_1 - 9x_2 + 8x_3 + 4x_4 - 13x_5 = 49$$

h)
$$x_1 - 2x_2 + x_3 + 3x_4 - x_5 = 1$$
$$-3x_1 + 6x_2 - 4x_3 - 9x_4 + 3x_5 = -1$$
$$-x_1 + 2x_2 - 2x_3 - 4x_4 - 3x_5 = 3$$
$$x_1 - 2x_2 + 2x_3 + 2x_4 - 5x_5 = 1$$

5. In your own words, can you describe an algorithm that will solve a system of linear equations for you?

6. In each of the systems of linear equations given in Exercise 4, calculate the rank of the corresponding augmented matrix, and find a connection with the number of variables, the number of solutions, and the number of parameters in the solution.

7. If a system of 5 equations in 7 variables has a solution, explain why there is more than one solution.

8. Consider the system $ax = b$ of one equation in one variable. Give conditions on a and b such that the system has no solution, a unique solution, and infinitely many solutions.

9. In each case find (if possible) conditions on the numbers a, b, and c that the given system has no solution, a unique solution, or infinitely many solutions.

a)
$$2x_1 - 3x_2 - 3x_3 = a$$
$$-x_1 + x_2 + 2x_3 = b$$
$$x_1 - 3x_2 = c$$

b)
$$x_1 - 2x_2 + 2x_3 = a$$
$$-2x_1 + x_2 + x_3 = b$$
$$x_1 - 5x_2 + 7x_3 = c$$

c)
$$x_1 + ax_2 = 1$$
$$bx_1 + 2x_2 = 5$$

d)
$$ax_1 + x_2 = -1$$
$$2x_1 + x_2 = b$$

10. Let $A = \begin{bmatrix} 1 & -2 & 0 & 3 \\ -4 & 1 & 5 & -2 \\ -1 & -5 & 5 & 7 \end{bmatrix}$. Show that A and A^T have the same rank. [Remark: We will see in Section 4.4 that this is true for *every* matrix A.]

11. In your own words, can you describe an algorithm that will compute the rank of a matrix?

12. Four one-way streets feed into a traffic circle as in the diagram, where the traffic flows are measured in cars per minute. In order to design the roads, the engineers must determine the flows f_1, f_2, f_3, and f_4 in the circle. Use the fact that the traffic flow into any intersection must equal the traffic flow out of that intersection to obtain four equations relating these flows. Solve the equations and express f_1, f_2, and f_3 in terms of f_4. Which part of the circle will carry the most traffic?

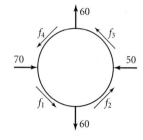

13. A man must take 5 units of vitamin A, 13 units of vitamin B, and 23 units of vitamin C each day. Three brands of vitamin pills are available and the number of units of each vitamin per pill are given in the table.

	Vitamin A	Vitamin B	Vitamin C
Brand 1	1	2	4
Brand 2	1	1	3
Brand 3	0	1	1

a) Find all combinations of pills that provide the exact daily requirement (no partial pills).

b) If brands 1, 2, and 3 cost $0.90, $0.60, and $1.50 per pill respectively, find the least expensive treatment.

14. In each case either show that the statement is true or give an example showing that it is false. Assume that a system of equations is given with augmented matrix A, coefficient matrix C, and reduced row-echelon form R.

a) A and R are the same size.

b) If R has a row of zeros, there are infinitely many solutions.

c) If there is more than one solution, R must have a row of zeros.

d) If there exists a solution, there are infinitely many solutions.

e) If there are more variables than equations, there are infinitely many solutions.

f) If every row of R has a leading 1, the system has at least one solution.

g) If the system has a solution, $rank(A) = rank(C)$.

h) $rank(C) \leq rank(A)$.

i) $rank(A) \leq 1 + rank(C)$.

j) If A is $m \times n$ and $rank A = m$, the system is consistent.

1.3   HOMOGENEOUS SYSTEMS

In this section, we concentrate on a particular class of systems of linear equations, that is, those systems where the constant term in each equation is 0.

1.3.1   Homogeneous Systems

A system of linear equations is called **homogeneous** if all the constant terms are zero. Thus a typical homogeneous linear equation in the n variables x_1, x_2, $\cdots$, x_n has the form

$$a_1x_1 + a_2x_2 + \cdots + a_nx_n = 0.$$

Because the constants are all zero, any homogeneous system always has the **trivial** solution

$$x_1 = 0, \ x_2 = 0, \ \cdots, \ x_n = 0$$

in which every variable is zero. Many practical problems come down to discovering whether or not some homogeneous system has a **nontrivial** solution, that is, a solution where at least one of the variables is nonzero. The next theorem gives an important situation where this *must* happen.

THEOREM 1   If a homogeneous system of linear equations has more variables than equations, then it has nontrivial solutions.

PROOF   Suppose there are m equations in n variables, so our assumption is that $n > m$. If r is the rank of the augmented matrix, then $r \leq m$ because the number r of leading 1's cannot exceed the number m of equations. Hence $r \leq m < n$, whence $r < n$. By Theorem 3 §1.2, this means that the number $n - r$ of parameters is not zero, so there are (infinitely many) nontrivial solutions.

The existence of a nontrivial solution is often the desired outcome for a homogeneous system. The following example provides an illustration of how Theorem 1 can be used in geometry.

Example 1   The graph of an equation $ax^2 + bxy + cy^2 + dx + ey + f = 0$ is called a **conic** if a, b, and c are not all zero. (Circles, ellipses, hyperbolas, and parabolas are all examples of conics.) Show that there is at least one conic through any five points in the plane that are not all on a line.

SOLUTION   Suppose that the coordinates of the five points are (p_1, q_1), (p_2, q_2), (p_3, q_3), (p_4, q_4), and (p_5, q_5). The graph of the equation $ax^2 + bxy + cy^2 + dx + ey + f = 0$ passes through the point (p_i, q_i) if

$$ap_i^2 + bp_iq_i + cq_i^2 + dp_i + eq_i + f = 0$$

Since there are five points, this gives five homogeneous linear equations in the six variables a, b, c, d, e, and f. Hence there is a nontrivial solution by Theorem 1. If $a = b = c = 0$ in this solution, then the five points all lie on the line with equation $dx + ey + f = 0$, contrary to our assumption. Hence one of a, b, and c is nonzero and we have a conic.

1.3.2 Basic Solutions

Of course, Gaussian elimination also works for homogeneous systems. In fact, it provides a way to write the solutions in a convenient form which will be needed later. This is illustrated in the following example.

Example 2 Solve the following homogeneous system

$$x_1 - 2x_2 + x_3 + x_4 = 0$$
$$-x_1 + 2x_2 \qquad + x_4 = 0$$
$$2x_1 - 4x_2 + x_3 \qquad = 0$$

and express the solutions as sums of scalar multiples of specific solutions.

SOLUTION The augmented matrix is reduced as follows:

$$\begin{bmatrix} 1 & -2 & 1 & 1 & 0 \\ -1 & 2 & 0 & 1 & 0 \\ 2 & -4 & 1 & 0 & 0 \end{bmatrix} \rightarrow \begin{bmatrix} 1 & -2 & 1 & 1 & 0 \\ 0 & 0 & 1 & 2 & 0 \\ 0 & 0 & -1 & -2 & 0 \end{bmatrix}$$

$$\rightarrow \begin{bmatrix} 1 & -2 & 0 & -1 & 0 \\ 0 & 0 & 1 & 2 & 0 \\ 0 & 0 & 0 & 0 & 0 \end{bmatrix}$$

Hence the leading variables are x_1 and x_3, and the nonleading variables x_2 and x_4 become parameters: $x_2 = s$ and $x_4 = t$. Then the equations in the final system determine the leading variables in terms of the parameters:

$$x_1 = 2s + t \quad \text{and} \quad x_3 = -2t$$

This means that the general solution is $X = [2s + t \quad s \quad -2t \quad t]^T$. The new idea here is to separate this into parts involving only s or t:

$$X = \begin{bmatrix} 2s+t \\ s \\ -2t \\ t \end{bmatrix} = \begin{bmatrix} 2s \\ s \\ 0 \\ 0 \end{bmatrix} + \begin{bmatrix} t \\ 0 \\ -2t \\ t \end{bmatrix} = s \begin{bmatrix} 2 \\ 1 \\ 0 \\ 0 \end{bmatrix} + t \begin{bmatrix} 1 \\ 0 \\ -2 \\ 1 \end{bmatrix}$$

Hence $X_1 = \begin{bmatrix} 2 \\ 1 \\ 0 \\ 0 \end{bmatrix}$ and $X_2 = \begin{bmatrix} 1 \\ 0 \\ -2 \\ 1 \end{bmatrix}$ are specific solutions, and the general solution X has the form $X = sX_1 + tX_2$.

The specific solutions X_1 and X_2 in Example 2 are called the basic solutions of the homogeneous system. They have the property that every solution X has the form

$$X = sX_1 + tX_2 \quad \text{where } s \text{ and } t \text{ are arbitrary numbers.}$$

This happens for every homogeneous system.

To describe the general situation, the following terminology is useful: If X_1, X_2, $\cdots$, X_k are columns, an expression of the form

$$s_1 X_1 + s_2 X_2 + \cdots + s_n X_k \quad \text{where } s_1, \ s_2, \ \cdots, \ s_k \text{ are arbitrary numbers}$$

is called a **linear combination** of the columns X_1, X_2, $\cdots$, X_k. Given *any* homogeneous system of linear equations, a computation like that in Example 2 expresses every solution to the system as a linear combination of certain particular solutions. These particular solutions are called **basic solutions** produced by the Gaussian algorithm. (Of course, the system may have only the trivial solution; in this case we say that the system has **no basic solutions**.)

THEOREM 2   Suppose a system of homogeneous linear equations in n variables is given. Assume that the rank of the augmented matrix is r. Then:

(1) The Gaussian algorithm produces exactly $n - r$ basic solutions.

(2) Every solution is a linear combination of these basic solutions.

PROOF   We already have observed that every solution is a linear combination of the basic ones produced by the Gaussian algorithm. By Theorem 3 §1.2 there are exactly $n - r$ parameters in the general solution, and so there are exactly $n - r$ basic solutions (one for each parameter).

Example 3   Find basic solutions for the following homogeneous system, and illustrate Theorem 2.

$$
\begin{aligned}
x_1 - 2x_2 + 4x_3 - x_4 + \quad\;\;\; 5x_6 &= 0 \\
-2x_1 + 4x_2 - 7x_3 + x_4 + 2x_5 - 8x_6 &= 0 \\
3x_1 - 6x_2 + 12x_3 - 3x_4 + x_5 + 15x_6 &= 0 \\
2x_1 - 4x_2 + 9x_3 - 3x_4 + 3x_5 + 12x_6 &= 0
\end{aligned}
$$

SOLUTION   The reduction of the augmented matrix to reduced form is as follows:

$$
\begin{bmatrix}
1 & -2 & 4 & -1 & 0 & 5 & 0 \\
-2 & 4 & -7 & 1 & 2 & -8 & 0 \\
3 & -6 & 12 & -3 & 1 & 15 & 0 \\
2 & -4 & 9 & -3 & 3 & 12 & 0
\end{bmatrix}
\rightarrow
\begin{bmatrix}
1 & -2 & 4 & -1 & 0 & 5 & 0 \\
0 & 0 & 1 & -1 & 2 & 2 & 0 \\
0 & 0 & 0 & 0 & 1 & 0 & 0 \\
0 & 0 & 1 & -1 & 3 & 2 & 0
\end{bmatrix}
$$

$$
\rightarrow
\begin{bmatrix}
1 & -2 & 0 & 3 & 0 & -3 & 0 \\
0 & 0 & 1 & -1 & 0 & 2 & 0 \\
0 & 0 & 0 & 0 & 1 & 0 & 0 \\
0 & 0 & 0 & 0 & 0 & 0 & 0
\end{bmatrix}
$$

Hence the nonleading variables are assigned as parameters: $x_2 = s$, $x_4 = t$, and $x_6 = u$. Then the equations give the leading variables: $x_1 = 2s - 3t + 3u$, $x_3 = t - 2u$, and $x_5 = 0$. Thus the general solution X is

$$
X = \begin{bmatrix} x_1 \\ x_2 \\ x_3 \\ x_4 \\ x_5 \\ x_6 \end{bmatrix} = \begin{bmatrix} 2s - 3t + 3u \\ s \\ t - 2u \\ t \\ 0 \\ u \end{bmatrix} = s\begin{bmatrix} 2 \\ 1 \\ 0 \\ 0 \\ 0 \\ 0 \end{bmatrix} + t\begin{bmatrix} -3 \\ 0 \\ 1 \\ 1 \\ 0 \\ 0 \end{bmatrix} + u\begin{bmatrix} 3 \\ 0 \\ -2 \\ 0 \\ 0 \\ 1 \end{bmatrix}
$$

so the basic solutions are $X_1 = \begin{bmatrix} 2 \\ 1 \\ 0 \\ 0 \\ 0 \\ 0 \end{bmatrix}$, $X_2 = \begin{bmatrix} -3 \\ 0 \\ 1 \\ 1 \\ 0 \\ 0 \end{bmatrix}$ and $X_3 = \begin{bmatrix} 3 \\ 0 \\ -2 \\ 0 \\ 0 \\ 1 \end{bmatrix}$.

Thus there are 3 basic solutions, which agrees with Theorem 2 because the rank of the augmented matrix is $r = 3$ in this case and there are $n = 6$ variables.

The basic solutions of a homogeneous system of linear equations are useful because they give an easy description of *all* solutions: Just take all linear combinations. However, the basic solutions have other uses as well, as we shall see in Section 2.3 when we use them to study diagonalization, one of the most useful techniques in linear algebra. We conclude with an example which applies homogeneous equations to balancing chemical reactions.

Example 4 A chemical reaction is a rearrangement of molecules to form new chemical units, where reactants are transformed into products. For example, $2Na + Cl_2 \rightarrow 2NaCl$ represents the reaction of two sodium molecules and one chlorine molecule to give two molecules of sodium chloride (table salt). This reaction is balanced in the sense that the number of atoms of each element on one side of the reaction is the same as the number on the other side. As another illustration, consider burning methane:

Methane (CH_4) + Oxygen (O_2) $\rightarrow$ Carbon Dioxide (CO_2) + Water (H_2O).

To balance this reaction, let $x, y, z,$ and w denote the number of molecules of methane, oxygen, carbon dioxide, and water, respectively, that must be present. Then the reaction can be represented by

$$xCH_4 + yO_2 \rightarrow zCO_2 + wH_2O.$$

The number of atoms of each element on each side of the reaction must be the same, giving the equations $x = z$ (to balance C), $4x = 2w$ (to balance H) and $2y = 2z + w$ (to balance O). These equations can be written as a homogeneous linear system

$$
\begin{aligned}
x \quad\quad - z \quad\quad &= 0 \\
4x \quad\quad\quad - 2w &= 0 \\
2y - 2z - w &= 0
\end{aligned}
$$

and the general solution is $X = [t \quad 2t \quad t \quad 2t]^T$ where t is arbitrary. Since $x, y, z,$ and w must be positive integers, taking $t = 1$ gives one solution $x = z = 1$ and $y = w = 2$. Hence the balanced reaction is

$$CH_4 + 2O_2 \rightarrow CO_2 + 2H_2O.$$

Exercises 1.3

1. In each case, consider the system of homogeneous equations with the given matrix as coefficient matrix, find basic solutions to the system, and express the general solution as a linear combination of these basic solutions.

a) $\begin{bmatrix} 1 & 2 & 3 \\ -1 & 3 & 0 \\ -1 & 8 & 3 \end{bmatrix}$

b) $\begin{bmatrix} 1 & 2 & 3 \\ -1 & 3 & 0 \\ 1 & 8 & 3 \end{bmatrix}$

c) $\begin{bmatrix} 1 & 3 & -2 & -1 \\ -2 & 1 & 0 & 4 \\ 1 & 10 & -6 & 1 \end{bmatrix}$

d) $\begin{bmatrix} 1 & -2 & 0 & 3 \\ -3 & 6 & 1 & -4 \\ 2 & -4 & -1 & 1 \end{bmatrix}$

e) $\begin{bmatrix} 1 & 2 & 0 \\ 2 & 3 & -1 \\ 3 & 4 & -2 \\ 1 & 3 & 1 \\ 6 & 9 & -3 \end{bmatrix}$

f) $\begin{bmatrix} 2 & -1 & 6 & 0 & -3 & 7 \\ -3 & 1 & 3 & -5 & 1 & 4 \end{bmatrix}$

g) $\begin{bmatrix} 1 & 2 & 1 & -1 & 3 \\ 1 & 2 & 2 & 1 & 2 \\ 2 & 4 & 2 & -1 & 7 \end{bmatrix}$

h) $\begin{bmatrix} 1 & 1 & -2 & 3 & 2 \\ 2 & -1 & 3 & 4 & 1 \\ -1 & -2 & 3 & 0 & 1 \\ 3 & 0 & 1 & 7 & 3 \end{bmatrix}$

2. Find a balanced equation for the following chemical reactions:

a) Ammonia (NH_3) + Copper Oxide (CuO)
$\rightarrow$ Nitrogen (N_2) + Copper (Cu) + Water (H_2O).

b) Octane (C_8H_{18}) + Oxygen (O_2)
$\rightarrow$ Carbon Dioxide (CO_2) + Water (H_2O).

3. Explain the difference between general and homogeneous systems of linear equations, and what the implications are for the solutions.

4. Suppose a homogeneous system has 4 equations and 6 variables, and let A denote the augmented matrix.
   a) Can the system have a unique solution? No solution? Support your answers.
   b) How many parameters are possible? Support your answer.
   c) How many parameters are possible if a row of A is a multiple of a different row? Support your answer.
   d) How many parameters are possible if $rank A = 4$? Support your answer.
   e) How many parameters are possible if $rank A = 2$? Support your answer.

5. Show that the converse of Theorem 1 is not true. That is, show that if a homogeneous system has a nontrivial solution, it may *not* have more variables than equations.

6. If a system has more equations than variables, can it have a unique solution? Justify your answer.

7. In each case either show that the statement is true or give an example showing that it is false. Assume that a system of equations is given with augmented matrix A and reduced row-echelon form R.
   a) If the system is homogeneous, every solution is trivial.
   b) If the system has a nontrivial solution, it cannot be homogeneous.
   c) If the system has a trivial solution, it must be homogeneous.
   d) If the system is homogeneous and has a nontrivial solution, R has a row of zeros.
   e) If the system is homogeneous and has a nontrivial solution, then it has infinitely many nontrivial solutions.
   f) If the system is homogeneous and R has a row of zeros, there are nontrivial solutions.
   g) If A is $m \times n$ and $rank A = m$, the system has only the trivial solution.

8. For a homogeneous system with coefficient matrix C and augmented matrix A, show that $rank A = rank C$.

1.4   MATRIX MULTIPLICATION

In addition to the operations in Section 1.1, there is another operation by which certain matrices can be multiplied together to yield another matrix. This is useful for systems of linear equations, and turns out to have many other applications. We begin with an example of how matrix multiplication arises in a commercial context.

1.4.1   Matrix Multiplication

Example 1   A store sells two brands of toasters, brand X and brand Y. The manager has the following two data matrices available, the first giving sales volumes for three months, and the second giving the retail price and the dealer cost (in dollars):

$$
\begin{array}{c}
\\ \text{Jan} \\ \text{Feb} \\ \text{Mar}
\end{array}
\begin{array}{c}
X \quad Y \\
\begin{bmatrix} 11 & 9 \\ 10 & 7 \\ 14 & 8 \end{bmatrix}
\end{array}
\quad \text{and} \quad
\begin{array}{c}
\\ X \\ Y
\end{array}
\begin{array}{c}
\text{Retail} \quad \text{Cost} \\
\begin{bmatrix} 29 & 22 \\ 31 & 26 \end{bmatrix}
\end{array}
$$

The manager wants a systematic way to calculate the new matrix

$$
\begin{array}{c}
\\ \text{Jan} \\ \text{Feb} \\ \text{Mar}
\end{array}
\begin{array}{c}
\text{Retail} \quad \text{Cost} \\
\begin{bmatrix} 598 & 476 \\ 507 & 402 \\ 654 & 516 \end{bmatrix}
\end{array}
$$

of total sales and costs for the three months. For example, for January, the total retail sales were

$$598 = 11 \cdot 29 + 9 \cdot 31$$

because there were 11 brand-X toasters sold at \$29 each, and 9 brand-Y toasters sold at \$31 each. This gives the $(1, 1)$-entry 598 of the new matrix. Observe that this entry can be calculated directly from the first two matrices by going along the first row $[11 \ 9]$ of the left matrix and the first column $\begin{bmatrix} 29 \\ 31 \end{bmatrix}$ of the right matrix, multiplying corresponding entries, and adding the results. This is called taking the dot product of this row and column. Similarly, the $(3, 2)$-entry, 516, of the new matrix is obtained by taking the dot product of row 3 of the left matrix and column 2 of the right matrix:

$$516 = 14 \cdot 22 + 8 \cdot 26$$

Every entry in the new matrix is calculated in the same way: The (i, j)-entry of the new matrix is the dot product of row i of the left matrix and column j of the right matrix.

The calculation in Example 1 is a special case of general matrix multiplication. To describe it we use the following terminology: If $R = [r_1 \ r_2 \ \cdots \ r_n]$ is a row matrix and $C = [c_1 \ c_2 \ \cdots \ c_n]^T$ is a column matrix, each with n entries, we define their **dot product** to be the number

$$r_1c_1 + r_2c_2 + \cdots + r_nc_n.$$

In other words, the dot product of R and C is the number formed by multiplying corresponding entries and adding the results. As in Example 1, this leads to a way to multiply two matrices:

*The **product** of an $m \times n$ matrix A and an $n \times p$ matrix B is the $m \times p$ matrix AB whose (i, j)-entry is the dot product of row i of A and column j of B.*

Thus computing the (i, j)-entry of the product AB means going across row i of A and down column j of B, multiplying corresponding entries, and adding the results. This is illustrated in Figure 1.2.

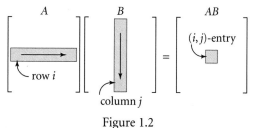

Figure 1.2

Example 2   Here are some typical matrix products.

$$\begin{bmatrix} 5 & 1 \\ 7 & 6 \\ -4 & 9 \end{bmatrix} \begin{bmatrix} 2 & -1 \\ 0 & 3 \end{bmatrix} = \begin{bmatrix} 5 \cdot 2 + 1 \cdot 0 & 5(-1) + 1 \cdot 3 \\ 7 \cdot 2 + 6 \cdot 0 & 7(-1) + 6 \cdot 3 \\ (-4)2 + 9 \cdot 0 & (-4)(-1) + 9 \cdot 3 \end{bmatrix} = \begin{bmatrix} 10 & -2 \\ 14 & 11 \\ -8 & 31 \end{bmatrix}$$

$$\begin{bmatrix} p & q & r \end{bmatrix} \begin{bmatrix} 5 & 7 \\ -3 & 9 \\ 2 & -5 \end{bmatrix} = \begin{bmatrix} 5p - 3q + 2r & 7p + 9q - 5r \end{bmatrix}$$

$$\begin{bmatrix} 2 & 7 & -5 \\ 3 & 0 & 1 \end{bmatrix} \begin{bmatrix} x \\ y \\ z \end{bmatrix} = \begin{bmatrix} 2x + 7y - 5z \\ 3x + z \end{bmatrix}$$

Note that forming the product AB is not always possible; it requires that the rows of A have the same length as the columns of B (so the dot products can be computed). The following rule is a useful way to remember when AB can be formed and what the size of AB is when A is $m \times n$ and B is $n' \times p$:

$$\begin{array}{cc} A & B \\ m \times \boxed{n \quad n'} \times p \end{array}$$

The product AB is defined if and only if $n = n'$, and in this case the matrix AB has size $m \times p$.

When these conditions are met we say that A and B are **compatible for multiplication**. Whenever we write a matrix product AB, it is tacitly assumed that this is the case.

The next example shows that matrix multiplication has properties not encountered in numerical arithmetic. If A is a square matrix, we write the **powers** of A as for numbers:

$$A^2 = AA$$
$$A^3 = AAA \quad \text{etc.}$$

Example 3   Show that the following can happen for 2×2 matrices A and B.

(1) $A^2 = 0$ even though $A \neq 0$.

(2) $AB \neq BA$.

SOLUTION   Let $A = \begin{bmatrix} 0 & 1 \\ 0 & 0 \end{bmatrix}$ and $B = \begin{bmatrix} 1 & 0 \\ 0 & 0 \end{bmatrix}$. Then $A^2 = \begin{bmatrix} 0 & 1 \\ 0 & 0 \end{bmatrix}\begin{bmatrix} 0 & 1 \\ 0 & 0 \end{bmatrix} = \begin{bmatrix} 0 & 0 \\ 0 & 0 \end{bmatrix} = 0$, even though

$A \neq 0$. Moreover $AB = \begin{bmatrix} 0 & 1 \\ 0 & 0 \end{bmatrix}\begin{bmatrix} 1 & 0 \\ 0 & 0 \end{bmatrix} = 0$ while $BA = \begin{bmatrix} 1 & 0 \\ 0 & 0 \end{bmatrix}\begin{bmatrix} 0 & 1 \\ 0 & 0 \end{bmatrix} = A$.

Hence $AB \neq BA$.

Two matrices A and B are said to **commute** if $AB = BA$. Thus Example 3 exhibits two matrices that do *not* commute. In fact commuting is relatively rare: Given two matrices, the chances are they will not commute.

Example 4   If $B = \begin{bmatrix} 1 & 1 \\ 0 & 0 \end{bmatrix}$, find all 2×2 matrices A that commute with B.

SOLUTION   The condition on A is that $AB = BA$. If we write $A = \begin{bmatrix} x & y \\ z & w \end{bmatrix}$ in terms of its entries, this condition becomes

$$\begin{bmatrix} x & y \\ z & w \end{bmatrix}\begin{bmatrix} 1 & 1 \\ 0 & 0 \end{bmatrix} = \begin{bmatrix} 1 & 1 \\ 0 & 0 \end{bmatrix}\begin{bmatrix} x & y \\ z & w \end{bmatrix},$$

that is

$$\begin{bmatrix} x & x \\ z & z \end{bmatrix} = \begin{bmatrix} x+z & y+w \\ 0 & 0 \end{bmatrix}.$$

Equating entries gives $z = 0$ and $x = y + w$, so A has the form $A = \begin{bmatrix} y+w & y \\ 0 & w \end{bmatrix}$ where y and w are arbitrary numbers.

1.4.2   Properties of Matrix Multiplication

Example 3 shows that matrix arithmetic differs in basic ways from ordinary numerical arithmetic. On the other hand, many similarities do occur (as seen for matrix addition in Theorem 1, §1.1).

The number 1 has the property that $1 \cdot a = a = a \cdot 1$ for every number a. An analogous role is played for matrix multiplication by square matrices of the following type:

$$I_2 = \begin{bmatrix} 1 & 0 \\ 0 & 1 \end{bmatrix} \quad I_3 = \begin{bmatrix} 1 & 0 & 0 \\ 0 & 1 & 0 \\ 0 & 0 & 1 \end{bmatrix} \quad I_4 = \begin{bmatrix} 1 & 0 & 0 & 0 \\ 0 & 1 & 0 & 0 \\ 0 & 0 & 1 & 0 \\ 0 & 0 & 0 & 1 \end{bmatrix} \quad \text{etc.}$$

In general the $n \times n$ **identity matrix** I_n is the square $n \times n$ matrix with 1's on the main diagonal and zeros elsewhere. It is often written simply as I when no confusion can result. It is routine to verify that identity matrices enjoy the following properties

$$IA = A \quad \text{and} \quad BI = B$$

whenever the products are defined. These are the first of the following important facts about matrix multiplication.

THEOREM **1** Let c be a scalar and let A, B, and C denote matrices of sizes such that the products below can be performed.

(1) $IA = A$ and $BI = B$.
(2) $A(BC) = (AB)C$.
(3) $A(B + C) = AB + AC$ and $A(B - C) = AB - AC$.
(4) $(B + C)A = BA + CA$ and $(B - C)A = BA - CA$.
(5) $c(AB) = (cA)B = A(cB)$.
(6) $(AB)^T = B^T A^T$.

The proofs of these properties are routine and are given at the end of this section.

The property that $A(BC) = (AB)C$ is called the **associative law** for matrix multiplication. It asserts that the product of three matrices A, B, and C (in that order) is the same no matter how it is formed and so is denoted simply as ABC. Similarly, the product $ABCD$ of four matrices can be formed in several ways (examples: $A[B(CD)]$, $(AB)(CD)$, $[A(BC)]D$, etc.). However the associative law shows that they are all equal, and so are written simply as $ABCD$. Similar remarks apply to products of five or more matrices.

However, a note of caution is needed here. The fact that AB and BA may not be equal (see Example 3) means that the *order* of the factors in a matrix product *is* important. For example, the products $ADCB$ and $ABCD$ may *not* be equal.

Warning If the order of the factors in a product of matrices is changed, the product matrix may change (or may not exist.)

Ignoring this is the source of many errors by linear algebra students! For example, when multiplying a matrix equation

$$B = C$$

by a matrix A care must be taken to multiply B and C on the *same side* by A. Hence we speak of *left-multiplying* by A to get $AB = AC$, and *right-multiplying* by A to get $BA = CA$.[12] The next example illustrates how this is used.

Example 5 If A, B, and C are matrices such that $AB = I$ and $CA = I$, show that $B = C$.

SOLUTION Left multiply the given equation $I = AB$ by C, and use (1) and (2) of Theorem 1, to get
$$C = CI = C(AB) = (CA)B = IB = B.$$

Properties (3) and (4) of Theorem 1 are called the **distributive laws**. They extend to sums of more than two terms, and they combine with property (5) to allow algebraic manipulations very much like those in numerical arithmetic. For example:
$$A(2B - C + 3D) = 2AB - AC + 3AD$$
$$(A + 2C - 3E + 5D)B = AB + 2CB - 3EB + 5DB$$
Note that the warning is still in effect: the order of each of the products here must not be changed.

---

[12] It is vital to realize that $AB = CA$ *can happen* even if $B = C$.

Example 6   Simplify the expression
$$A(BC - 2CD) + A(2C - B)D + (BA - AB)C.$$

SOLUTION   We use the properties in Theorem 1 and the extended distributive laws
$$A(BC - 2CD) + A(2C - B)D + (BA - AB)C$$
$$= ABC - 2ACD + 2ACD - ABD + BAC - ABC$$
$$= BAC - ABD.$$

Recall that two matrices A and B are said to commute if $AB = BA$. Many formulas that are valid for numbers will fail for noncommuting matrices. For example, the well-known "difference of squares" formula $a^2 - b^2 = (a - b)(a + b)$ of arithmetic may not hold for matrices; the whole thing depends upon whether the matrices commute.

Example 7   Let A and B denote $n \times n$ matrices.
    (a) If $AB = BA$, show that $A^2 - B^2 = (A - B)(A + B)$.
    (b) If $A^2 - B^2 = (A - B)(A + B)$, show that necessarily $AB = BA$

SOLUTION   The distributive laws give
$$(A - B)(A + B) = A(A + B) - B(A + B) = A^2 + AB - BA - B^2. \qquad (*)$$
This holds whether or not $AB = BA$, and so is helpful in both (a) and (b).
    (a) If $AB = BA$, the right side of equation $(*)$ equals $A^2 - B^2$, giving (a).
    (b) If $A^2 - B^2 = (A - B)(A + B)$, equation $(*)$ becomes
$A^2 - B^2 = A^2 + AB - BA - B^2$. Subtracting $A^2 - B^2$ from both sides gives
$0 = AB - BA$, whence $AB = BA$. This proves (b).

Recall that a matrix A is called symmetric if $A^T = A$ where A^T is the transpose of A.

Example 8   If A and B are symmetric matrices such that $AB = BA$, show that AB is also symmetric.

SOLUTION   We are given $A^T = A$ and $B^T = B$. Compute the transpose of AB using (6) of Theorem 1:
$$(AB)^T = B^T A^T = BA.$$
Since we are assuming that $AB = BA$, this gives $(AB)^T = AB$; that is, AB is symmetric.

1.4.3   Matrix Multiplication and Linear Equations

One of the most important motivations for matrix multiplication is in the study of systems of linear equations begun in Section 1.2. Consider the following system of 3 linear equations in 4 variables:
$$x_1 - 2x_2 + 2x_3 - x_4 = 1$$
$$2x_1 - 4x_2 + 3x_3 + x_4 = 3$$
$$3x_1 - 6x_2 + 5x_3 \qquad = 4$$
This system can be written as a single matrix equation
$$\begin{bmatrix} x_1 & - & 2x_2 & + & 2x_3 & - & x_4 \\ 2x_1 & - & 4x_2 & + & 3x_3 & + & x_4 \\ 3x_1 & - & 6x_2 & + & 5x_3 & & \end{bmatrix} = \begin{bmatrix} 1 \\ 3 \\ 4 \end{bmatrix}.$$

THEOREM 3

Let A be an $m \times n$ matrix of rank r. Then there exist invertible matrices U and V (of sizes $m \times m$ and $n \times n$ respectively) such that

$$UAV = \begin{bmatrix} I_r & 0 \\ 0 & 0 \end{bmatrix}.$$

Moreover, U and V can be computed in two steps:

Step 1. $[A \ \ I_m] \to [R \ \ U]$ where R is a reduced row-echelon matrix.

Step 2. $[R^T \ \ I_n] \to \left[\begin{bmatrix} I_r & 0 \\ 0 & 0 \end{bmatrix} \ V^T \right]$.

The procedure in Theorem 3 to compute U and V is easily adapted for a computer.

Example 5

If $A = \begin{bmatrix} 1 & -2 & 3 & 1 \\ -1 & 2 & -1 & 1 \\ 2 & -4 & 5 & 1 \end{bmatrix}$, show that $rank A = 2$, and find invertible matrices U and V such that $UAV = \begin{bmatrix} I_2 & 0 \\ 0 & 0 \end{bmatrix}$.

SOLUTION

The reduction in Step 1 of Theorem 3 is $[A \ \ I_3] \to [R \ \ U]$ where, as the reader can verify,

$$R = \begin{bmatrix} 1 & -2 & 0 & -2 \\ 0 & 0 & 1 & 1 \\ 0 & 0 & 0 & 0 \end{bmatrix} \quad \text{and} \quad U = \begin{bmatrix} -5 & 0 & 3 \\ 2 & 0 & -1 \\ -3 & 1 & 2 \end{bmatrix}$$

Thus $rank A = 2$, so Step 2 of Theorem 3 is the reduction

$$[R^T \ \ I_4] \to \left[\begin{bmatrix} I_2 & 0 \\ 0 & 0 \end{bmatrix} \ V^T \right]$$

where

$V = \begin{bmatrix} 1 & 0 & 2 & 2 \\ 0 & 0 & 1 & 0 \\ 0 & 1 & 0 & -1 \\ 0 & 0 & 0 & 1 \end{bmatrix}$. The reader can verify that $UAV = \begin{bmatrix} I_2 & 0 \\ 0 & 0 \end{bmatrix}$.

1.6.3 Uniqueness of Reduced Row-echelon Matrices[20]

We stated earlier that the reduced row-echelon form of a matrix is uniquely determined. We conclude this section with a proof of this.

THEOREM 4

If A is a matrix and $A \to R$ and $A \to S$ by row operations where R and S are both reduced row-echelon matrices, then $R = S$.

By Theorem 1 there are invertible matrices P and Q such that $R = PA$ and $S = QA$. Then $U = QP^{-1}$ is an invertible matrix with the property that $UR = S$. Hence we prove the following statement:

---

[20] This section is not used in the sequel, and so may be omitted.

PROPOSITION   Suppose $UR = S$ where R and S are $m \times n$ reduced row-echelon matrices and U is invertible. Then $R = S$.

PROOF   We proceed by induction on m. The case $m = 1$ is left to the reader. Let R_j and S_j denote column j of R and S respectively. Then matrix multiplication gives

$$UR_j = S_j \quad \text{for each } j. \tag{$*$}$$

Since U is invertible, it follows that $R_j = 0$ if and only if $S_j = 0$; that is R and S have the same zero columns. Hence, by passing to the matrices obtained by deleting all zero columns from R and S, we may assume that there are no zero columns.

But then the first column from the left in R and S is column 1 of I_m (both are row-echelon). Applying $(*)$ to this column shows that column 1 of U equals column 1 of I_m. Hence write U, R, and S in block form as follows:

$$U = \begin{bmatrix} 1 & X \\ 0 & V \end{bmatrix}, \quad R = \begin{bmatrix} 1 & Y \\ 0 & R' \end{bmatrix}, \quad \text{and} \quad S = \begin{bmatrix} 1 & Z \\ 0 & S' \end{bmatrix}$$

Since $UR = S$, block multiplication shows that $VR' = S'$. Hence $R' = S'$ by induction because V is invertible (U is invertible).

It follows that R and S have leading 1's in the same columns, say k of them. Applying $(*)$ to these columns then yields that the first k columns of U are the first k columns of I_m. Hence we can write U, R, and S in block form as follows:

$$U = \begin{bmatrix} I_k & M \\ 0 & W \end{bmatrix}, \quad R = \begin{bmatrix} R_1 & R_2 \\ 0 & 0 \end{bmatrix}, \quad S = \begin{bmatrix} S_1 & S_2 \\ 0 & 0 \end{bmatrix}$$

where R_1 and S_1 are $k \times k$. But then $UR = R$ by block multiplication, that is $S = R$. This completes the proof.

Exercises 1.6

1. For each of the following elementary matrices, describe the corresponding row operation and write the inverse.

   a) $E = \begin{bmatrix} 0 & 1 & 0 \\ 1 & 0 & 0 \\ 0 & 0 & 1 \end{bmatrix}$ b) $E = \begin{bmatrix} 1 & 0 & 0 \\ 5 & 1 & 0 \\ 0 & 0 & 1 \end{bmatrix}$

   c) $E = \begin{bmatrix} 2 & 0 & 0 \\ 0 & 1 & 0 \\ 0 & 0 & 1 \end{bmatrix}$ d) $E = \begin{bmatrix} 1 & 0 & -3 \\ 0 & 1 & 0 \\ 0 & 0 & 1 \end{bmatrix}$

2. In each case find elementary matrices E and F such that $B = EA$ and $A = FB$. What is the relationship between E and F?

   a) $A = \begin{bmatrix} 2 & -1 \\ 5 & 3 \end{bmatrix}$ $B = \begin{bmatrix} 2 & -1 \\ 1 & 5 \end{bmatrix}$

   b) $A = \begin{bmatrix} 3 & 2 \\ -5 & 7 \end{bmatrix}$ $B = \begin{bmatrix} -2 & 9 \\ -5 & 7 \end{bmatrix}$

   c) $A = \begin{bmatrix} 3 & -2 & 0 \\ 1 & 5 & 6 \\ -2 & 1 & 3 \end{bmatrix}$ $B = \begin{bmatrix} 3 & -2 & 0 \\ -3 & 7 & 12 \\ -2 & 1 & 3 \end{bmatrix}$

   d) $A = \begin{bmatrix} 1 & 3 & -7 \\ -1 & 2 & -5 \\ -3 & 0 & 6 \end{bmatrix}$ $B = \begin{bmatrix} 1 & 3 & -7 \\ -1 & 2 & -5 \\ -1 & 6 & -8 \end{bmatrix}$

3. In each case find elementary matrices E_1 and E_2 such that $B = E_2 E_1 A$.

   a) $A = \begin{bmatrix} 3 & -5 \\ 2 & 4 \end{bmatrix}$ $B = \begin{bmatrix} 0 & -11 \\ 1 & 2 \end{bmatrix}$

   b) $A = \begin{bmatrix} 5 & -3 \\ 2 & 1 \end{bmatrix}$ $B = \begin{bmatrix} 2 & 1 \\ 1 & -5 \end{bmatrix}$

4. Describe the connection between elementary row operations and elementary matrices.

5. In each case express the invertible matrix A as a product of elementary matrices.

   a) $A = \begin{bmatrix} 3 & -1 \\ 1 & 0 \end{bmatrix}$ b) $A = \begin{bmatrix} 2 & -1 \\ 1 & -1 \end{bmatrix}$

6. In each case find an invertible matrix U such that $UA = R$ is the reduced row-echelon form of A.

   a) $A = \begin{bmatrix} 3 & -1 \\ -2 & 0 \end{bmatrix}$ b) $A = \begin{bmatrix} 3 & -1 \\ 1 & -3 \end{bmatrix}$

   c) $A = \begin{bmatrix} 3 & -1 & 4 \\ -2 & 0 & -3 \\ -1 & 3 & 0 \end{bmatrix}$ d) $A = \begin{bmatrix} 1 & -3 & -1 \\ 1 & -3 & 5 \\ 3 & -9 & -1 \end{bmatrix}$

7. Explain why a matrix can have many row-echelon forms.

8. In each case find an invertible matrix U such that $UA = B$.

a) $A = \begin{bmatrix} 3 & 1 \\ 2 & 5 \end{bmatrix}$ $B = \begin{bmatrix} 1 & -4 \\ 4 & -3 \end{bmatrix}$

b) $A = \begin{bmatrix} 2 & -3 \\ 5 & 1 \end{bmatrix}$ $B = \begin{bmatrix} 1 & 7 \\ 2 & -3 \end{bmatrix}$

9. What is the connection between invertible matrices and elementary matrices?

10. Find an elementary matrix F such that $B = AF$, where $A = \begin{bmatrix} 2 & -3 \\ 5 & 7 \end{bmatrix}$ and $B = \begin{bmatrix} 8 & -3 \\ -9 & 7 \end{bmatrix}$.

11. Let E be an elementary matrix. Show that E^T is also elementary of the same type as E.

12. In each case either show that the statement is true or give an example showing that it is false.
a) If $B = EA$ where E is elementary, then $A = FB$ for some elementary F.
b) The product of two elementary matrices is again elementary.
c) The transpose of an elementary matrix is again elementary.
d) If $A \to R$ and $B \to R$ where R is a reduced row-echelon matrix, then $A = B$.

13. In each case determine $r = rank A$ and find invertible matrices U and V such that $UAV = \begin{bmatrix} I_r & 0 \\ 0 & 0 \end{bmatrix}$.

a) $A = \begin{bmatrix} 1 & -1 & 2 & 1 \\ 2 & -1 & 0 & 3 \\ 0 & 1 & -4 & 1 \end{bmatrix}$ **b)** $A = \begin{bmatrix} 1 & 1 & 0 & -1 \\ 3 & 2 & 1 & 1 \\ 1 & 0 & 1 & 3 \end{bmatrix}$

14. While trying to invert A, the double matrix $[A \ I]$ is carried to $[P \ Q]$. Show that $P = QA$.

15. Use Theorem 1 to show that the only matrix A that can be carried to 0 by row operations is $A = 0$.

16. If $B = UA$ where U is invertible, show that $A \to B$ by row operations.

17. a) Show that every $m \times n$ matrix A can be factored as $A = UR$ where U is invertible and R is in reduced row-echelon form.
b) Show that R in the factorization in **a)** is unique, that is, if $A = U_1 R_1$ as in **a)**, then $R_1 = R$.
c) Show that the factorization in **a)** may not be unique in general.

18. Suppose that $A \to B$ by column operations, and we apply these same column operations to the double matrix $[A \ I]$ and get $[A \ I] \to [B \ V]$, explain why V is invertible and $AV = B$.

19. Two matrices A and B are called **row-equivalent** (written $A \overset{r}{\sim} B$) if A can be carried to B by row operations.
a) Show that $A \overset{r}{\sim} B$ if and only if $B = UA$ for some invertible matrix U.
b) If $A \overset{r}{\sim} B$, show that also $B \overset{r}{\sim} A$.
c) If $A \overset{r}{\sim} B$ and $B \overset{r}{\sim} C$, show that $A \overset{r}{\sim} C$.
d) If A and B are both row-equivalent to some third matrix, show that $A \overset{r}{\sim} B$.
e) If $A \overset{r}{\sim} B$, show that $rank A = rank B$.
f) If $A \overset{r}{\sim} B$ and A is invertible, show that B is also invertible.

1.7 LU-FACTORIZATION

The solution of a system of linear equations $AX = B$ can be computed much more quickly if the matrix A can be factored in the form $A = LU$ where L and U are matrices of a particularly nice form. Such factorizations play an important role in countless numerical applications. In this section we show that Gaussian elimination can be used to find such factorizations.

1.7.1 Triangular Matrices

As for square matrices, an $m \times n$ matrix A is called **upper triangular** if each entry below and to the left of the main diagonal is zero. For example, every row-echelon matrix is upper triangular, as is each of the following matrices:

$$\begin{bmatrix} 2 & -3 & 0 & 1 \\ 0 & 1 & 3 & 0 \\ 0 & 0 & 0 & 2 \end{bmatrix} \quad \begin{bmatrix} 0 & -1 & 0 & 5 & 2 \\ 0 & 0 & 0 & 5 & -2 \\ 0 & 0 & 1 & 0 & 3 \end{bmatrix} \quad \begin{bmatrix} 1 & 2 & 3 \\ 0 & -2 & 5 \\ 0 & 0 & 0 \\ 0 & 0 & 0 \end{bmatrix}$$

Similarly, a matrix A is called **lower triangular** if every entry above and to the right of the main diagonal is zero, equivalently if A^T is upper triangular. A matrix is called **triangular** if it is either upper or lower triangular. The following result will be needed, and follows from the definition of matrix multiplication.

LEMMA 1   The product of two lower (upper) triangular matrices is again lower (upper) triangular.

One reason for the importance of triangular matrices is the ease with which a linear system $AX = B$ can be solved when the coefficient matrix A is triangular.

Example 1   Solve the system

$$-x_1 - 2x_2 + x_3 + 3x_4 + 2x_5 = 2$$
$$x_3 + 5x_4 - 3x_5 = -1$$
$$2x_5 = 3$$

where the coefficient matrix is upper triangular.

SOLUTION   As for a row-echelon matrix, let $x_2 = s$ and $x_4 = t$ be parameters. We solve for x_5, x_3, and x_1 in that order. The third equation gives

$$x_5 = \tfrac{3}{2}$$

Then substitution into the second equation gives

$$x_3 = \tfrac{7}{2} - 5t$$

as the reader can verify. Finally substitute these into the first equation to get

$$x_1 = \tfrac{9}{2} - 2s - 2t.$$

This gives the general solution.

The method used in Example 1 is called **back substitution** because later variables are substituted into earlier equations. It works because the coefficient matrix is upper triangular. Similarly, if the matrix of coefficients is lower triangular, the system can be solved by **forward substitution** where earlier variables are substituted in later equations.

Now consider a system $AX = B$ where A is an arbitrary matrix. If A can be factored as $A = LU$ where L is an invertible lower triangular and U is upper triangular, the system $AX = B$ can be solved in two stages as follows:

1. First solve $LY = B$ for Y by forward substitution.
2. Then solve $UX = Y$ for X by back substitution.

Then X is the solution to the system $AX = B$. Indeed, since $A = LU$, we have $AX = LUX = LY = B$ as required. The method adapts easily for use in computer programs.

1.7.2   LU-Factorization

Hence if A is any $m \times n$ matrix, we try to factor A as $A = LU$ where L is lower triangular and U is upper triangular. The idea is to carry A by row operations to a row-echelon matrix U (which is upper triangular), and look for ways to find L. Suppose that k row operations are needed, and that the corresponding elementary matrices are $E_1, E_2, \cdots, E_k$. Then the reduction takes the form

$$A \to E_1 A \to E_2 E_1 A \to \cdots \to E_k \cdots E_2 E_1 A = U.$$

Thus $PA = U$ where $P = E_k \cdots E_2 E_1$ is invertible because each E_i is invertible.

If we do not insist that U is reduced, the row-reduction can be carried out by adding multiples of a row to rows below it, and possibly by row interchanges. The point is that no row of A need ever be added to a row *above* it. Thus, apart from row-interchanges, the only row operations needed are those for which the corresponding elementary matrix E_i is *lower* triangular. In particular, if no row interchanges are needed, the matrix P is lower triangular by Lemma 1. Since $PA = U$ we obtain $A = P^{-1}U$, and P^{-1} is also lower triangular by Theorem 4 §1.5. If we write $L = P^{-1}$, this proves the first part of the following theorem.

For convenience we say that a matrix A can be **lower reduced** if it can be carried to a row-echelon matrix using no row interchanges (and adding no multiple of a row to a row above it). A square matrix D is called **diagonal** if every entry off the main diagonal is zero.

THEOREM 1   Suppose that a matrix A can be lower reduced to a row-echelon matrix U. Then A can be factored as

$$A = LU$$

where L is lower triangular and invertible, and U is upper triangular and row-echelon. Moreover, if A is invertible, this factorization is unique; that is, if $A = L_1U_1$ is another such factorization, then $L_1 = L$ and $U_1 = U$.

PROOF   It remains to prove uniqueness. If $LU = A = L_1U_1$, then $L_1^{-1}L = U_1U^{-1} = D$, say. This matrix D is lower triangular ($L_1^{-1}L$) and upper triangular (U_1U^{-1}), and so is actually diagonal. But $D = U_1U^{-1}$ has 1's on the main diagonal (this is true of U and U_1 since they are invertible and row-echelon). It follows that $D = I$, and so $L_1^{-1}L = I$ and $U_1U^{-1} = I$. Hence $L_1 = L$ and $U_1 = U$, as asserted.

A factorization $A = LU$ as in Theorem 1 is called an **LU-factorization** of A. Such a factorization may not exist (Exercise 6) because A cannot be carried to row-echelon form without using at least one row interchange. A procedure for dealing with this situation will be outlined later.

If an LU-factorization $A = LU$ does exist, the above discussion shows that U can be any row-echelon form for A (obtained by lower reduction), and L is the inverse of the product of elementary matrices needed to carry $A \to U$. However, there is a simpler way to obtain L whereby the columns of L are obtained one by one. The following examples illustrate the technique. For convenience, the first nonzero column from the left in a matrix A is called the **leading column** of A.

Example 2   Find an LU-factorization for $A = \begin{bmatrix} 0 & 2 & -6 & -2 & 4 \\ 0 & -1 & 3 & 3 & 2 \\ 0 & -1 & 3 & 7 & 10 \end{bmatrix}$.

SOLUTION   We lower reduce A to row echelon form as follows:

$$A = \begin{bmatrix} 0 & 2 & -6 & -2 & 4 \\ 0 & -1 & 3 & 3 & 2 \\ 0 & -1 & 3 & 7 & 10 \end{bmatrix}$$

$$\rightarrow \begin{bmatrix} 0 & 1 & -3 & -1 & 2 \\ 0 & 0 & 0 & 2 & 4 \\ 0 & 0 & 0 & 6 & 12 \end{bmatrix}$$

$$\rightarrow \begin{bmatrix} 0 & 1 & -3 & -1 & 2 \\ 0 & 0 & 0 & 1 & 2 \\ 0 & 0 & 0 & 0 & 0 \end{bmatrix} = U$$

The shaded columns are determined as follows: The first is the leading column of A, and it is used to create the first leading 1 (using lower reduction). At this stage, we are finished with row 1, and we repeat the procedure on the matrix consisting of the remaining rows. Thus the second shaded column is the leading column of this smaller matrix, and we create the second leading 1. As the remaining row is zero in this case, we are finished. Then $A = LU$ where

$$L = \begin{bmatrix} 2 & 0 & 0 \\ -1 & 2 & 0 \\ -1 & 6 & 1 \end{bmatrix}.$$

This matrix L is obtained from the identity matrix by replacing the bottom of columns 1 and 2 by the leading columns (in order) that were shaded in the lower reduction. Note that $rank A = 2$ here, and this is the number of shaded columns.

The calculation in Example 2 works for any $m \times n$ matrix A that can be lower reduced to row-echelon form. The procedure can be stated formally as follows:

LU-ALGORITHM   Let A be an $m \times n$ matrix, and suppose $A \rightarrow U$ by lower reduction where U is a row-echelon matrix. Then $A = LU$ where the lower triangular, invertible matrix L is created as follows:

(1) If $A = 0$ take $L = I_m$ and $U = 0$.
(2) If $A \neq 0$ let C_1 denote the leading column of A. Then use C_1 to create the first leading 1 and make the rest of the entries in that column zero (using lower reduction). When this is done, let A_2 denote the resulting matrix with the first row deleted.
(3) If $A_2 \neq 0$ let C_2 denote its leading column and repeat Step 2 on A_2 to create A_3.
(4) Continue in this way until U is reached where all rows below the last leading 1 consist of zeros.
(5) Create L by placing $C_1, C_2, C_3, \cdots, C_r$ at the bottom of the first r columns of I_m, where $r = rank A$.

The proof that $LU = A$ in the LU-algorithm involves induction and block multiplication; we omit the details.

Example 3   Find an LU-factorization for $A = \begin{bmatrix} 5 & -5 & 10 & 0 & 5 \\ -3 & 3 & 2 & 2 & 1 \\ -2 & 2 & 0 & -1 & 0 \\ 1 & -1 & 10 & 2 & 5 \end{bmatrix}.$

SOLUTION   The lower reduction to row-echelon form is as follows:

$$\begin{bmatrix} 5 & -5 & 10 & 0 & 5 \\ -3 & 3 & 2 & 2 & 1 \\ -2 & 2 & 0 & -1 & 0 \\ 1 & -1 & 10 & 2 & 5 \end{bmatrix} \rightarrow \begin{bmatrix} 1 & -1 & 2 & 0 & 1 \\ 0 & 0 & 8 & 2 & 4 \\ 0 & 0 & 4 & -1 & 2 \\ 0 & 0 & 8 & 2 & 4 \end{bmatrix}$$

$$\rightarrow \begin{bmatrix} 1 & -1 & 2 & 0 & 1 \\ 0 & 0 & 1 & \frac{1}{4} & \frac{1}{2} \\ 0 & 0 & 0 & -2 & 0 \\ 0 & 0 & 0 & 0 & 0 \end{bmatrix}$$

$$\rightarrow \begin{bmatrix} 1 & -1 & 2 & 0 & 1 \\ 0 & 0 & 1 & \frac{1}{4} & \frac{1}{2} \\ 0 & 0 & 0 & 1 & 0 \\ 0 & 0 & 0 & 0 & 0 \end{bmatrix}.$$

Hence $A = LU$ where $L = \begin{bmatrix} 5 & 0 & 0 & 0 \\ -3 & 8 & 0 & 0 \\ -2 & 4 & -2 & 0 \\ 1 & 8 & 0 & 1 \end{bmatrix}$ and $U = \begin{bmatrix} 1 & -1 & 2 & 0 & 1 \\ 0 & 0 & 1 & \frac{1}{4} & \frac{1}{2} \\ 0 & 0 & 0 & 1 & 0 \\ 0 & 0 & 0 & 0 & 0 \end{bmatrix}$ as the reader can verify.

Example 4 Find an LU-factorization for the invertible matrix

$$A = \begin{bmatrix} 1 & 2 & 1 \\ 2 & -1 & 1 \\ 1 & 1 & 2 \end{bmatrix}.$$

SOLUTION The lower reduction to row-echelon form is

$$A = \begin{bmatrix} 1 & 2 & 1 \\ 2 & -1 & 1 \\ 1 & 1 & 2 \end{bmatrix} \rightarrow \begin{bmatrix} 1 & 2 & 1 \\ 0 & -5 & -1 \\ 0 & -1 & 1 \end{bmatrix}$$

$$\rightarrow \begin{bmatrix} 1 & 2 & 1 \\ 0 & 1 & \frac{1}{5} \\ 0 & 0 & \frac{6}{5} \end{bmatrix} \rightarrow \begin{bmatrix} 1 & 2 & 1 \\ 0 & 1 & \frac{1}{5} \\ 0 & 0 & 1 \end{bmatrix}$$

Hence $A = LU$ where $L = \begin{bmatrix} 1 & 0 & 0 \\ 2 & -5 & 0 \\ 1 & -1 & \frac{6}{5} \end{bmatrix}$ and $U = \begin{bmatrix} 1 & 2 & 1 \\ 0 & 1 & \frac{1}{5} \\ 0 & 0 & 1 \end{bmatrix}$.

If an invertible symmetric matrix A has an LU-factorization, we can get a better result.[21] More precisely, suppose $A = MU$ where U is a row-echelon form for A and M is lower triangular (the reason for denoting it as M will be apparent soon). Then

$$MU = A = A^T = U^T M^T.$$

Now observe that M and U are both invertible (by Corollary 1 of Theorem 5 §1.5, since A is invertible). Hence we get

$$(U^T)^{-1}M = M^T U^{-1} = D, \text{ say.}$$

This matrix D is lower triangular $((U^T)^{-1}M)$ and upper triangular $(M^T U^{-1})$, and so is actually diagonal. Since $M = U^T D$, the factorization $A = MU$ becomes

$$A = U^T DU.$$

Finally, write $L = U^T$, so that L is lower triangular with 1's on the main triangular (because U is row-echelon and invertible). This proves the following theorem which is important in numerical analysis. (The proof of uniqueness is like that in Theorem 1, and is left as an exercise for the reader.)

THEOREM 2 If A is a symmetric, invertible matrix which has an LU-factorization, then

$$A = LDL^T$$

where D is diagonal and L is lower triangular with 1's on the main diagonal. Moreover, this factorization is unique; that is, if $A = L_1 D_1 L_1^T$ is another such factorization, then $L_1 = L$ and $D_1 = D$.

The factorization in Theorem 2 is called an **LDLT-factorization** of the symmetric matrix A.

---

[21] But note that $\begin{bmatrix} 0 & 1 \\ 1 & 0 \end{bmatrix}$ does not have an LU-factorization.

Example 5

If A is the symmetric invertible matrix in Example 4, we have (in the notation of that example but writing M in place of L)

$$D = M^T U^{-1} = \begin{bmatrix} 1 & 2 & 1 \\ 0 & -5 & -1 \\ 0 & 0 & \frac{6}{5} \end{bmatrix} \begin{bmatrix} 1 & -2 & -\frac{3}{5} \\ 0 & 1 & -\frac{1}{5} \\ 0 & 0 & 1 \end{bmatrix} = \begin{bmatrix} 1 & 0 & 0 \\ 0 & -5 & 0 \\ 0 & 0 & \frac{6}{5} \end{bmatrix}.$$

The reader can verify that $A = LDL^T$ where $L = U^T$.

There is one special case of Theorem 2 that deserves mention. A symmetric matrix is called **positive definite** if $X^T A X > 0$ for every column $X \neq 0$ (here we regard the 1×1 matrix $X^T A X$ as a number). These matrices arise in geometry and in numerical analysis. They will be studied in Section 4.8.2 where several other characterizations are given and, in addition, it is shown that every positive definite matrix is invertible and admits an LU-factorization, and hence an LDLT-factorization.

1.7.3 Dealing with Row Interchanges

Every matrix A can be carried to a row-echelon matrix U by row operations. If we do not insist that U is reduced, this can be done without adding any multiples of a row of A to a row above it. If no row interchanges are required, we have seen that A admits an LU-factorization. But some matrices have no LU-factorization (for example $A = \begin{bmatrix} 0 & 1 \\ 1 & 0 \end{bmatrix}$) and so require at least one row interchange. However, it turns out that if all the necessary row interchanges are carried out first, the resulting matrix requires no interchanges and so has an LU-factorization.

THEOREM 3

Suppose an $m \times n$ matrix A is carried to a row-echelon matrix U using no row operations that add a multiple of a row to a row above it. Let $P_1, P_2, \cdots, P_{s-1}, P_s$ denote the elementary matrices corresponding (in order) to the row interchanges used. Write $P = P_s P_{s-1} \cdots P_2 P_1$ (if no interchanges are used, take $P = I_m$). Then:

(1) PA is the matrix obtained by doing these interchanges (in order) to A.

(2) PA has an LU-factorization.

The proof of Theorem 3 is omitted.

If $P_1, P_2, \cdots, P_{s-1}, P_s$ are elementary matrices corresponding to row interchanges, the matrix $P = P_s P_{s-1} \cdots P_2 P_1$ is called a **permutation matrix**. Such a matrix is obtained from the identity matrix by doing the same interchanges in order to I (starting with the one corresponding to P_1). Thus P is obtained from I by placing the rows in a different order (hence the name), and so has exactly one 1 in each row and column. We regard the identity matrix as a permutation matrix.

Example 6

If $A = \begin{bmatrix} 0 & 0 & -2 \\ 2 & 4 & 2 \\ 1 & -1 & 4 \end{bmatrix}$, find a permutation matrix P such that PA has an LU-factorization, and then find the factorization.

SOLUTION | First carry A to row-echelon form:

$$A = \begin{bmatrix} 0 & 0 & -2 \\ 2 & 4 & 2 \\ 1 & -1 & 4 \end{bmatrix} \rightarrow \begin{bmatrix} 1 & 2 & 1 \\ 0 & 0 & 1 \\ 1 & -1 & 4 \end{bmatrix}$$

$$\rightarrow \begin{bmatrix} 1 & 2 & 1 \\ 0 & 0 & 1 \\ 0 & -3 & 3 \end{bmatrix} \rightarrow \begin{bmatrix} 1 & 2 & 1 \\ 0 & 1 & -1 \\ 0 & 0 & 1 \end{bmatrix}$$

Only two row interchanges were used, first rows 1 and 2, and then rows 2 and 3. Hence, as in Theorem 3, the required permutation matrix is

$$P = P_2 P_1 = \begin{bmatrix} 1 & 0 & 0 \\ 0 & 0 & 1 \\ 0 & 1 & 0 \end{bmatrix} \begin{bmatrix} 0 & 1 & 0 \\ 1 & 0 & 0 \\ 0 & 0 & 1 \end{bmatrix} = \begin{bmatrix} 0 & 1 & 0 \\ 0 & 0 & 1 \\ 1 & 0 & 0 \end{bmatrix}.$$

If we do these interchanges in order to A, the result is PA. Applying the LU-algorithm to PA gives

$$PA = \begin{bmatrix} 2 & 4 & 2 \\ 1 & -1 & 4 \\ 0 & 0 & -2 \end{bmatrix} \rightarrow \begin{bmatrix} 1 & 2 & 1 \\ 0 & -3 & 3 \\ 0 & 0 & -2 \end{bmatrix}$$

$$\rightarrow \begin{bmatrix} 1 & 2 & 1 \\ 0 & 1 & -1 \\ 0 & 0 & -2 \end{bmatrix} \rightarrow \begin{bmatrix} 1 & 2 & 1 \\ 0 & 1 & -1 \\ 0 & 0 & 1 \end{bmatrix} = U.$$

Hence $PA = LU$ where $L = \begin{bmatrix} 2 & 0 & 0 \\ 1 & -3 & 0 \\ 0 & 0 & -2 \end{bmatrix}$ and $U = \begin{bmatrix} 1 & 2 & 1 \\ 0 & 1 & -1 \\ 0 & 0 & 1 \end{bmatrix}$.

Note that A can be carried also to row-echelon form using only one row interchange (1 and 3). The reader should obtain the corresponding factorization.

Consider the system $AX = B$ of linear equations where A is $m \times n$. If P is any permutation matrix, the matrix PA is obtained from A by writing the rows in a different order. Hence the system of equations

$$(PA)X = PB$$

is identical to the system $AX = B$ except for the order in which the equations are written, and so the two systems have the same solutions. Since the permutation matrix P can be chosen so that PA has an LU-factorization, the system $(PA)X = PB$ can be solved by forward and backward substitution.

Exercises 1.7

1. In each case use the given LU-factorization of A to solve the system $AX = B$ by solving $LY = B$ and $UX = Y$ by forward and backward substition respectively.

a) $A = \begin{bmatrix} 2 & 0 & 0 & 0 \\ 3 & -1 & 0 & 0 \\ 7 & 0 & 1 & 0 \\ 2 & -3 & 5 & 2 \end{bmatrix} \begin{bmatrix} 2 & -1 & 0 & 0 & 3 \\ 0 & 5 & 7 & -3 & 2 \\ 0 & 0 & -1 & 0 & 3 \\ 0 & 0 & 0 & 0 & 0 \end{bmatrix}$, $B = \begin{bmatrix} 8 \\ 1 \\ 30 \\ -15 \end{bmatrix}$

b) $A = \begin{bmatrix} 1 & 0 & 0 & 0 \\ 5 & -3 & 0 & 0 \\ 2 & 0 & -1 & 0 \\ -1 & 7 & 0 & 1 \end{bmatrix} \begin{bmatrix} 1 & -3 & 7 & 11 & -4 \\ 0 & 2 & -5 & 6 & 1 \\ 0 & 0 & 0 & 0 & 0 \\ 0 & 0 & 0 & 0 & 0 \end{bmatrix}$, $B = \begin{bmatrix} 2 \\ -1 \\ 7 \\ 2 \end{bmatrix}$

2. In each case find a LU-factorization of the given matrix.

a) $\begin{bmatrix} 2 & 4 & 2 \\ 1 & -1 & 3 \\ -1 & 7 & -7 \end{bmatrix}$

b) $\begin{bmatrix} -3 & 6 & 9 \\ 2 & -4 & 1 \\ -1 & 2 & -7 \end{bmatrix}$

c) $\begin{bmatrix} 2 & 6 & -2 & 0 & 2 \\ 3 & 9 & -3 & 3 & 1 \\ -1 & -3 & 1 & -3 & 1 \end{bmatrix}$

d) $\begin{bmatrix} 3 & -9 & 6 & 0 & -9 \\ -2 & 6 & 1 & 1 & 1 \\ -1 & 3 & 0 & 4 & 3 \end{bmatrix}$

e) $\begin{bmatrix} -5 & 10 & 0 & -15 \\ 2 & -3 & 1 & 5 \\ 1 & -2 & 4 & 0 \\ 1 & 1 & 1 & 1 \end{bmatrix}$

f) $\begin{bmatrix} 1 & -3 & 2 & 0 \\ 2 & -5 & -3 & 1 \\ 0 & -1 & 3 & 7 \\ -1 & 3 & 2 & 5 \end{bmatrix}$

g) $\begin{bmatrix} 2 & 2 & -2 & 4 & 2 \\ 1 & -1 & 0 & 2 & 1 \\ 3 & 1 & -2 & 6 & 3 \\ 1 & 3 & -2 & 2 & 1 \end{bmatrix}$ **h)** $\begin{bmatrix} -1 & -3 & 1 & 0 & -1 \\ 1 & 4 & 1 & 1 & 1 \\ 1 & 2 & -3 & -1 & 1 \\ 0 & -2 & -4 & -2 & 0 \end{bmatrix}$

3. In your own words, write the procedure to find an LU-factorization of a matrix A, and describe how it is used to solve a system $AX = B$.

4. In each case find a permutation matrix P such that PA has an LU-factorization, and find that factorization.

a) $A = \begin{bmatrix} -1 & 4 & 5 & 2 \\ 0 & 0 & 0 & -1 \\ 1 & -2 & -2 & 0 \\ 0 & -1 & -1 & 0 \end{bmatrix}$ **b)** $A = \begin{bmatrix} 0 & 0 & 0 & 3 \\ 0 & 0 & 2 & -4 \\ 0 & -1 & 0 & 5 \\ 1 & 3 & -2 & 3 \end{bmatrix}$

5. In each case either show that the statement is true or give an example showing that it is false.
   a) The sum of two upper triangular matrices is again upper triangular.
   b) Every invertible matrix has an LU-factorization.
   c) Every permutation matrix is invertible.
   d) If B is symmetric, so also is LBL^T for any matrix L.

6. If $A = \begin{bmatrix} 0 & 1 \\ 1 & 0 \end{bmatrix}$, show that $A = LU$ is impossible for *any* lower triangular 2×2 matrix L and upper triangular 2×2 matrix U. In particular, show that A has no LU-factorization.

7. If A is lower triangular and invertible, give an LU-factorization of A.

8. Show that any row interchange can be accomplished by row operations of other types.

9. Show that any multiple of a row can be added to a row above it by row operations of other types.

10. a) Show that every permutation matrix is invertible.
   b) Show that the inverse of a permutation matrix is again a permutation matrix.

11. Show that the $LDLT$ factorization in Theorem 2 is unique.

12. A triangular matrix is called *unit triangular* if it is square and every main diagonal element is 1.
   a) If A has an LU-factorization, show that $A = LU$ where L is unit lower triangular and U is upper triangular.
   b) Show that the factorization in **a)** is unique if A is invertible.

13. If $A = \begin{bmatrix} a & b \\ b & c \end{bmatrix}$ where $a \neq 0$ and $ac \neq b^2$, show that A has an $LDLT$ factorization, $A = LDL^T$, and find D and L.

1.8   APPLICATION TO MARKOV CHAINS[22]

A Markov chain is a mathematical model that provides insight and information about a wide variety of applications, but is simple enough to be described using only linear equations and matrix multiplication. The model requires an acquaintance with probability theory, but this is no hindrance as we can proceed informally.

The probability of getting a head when flipping a fair coin is $\frac{1}{2}$ because, in a long series of flips, the coin will fall heads half the time. In general, the **probability** of an event is the long-term proportion of the time that the event will occur. For example, the probability of obtaining a 6 on the roll of a die is $\frac{1}{6}$ because each of the 6 faces of the die is equally likely to appear. Probabilities of events are thus numbers between 0 and 1, with impossible events having probability 0, and certain events having probability 1. Our use of probabilities arises in applications like the following.

1.8.1   A Model of the Weather

Consider the weather in a certain city. We assume for simplicity that it is always in one of two *states*: sunny or cloudy. The weather evolves in daily stages, changing from one state to another. We are interested in finding the answers to questions of the following type:

---

[22] The material in this section will not be used elsewhere in the text.

Question 1. *If it is sunny on Monday, what is the probability that it is sunny on Thursday?*

Question 2. *What is the long-term proportion of the time that it is sunny?*

To answer such questions, we need to know the probability that the weather will change or remain the same from one day to the next. Suppose that long-term weather records show that:

(1) If it is sunny one day, it is equally likely to be sunny or cloudy next day.
(2) If it is cloudy one day, the probabilities it is sunny and cloudy the next day are $\frac{3}{4}$ and $\frac{1}{4}$ respectively.

With the help of matrix algebra, this information provides answers to the above questions.

The given weather data are summarized in the accompanying table. Note that, if it is sunny on a given day, the first column lists the probabilities for the weather on the next day. Similarly, the second column gives the probabilities for the weather the day after a cloudy day. In particular, each column sums to 1 because, in this model, it *must* be either sunny or cloudy the next day. The corresponding matrix of probabilities

Present day

	S	C
Next day S	$\frac{1}{2}$	$\frac{3}{4}$
C	$\frac{1}{2}$	$\frac{1}{4}$

$$P = \begin{bmatrix} \frac{1}{2} & \frac{3}{4} \\ \frac{1}{2} & \frac{1}{4} \end{bmatrix}$$

is called the *probability transition matrix* for this model of the weather.

Of course the weather each day is not determined; all we can hope to know is the *probability* that it is sunny or cloudy on any given day. Hence we introduce the *state vector* for day m:

$$S_m = \begin{bmatrix} s_1 \\ s_2 \end{bmatrix}$$

Here s_1 and s_2 are the probabilities that the weather is sunny and cloudy, respectively, on day m. In particular S_0 represents the initial situation. Note that $s_1 + s_2 = 1$ because the weather must be in *some* state on day m. The remarkable thing is that we can use matrix multiplication to compute these state vectors. More precisely, the following matrix equations hold:

$$S_{m+1} = PS_m \quad \text{for each} \quad m = 0, 1, \cdots. \tag{$*$}$$

In other words, the state vector S_{m+1} for a given day can be computed by multiplying S_m by the transition matrix P. To apply this to our situation, choose the initial day to be Monday. Then $S_0 = \begin{bmatrix} 1 \\ 0 \end{bmatrix}$ because we are assuming that the weather is sunny on Monday. With this, we can apply $(*)$ repeatedly to compute

$$S_1 = PS_0 = \begin{bmatrix} \frac{1}{2} & \frac{3}{4} \\ \frac{1}{2} & \frac{1}{4} \end{bmatrix}\begin{bmatrix} 1 \\ 0 \end{bmatrix} = \begin{bmatrix} \frac{1}{2} \\ \frac{1}{2} \end{bmatrix},$$

$$S_2 = PS_1 = \begin{bmatrix} \frac{1}{2} & \frac{3}{4} \\ \frac{1}{2} & \frac{1}{4} \end{bmatrix}\begin{bmatrix} \frac{1}{2} \\ \frac{1}{2} \end{bmatrix} = \begin{bmatrix} \frac{5}{8} \\ \frac{3}{8} \end{bmatrix},$$

$$S_3 = PS_2 = \begin{bmatrix} \frac{1}{2} & \frac{3}{4} \\ \frac{1}{2} & \frac{1}{4} \end{bmatrix}\begin{bmatrix} \frac{5}{8} \\ \frac{3}{8} \end{bmatrix} = \begin{bmatrix} \frac{19}{32} \\ \frac{13}{32} \end{bmatrix}.$$

Since we are taking Monday to be day 0, Thursday is day 3. Hence the probability that it is sunny Thursday is $\frac{19}{32}$, answering Question 1 above. Of course we have also determined that the probability it is cloudy on Thursday is $\frac{13}{32}$.

Turning to Question 2, we compute successively

$$S_4 = \begin{bmatrix} 0.6015625 \\ 0.3984375 \end{bmatrix}, \quad S_5 = \begin{bmatrix} 0.599609375 \\ 0.400390625 \end{bmatrix}, \quad S_6 = \begin{bmatrix} 0.600097656 \\ 0.399902344 \end{bmatrix}, \cdots.$$

Clearly S_m is getting closer and closer to $\begin{bmatrix} 0.6 \\ 0.4 \end{bmatrix}$ as m increases. It follows that, in the long run, the weather is sunny with probability 0.6, and cloudy with probability 0.4. This answers Question 2.

The vector $S = \begin{bmatrix} 0.6 \\ 0.4 \end{bmatrix}$ is called the *steady-state vector* for the weather. There is another way to compute it that is much better (and simpler) than computing several state vectors $S_1, S_2, \cdots$ and observing their behaviour. Assume that S_m is indeed very close to some fixed vector S for all sufficiently large m. Then S_{m+1} is also very close to S, and so the equation $S_{m+1} = PS_m$ is closely approximated by $S = PS$. This can be written

$$(I - P)S = 0$$

which is a system of linear homogeneous equations for S. In the above model of the weather, reduction of the augmented matrix to reduced form is

$$\begin{bmatrix} \frac{1}{2} & -\frac{3}{4} & 0 \\ -\frac{1}{2} & \frac{3}{4} & 0 \end{bmatrix} \rightarrow \begin{bmatrix} 1 & -\frac{3}{2} & 0 \\ 0 & 0 & 0 \end{bmatrix}$$

so the general solution to the system $(I - P)S = 0$ is $\begin{bmatrix} \frac{3}{2}t \\ t \end{bmatrix}$ where t is a parameter. Since the entries of S must sum to 1, we must have $\frac{3}{2}t + t = 1$, and so $t = \frac{2}{5}$. This gives $S = \begin{bmatrix} \frac{3}{5} \\ \frac{2}{5} \end{bmatrix} = \begin{bmatrix} 0.6 \\ 0.4 \end{bmatrix}$, which is what we had before.

1.8.2   Markov Chains

This model of the weather is an example of a Markov chain. In general, a **Markov**[23] **chain** is a system that evolves through a series of **stages** (the consecutive days in the above discussion) and, at any stage, must be in one of a finite number of **states** (sunny or cloudy). To analyze the chain, we must know each **transition probability** p_{ij}; that is, the probability that, if the chain is in state j at some stage, it will be in state i after one more transition. If the chain has n states, the $n \times n$ matrix $P = [p_{ij}]$ is called the **transition matrix** for the chain. The 3×3 case is illustrated as follows:

		Present stage		
		State 1	State 2	State 3
Next stage	State 1	p_{11}	p_{12}	p_{13}
	State 2	p_{21}	p_{22}	p_{23}
	State 3	p_{31}	p_{32}	p_{33}

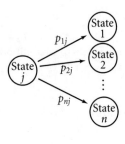

Observe that each column of P sums to 1 because, starting in state j at present, the chain must go to *some* state at the next stage. In general, a square matrix is called **stochastic** if the entries are all nonnegative and each column sum is 1.

---

[23] Named after the Russian mathematician Andreĭ Andreevič Markov (1856–1922).

In general, columns whose entries are probabilities that sum to 1 are called **probability vectors**. At the mth stage, the chain is described by the **state vector**

$$S_m = \begin{bmatrix} s_1^{(m)} \\ s_2^{(m)} \\ \vdots \\ s_n^{(m)} \end{bmatrix}$$

where $s_k^{(m)}$ is the probability that the chain is in state k after m transitions. Note that each S_m is a probability vector because the chain must be in *some* state after m transitions. A probability vector S is called a **steady-state vector** for the Markov chain if the state vectors S_m get closer and closer to S as m increases. Thus the entries of S are the long-term probabilities that the chain will be in the various states.

It can happen that a Markov chain does not have a steady-state vector. One condition that guarantees that a steady-state vector exists is that the chain is **regular**; that is, some power P^k of the transition matrix has all its entries positive. For small chains this can be checked graphically as follows: Represent the states as the vertices $v_1, v_2, \cdots, v_n$ of a directed graph (called the **graph** of the chain) and draw an arrow from state v_j to v_i when it is possible to go from state v_j to state v_i (that is, when the probability $p_{ij} > 0$). Then the chain is regular if there exists an integer k such that it is possible to go from any vertex to any other vertex in exactly k transitions.

Thus, for example, the weather chain discussed above is regular because it is possible to go from any state to any other state in *one* transition. The graph is given in the diagram.

The behaviour of regular Markov chains is summarized in the following theorem.

THEOREM 1

Consider a Markov chain with transition matrix P.

(1) $S_{m+1} = PS_m$ for all $m = 0, 1, 2, \cdots$.

(2) Suppose the chain is regular. Then the steady state vector S is the unique solution to the homogeneous system

$$(I - P)S = 0$$

whose entries sum to 1.

We give a proof of (1) of Theorem 1 at the end of this section which illustrates how it is that matrix multiplication arises here. Part (2) of Theorem 1 will not be proved in this book.[24]

Example 1

Consider a mouse in the maze shown. If it is in any cell, assume that it is equally likely to stay in the cell, leave by the first exit, leave by the second exit, etc.

(a) If it starts in cell 1, what is the probability it is in each of the cells after three moves?

(b) What proportion of the time does it spend in each of the cells?

SOLUTION

The states here are the cells 1, 2, and 3, and the stages are the successive moves. If the mouse is in cell 1, it has two options: stay or go to cell 2. By assumption these are equally likely, so both have probability $\frac{1}{2}$. Since it has probability 0 of going to cell 3,

this gives the first column of the transition matrix $P = \begin{bmatrix} \frac{1}{2} & \frac{1}{3} & 0 \\ \frac{1}{2} & \frac{1}{3} & \frac{1}{2} \\ 0 & \frac{1}{3} & \frac{1}{2} \end{bmatrix}$.

---

[24] A proof can be found in Kemeny, Mirkil, Snell, and Thompson: *Finite Mathematical Structures*, Prentice-Hall, 1958.

If the mouse is in cell 2 it can stay, go to cell 1, or go to cell 3, and these all have probability $\frac{1}{3}$ (being equally likely). This gives column 2 of P, and column 3 is found in a similar way.

If the mouse starts in cell 1, we have $S_0 = [1 \quad 0 \quad 0]^T$. Hence we compute

$$S_1 = PS_0 = \begin{bmatrix} \frac{1}{2} \\ \frac{1}{2} \\ 0 \end{bmatrix}, \quad S_2 = PS_1 = \begin{bmatrix} \frac{5}{12} \\ \frac{5}{12} \\ \frac{2}{12} \end{bmatrix}, \quad S_3 = PS_2 = \begin{bmatrix} \frac{25}{72} \\ \frac{31}{72} \\ \frac{16}{72} \end{bmatrix}.$$

Thus the probabilities the mouse is in cells 1, 2, and 3 after three moves are $\frac{25}{72}$, $\frac{31}{72}$, and $\frac{16}{72}$ respectively.

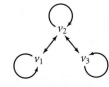

The graph of this chain is as shown, so any cell is reachable from any other cell in exactly 2 transitions. Hence the chain is regular and we can find the steady-state vector S by solving the system of linear equations

$$(I - P)S = 0.$$

The reduction of the augmented matrix to reduced form is as follows:

$$\begin{bmatrix} \frac{1}{2} & -\frac{1}{3} & 0 & 0 \\ -\frac{1}{2} & \frac{2}{3} & -\frac{1}{2} & 0 \\ 0 & -\frac{1}{3} & \frac{1}{2} & 0 \end{bmatrix} \rightarrow \begin{bmatrix} \frac{1}{2} & -\frac{1}{3} & 0 & 0 \\ 0 & \frac{1}{3} & -\frac{1}{2} & 0 \\ 0 & 0 & 0 & 0 \end{bmatrix}$$

$$\rightarrow \begin{bmatrix} 1 & 0 & -1 & 0 \\ 0 & 1 & -\frac{3}{2} & 0 \\ 0 & 0 & 0 & 0 \end{bmatrix}$$

Thus the general solution to $(I - P)S = 0$ is $\begin{bmatrix} t & \frac{3}{2}t & t \end{bmatrix}^T$. This is a probability vector if the entries sum to 1, that is if $t + \frac{3}{2}t + t = 1$. This gives $t = \frac{2}{7}$, so the steady-state vector is $S = \begin{bmatrix} \frac{2}{7} & \frac{3}{7} & \frac{2}{7} \end{bmatrix}^T$. Thus the mouse spends $\frac{3}{7}$ of his time in cell 2, and $\frac{2}{7}$ of his time in each of cells 1 and 3.

For any regular Markov chain, it can be shown that the solution S of the homogeneous system $(I - P)S = 0$ always involves exactly one parameter t (as in Example 1). Then t is determined by the requirement that the entries of the steady-state vector S must sum to 1.

We conclude with one final observation. Let P be the transition matrix of a Markov chain, and let S_0, S_1, S_2, $\cdots$ S_m, $\cdots$ be the state vectors. Then $S_1 = PS_0$ by Theorem 1, so $S_2 = PS_1 = P(PS_0) = P^2S_0$, again by Theorem 1. Next $S_3 = PS_2 = P(P^2S_0) = P^3S_0$. The pattern is clear:

$$S_m = P^m S_0 \quad \text{for each} \quad m = 1, 2, 3, \cdots.$$

Hence the behaviour of the chain is entirely determined by the initial state vector S_0 and the powers P^m of the transition matrix. In Section 2.3 we develop methods to calculate the powers of any square matrix.

1.8.3   Proof of (1) of Theorem 1

Think of the chain as having been run N times where N is large. Recall that the mth state vector is

$$S_m = \begin{bmatrix} s_1^{(m)} & s_2^{(m)} & \cdots & s_n^{(m)} \end{bmatrix}^T$$

where $s_i^{(m)}$ is the probability that it is in state i at stage m. Looking at stage $m + 1$, we have that, approximately,

$$s_i^{(m+1)}N \text{ is the number of times it is in state } i \text{ at stage } m + 1.$$

We count this number a different way. To get to state i at stage $m + 1$ the chain had to be in *some* state j at stage m. Since the approximate number of times it is in state j at stage m is $s_j^{(m)}N$, and since p_{ij} is the probability that it goes from state j to state i in one transition, the number of times it got to state i via state j is $p_{ij}(s_j^{(m)}N)$. Summing over j gives the total number of times it got to state i. This is the number we got before, so

$$s_i^{(m+1)}N = p_{i1} s_1^{(m)}N + p_{i2} s_2^{(m)}N + \cdots + p_{in} s_n^{(m)}N.$$

Cancelling N gives $s_i^{(m+1)} = p_{i1} s_1^{(m)} + p_{i2} s_2^{(m)} + \cdots + p_{in} s_n^{(m)}$. This asserts that entry i of the column matrix S_{m+1} is equal to entry i of the matrix product PS_m. Hence $S_{m+1} = PS_m$, which is (1) of Theorem 1.

Exercises 1.8

1. A city has only rainy or sunny days. Assume that there is an 80% probability of having sun the day following a sunny day, and a 60% probability of having rain the day following a rainy day. If there is an 80% probability of having a sunny day today, calculate the probabilities of rain and shine for each of the following 10 days, calculate the long-term probabilities of rain and shine, and find out how many days it will take to reach this steady-state vector with 2 decimal accuracy.

2. In each case find the steady-state vector and, assuming the chain starts in state 1, find the probability that it is in state 2 after 3 transitions.

a) $P = \begin{bmatrix} 0.5 & 0.3 \\ 0.5 & 0.7 \end{bmatrix}$ **b)** $P = \begin{bmatrix} \frac{1}{2} & 1 \\ \frac{1}{2} & 0 \end{bmatrix}$

c) $P = \begin{bmatrix} 0 & \frac{1}{2} & \frac{1}{4} \\ 1 & 0 & \frac{1}{4} \\ 0 & \frac{1}{2} & \frac{1}{2} \end{bmatrix}$ **d)** $P = \begin{bmatrix} 0.4 & 0.1 & 0.5 \\ 0.2 & 0.6 & 0.2 \\ 0.4 & 0.3 & 0.3 \end{bmatrix}$

e) $P = \begin{bmatrix} 0.8 & 0.0 & 0.2 \\ 0.1 & 0.6 & 0.1 \\ 0.1 & 0.4 & 0.7 \end{bmatrix}$ **f)** $P = \begin{bmatrix} 0.1 & 0.3 & 0.3 \\ 0.3 & 0.1 & 0.6 \\ 0.6 & 0.6 & 0.1 \end{bmatrix}$

3. In each case determine whether the given probability transition matrix is regular by drawing the graph.

a) $P = \begin{bmatrix} 0 & 0 & \frac{1}{2} \\ 1 & 0 & \frac{1}{2} \\ 0 & 1 & 0 \end{bmatrix}$ **b)** $P = \begin{bmatrix} \frac{1}{2} & 0 & \frac{1}{3} \\ \frac{1}{4} & 1 & \frac{1}{3} \\ \frac{1}{4} & 0 & \frac{1}{3} \end{bmatrix}$

c) $P = \begin{bmatrix} \frac{1}{2} & 0 & 0 \\ \frac{1}{2} & \frac{1}{4} & \frac{2}{3} \\ 0 & \frac{3}{4} & \frac{1}{3} \end{bmatrix}$ **d)** $P = \begin{bmatrix} 0 & 0 & \frac{1}{3} \\ \frac{1}{2} & 0 & \frac{1}{2} \\ \frac{1}{2} & 1 & \frac{1}{6} \end{bmatrix}$

4. A man eats one of three soups for lunch each day—beef, chicken, or vegetable. He never eats the same soup two days in a row. If he eats beef soup one day, he is equally likely to eat each of the others next day; if he does not eat beef soup one day, he is twice as likely to eat it next day as the alternative.

a) If he has beef soup one day, what is the probability he has it again two days later?

b) Find the long-run probabilities he eats each of the soups.

5. A wolf pack always hunts in one of four regions, R_1, R_2, R_3, or R_4. Its hunting habits are as follows:
(1) If it hunts in some region, it is as likely as not to hunt there the next day.
(2) If it hunts in R_1, it never hunts in R_2 or in R_3 the next day.
(3) If it hunts in R_2 or R_3, it is equally likely to hunt in each of the other regions the next day.
(4) If it hunts in R_4, it is equally likely to hunt in regions R_2 and R_3 on the next day, but twice as likely to hunt in R_1 than in either R_2 or R_3.

a) Find the proportion of the time the pack hunts in R_1, R_2, R_3, and R_4.

b) If the pack hunts in R_1 on Monday, find the probability it hunts there on Thursday.

6. A gambler always plays one of three slot machines, A, B, or C. He never plays the same machine on two successive days. If he plays A, he plays C the next day. If he plays B or C, he is twice as likely to play A the next day as the alternative.

a) What proportion of his time does he spend playing A, B, and C?

b) If he plays C one day, find the probability he plays it again three days later.

7. A lab rat has a choice of three foods P, Q, and R each day. On any given day it has a 60% chance of choosing the same food as it chose the previous day, and is equally likely to choose either of the other foods.

a) If it chooses P one day, find the probability it chooses Q three days later.

b) What percentage of its meals are food P, Q, and R?

8. Assume that there are three classes—upper U, middle M, and lower L—and that social mobility is modelled as follows:
   (1) Of children of U parents, 70% remain U while 20% become L and 10% become M.
   (2) Of children of M parents, 80% remain M while 10% become L and 10% become U.
   (3) Of children of L parents, 60% remain L while 10% become U and 30% become M.
   a) Find the probability that the grandchild of L parents becomes U.
   b) Find the long-term breakdown of society into classes.

9. John makes it to work on time one Monday out of four. On other work days his behaviour is as follows: If he is late one day, he is twice as likely to be on time next day as to be late. If he is on time one day, he is equally likely to be on time or late next day. Find the probability of his being on time Thursdays.

10. The governor says she will call an election. This gossip is passed from person to person with probability $p \neq 0$ that the information is passed incorrectly at any stage. Assume that when a person hears the news he or she passes it to one person who does not know. Find the long-term probability that a person will hear that there is going to be an election.

11. Suppose you play a game with a friend in which you either win or lose $1 at each round with equal probabilities. You start with $1 and you decide in advance to quit if you ever go broke or get $4. Assume that your friend never quits.
   a) If the states are 0, 1, 2, 3, and 4 (representing your wealth), show that the transition matrix is not regular.

   b) Find the probability that you go broke after exactly 3 matches.
   c) Find a steady-state vector by calculating S_n for large values of n, and make an argument whether, as a casino owner, you would profit from playing such a game in the long run against your customers.

12. In each case either show that the statement is true or give an example showing that it is false. Throughout, P denotes a probability transition matrix.
   a) If all rows but the last in P are known, then the last row is also known.
   b) If P has a 1 on the main diagonal, it is regular.
   c) If P is regular, then it is invertible.
   d) If P is invertible, then it is regular.

13. Let $E = [1 \; 1 \; \cdots \; 1]$ denote the $1 \times n$ matrix with each entry 1.
   a) If an $n \times n$ matrix P has nonnegative entries, show that P is stochastic if and only if $EP = E$.
   b) Show that the product of two stochastic matrices is stochastic.
   c) If P is stochastic, show that there exists a column $S \neq 0$ such that $PS = S$. [In fact S can be chosen to be a probability vector.]

14. Let $P = \begin{bmatrix} 0 & 0 & 1 \\ 1 & 0 & 0 \\ 0 & 1 & 0 \end{bmatrix}$. Is the corresponding chain regular? Draw the graph of the chain. Can you get from any vector to any other vector? Why does the graphical test fail? Show that $PS = S$ when $S = \begin{bmatrix} \frac{1}{3} & \frac{1}{3} & \frac{1}{3} \end{bmatrix}^T$. Do the state vectors get closer and closer to S?

1.9 FINITE FIELDS AND CRYPTOGRAPHY

Up to now, virtually all matrices have had entries that are real (possibly complex) numbers. The real numbers have the properties that they can be added and multiplied, that the usual laws of arithmetic hold, and that we can divide by any nonzero real number. As such the real numbers are an example of an algebraic system called a **field**. The set of complex numbers is also a field, as is the set of rational numbers (fractions). Our motivation for isolating the concept of a field is that nearly everything we have done remains valid if the scalars are restricted to some field: The Gaussian algorithm can be used to solve systems of linear equations with coefficients in the field, the matrix inversion algorithm works in the same way, and so on. The reason is that the field has all the properties used in the proofs of these results, so all the theorems remain valid.

It turns out that there are finite fields—that is, finite sets that satisfy the usual laws of arithmetic and in which every nonzero member has an inverse. This section is an informal introduction to some of these finite fields, with an application to cryptography.

1.9.1 Finite Fields

Our construction of a finite field is based on the process of "long division" familiar from arithmetic. For example, we can divide an integer[25] n by 5 and leave a remainder in the set $\{0, 1, 2, 3, 4\}$ (called the remainder of n modulo 5). For example

$$19 = 3 \cdot 5 + 4,$$

so the remainder of 19 modulo 5 is 4. Similarly the remainder of 137 modulo 5 is 2 because $137 = 27 \cdot 5 + 2$. This even works for negative integers: For example,

$$-17 = (-4) \cdot 5 + 3$$

so the remainder of -17 modulo 5 is 3.

This process is called the **division algorithm**. More formally, let $p \geq 2$ denote a positive integer. Then every integer n can be written uniquely in the form

$$n = qp + r \quad \text{where } q \text{ and } r \text{ are integers and } 0 \leq r \leq p - 1.$$

Here q is called the **quotient**, and r is called the **remainder** of n **modulo** p, and we refer to p as the **modulus**. Thus if $p = 6$, then the fact that $134 = 22 \cdot 6 + 2$ means that 134 has quotient 22 and remainder 2 modulo 6.

Returning to the case $p = 5$, consider the set $\mathbb{F}_5 = \{0, 1, 2, 3, 4\}$ of possible remainders. We are going to turn $\mathbb{F}_5$ into a field by adding and multiplying modulo 5: That is we add or multiply two numbers in $\mathbb{F}_5$ by calculating the usual sum or product and taking the remainder modulo 5. Hence $2 + 4 = 1$ and $2 \cdot 4 = 3$ in $\mathbb{F}_5$, while $3 + 4 = 2$, and $3 \cdot 4 = 2$. In this way we can fill in the addition and multiplication tables for $\mathbb{F}_5$; the result is:

+	0	1	2	3	4
0	0	1	2	3	4
1	1	2	3	4	0
2	2	3	4	0	1
3	3	4	0	1	2
4	4	0	1	2	3

×	0	1	2	3	4
0	0	0	0	0	0
1	0	1	2	3	4
2	0	2	4	1	3
3	0	3	1	4	2
4	0	4	3	2	1

The remarkable thing about this is that addition and multiplication modulo 5 make $\mathbb{F}_5$ into a field. That the usual laws of arithmetic hold is not too surprising since they are true for ordinary addition and multiplication and all we are doing is reducing modulo 5. Perhaps more surprising is the fact that $\mathbb{F}_5$ is a field as the multiplication table shows: We have $1 \cdot 1 = 1$, $2 \cdot 3 = 1 (= 3 \cdot 2)$, and $4 \cdot 4 = 1$, so 1 and 4 are selfinverse in $\mathbb{F}_5$, and 2 and 3 are inverses of each other. In other words, *every nonzero element* of $\mathbb{F}_5$ has an inverse!

Note that if we do all of this using 6 as the modulus, we do not get a field. For in that case we have $\mathbb{F}_6 = \{0, 1, 2, 3, 4, 5\}$, and $2 \cdot 3 = 0$ so neither 2 nor 3 has an inverse in $\mathbb{F}_6$ (verify this). The reason, of course, is that 6 factors as 2 times 3 in ordinary arithmetic, and so leaves a remainder of 0 modulo 6. Of course 5 has no such factorization, and it is this fact that makes $\mathbb{F}_5$ into a field. More generally, an integer $p \geq 2$ is called a **prime** if p cannot be factored as $p = ab$ where a and b are positive integers, and neither a nor b equals 1. Thus the first few primes are 2, 3, 5, 7, 11, 13, 17, $\cdots$.

If p is a prime, let

$$\mathbb{F}_p = \{0, 1, 2, 3, \cdots, p - 1\}$$

---

[25] The **integers** are the numbers 0, ± 1, ± 2, ± 3, $\cdots$.

denote the set of possible remainders modulo p. We add and multiply in $\mathbb{F}_p$ by finding the usual sum or product and taking the remainder modulo p. The important fact that we need is the following result.

THEOREM ①   If p is a prime and we write $\mathbb{F}_p = \{0, \ 1, \ 2, \ 3, \cdots, \ p-1\}$, then $\mathbb{F}_p$ is a field using addition and multiplication modulo p.

The proof can be found in books on abstract algebra.[26]

Note that we will make statements like $-16 = 4$ in $\mathbb{F}_5$; it means that -16 and 4 leave the same remainder when divided by 5, and so are equal in $\mathbb{F}_5$ (and we say that $-16 = 4$ modulo 5). In general, if p is any prime, the operative fact is that $n = m$ modulo p if $n - m$ is a multiple of p.

Example 1   If $p = 2$, then $\mathbb{F}_2 = \{0, \ 1\}$ with addition and multiplication modulo 2 given by the tables

+	0	1
0	0	1
1	1	0

and

×	0	1
0	0	0
1	0	1

This is binary arithmetic, the basis of computers.

Arithmetic in $\mathbb{F}_p$ is in a sense simpler than that for the real numbers. For example, consider negatives. Given the element 8 in $\mathbb{F}_{17}$, what is -8? The answer lies in the observation that $8 + 9 = 0$ in $\mathbb{F}_{17}$, so $-8 = 9$ (and $-9 = 8$). In the same way, finding negatives is not difficult in $\mathbb{F}_p$ for any prime p.

However, as for matrices, it is more difficult to find inverses in $\mathbb{F}_p$. For example, how does one find $\frac{1}{14}$ in $\mathbb{F}_{17}$? Since $\frac{1}{14} \cdot 14 = 1$ in $\mathbb{F}_{17}$, we are looking for an integer a with the property that $a \cdot 14 = 1$ modulo 17. Of course we can try all possibilities (there are only 17 of them!), and the result is $a = 11$ (verify). However this method is of little use for large primes p, and it is a comfort to know that there is a systematic procedure (called the **Euclidean algorithm**) for finding inverses in $\mathbb{F}_p$ for any prime p. Furthermore, this algorithm is easy to program for a computer. To illustrate the method, let us once again find the inverse of 14 in $\mathbb{F}_{17}$.

Example 2   Find the inverse of 14 in $\mathbb{F}_{17}$.

SOLUTION   The idea is to first divide $p = 17$ by 14:

$$17 = 1 \cdot 14 + 3.$$

Now divide 14 by the new remainder 3 to get

$$14 = 4 \cdot 3 + 2,$$

and then divide 3 by the new remainder 2 to get

$$3 = 1 \cdot 2 + 1.$$

It is a theorem of number theory that, because 17 is a prime, this procedure will always lead to a remainder of 1 as is the case here. At this point we eliminate remainders in these equations from the bottom up. In the present example, we get:

---

[26] For example, W.K. Nicholson, *Introduction to Abstract Algebra*, 2nd ed., Wiley, 1999.

$$1 = 3 - 1 \cdot 2$$
$$= 3 - 1 \cdot (14 - 4 \cdot 3) \;=\; 5 \cdot 3 - 1 \cdot 14$$
$$= 5 \cdot (17 - 1 \cdot 14) - 1 \cdot 14 \;=\; 5 \cdot 17 - 6 \cdot 14.$$

Hence $(-6) \cdot 14 = 1$ in $\mathbb{F}_{17}$, that is $11 \cdot 14 = 1$. So $\frac{1}{14} = 11$ in $\mathbb{F}_{17}$.

As mentioned above, nearly everything we have done with matrices over the field of real numbers can be done in the same way for matrices with entries from $\mathbb{F}_p$. We illustrate with one example.

Example 3   Determine if the matrix $A = \begin{bmatrix} 1 & 4 \\ 6 & 5 \end{bmatrix}$ from $\mathbb{F}_7$ is invertible, and if so find its inverse.

PROOF   Working in $\mathbb{F}_7$, $det\,A = 1 \cdot 5 - 6 \cdot 4 = 5 - 3 = 2 \neq 0$ in $\mathbb{F}_7$, so A is invertible. Hence Example 5 §1.5 gives $A^{-1} = \frac{1}{2}\begin{bmatrix} 5 & -4 \\ -6 & 1 \end{bmatrix}$. Now $2 \cdot 4 = 1$ in $\mathbb{F}_7$, so $\frac{1}{2} = 4$. Also, $-4 = 3$ and $-6 = 1$ in $\mathbb{F}_7$ so, finally, $A^{-1} = 4\begin{bmatrix} 5 & 3 \\ 1 & 1 \end{bmatrix} = \begin{bmatrix} 6 & 5 \\ 4 & 4 \end{bmatrix}$. Thus $\begin{bmatrix} 1 & 4 \\ 6 & 5 \end{bmatrix}\begin{bmatrix} 6 & 5 \\ 4 & 4 \end{bmatrix} = \begin{bmatrix} 1 & 0 \\ 0 & 1 \end{bmatrix}$ in $\mathbb{F}_7$ as the reader can verify.

1.9.2 **An Application to Cryptography**[27]

Cryptography is the science of encoding messages so that they will not be understood if they are intercepted, but which can be easily decoded by the intended recipient. We conclude with one simple example in this large and rapidly growing field.

Suppose a general wants to send the message

ATTACK AT DAWN

to his major in the field, but does not want the message to be understood by the opposing forces. We use the following method of coding the message: Convert every letter and punctuation mark into a number as follows

a	b	c	d	e	f	g	h	i	j	k	l	m	n	o	p
0	1	2	3	4	5	6	7	8	9	10	11	12	13	14	15

q	r	s	t	u	v	w	x	y	z	,	.	–
16	17	18	19	20	21	22	23	24	25	26	27	28

where 28 represents a space. Then the message ATTACK AT DAWN becomes

0 19 19 0 2 10 28 0 19 28 3 0 22 13

in numerical form.

Now we encode the message for transmission as follows: Since there are 29 symbols, and since the number 29 is a prime, we choose an invertible 2×2 matrix over $\mathbb{F}_{29}$, say

$$A = \begin{bmatrix} 2 & 15 \\ 7 & 22 \end{bmatrix}.$$

Then break the message into 1×2 segments as follows:

$$[0 \;\; 19]\,[19 \;\; 0]\,[2 \;\; 10]\,[28 \;\; 0]\,[19 \;\; 28]\,[3 \;\; 0]\,[22 \;\; 13].$$

Next encode the message by right multiplying each 1×2 segment by A to get

$$[17 \;\; 12]\,[9 \;\; 24]\,[16 \;\; 18]\,[27 \;\; 14]\,[2 \;\; 2]\,[6 \;\; 16]\,[19 \;\; 7]$$

[27] We acknowledge the contribution of Murray Bremner, University of Saskatchewan.

(corresponding to the message RMJYQS.OCCGQTH). It is this sequence that is transmitted to the major who, being in possession of A, finds A^{-1} and decodes the message by right multiplying each of these new segments by A^{-1}.

More precisely, $det A = -61 = 26$ in $\mathbb{F}_{29}$, so A is invertible. Using the Euclidean algorithm, we find $\frac{1}{26}$ as follows: $29 = 1 \cdot 26 + 3$, $26 = 8 \cdot 3 + 2$, $3 = 1 \cdot 2 + 1$; and eliminating remainders gives

$$1 = 3 - 1 \cdot (26 - 8 \cdot 3) = 9 \cdot 3 - 1 \cdot 26 = 9(29 - 1 \cdot 26) - 1 \cdot 26 = 9 \cdot 29 - 10 \cdot 26.$$

Hence $(-10) \cdot 26 = 1$ modulo 29, that is $19 \cdot 26 = 1$. Hence $\frac{1}{26} = 19$ in $\mathbb{F}_{29}$.
Now

$$A^{-1} = \tfrac{1}{26}\begin{bmatrix} 22 & -15 \\ -7 & 2 \end{bmatrix} = 19\begin{bmatrix} 22 & 14 \\ 22 & 2 \end{bmatrix} = \begin{bmatrix} 12 & 5 \\ 12 & 9 \end{bmatrix}.$$

Hence the first segment $[17 \quad 12]$ of the transmitted message is decoded by right multiplication by A^{-1} to give $[17 \quad 12]\begin{bmatrix} 12 & 5 \\ 12 & 9 \end{bmatrix} = [0 \quad 19]$, which is the first segment of the original messsage. Similarly each segment is decoded, and so the original message is recreated.

Of course this can be varied: The original message can be broken into segments of length 3, say, and then encoded by right multiplication by an invertible 3×3 matrix A. And more symbols can be introduced by choosing a larger prime as the modulus.

Exercises 1.9

1. In each case write the addition and multiplication table of the finite field.

   a) $\mathbb{F}_3$ **b)** $\mathbb{F}_7$ **c)** $\mathbb{F}_{11}$

2. In each case find $\frac{1}{a}$ in $\mathbb{F}_p$.

   a) $a = 12$ in $\mathbb{F}_{41}$.   **b)** $a = 17$ in $\mathbb{F}_{37}$.
   c) $a = 11$ in $\mathbb{F}_{23}$.   **d)** $a = 8$ in $\mathbb{F}_{29}$.

3. In each case either show that A has no inverse or find A^{-1}.

   a) $A = \begin{bmatrix} 2 & 1 \\ 5 & 2 \end{bmatrix}$ in $\mathbb{F}_7$.   **b)** $A = \begin{bmatrix} 3 & 4 \\ 7 & 8 \end{bmatrix}$ in $\mathbb{F}_{11}$.

   c) $A = \begin{bmatrix} 3 & 11 \\ 2 & 8 \end{bmatrix}$ in $\mathbb{F}_{13}$.   **d)** $A = \begin{bmatrix} 2 & 1 \\ 3 & 4 \end{bmatrix}$ in $\mathbb{F}_5$.

4. Encode the message MEET AT NOON using the setup in the text, but using $A = \begin{bmatrix} 6 & 2 \\ 12 & 7 \end{bmatrix}$. What is A^{-1}?

5. Show that the elements of the last column of the multiplication table for $\mathbb{F}_p$ are $0,\ p-1,\ p-2, \cdots,\ 2,\ 1$ in that order.

CHAPTER 2

Determinants and Eigenvalues

2.1 COFACTOR EXPANSIONS

In Section 1.5 we defined the determinant of a 2×2 matrix $A = \begin{bmatrix} a & b \\ c & d \end{bmatrix}$ as follows:

$$det A = det \begin{bmatrix} a & b \\ c & d \end{bmatrix} = ad - bc$$

We then showed (Example 5 §1.5) that A has an inverse if $det A \neq 0$, and gave a formula for the inverse in that case. One goal of this chapter is to do this for *any* square matrix A.

There is no problem if A is 1×1, say $A = [a]$. In that case we define

$$det[a] = a$$

and note that $[a]$ is invertible if (and only if) $a \neq 0$, and that then the formula for the inverse is $[a]^{-1} = \left[\frac{1}{a} \right]$.

So what do we do if A is $n \times n$ where $n \geq 3$? The formula for the determinant of a 3×3 matrix turns out to be:

$$det \begin{bmatrix} a & b & c \\ d & e & f \\ g & h & i \end{bmatrix} = aei + bfg + cdh - ceg - afh - bdi \qquad (*)$$

and the expression for the inverse is even more involved.[1] The situation is much more complicated for $n \times n$ matrices where $n > 3$.

2.1.1 Cofactor Expansion

There is, however, an inductive way to define the determinant $det A$ of any square matrix A. The idea is to define the determinant of a 3×3 matrix in terms of determinants of 2×2 matrices, then give the determinant of any 4×4 matrix in terms of determinants of 3×3 matrices, and so on.

---

[1] One way to remember the formula $(*)$ is to adjoin columns 1 and 2 of A on the right to obtain $\begin{bmatrix} a & b & c & a & b \\ d & e & f & d & e \\ g & h & i & g & h \end{bmatrix}$.

Then the terms *aei*, *bfg*, and *cdh* in $(*)$ are the products down to the right, starting at *a*, *b*, and *c*, while the terms −*ceg*, −*afh*, and −*bdi* come from products down to the left, starting at *c*, *a*, and *b*. I hesitate to reveal this rule because it does **not**, repeat **not**, extend to $n \times n$ matrices for $n > 3$.

To motivate the procedure[2], we collect the terms in (∗) involving the first row entries a, b, and c, and observe that the multipliers are 2×2 determinants:

$$det \begin{bmatrix} a & b & c \\ d & e & f \\ g & h & i \end{bmatrix} = aei + bfg + cdh - ceg - afh - bdi$$

$$= a(ei - fh) - b(di - fg) + c(dh - eg)$$

$$= a\,det \begin{bmatrix} e & f \\ h & i \end{bmatrix} - b\,det \begin{bmatrix} d & f \\ g & i \end{bmatrix} + c\,det \begin{bmatrix} d & e \\ g & h \end{bmatrix}$$

This last expression can be described as follows: To compute the determinant of a 3×3 matrix A, multiply each entry in the first row by ± 1 times the determinant of a certain 2×2 matrix, namely the one obtained from A by deleting the row and column of the entry in question and add the results. Here the signs alternate down the row (starting with +1).

Example 1   Find the determinant of

$$A = \begin{bmatrix} 2 & -3 & 7 \\ 5 & -1 & 6 \\ 4 & 0 & 8 \end{bmatrix}.$$

SOLUTION   Using the above procedure, we get:

$$det A = 2\,det \begin{bmatrix} -1 & 6 \\ 0 & 8 \end{bmatrix} - (-3)\,det \begin{bmatrix} 5 & 6 \\ 4 & 8 \end{bmatrix} + 7\,det \begin{bmatrix} 5 & -1 \\ 4 & 0 \end{bmatrix}$$

$$= 2(-8 - 0) + 3(40 - 24) + 7(0 - (-4))$$

$$= -16 + 48 + 28 = 60.$$

In this form the procedure can be generalized. To do so, it is convenient to introduce some terminology. Suppose that we have already defined how to compute the determinant of any $(n-1) \times (n-1)$ matrix. Given an $n \times n$ matrix A, let A_{ij} denote the $(n-1) \times (n-1)$ matrix obtained from A by deleting row i and column j. Then we define the (i, j)-**cofactor** $C_{ij}(A)$ of A by

$$C_{ij}(A) = (-1)^{i+j} det(A_{ij}) \text{ for each } i \text{ and } j.$$

Here $(-1)^{i+j}$ is called the **sign** of the (i, j)-position in the matrix. The following diagram is useful for remembering the sign of a position.

$$\begin{bmatrix} +1 & -1 & +1 & -1 & \cdots \\ -1 & +1 & -1 & +1 & \cdots \\ +1 & -1 & +1 & -1 & \cdots \\ -1 & +1 & -1 & +1 & \cdots \\ \vdots & \vdots & \vdots & \vdots & \end{bmatrix}$$

Note that the signs alternate along each row or column, starting with +1 in the upper left corner.

Since we already know how to compute 2×2 determinants, we can find the cofactors of any 3×3 matrix.

Example 2   Find $C_{12}(A)$, $C_{32}(A)$, and $C_{33}(A)$ for the matrix

$$A = \begin{bmatrix} 2 & -3 & 7 \\ 5 & -1 & 6 \\ 4 & 0 & 8 \end{bmatrix}.$$

---

[2] Another way to generalize (∗) is to notice that the right side is the sum of all products of entries of the matrix which have exactly one factor from each row and column, and which have a sign + or −. When it is clarified which products get which sign, this gives a very satisfactory definition of the determinant.

SOLUTION The sign of the $(1, 2)$-position is -1, and A_{12} is obtained from A by deleting row 1 and column 2. Hence

$$C_{12}(A) = -\det(A_{12}) = -\det\begin{bmatrix} 5 & 6 \\ 4 & 8 \end{bmatrix} = -(40 - 24) = -16.$$

Similarly,

$$C_{32}(A) = -\det(A_{32}) = -\det\begin{bmatrix} 2 & 7 \\ 5 & 6 \end{bmatrix} = -(12 - 35) = 23,$$

$$C_{33}(A) = +\det(A_{33}) = \det\begin{bmatrix} 2 & -3 \\ 5 & -1 \end{bmatrix} = -2 + 15 = 13.$$

Clearly there are $9 = 3^2$ different cofactors for A, and they all can be computed in a similar way.

Again, suppose that we have already defined how to compute the determinant of any $(n - 1) \times (n - 1)$ matrix. Then if $A = [a_{ij}]$ is any $n \times n$ matrix, we define the **determinant** $\det A$ of A as follows:

$$\det A = a_{11}C_{11}(A) + a_{12}C_{12}(A) + \cdots + a_{1n}C_{1n}(A).$$

In other words, $\det A$ is obtained as in (*) by multiplying each entry in row 1 of A by the corresponding cofactor, and adding the results. This is called the cofactor expansion of A along row 1. More generally:

> If A is any square matrix, the **cofactor expansion**[3] along any row (or column) is a number defined as follows: *Multiply each entry in the row (or column) by the corresponding cofactor, and add the results.*

Thus a square matrix A has many cofactor expansions, one along each row or column. The astonishing thing about these expansions is that they are all equal. This common value is the determinant $\det A$.

THEOREM ① **Cofactor Expansion Theorem.** If A is any square matrix, the determinant $\det A$ is equal to the Laplace expansion along any row or column of A.

We omit the proof of Theorem 1.

Note that if a row or column of a square matrix A consists *entirely* of zeros, then $\det A = 0$ by the cofactor expansion along that row or column. This observation will be used frequently, and we record it for reference.

COROLLARY If a square matrix A has a row or column of zeros, then $\det A = 0$.

Example 3 Compute the determinant of $A = \begin{bmatrix} 5 & -1 & 7 \\ 9 & -3 & 6 \\ 4 & 8 & 0 \end{bmatrix}$ using the cofactor expansion along column 2 and then by using the expansion along row 3.

---

[3] This is sometimes called the *Laplace expansion* because (a more general version of) it was given in 1772 by Pierre-Simon de Laplace (1749–1827).

SOLUTION   The expansion along column 2 is as follows:

$$detA = (-1)C_{12}(A) + (-3)C_{22}(A) + 8\,C_{32}(A)$$

$$= (-1)\left\{-det\begin{bmatrix} 9 & 6 \\ 4 & 0 \end{bmatrix}\right\} + (-3)\left\{det\begin{bmatrix} 5 & 7 \\ 4 & 0 \end{bmatrix}\right\} + 8\left\{-det\begin{bmatrix} 5 & 7 \\ 9 & 6 \end{bmatrix}\right\}$$

$$= (-1)(24) + (-3)(-28) + 8(33)$$

$$= 324.$$

Similarly, the expansion along row 3 is

$$detA = 4\,det\begin{bmatrix} -1 & 7 \\ -3 & 6 \end{bmatrix} + 8\left\{-det\begin{bmatrix} 5 & 7 \\ 9 & 6 \end{bmatrix}\right\} + 0\,det\begin{bmatrix} 5 & -1 \\ 9 & -3 \end{bmatrix}$$

$$= 4 \cdot 15 + 8 \cdot 33 + 0 = 324.$$

Of course the two values are equal as Theorem 1 guarantees.

When computing the determinant of a 4×4 matrix, the cofactor expansion involves computing determinants of 3×3 matrices. These in turn are evaluated by calculating 2×2 determinants. Here is an example.

Example 4   Compute $detA$ where $A = \begin{bmatrix} 2 & -1 & 0 & 3 \\ 1 & 0 & 5 & 7 \\ 7 & 9 & 0 & 2 \\ 4 & 0 & 0 & 8 \end{bmatrix}$.

SOLUTION   Since (by Theorem 1) we may expand $detA$ along any row or column, we choose one that simplifies the calculation. One way to do this is to choose a row or column with as many zeros as possible. Hence we use column 3 in A because it contains three zeros.

$$detA = 0\,C_{13}(A) + 5\,C_{23}(A) + 0\,C_{33}(A) + 0\,C_{43}(A)$$

$$= 5\,C_{23}(A) = -5\,det\begin{bmatrix} 2 & -1 & 3 \\ 7 & 9 & 2 \\ 4 & 0 & 8 \end{bmatrix}$$

where we used the fact that the sign of the $(2,\ 3)$-position is -1. This reduces the calculation to finding a 3×3 determinant, and again we choose a row or column with as many zeros as possible. Using row 3 gives

$$detA = -5\left\{4\,det\begin{bmatrix} -1 & 3 \\ 9 & 2 \end{bmatrix} + 0 + 8\,det\begin{bmatrix} 2 & -1 \\ 7 & 9 \end{bmatrix}\right\}$$

$$= -5\,\{4(-29) + 8(25)\} = -420$$

as required.

2.1.2   Elementary Operations and Determinants

One way to create zeros in a matrix (and so simplify the computation of the determinant) is by using elementary row operations. The next theorem shows that row operations have a simple effect on the determinant, and that *column* operations can also be used. This can be combined with the cofactor expansion to greatly reduce the computing time involved in finding determinants.

THEOREM 2 Let A denote any $n \times n$ matrix.

(1) If B is obtained from A by interchanging two different rows (columns), then $detB = -detA$.

(2) If B is obtained from A by multiplying a row (column) by a number k, then $detB = k\,detA$.

(3) If B is obtained from A by adding a multiple of some row (column) of A to a different row (column), then $detB = detA$.

PROOF We prove the theorem for row operations; the proof for column operations is analogous.

(1) We proceed by induction on n. The cases $n = 1$ and $n = 2$ are left to the reader. If $n > 2$, expand $detB$ along a row other than the two that were interchanged. The entries of this row are the same for both A and B, but the cofactors in B are the negatives of those in A by induction, because the corresponding $(n-1) \times (n-1)$ matrices have two rows interchanged. It follows that $detB = -detA$.

(2) Expand $detB$ along the row that is multiplied by k. The entries in this row of B are k times the entries of the same row of A, and the corresponding cofactors are the same as those for A (because B and A differ only in this row). It follows that $detB = k\,detA$.

(3) Let B be obtained from $A = [a_{ij}]$ by adding u times row p to row q. Thus row q of B is

$$[a_{q1} + u\,a_{p1},\ a_{q2} + u\,a_{p2},\ \cdots,\ a_{qn} + u\,a_{pn}].$$

The cofactors of the positions in this row are the same as those for A (they do not involve row q), that is $C_{qj}(B) = C_{qj}(A)$ for each j. Hence expanding $detB$ along row q gives

$$\begin{aligned}
detB &= (a_{q1} + u\,a_{p1})C_{q1}(B) + \cdots + (a_{qn} + u\,a_{pn})C_{qn}(B) \\
&= [a_{q1}C_{q1}(B) + \cdots + a_{qn}C_{qn}(B)] + u[\,a_{p1}C_{q1}(B) + \cdots + a_{pn}C_{qn}(B)] \\
&= [a_{q1}C_{q1}(A) + \cdots + a_{qn}C_{qn}(A)] + u[\,a_{p1}C_{q1}(A) + \cdots + a_{pn}C_{qn}(A)] \\
&= detA + u\,detA_1
\end{aligned}$$

where A_1 is the matrix obtained from A by replacing row q by row p, and both expansions are along row q. It remains to show that $detA_1 = 0$. But A_1 has two identical rows, so A_1 is unchanged if these rows are interchanged. Hence $detA_1 = -detA_1$ by (1), whence $detA_1 = 0$. Thus $detB = detA$ as required.

The proof of (3) in Theorem 2 establishes the following useful fact.

COROLLARY If a square matrix A has two identical rows (or columns), then $detA = 0$.

The properties in Theorem 2 can be stated in other words as follows:

(1) If two distinct rows (columns) are interchanged, the determinant changes sign.

(2) A common factor in any row (column) can be "taken out" of the determinant.

(3) Adding a multiple of any row (column) to another row (column) has no effect on the determinant.

These facts are very useful in computing determinants because they reduce the amount of computation required (and for other reasons as well). This is illustrated by the following three examples.

Example 7   Show that the matrix $A = \begin{bmatrix} 1 & 1 \\ 0 & 1 \end{bmatrix}$ is not diagonalizable.

SOLUTION 1   The characteristic polynomial of A is $c_A(x) = (x-1)^2$, so A has only one eigenvalue $\lambda_1 = 1$, which is of multiplicity 2. But the system of equations $(\lambda_1 I - A)X = 0$ has general solution $X = t\begin{bmatrix} 1 \\ 0 \end{bmatrix}$, so there is only one basic solution $\begin{bmatrix} 1 \\ 0 \end{bmatrix}$. Hence A is not diagonalizable by Theorem 5.

SOLUTION 2   If A were diagonalizable, there would be an invertible matrix P such that $P^{-1}AP = D$ is diagonal. By Theorem 3, the diagonal entries of D must be eigenvalues of A, so $D = I$ because 1 is the only eigenvalue of A. Hence $P^{-1}AP = I$, so $A = PIP^{-1} = I$, a contradiction. Hence A is not diagonalizable.

2.3.4   Similar Matrices

If A and B are $n \times n$ matrices, we say that A and B are *similar* if

$$B = P^{-1}AP \text{ for some invertible matrix } P.$$

When this is the case, we write $A \sim B$. The language of similarity is used throughout linear algebra. For example, in this terminology a matrix A is diagonalizable if and only if it is similar to a diagonal matrix.

If $A \sim B$, then necessarily $B \sim A$. To see why, suppose that $B = P^{-1}AP$. Then $A = PBP^{-1} = Q^{-1}BQ$ where $Q = P^{-1}$. Since Q is invertible, this proves the second of the following properties of similarity (the others are Exercise 18):

1. $A \sim A$ for all square matrices A.
2. If $A \sim B$, then $B \sim A$.
3. If $A \sim B$ and $B \sim C$, then $A \sim C$.

$(*)$

These properties are often expressed by saying that the similarity relation $\sim$ is an *equivalence relation* on the set of $n \times n$ matrices. Moreover, similarity is compatible with inverses, transposes, and powers in the following sense:

$$\text{If } A \sim B, \text{ then } \begin{cases} A^{-1} \sim B^{-1} \\ A^T \sim B^T \\ A^k \sim B^k \text{ for all } k \geq 0. \end{cases}$$

$(**)$

The proofs are routine matrix computations (Exercise 18). In addition, similar matrices share many properties, some of which are collected in the next theorem for reference.

THEOREM 6   If A and B are similar $n \times n$ matrices, then:

(1) $det A = det B$.
(2) $c_A(x) = c_B(x)$.
(3) A and B have the same eigenvalues.

PROOF   Let $B = P^{-1}AP$ for some invertible matrix P.

(1) $det B = det(P^{-1}) \, det A \, det P = det A$ because $det(P^{-1}) = 1/det P$.
(2) One verifies that $xI - B = P^{-1}(xI - A)P$. Hence (1) gives
$$c_B(x) = det(xI - B) = det\{P^{-1}(xI - A)P\} = det(xI - A) = c_A(x).$$
(3) The eigenvalues of a matrix are the roots of its characteristic polynomial, so (2) applies.

The class of diagonalizable matrices is well-behaved because these matrices are similar to diagonal matrices. Here are two illustrations.

Example 8   If A is similar to B and either A or B is diagonalizable, show that the other is also diagonalizable.

SOLUTION   We have $A \sim B$. Suppose that A is diagonalizable, say $A \sim D$, where D is diagonal. Since $B \sim A$ by (*), we have $B \sim A$ and $A \sim D$. Hence $B \sim D$ by (*), so B is diagonalizable too. A similar argument works if we assume instead that B is diagonalizable.

Example 9   If A is diagonalizable, show that A^T, A^{-1} (if it exists), and A^k (for each $k \geq 1$) are all diagonalizable.

SOLUTION   Since A is diagonalizable, we have $A \sim D$ where D is a diagonal matrix. Hence (**) gives $A^T \sim D^T$, $A^{-1} \sim D^{-1}$, and $A^k \sim D^k$, and the result follows because D^T, D^{-1}, and D^k are all diagonal.

Suppose that A is diagonalizable, say $P^{-1}AP = D$ is diagonal. Theorem 6 shows that A and D have the same eigenvalues. But the eigenvalues of the diagonal matrix D are just the main diagonal entries (verify), so the diagonal entries of D must be the eigenvalues of A in some order. This means that A inherits many properties of D, and hence of its eigenvalues. The following example illustrates how this happens.

Example 10   Let A be a diagonalizable 2×2 matrix. If $\lambda^4 = 5\lambda$ for each eigenvalue λ of A, show that $A^4 = 5A$.

SOLUTION   Let $P^{-1}AP = D = \begin{bmatrix} \lambda_1 & 0 \\ 0 & \lambda_2 \end{bmatrix}$ where λ_1 and λ_2 are the eigenvalues of A, and P is invertible. Then

$$D^4 = \begin{bmatrix} \lambda_1^4 & 0 \\ 0 & \lambda_2^4 \end{bmatrix} = \begin{bmatrix} 5\lambda_1 & 0 \\ 0 & 5\lambda_2 \end{bmatrix} = 5\begin{bmatrix} \lambda_1 & 0 \\ 0 & \lambda_2 \end{bmatrix} = 5D.$$

Since $A = PDP^{-1}$ (obtained by solving $P^{-1}AP = D$ for A), this gives

$$A^4 = (PDP^{-1})^4 = PD^4P^{-1} = P(5D)P^{-1} = 5(PDP^{-1}) = 5A$$

using Theorem 1.

The result in Example 10 can be reformulated as follows: Write $p(x) = x^4 - 5x$. Then the example asserts that, if $p(\lambda) = 0$ for every eigenvalue λ of A, then $p(A) = 0$. This holds much more generally.

If $p(x) = a_0 + a_1x + a_2x^2 + \cdots + a_kx^k$ is any polynomial, the **evaluation** of $p(x)$ at the (square) matrix A is defined to be

$$p(A) = a_0I + a_1A + a_2A^2 + \cdots + a_kA^k$$

where I is the identity matrix of the same size as A. Then the method used in Example 10 shows that if A is diagonalizable, and if $p(x)$ is any polynomial such that $p(\lambda) = 0$ for all eigenvalues λ of A, then necessarily $p(A) = 0$. In particular, the characteristic polynomial $c_A(x)$ certainly has the property that $c_A(\lambda) = 0$ for each eigenvalue of A, so we must have that $c_A(A) = 0$. In other words, this shows that $c_A(A) = 0$ for every diagonalizable matrix A. In fact, this holds for *every* square matrix A and, in full generality, is called the

| CAYLEY-HAMILTON THEOREM | If A is a square matrix, then $c_A(A) = 0$. |

The proof is given in Section 5.6.

Exercises 2.3

1. Consider the matrix $A = \begin{bmatrix} 1 & 1 & 1 \\ 1 & 1 & -1 \\ 1 & 1 & 1 \end{bmatrix}$.

  a)[†] Directly calculate the matrix power A^{20}.

  b) Use the fact that A is diagonalizable to compute A^{20}; that is, there are matrices P and D such that $P^{-1}AP = D$

$$\text{where } P^{-1}AP = \begin{bmatrix} -1 & 0 & 1 \\ 1 & 1 & 0 \\ -1 & -1 & 1 \end{bmatrix}\begin{bmatrix} 1 & 1 & 1 \\ 1 & 1 & -1 \\ 1 & 1 & 1 \end{bmatrix}\begin{bmatrix} -1 & 1 & 1 \\ 1 & 0 & -1 \\ 0 & 1 & 1 \end{bmatrix}$$

$$= \begin{bmatrix} 0 & 0 & 0 \\ 0 & 2 & 0 \\ 0 & 0 & 1 \end{bmatrix} = D.$$

  c) Explain the benefits of diagonalizing a matrix to compute its powers.

2. In each case find the characteristic polynomial, eigenvalues, and eigenvectors and, if possible, find an invertible matrix P such that $P^{-1}AP = D$.

  a) $A = \begin{bmatrix} 1 & 3 \\ 2 & 2 \end{bmatrix}$ **b)** $A = \begin{bmatrix} 2 & -1 \\ -4 & -1 \end{bmatrix}$

  c) $A = \begin{bmatrix} 7 & 0 & 5 \\ 0 & 5 & 0 \\ -4 & 0 & -2 \end{bmatrix}$ **d)** $A = \begin{bmatrix} 3 & -4 & 2 \\ 1 & -2 & 2 \\ 1 & -5 & 5 \end{bmatrix}$

  e) $A = \begin{bmatrix} 1 & 1 & 0 \\ 1 & 1 & -1 \\ 0 & 1 & 1 \end{bmatrix}$ **f)** $A = \begin{bmatrix} 7 & 4 & -16 \\ 2 & 5 & -8 \\ 2 & 2 & -5 \end{bmatrix}$

3. Write your own short description of how to find eigenvalues of a matrix A, the corresponding eigenvectors, and an invertible matrix P such that $P^{-1}AP$ is a diagonal matrix.

4. If $P^{-1}AP = D$ is a diagonal matrix, what are the diagonal entries of D and the columns of P?

5. a) Show that $A = \begin{bmatrix} 1 & 3 \\ -3 & -5 \end{bmatrix}$ is not diagonalizable.

  b) Show that $A = \begin{bmatrix} 1 & c \\ 0 & 1 \end{bmatrix}$ is not diagonalizable unless $c = 0$.

6. In each case determine whether A is diagonalizable. Give reasons for your answer.

  a) $A = \begin{bmatrix} 5 & -2 & 2 \\ 4 & 1 & 4 \\ 4 & -4 & 9 \end{bmatrix}$ **b)** $A = \begin{bmatrix} 2 & 2 & -1 \\ 1 & 1 & 0 \\ 1 & -2 & -2 \end{bmatrix}$

[†] Requires computer assistance (e.g., Matlab).

7. In each case either show that the statement is true or give an example showing that it is false. Throughout, A represents a square matrix.

  a) If A has real eigenvalues, then it is diagonalizable.

  b) If A is diagonalizable, then it has distinct eigenvalues.

  c) If all of the eigenvalues of A are real and distinct, then A is diagonalizable.

  d) If A is diagonalizable, then its transpose A^T is also diagonalizable.

  e) Every invertible matrix is diagonalizable.

  f) Every diagonalizable matrix is symmetric.

  g) If A has no inverse, then $\lambda = 0$ is an eigenvalue of A.

  h) If $\lambda = 0$ is an eigenvalue of A, then A has no inverse.

8. If λ is an eigenvalue of A, and if α is a number, show that $\lambda - \alpha$ is an eigenvalue of $A_1 = A - \alpha I$. How do the eigenvectors compare?

9. Find the eigenvalues of $A = \begin{bmatrix} \cos\theta & -\sin\theta \\ \sin\theta & \cos\theta \end{bmatrix}$.

10. If X and Y are eigenvectors of A corresponding to λ, show that the same is true of $X + Y$ and aX for any number a (provided that $X + Y$ and aX are not zero).

11. If λ is an eigenvalue of A, show that:

  a) $k\lambda$ is an eigenvalue of kA for each real number k.

  b) λ^2 is an eigenvalue of A^2.

  c) $3 - 2\lambda + 5\lambda^3$ is an eigenvalue of $3I - 2A + 5A^3$.

12. Let A denote an invertible matrix.

  a) If λ is an eigenvalue of A, show that $\lambda \neq 0$ and that $\frac{1}{\lambda}$ is an eigenvalue of A^{-1}.

  b) Show that every eigenvalue μ of A^{-1} has the form $\mu = \frac{1}{\lambda}$ where λ is some eigenvalue of A.

13. If $D = diag(\lambda_1, \lambda_2, \cdots, \lambda_n)$ and $E = diag(\mu_1, \mu_2, \cdots, \mu_n)$, show that

  a) $D + E = diag(\lambda_1 + \mu_1, \lambda_2 + \mu_2, \cdots, \lambda_n + \mu_n)$

  b) $DE = diag(\lambda_1\mu_1, \lambda_2\mu_2, \cdots, \lambda_n\mu_n)$

  c) $D^k = diag(\lambda_1^k, \lambda_2^k, \cdots, \lambda_n^k)$ for each integer $k \geq 1$.

14. a) Show that A and its transpose A^T have the same characteristic polynomial. [Hint: $xI = (xI)^T$.]

  b) If A is diagonalizable, show that A^T is diagonalizable.

15. If A is diagonalizable with eigenvalues $\lambda_1, \lambda_2, \cdots, \lambda_n$, show that $det A = \lambda_1\lambda_2 \cdots \lambda_n$.

16. a) If $A^{-1} = A$ and λ is an eigenvalue of A, show that $\lambda = \pm 1$.

  b) If A is diagonalizable and every eigenvalue is ± 1, show that $A^{-1} = A$.

17. a) If $A^2 = A$ and λ is an eigenvalue of A, show that $\lambda = 0, 1$.

  b) If A is diagonalizable and every eigenvalue is 0 or 1, show that $A^2 = A$.

18. If A and B are square matrices, show that:

  a) If $B = QAQ^{-1}$ for some invertible matrix Q, then $A \sim B$.

  b) $A \sim A$ for all square matrices A.

  c) If $A \sim B$, then $B \sim A$.

  d) If $A \sim B$ and $B \sim C$, then $A \sim C$.

  e) If $A \sim B$, then $\det A = \det B$.

  f) If $A \sim B$, then $A^{-1} \sim B^{-1}$.

  g) If $A \sim B$, then $A^k \sim B^k$ for all integers $k \geq 1$.

  h) If $A \sim B$, then $A^T \sim B^T$.

19. Assume that A has eigenvalues λ_1 and λ_2 with corresponding eigenvectors X_1 and X_2.

  a) Find A if $\lambda_1 = 2$, $\lambda_2 = 5$, $X_1 = \begin{bmatrix} 2 \\ 1 \end{bmatrix}$, and $X_2 = \begin{bmatrix} 3 \\ 2 \end{bmatrix}$.

  b) Find A if $\lambda_1 = -1$, $\lambda_2 = 0$, $X_1 = \begin{bmatrix} 1 \\ 1 \end{bmatrix}$, and $X_2 = \begin{bmatrix} -1 \\ 2 \end{bmatrix}$.

20. If $A = \begin{bmatrix} a & b \\ c & d \end{bmatrix}$, show that:

  a) $c_A(x) = x^2 - (trA)x + \det A$ where $trA = a + d$ is called the **trace** of A.

  b) The eigenvalues of A are
$$\lambda = \tfrac{1}{2}\left[(a+d) \pm \sqrt{(a-d)^2 + 4bc}\right].$$

21. a) If D is diagonal with distinct eigenvalues, and if $CD = DC$, show that C is also diagonal. [Hint: Compare (i, j)-entries in $CD = DC$.]

  b) If A is diagonalizable with distinct eigenvalues, and if $BA = AB$, show that B is also diagonalizable. [Hint: Use **a)**.]

2.4 LINEAR DYNAMICAL SYSTEMS

We began Section 2.3 with an example from ecology which models the evolution of the population of a species of birds as time goes on. As promised, we now complete the example and extend it to other situations.

2.4.1 Linear Dynamical Systems

The bird population was described by computing the female population profile $V_k = \begin{bmatrix} a_k \\ j_k \end{bmatrix}$ of the species, where a_k and j_k represent the number of adult and juvenile females present k years after the initial values a_0 and j_0 were observed. The model assumes that these numbers are related by the following equations:

$$a_{k+1} = \tfrac{1}{2}a_k + \tfrac{1}{4}j_k$$
$$j_{k+1} = 2a_k$$

If we write $A = \begin{bmatrix} \tfrac{1}{2} & \tfrac{1}{4} \\ 2 & 0 \end{bmatrix}$, this system takes the following matrix form

$$V_{k+1} = AV_k \text{ for each } k = 1, 2, \cdots.$$

Hence $V_1 = AV_0$, whence $V_2 = AV_1 = A^2V_0$ and, in general,

$$V_k = A^kV_0 \text{ for } k = 1, 2, \cdots.$$

We can now use our diagonalization techniques to determine the population profile V_k for all values of k in terms of the initial values.

Example 1   Assuming that the initial values were $a_0 = 100$ adult females and $j_0 = 40$ juvenile females, compute a_k and j_k for $k = 1, 2, \cdots$.

SOLUTION   The characteristic polynomial of the matrix $A = \begin{bmatrix} \tfrac{1}{2} & \tfrac{1}{4} \\ 2 & 0 \end{bmatrix}$ is

$c_A(x) = x^2 - \frac{1}{2}x - \frac{1}{2} = (x-1)\left(x + \frac{1}{2}\right)$, so the eigenvalues are $\lambda_1 = 1$ and $\lambda_2 = -\frac{1}{2}$ and Gaussian elimination gives corresponding basic eigenvectors $\begin{bmatrix} \frac{1}{2} \\ 1 \end{bmatrix}$ and $\begin{bmatrix} -\frac{1}{4} \\ 1 \end{bmatrix}$. For convenience (see Remark 5 §2.3), we can use multiples $X_1 = \begin{bmatrix} 1 \\ 2 \end{bmatrix}$ and $X_2 = \begin{bmatrix} -1 \\ 4 \end{bmatrix}$ respectively. Hence a diagonalizing matrix is $P = \begin{bmatrix} 1 & -1 \\ 2 & 4 \end{bmatrix}$ and we obtain

$$P^{-1}AP = D \quad \text{where} \quad D = \begin{bmatrix} 1 & 0 \\ 0 & -\frac{1}{2} \end{bmatrix}.$$

This gives $A = PDP^{-1}$ so, for each $k \geq 0$, we can compute A^k explicitly:

$$A^k = PD^kP^{-1} = \begin{bmatrix} 1 & -1 \\ 2 & 4 \end{bmatrix} \begin{bmatrix} 1 & 0 \\ 0 & (-\frac{1}{2})^k \end{bmatrix} \frac{1}{6} \begin{bmatrix} 4 & 1 \\ -2 & 1 \end{bmatrix}$$

$$= \frac{1}{6} \begin{bmatrix} 4 + 2(-\frac{1}{2})^k & 1 - (-\frac{1}{2})^k \\ 8 - 8(-\frac{1}{2})^k & 2 + 4(-\frac{1}{2})^k \end{bmatrix}.$$

Hence we obtain

$$\begin{bmatrix} a_k \\ j_k \end{bmatrix} = V_k = A^k V_0 = \frac{1}{6} \begin{bmatrix} 4 + 2(-\frac{1}{2})^k & 1 - (-\frac{1}{2})^k \\ 8 - 8(-\frac{1}{2})^k & 2 + 4(-\frac{1}{2})^k \end{bmatrix} \begin{bmatrix} 100 \\ 40 \end{bmatrix}$$

$$= \frac{1}{6} \begin{bmatrix} 440 + 160(-\frac{1}{2})^k \\ 880 - 640(-\frac{1}{2})^k \end{bmatrix}.$$

Equating top and bottom entries, we obtain exact formulas for a_k and j_k:

$$a_k = \frac{220}{3} + \frac{80}{3}\left(-\frac{1}{2}\right)^k \quad \text{and} \quad j_k = \frac{440}{3} - \frac{320}{3}\left(-\frac{1}{2}\right)^k \quad \text{for } k = 1, 2, \cdots.$$

In practice, the exact values of a_k and j_k usually are not required. What is needed is a measure of how these numbers behave for large values of k. This is easy to obtain here. Since $\left(-\frac{1}{2}\right)^k$ is nearly zero for large k, we have the following approximate values

$$a_k \approx \frac{220}{3} \quad \text{and} \quad j_k \approx \frac{440}{3} \quad \text{if } k \text{ is large.}$$

Hence, in the long term, the female population stabilizes with approximately twice as many juveniles as adults.

The population model in Example 1 is an example of a **dynamical system**; that is, a sequence of columns V_0, V_1, V_2, $\cdots$ where the initial column V_0 is known and the other columns are determined by the condition

$$V_{k+1} = AV_k \text{ for each } k \geq 0$$

where A is a square matrix.[7] The condition $V_{k+1} = AV_k$ is called a **matrix recurrence** for the columns V_k. While this example is from ecology, dynamical systems arise in many parts of science and engineering,[8] and in other areas such as economics.

Since V_0 is known, the matrix recurrence $V_{k+1} = AV_k$ gives successively

$$V_1 = AV_0,$$
$$V_2 = AV_1 = A(AV_0) = A^2V_0,$$
$$V_3 = AV_2 = A(A^2V_0) = A^3V_0,$$

$$\vdots$$

---

[7] More precisely, this is a *linear discrete* dynamical system. Many models use differential relationships between V_{k+1} and V_k, viewed as functions of time.

[8] A Markov Chain (Section 1.8) is a dynamical system where the matrix recursion $S_{k+1} = PS_k$ relates the state vectors S_k, and P is the transition matrix.

Continuing in this way, we get
$$V_k = A^k V_0 \text{ for each } k = 1, 2, \cdots. \qquad (*)$$

Hence we can determine the columns V_k if we can compute the powers A^k of the matrix A. As we have seen, this can be done if A is diagonalizable; indeed $(*)$ can be used (as in Example 1) to give a nice "formula" for the columns V_k in this case.

To see what happens in general, assume that A is diagonalizable with eigenvalues λ_1, $\lambda_2, \cdots, \lambda_n$ and corresponding eigenvectors $X_1, X_2, \cdots, X_n$. If $P = [X_1 \ X_2 \ \cdots \ X_n]$ is the matrix with the X_i as its columns, then P is invertible and
$$P^{-1}AP = D = diag(\lambda_1, \lambda_2, \cdots, \lambda_n)$$

by Theorem 3 §2.3. Hence $A = PDP^{-1}$ so $(*)$ and Theorem 1 §2.3 give
$$V_k = A^k V_0 = (PDP^{-1})^k V_0 = (PD^k P^{-1})V_0 = PD^k(P^{-1}V_0)$$

for each $k = 1, 2, \cdots$. For convenience, we denote the column $P^{-1}V_0$ arising here as follows
$$P^{-1}V_0 = \begin{bmatrix} b_1 \\ b_2 \\ \vdots \\ b_n \end{bmatrix} = [b_1 \ b_2 \ \cdots \ b_n]^T.$$

Then matrix multiplication gives (see Theorem 3 §1.4)
$$V_k = PD^k(P^{-1}V_0)$$

$$= [X_1 \ X_2 \ \cdots \ X_n] \begin{bmatrix} \lambda_1^k & 0 & \cdots & 0 \\ 0 & \lambda_2^k & \cdots & 0 \\ \vdots & \vdots & \ddots & \vdots \\ 0 & 0 & \cdots & \lambda_n^k \end{bmatrix} \begin{bmatrix} b_1 \\ b_2 \\ \vdots \\ b_n \end{bmatrix}$$

$$= [\lambda_1^k X_1 \ \lambda_2^k X_2 \ \cdots \ \lambda_n^k X_n] \begin{bmatrix} b_1 \\ b_2 \\ \vdots \\ b_n \end{bmatrix}$$

$$= b_1 \lambda_1^k X_1 + b_2 \lambda_2^k X_2 + \cdots + b_n \lambda_n^k X_n$$

for each $k \geq 0$. This is a useful explicit formula for the columns V_k. Note that, in particular, $V_0 = b_1 X_1 + b_2 X_2 + \cdots + b_n X_n$.

However, such an exact formula for V_k is often not required in practice; all that is needed is to *estimate* V_k for large values of k (as in Example 1). This can be done easily if the diagonalizable $n \times n$ matrix A has a largest eigenvalue.

2.4.2 Dominant Eigenvalues

An eigenvalue λ of an $n \times n$ matrix A is called a **dominant eigenvalue** of A if
$$|\lambda| > |\mu| \text{ for all eigenvalues } \mu \neq \lambda$$

where $|\lambda|$ denotes the absolute value[9] of the number λ. For example, $\lambda_1 = 1$ is dominant in Example 1 because $\lambda_2 = -\frac{1}{2}$ is smaller in absolute value.

Returning to the above discussion, suppose A has a dominant eigenvalue. By choosing the order in which the columns X_i are placed in P, we may assume that λ_1 is dominant among the eigenvalues $\lambda_1, \lambda_2, \cdots, \lambda_n$ of A. In this case, take λ_1^k out as a common factor in the expression $V_k = b_1 \lambda_1^k X_1 + b_2 \lambda_2^k X_2 + \cdots + b_n \lambda_n^k X_n$ for V_k. The result is

---

[9] The **absolute value** $|a|$ of a number a is defined as follows: $|a| = \begin{cases} a & \text{if } a \geq 0 \\ -a & \text{if } a < 0 \end{cases}$. Thus, for example, $|3| = 3$ and $|-2| = 2$. It is useful to note that the absolute value is also given by the formula $|a| = \sqrt{a^2}$, where $\sqrt{a^2}$ denotes the positive square root of a^2.

$$V_k = \lambda_1^k \left[b_1 X_1 + b_2 \left(\tfrac{\lambda_2}{\lambda_1} \right)^k X_2 + \cdots + b_n \left(\tfrac{\lambda_n}{\lambda_1} \right)^k X_n \right]$$

for each $k \geq 0$. Since λ_1 is dominant, we have $|\lambda_i| < |\lambda_1|$ for each $i \geq 2$, so each of the numbers $\left(\tfrac{\lambda_i}{\lambda_1} \right)^k$ becomes small in absolute value as k increases. Hence V_k is approximately equal to the first term $\lambda_1^k b_1 X_1$, and we write this as $V_k \approx \lambda_1^k b_1 X_1$. These observations are summarized in the following theorem (together with the above exact formula for V_k).

THEOREM 1

Consider the dynamical system with matrix recurrence
$$V_{k+1} = A V_k \text{ for } k \geq 0$$
where A and V_0 are given. Assume that A is a diagonalizable $n \times n$ matrix with eigenvalues $\lambda_1, \lambda_2, \cdots, \lambda_n$ and corresponding eigenvectors $X_1, X_2, \cdots, X_n$, and let $P = [X_1 \ X_2 \ \cdots \ X_n]$ be the corresponding diagonalizing matrix. Then an exact formula for the V_k is
$$V_k = b_1 \lambda_1^k X_1 + b_2 \lambda_2^k X_2 + \cdots + b_n \lambda_n^k X_n \quad \text{for each} \quad k \geq 0$$
where the coefficients b_i come from $P^{-1} V_0 = [b_1 \ b_2 \ \cdots \ b_n]^T$. Moreover, if A has dominant eigenvalue λ_1, of multiplicity 1, then[10] V_k is approximated by
$$V_k \approx \lambda_1^k b_1 X_1 \text{ for sufficiently large } k.$$

Remark

Suppose the dynamical system in Theorem 1 has a dominant eigenvalue λ_1. If $\lambda_1 = 1$, Theorem 1 shows that the V_k become constant in the long run. If $|\lambda_1| < 1$, then the powers λ_1^k will become close to zero for large k, so the columns V_k will converge to 0. On the other hand, if $|\lambda_1| > 1$, then the V_k will become large as k increases. We give some examples of this behaviour below.

In Example 1 the numbers a_k and j_k of adult and juvenile female birds alive were related by the equations
$$a_{k+1} = \tfrac{1}{2} a_k + \tfrac{1}{4} j_k$$
$$j_{k+1} = 2 a_k.$$

This means that $\tfrac{1}{2}$ of the adults and $\tfrac{1}{4}$ of the juveniles alive in year k survive to year $k + 1$, and that each female produces 2 juveniles per year on average. In Example 1 we showed that the species population becomes stable under these conditions. We now examine what happens if we lower the juvenile survival rate to $\tfrac{1}{8}$. It turns out that this drives the species to extinction.

Example 2

Assume that the numbers a_k and j_k of adult and juvenile birds in Example 1 satisfy the equations
$$a_{k+1} = \tfrac{1}{2} a_k + \tfrac{1}{8} j_k$$
$$j_{k+1} = 2 a_k.$$
If $a_0 = 100$ and $j_0 = 40$ as in Example 1, estimate the population profile $V_k = \begin{bmatrix} a_k \\ j_k \end{bmatrix}$ for large k.

SOLUTION

Now $V_{k+1} = A V_k$ where $A = \begin{bmatrix} \tfrac{1}{2} & \tfrac{1}{8} \\ 2 & 0 \end{bmatrix}$. The characteristic polynomial is $c_A(x) = x^2 - \tfrac{1}{2} x - \tfrac{1}{4}$, so the eigenvalues are $\lambda_1 = \tfrac{1}{4} \left[1 + \sqrt{5} \right] = 0.809$ and $\lambda_2 = \tfrac{1}{4} \left[1 - \sqrt{5} \right] = -0.309$. Corresponding eigenvectors are $X_1 = \begin{bmatrix} 0.809 \\ 2 \end{bmatrix}$ and $X_2 = \begin{bmatrix} -0.309 \\ 2 \end{bmatrix}$, so a diagonalizing matrix

---

[10] More can be said here. Suppose, for example, that $|\lambda_1| = |\lambda_2| > \lambda_i$ for each $i \geq 3$. Then $V_k \approx \lambda_1^k b_1 X_1 + \lambda_2^k b_2 X_2$ for sufficiently large k.

is $P = \begin{bmatrix} 0.809 & -0.309 \\ 2 & 2 \end{bmatrix}$. Since we are still assuming that $V_0 = \begin{bmatrix} 100 \\ 40 \end{bmatrix}$, the coefficients b_1 and b_2 are given by

$$\begin{bmatrix} b_1 \\ b_2 \end{bmatrix} = P^{-1}V_0 = \frac{1}{2.236}\begin{bmatrix} 2 & 0.309 \\ -2 & 0.809 \end{bmatrix}\begin{bmatrix} 100 \\ 40 \end{bmatrix} = \begin{bmatrix} 94.97 \\ -74.97 \end{bmatrix}$$

Since λ_1 is dominant and of multiplicity 1, an estimate for V_k is given by

$$\begin{bmatrix} a_k \\ j_k \end{bmatrix} = V_k \cong b_1\lambda_1^k X_1 = 94.97(0.809)^k\begin{bmatrix} 0.809 \\ 2 \end{bmatrix}$$

Comparing entries gives

$$a_k \approx 76.83(0.809)^k \quad \text{and} \quad j_k \approx 189.94(0.809)^k$$

for sufficiently large k. We thus obtain the total female population $a_k + j_k \cong 266.77\,(0.809)^k$ so, since $0.809 < 1$, the population becomes smaller and smaller as k increases. In other words, the species becomes extinct. Note that this also shows that the breakdown of the (decreasing) female population into adults and juveniles stabilizes with approximately $\frac{76.83}{266.77} = 0.288 = 28.8\%$ adults and $\frac{189.94}{266.77} = 0.712 = 71.2\%$ juveniles.

Much of the computation in Examples 1 and 2 can in fact be carried out for a much more general model. As before, let a_k and j_k denote the number of adult and juvenile female birds alive in year k, and assume they satisfy the equations

$$a_{k+1} = \alpha a_k + \beta j_k$$
$$j_{k+1} = ma_k$$

for $k \geq 0$. Here α and β are the *adult and juvenile survival rates*; that is, the proportions of adult and juvenile females respectively to survive from one year to the next. Similarly, m is the *reproduction rate*, that is the number of juveniles hatched (per adult female) in any year. We assume that α, β, and m are all positive.

Writing $V_k = \begin{bmatrix} a_k \\ j_k \end{bmatrix}$ and $A = \begin{bmatrix} \alpha & \beta \\ m & 0 \end{bmatrix}$ as before, the above equations become the matrix recurrence $V_{k+1} = AV_k$. The characteristic polynomial of A is

$$c_A(x) = det\begin{bmatrix} x-\alpha & -\beta \\ -m & x \end{bmatrix} = x^2 - \alpha x - \beta m.$$ Hence the quadratic formula gives the eigenvalues

$$\lambda_1 = \tfrac{1}{2}(\alpha + r) \quad \text{and} \quad \lambda_2 = \tfrac{1}{2}(\alpha - r)$$

where, for convenience, we write $r = \sqrt{\alpha^2 + 4\beta m}$. Since the eigenvalues λ_i are roots of the characteristic polynomial, we have $\lambda_i^2 = \alpha\lambda_i + \beta m$ for each i. This shows that corresponding eigenvectors are

$$X_1 = \begin{bmatrix} \lambda_1 \\ m \end{bmatrix} \quad \text{and} \quad X_2 = \begin{bmatrix} \lambda_2 \\ m \end{bmatrix}$$

(because $AX_i = \lambda_i X_i$ for each i as the reader can verify). Furthermore, $r = \sqrt{\alpha^2 + 4\beta m} > \alpha$, so $\lambda_2 < 0$. Thus

$$|\lambda_2| = -\lambda_2 = \tfrac{1}{2}(r - \alpha) < \tfrac{1}{2}(\alpha + r) = \lambda_1 = |\lambda_1|,$$

so λ_1 is the dominant eigenvalue no matter what choice of α, β, and m is made. Hence Theorem 1 gives

$$V_k \approx b_1\lambda_1^k X_1 = b_1\lambda_1^k\begin{bmatrix} \lambda_1 \\ m \end{bmatrix}$$

where b_1 is computed as in Theorem 1 ($b_1 > 0$ as the reader can verify). Thus, in this model, the magnitude of $\lambda_1 > 0$ determines the ultimate population size as follows:

If $\lambda_1 > 1$, the population becomes very large as k increases.

If $\lambda_1 = 1$, the population stabilizes as k increases.

If $\lambda_1 < 1$, the population becomes very small as k increases.

In the last case, the population will become extinct unless something happens to change the values of α, β, and m.

2.4.3 A Predator-Prey Model

Examples 1 and 2 describe a single population and its evolution over time. The following example uses a matrix recurrence to study the dynamics between two interrelated populations.

Example 3 Let h_k and m_k denote the number of hawks and mice respectively in a certain region in year k. Assume that they are related as follows:

$$h_{k+1} = \tfrac{1}{2}h_k + \tfrac{1}{100}m_k$$
$$m_{k+1} = -\tfrac{50}{4}h_k + \tfrac{5}{4}m_k \quad \text{for } k \geq 0.$$

Find the limiting values of the populations of hawks and mice if the populations begin with 50 hawks and 1600 mice.

SOLUTION If we write $V_k = \begin{bmatrix} h_k \\ m_k \end{bmatrix}$ and $A = \begin{bmatrix} \tfrac{1}{2} & \tfrac{1}{100} \\ -\tfrac{50}{4} & \tfrac{5}{4} \end{bmatrix}$, then the equations become $V_{k+1} = AV_k$ and

we have a matrix recurrence. The characteristic polynomial is $x^2 - \tfrac{7}{4}x + \tfrac{3}{4} = (x - 1)\left(x - \tfrac{3}{4}\right)$, so the eigenvalues are $\lambda_1 = 1$ and $\lambda_2 = \tfrac{3}{4}$ with corresponding eigenvectors $X_1 = \begin{bmatrix} 1 \\ 50 \end{bmatrix}$ and $X_2 = \begin{bmatrix} 1 \\ 25 \end{bmatrix}$. Since λ_1 is dominant here, we can estimate the limiting value of V_k. Because $P = \begin{bmatrix} 1 & 1 \\ 50 & 25 \end{bmatrix}$ is a diagonalizing matrix, we obtain

$$\begin{bmatrix} b_1 \\ b_2 \end{bmatrix} = P^{-1}V_0 = \begin{bmatrix} -1 & \tfrac{1}{25} \\ 2 & -\tfrac{1}{25} \end{bmatrix} \begin{bmatrix} 50 \\ 1600 \end{bmatrix} = \begin{bmatrix} 14 \\ 36 \end{bmatrix} \quad \text{as in Theorem 1. Hence, for large } k,$$

$$V_k \approx \lambda_1^k b_1 X_1 = 14 \begin{bmatrix} 1 \\ 50 \end{bmatrix}$$

Thus the populations stabilize at approximately 14 hawks and 700 mice.

Of course, if the matrix A is changed in Example 3 the populations may not stabilize. One way to guarantee stability is to insist that $\lambda_1 = 1$ is a dominant eigenvalue. It turns out that this can be done in a whole class of models.

To see what happens in general, assume that the numbers h_k and m_k of hawks and mice are related as follows:

$$h_{k+1} = ph_k + \gamma m_k$$
$$m_{k+1} = -\delta h_k + qm_k \quad \text{for } k \geq 0 \quad\quad (**)$$

where p and q are the survival rate parameters, and γ and δ are the correlation parameters. We are looking for a "stable range" for these parameters, that is for values of the parameters that will ensure that the two populations will reach equilibrium levels. The following conditions on the parameters are inherent in the model:

$p > 0$ because more hawks one year means more the next year.

$p < 1$ because few mice one year means the number of hawks decreases.

$q > 1$ because few hawks one year means the number of mice increases.

$\gamma > 0$ because more mice one year means more hawks the next year.

$\delta > 0$ because more hawks one year means fewer mice the next year.

If we write $A = \begin{bmatrix} p & \gamma \\ -\delta & q \end{bmatrix}$ and $V_k = \begin{bmatrix} h_k \\ m_k \end{bmatrix}$, the equations (**) become the matrix recursion

$$V_{k+1} = A\,V_k \text{ for } k = 0, 1, 2, \cdots$$

where the initial situation V_0 is assumed to be known. We compute the characteristic polynomial

$$c_A(x) = det\begin{bmatrix} x-p & -\gamma \\ \delta & x-q \end{bmatrix} = x^2 - (p+q)x + (pq + \gamma\delta).$$

This has roots

$$\tfrac{1}{2}\left\{(p+q) \pm \sqrt{(p+q)^2 - 4(pq + \gamma\delta)}\right\} = \tfrac{1}{2}\left\{(p+q) \pm \sqrt{(q-p)^2 - 4\gamma\delta}\right\}$$

by the quadratic formula so, if we write

$$r = \sqrt{(q-p)^2 - 4\gamma\delta} = \sqrt{(p+q)^2 - 4(pq + \gamma\delta)},$$

the eigenvalues are

$$\lambda_1 = \tfrac{1}{2}\big[(p+q) + r\big] \quad \text{and} \quad \lambda_2 = \tfrac{1}{2}\big[(p+q) - r\big].$$

For r to be a real number, we require that $4\gamma\delta \leq (q-p)^2$. In addition, we want $r > 0$ because the eigenvalues should be distinct (so A is diagonalizable). So we insist that

$$4\gamma\delta < (q-p)^2. \tag{***}$$

Hence $\lambda_1 > \lambda_2 > 0$ (because $p + q > r > 0$), so λ_1 is the dominant eigenvalue. By Theorem 1 the columns V_k become constant for large k if $\lambda_1 = 1$, that is if $p + q + r = 2$. This gives $(p + q - 2)^2 = r^2 = (q-p)^2 - 4\gamma\delta$, which simplifies to the equation

$$\gamma\delta = (1 - p)(q - 1)$$

as the reader can verify. This condition leads to equilibrium.

EQUILIBRIUM CONDITION   Choose numbers p and q such that $0 < p < 1$, $q > 1$, and $p + q < 2$, and then choose $\gamma > 0$ and $\delta > 0$ satisfying

$$\gamma\delta = (1 - p)(q - 1).$$

If we use the model given by (**), the populations of hawks and mice become constant for large k.

PROOF   In fact, using the condition that $\gamma\delta = (1 - p)(q - 1)$, we have

$$(q - p)^2 - 4\gamma\delta = [2 - (p+q)]^2.$$

Since $p + q < 2$, it follows that (***) holds and $r = 2 - (p + q)$. This means that $\lambda_1 = \tfrac{1}{2}[(p+q) + r] = 1$, so $V_k = \begin{bmatrix} h_k \\ m_k \end{bmatrix}$ becomes constant for large k by Theorem 1 as required.

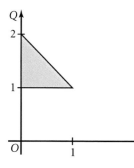

The constraints on p and q in the equilibrium condition are:
$$0 < p < 1$$
$$1 < q$$
$$p + q < 2$$
The region of acceptable pairs (p, q) is shown in the diagram. Having chosen such p and q, any positive numbers γ and δ can be chosen so that $\gamma\delta = (1 - p)(q - 1)$ and the populations in the resulting model will be in equilibrium.

In fact we can find formulas for the limiting values for h_k and m_k. First
$$X_1 = \begin{bmatrix} \gamma \\ \lambda_1 - p \end{bmatrix} \quad \text{and} \quad X_2 = \begin{bmatrix} \gamma \\ \lambda_2 - p \end{bmatrix}$$
are eigenvectors corresponding to λ_1 and λ_2 respectively because $AX_i = \lambda_i X_i$ for each i. (This is because λ_i is a root of the characteristic equation, so $\lambda_i^2 - (p + q)\lambda_i + (pq + \gamma\delta) = 0$.) Then Theorem 1 gives
$$\begin{bmatrix} h_k \\ m_k \end{bmatrix} = V_k \approx \lambda_1^k b_1 X_1 = b_1 X_1$$
where b_1 is obtained from $[b_1 \; b_2]^T = P^{-1}V_0$, and $P = [X_1 \; X_2]$ is the diagonalizing matrix for A. Since $\lambda_1 = 1$ for equilibrium, this gives
$$h_k = b_1\gamma \quad \text{and} \quad m_k = b_1(1 - p).$$
Thus, in this model the limiting ratio of hawks to mice is $\frac{\gamma}{1-p}$.

2.4.4   Graphical Description of Solutions

If a dynamical system $V_{k+1} = AV_k$ is given, the sequence $V_0, V_1, V_2, \cdots$ is called the **trajectory** of the system starting at V_0. It is instructive to obtain a graphical plot of the system by writing $V_k = \begin{bmatrix} x_k \\ y_k \end{bmatrix}$ and plotting the successive values as points in the plane, identifying V_k with the point $P(x_k, y_k)$. We give several examples which illustrate properties of dynamical systems. For ease of calculation we assume that the matrix A is simple, usually diagonal.

Example 4

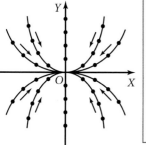

Let $A = \begin{bmatrix} \frac{1}{2} & 0 \\ 0 & \frac{1}{3} \end{bmatrix}$. Then the eigenvalues are $\frac{1}{2}$ and $\frac{1}{3}$, with corresponding eigenvectors $X_1 = \begin{bmatrix} 1 \\ 0 \end{bmatrix}$ and $X_2 = \begin{bmatrix} 0 \\ 1 \end{bmatrix}$. The general solution is
$$V_k = b_1 \left(\frac{1}{2}\right)^k \begin{bmatrix} 1 \\ 0 \end{bmatrix} + b_2 \left(\frac{1}{3}\right)^k \begin{bmatrix} 0 \\ 1 \end{bmatrix}$$
for $k = 0, 1, 2, \cdots$ by Theorem 1, where the coefficients b_1 and b_2 depend[11] on the initial point V_0. Several trajectories are plotted in the diagram and, for each choice of V_0, the trajectories converge toward the origin because both eigenvalues are less than 1 in absolute value. For this reason, the origin is called an **attractor** for the system.

---

[11] In fact, $P = I$ here, so $V_0 = \begin{bmatrix} b_1 \\ b_2 \end{bmatrix}$.

Example 5   Let $A = \begin{bmatrix} \frac{3}{2} & 0 \\ 0 & \frac{4}{3} \end{bmatrix}$. Here the eigenvalues are $\frac{3}{2}$ and $\frac{4}{3}$, with corresponding eigenvectors

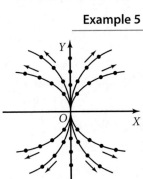

$X_1 = \begin{bmatrix} 1 \\ 0 \end{bmatrix}$ and $X_2 = \begin{bmatrix} 0 \\ 1 \end{bmatrix}$ as before. The general solution is

$$V_k = b_1 \left(\frac{3}{2}\right)^k \begin{bmatrix} 1 \\ 0 \end{bmatrix} + b_2 \left(\frac{4}{3}\right)^k \begin{bmatrix} 0 \\ 1 \end{bmatrix}$$

for $k = 0, 1, 2, \cdots$. Since both eigenvalues are greater than 1 in absolute value, the trajectories diverge away from the origin for every choice of initial point V_0. For this reason, the origin is called a **repellor** for the system.

Example 6   Let $A = \begin{bmatrix} 1 & -\frac{1}{2} \\ -\frac{1}{2} & 1 \end{bmatrix}$. Now the eigenvalues are $\frac{3}{2}$ and $\frac{1}{2}$, with corresponding eigenvectors

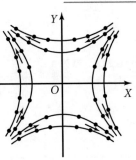

$X_1 = \begin{bmatrix} -1 \\ 1 \end{bmatrix}$ and $X_2 = \begin{bmatrix} 1 \\ 1 \end{bmatrix}$. The general solution is

$$V_k = b_1 \left(\frac{3}{2}\right)^k \begin{bmatrix} -1 \\ 1 \end{bmatrix} + b_2 \left(\frac{1}{2}\right)^k \begin{bmatrix} 1 \\ 1 \end{bmatrix}$$

for $k = 0, 1, 2, \cdots$. In this case $\frac{3}{2}$ is the dominant eigenvalue so, if $b_1 \neq 0$, we have $V_k \approx b_1 \left(\frac{3}{2}\right)^k \begin{bmatrix} -1 \\ 1 \end{bmatrix}$ for large k and V_k is approaching the line $y = -x$. However, if $b_1 = 0$, then $V_k = b_2 \left(\frac{1}{2}\right)^k \begin{bmatrix} 1 \\ 1 \end{bmatrix}$ and so approaches the origin along the line $y = x$. In general the trajectories appear as in the diagram, and the origin is called a **saddle point** for the dynamical system in this case.

Example 7   Let $A = \begin{bmatrix} 0 & \frac{1}{2} \\ -\frac{1}{2} & 0 \end{bmatrix}$. Now the characteristic polynomial is $c_A(x) = x^2 + \frac{1}{4}$, so the eigenvalues are the complex numbers $\frac{i}{2}$ and $-\frac{i}{2}$ where $i^2 = -1$. Hence A is not diagonalizable as a real matrix[12]. However, the trajectories are not difficult to describe. If we start with

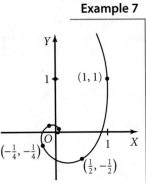

$V_0 = \begin{bmatrix} 1 \\ 1 \end{bmatrix}$, then the trajectory begins as

$$V_1 = \begin{bmatrix} \frac{1}{2} \\ -\frac{1}{2} \end{bmatrix}, \quad V_2 = \begin{bmatrix} -\frac{1}{4} \\ -\frac{1}{4} \end{bmatrix}, \quad V_3 = \begin{bmatrix} -\frac{1}{8} \\ \frac{1}{8} \end{bmatrix},$$
$$V_4 = \begin{bmatrix} \frac{1}{16} \\ \frac{1}{16} \end{bmatrix}, \quad V_5 = \begin{bmatrix} \frac{1}{32} \\ -\frac{1}{32} \end{bmatrix}, \quad V_6 = \begin{bmatrix} -\frac{1}{64} \\ -\frac{1}{64} \end{bmatrix}, \cdots$$

Five of these points are plotted in the diagram. Here each trajectory spirals in toward the origin, so the origin is an attractor. Note that the two (complex) eigenvalues have absolute value less than 1 here. If they had absolute value greater than 1, the trajectories would spiral out from the origin.

---

[12] Corresponding eigenvectors are $X_1 = \begin{bmatrix} 1 \\ i \end{bmatrix}$ and $X_2 = \begin{bmatrix} 1 \\ -i \end{bmatrix}$ so the theory works for the complex numbers. We return to this in Section 2.5.

Exercises 2.4

1. Consider the female bird population model where the adult survival rate is $\frac{1}{2}$, the juvenile survival rate is $\frac{1}{3}$, and the reproduction rate is 2; that is, the matrix A is
$$\begin{bmatrix} \frac{1}{2} & \frac{1}{3} \\ 2 & 0 \end{bmatrix}.$$

   a) Using an initial population of 100 adults and 60 juveniles, calculate the population for the next few years.

   b) Does the population become extinct? Stabilize? Diverge?

   c) Does it depend on the initial population?

   d) In the long term, what percentage of the total female population is made up of juveniles?

2. Consider once again the female bird population model where the adult survival rate is $\frac{3}{10}$, the juvenile survival rate is $\frac{1}{3}$, the reproduction rate is 2, and the initial population is 100 adults and 50 juveniles.

   a) Write a matrix recurrence for the bird population in the form $V_{k+1} = AV_k = A^k V_0$, where A is a matrix.

   b) Find the eigenvalues of A, corresponding eigenvectors, and an invertible matrix P which diagonalizes the matrix A.

   c) Find an exact formula for V_k in term of the eigenvalues and eigenvectors.

   d) Use the formula found in **c)** to calculate the population 5 years from now.

   e) Find the dominant eigenvalue.

   f) Find an approximating formula for V_k using the dominant eigenvalue.

   g) Use the formula found in **f)** to approximate the population 10 years from now.

   h) Compare the results found in **d)** and **g)**.

   i) Does the population become extinct? Stabilize? Diverge?

   j) Does it depend on the initial population?

   k) In the long term, what percentage of the total female population is made up of juveniles?

3. Consider the female bird population model where the adult survival rate is $\frac{2}{5}$, and the reproduction rate is 4. Find

β, the required value of the juvenile survival rate, to ensure that the population will stabilize in the long term.

4. In the general bird population model, assume that the adult survival rate α and the reproduction rate m are fixed. If β denotes the juvenile survival rate, show that the population:

   a) stabilizes if $\beta = \frac{1-\alpha}{m}$;

   b) becomes extinct if $\beta < \frac{1-\alpha}{m}$;

   c) becomes very large if $\beta > \frac{1-\alpha}{m}$.

5. The population of an endangered hawk species and its natural prey the field mouse, originally 30 hawks and 2000 mice, is represented by the following model:
$$h_{k+1} = 0.55 h_k + 0.005 m_k$$
$$m_{k+1} = -18 h_k + 1.2 m_k$$
where h_k and m_k represent the hawk and mice population respectively in year k.

   a) Make sure you understand what each parameter means.

   b) Express the model in the matrix form $V_{k+1} = AV_k$, and write $V_0 = \begin{bmatrix} 30 \\ 2000 \end{bmatrix}$.

   c) Find the eigenvalues and corresponding eigenvectors of A, use them to diagonalize the matrix A, and write a general formula to calculate V_k.

   d) Calculate the predicted population every few years for the next 30 years or so and, using eigenvalues, reason whether an equilibrium will be reached.

   e) In 5 years, biologists try to improve the hawk population by introducing 1000 mice in the hawk hunting area. Predict and compare the new hawk population 10 years from now.

   f) From that point on, the hawk survival rate drops to 0.50. The biologists are alarmed that this may wipe out the hawk population. Test to see what the model is predicting and explain what is happening.

6. Describe the trajectories of the dynamical system with matrix
$$A = \begin{bmatrix} 0 & 1 \\ -1 & 0 \end{bmatrix}.$$

2.5 COMPLEX EIGENVALUES

For the most part the matrices we have been dealing with have had real eigenvalues. However there are important matrices for which this is not the case. For example, the matrix $A = \begin{bmatrix} 0 & -1 \\ 1 & 0 \end{bmatrix}$ has characteristic polynomial $c_A(x) = x^2 + 1$, and this has no real root because $x^2 \geq 0$ for every real number x. Nonetheless, we can find eigenvalues for A and diagonalize it, but we have to use complex numbers. This section develops the basic properties of these numbers.

The concept of complex numbers depends on the existence of a number i such that $i^2 = -1$. Because such a number i cannot be real, it is usually called an "imaginary" number. But it is no more imaginary than the number -1 or the number 2 for that matter. Numbers exist only in our minds and so are *all* imaginary. The integers $1, 2, 3, \cdots$ were undoubtedly invented to count things (enemy warriors or animals to hunt), the positive real numbers were used to measure distances and areas, and the negative numbers enabled people to systematically denote phenomena like debt. In each case the numbers were invented (some would say "discovered") to describe some aspect of the world. This proved to be very useful because the algebraic properties of numbers could then be used to describe "laws" of nature. For example, $A = lw$ is the area of a rectangle of length l and width w; and $f = ma$ relates the force f, mass m, and acceleration a of a particle moving in a straight line (Newton's second law of motion). Thus it is important that the new numbers being created satisfy the rules of arithmetic.

2.5.1   Complex Numbers

In any event, mathematicians in the 1700s introduced a new (nonreal) number i with the property that

$$i^2 = -1$$

and they called expressions of the form

$$a + ib \quad \text{where } a \text{ and } b \text{ are real}$$

complex numbers. The set of all complex numbers is denoted $\mathbb{C}$. The rules of real arithmetic hold for these complex numbers with the single exception that $i^2 = -1$.

Given a complex number $z = a + ib$, the real number a is called the **real part** of z, and b is the **imaginary part** of z. Every real number a is a complex number, namely $a = a + 0i$, and complex numbers of the form $bi = 0 + bi$ are sometimes called **pure imaginary** numbers. The number i itself is called the **imaginary unit**.

If two complex numbers are equal, they must have the same real and imaginary parts. That is

$$\text{If } a + bi = a' + b'i \quad \text{then} \quad a = a' \text{ and } b = b'.$$

Indeed, if b were not equal to b' then we could solve for $i = \frac{a - a'}{b' - b}$, so i would be a real number, a contradiction. Hence $b = b'$, and so $a = a'$ (because $a + bi = a' + b'i$).

Because of this, it is possible to display the complex numbers geometrically as the points in the plane. This is accomplished by identifying the complex number $z = a + bi$ with the point $P(a, b)$.

Some examples are given in the diagram. When this is done the plane is called the **complex plane**. Note that the real numbers are identified with the points on the X-axis in the usual way. For this reason, the X-axis is called the **real axis**. Similarly, the Y-axis is called the **imaginary axis**.

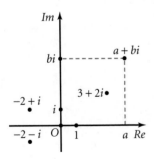

Complex numbers are added and multiplied in much the same way as linear polynomials $a + bx$, except that $i^2 = -1$. Thus

$$\text{If } z = a + ib \text{ and } w = a' + ib' \text{ then } \begin{cases} z + w = (a + a') + (b + b')i, \\ zw = (aa' - bb') + (ab' + ba')i. \end{cases}$$

Example 1 If $z = 3 - 2i$ and $w = -5 + 7i$, compute $z + w$, $z - w$, $5z$, zw, and z^2.

SOLUTION $\quad z + w = (3 - 5) + (-2 + 7)i = -2 + 5i.$
$z - w = (3 + 5) + (-2 - 7)i = 8 - 9i.$
$5z = 15 - 10i.$
$zw = (-15 - 14i^2) + (21 + 10)i = -1 + 31i.$
$z^2 = (9 + 4i^2) + (-6 - 6)i = 5 - 12i.$

Before describing the process of dividing one complex number by another we must introduce two important notions. If $z = a + ib$ is any complex number, the **conjugate** of z is another complex number, denoted $\bar{z}$, given by

$$\bar{z} = a - ib.$$

That is, $\bar{z}$ is formed by negating the imaginary part of z. Thus, in the complex plane, z and $\bar{z}$ are reflections of each other in the real axis (see the diagram).

Here are four useful properties of conjugation:

C1 $\overline{(z \pm w)} = \bar{z} \pm \bar{w}.$
C2 $\overline{(zw)} = \bar{z}\,\bar{w}.$
C3 $\overline{(\bar{z})} = z.$
C4 z is real if and only if $\bar{z} = z.$

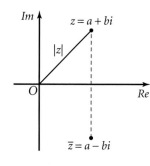

The routine verifications of C1, C2, and C3 are left as Exercise 6. As to C4, if $z = a + 0i$ is real, then $\bar{z} = a - 0i = z$. Conversely, if $z = a + bi$ and $\bar{z} = z$, then $a - bi = a + bi$. Hence equating imaginary parts gives $-b = b$. This means $b = 0$, whence $z = a + 0i = a$ is real.

Given any complex number $z = a + bi$, the distance from z to the origin 0 is

$$\sqrt{a^2 + b^2}$$

by Pythagoras' theorem[13]. This number is called the **absolute value** or **modulus** of the complex number $z = a + bi$, and is denoted (see the preceding diagram)

$$|z| = \sqrt{a^2 + b^2}.$$

It is routine to verify that

$$z\bar{z} = a^2 + b^2$$

which gives the following useful formula:

$$|z|^2 = z\bar{z} \quad \text{for every complex number } z.$$

Note that, if $z = a + 0i$ is real, then $|z| = \sqrt{a^2}$ is the absolute value of z viewed as a real number.

We list some basic properties of the absolute value.

A1 $\quad |z| \geq 0$ for all complex numbers z.
A2 $\quad |z| = 0$ if and only if $z = 0$.
A3 $\quad |zw| = |z|\,|w|$.

A1 and A2 follow immediately from the fact that $|z|$ is the distance from z to the origin O. To see why A3 holds, we use the fact (above) that $|z|^2 = z\bar{z}$ holds for every complex number z. Combining this with C2, we compute

$$|zw|^2 = (zw)\overline{(zw)} = zw\,\bar{z}\,\bar{w} = (z\bar{z})(w\bar{w}) = |z|^2\,|w|^2 = (|z|\,|w|)^2.$$

Now A3 follows by taking positive square roots.

---

[13] $\sqrt{p}$ denotes the *positive* square root of the real number $p \geq 0$.

We can now describe division by a complex number.

Example 2   Compute $\frac{3-5i}{2+7i}$.

SOLUTION   The idea is to multiply top and bottom by the conjugate of the denominator (and so turn the denominator into a real number):

$$\frac{3-5i}{2+7i} = \frac{(3-5i)(2-7i)}{(2+7i)(2-7i)} = \frac{-29-31i}{2^2+7^2} = -\frac{29}{53} - \frac{31}{53}i.$$

2.5.2   Quadratics

While the introduction of the imaginary unit i has been motivated by the problem of finding a root of the equation $x^2 + 1 = 0$, the complex numbers easily give the roots of any real quadratic. In fact, if a, b, and c are real numbers with $a \neq 0$, the quadratic equation $ax^2 + bx + c = 0$ has roots given by the famous **quadratic formula**:

$$x = \frac{-b \pm \sqrt{b^2 - 4ac}}{2a}.$$

The quantity $d = b^2 - 4ac$ is called the **discriminant** of the quadratic $ax^2 + bx + c$. It determines the nature of the roots:

If $d > 0$, there are two real roots.

If $d = 0$, there is one (repeated) real root.

If $d < 0$, there is no real root.

When $d < 0$ the quadratic $ax^2 + bx + c$ is said to be **irreducible**, and the quadratic formula gives two complex roots which are conjugates of each other:

$$\lambda = \tfrac{1}{2a}(-b + i\sqrt{|d|}) \quad \text{and} \quad \overline{\lambda} = \tfrac{1}{2a}(-b - i\sqrt{|d|})$$

The converse of this is also true: Given any nonreal complex number λ, then λ and $\overline{\lambda}$ are the roots of some real irreducible quadratic. Indeed, the quadratic

$$x^2 - (\lambda + \overline{\lambda})x + (\lambda\overline{\lambda}) = (x - \lambda)(x - \overline{\lambda})$$

is irreducible (the roots λ and $\overline{\lambda}$ are not real) and has real coefficients ($\lambda\overline{\lambda} = \left|\lambda\right|^2$ and $\lambda + \overline{\lambda}$ is twice the real part of λ).

Example 3   Find a real irreducible quadratic with $\lambda = 3 - 4i$ as a root.

SOLUTION   We have $\lambda + \overline{\lambda} = 6$ and $\left|\lambda\right|^2 = 25$, so $x^2 - 6x + 25$ is irreducible with roots λ and $\overline{\lambda} = 3 + 4i$.

2.5.3   Complex Linear Algebra

Everything we have done for real matrices can be done for complex matrices. The methods are the same; the only difference is that the arithmetic is carried out with complex numbers rather than real ones. We give three examples.

Example 4   Solve the system
$$\begin{aligned}
x + (1+i)y &= 1 - 2i \\
ix - \quad\ \ y + iz &= 2 \\
(i-1)x - \quad\ \ y - z &= 2i + 3
\end{aligned}$$

SOLUTION | The augmented matrix is reduced as follows:

$$
\begin{bmatrix} 1 & 1+i & 0 & 1-2i \\ i & -1 & i & 2 \\ i-1 & -1 & -1 & 2+3i \end{bmatrix} \rightarrow \begin{bmatrix} 1 & 1+i & 0 & 1-2i \\ 0 & -i & i & -i \\ 0 & 1 & -1 & 1 \end{bmatrix}
$$

$$
\rightarrow \begin{bmatrix} 1 & 1+i & 0 & 1-2i \\ 0 & 1 & -1 & 1 \\ 0 & 0 & 0 & 0 \end{bmatrix}
$$

$$
\rightarrow \begin{bmatrix} 1 & 0 & 1+i & -3i \\ 0 & 1 & -1 & 1 \\ 0 & 0 & 0 & 0 \end{bmatrix}.
$$

Hence we take $z = t$ where t is an arbitrary (complex) parameter, and then solve for $x = -3i - (1+i)t$ and $y = 1 + t$.

Example 5 | Find the inverse of $A = \begin{bmatrix} i & -1 \\ -i & 2 \end{bmatrix}$.

SOLUTION | We have $det A = 2i - (-1)(-i) = i \neq 0$. So A has an inverse and (the complex version of) Example 5 §1.5 gives

$$
A^{-1} = \tfrac{1}{i}\begin{bmatrix} 2 & 1 \\ i & i \end{bmatrix} = (-i)\begin{bmatrix} 2 & 1 \\ i & i \end{bmatrix} = \begin{bmatrix} -2i & -i \\ 1 & 1 \end{bmatrix}.
$$

The reader can check this directly. Of course the inverse can also be found using the matrix inversion algorithm.

Example 6 | Diagonalize the matrix $A = \begin{bmatrix} 0 & -1 \\ 1 & 0 \end{bmatrix}$.

SOLUTION | The characteristic polynomial of A is $c_A(x) = det(xI - A) = det\begin{bmatrix} x & 1 \\ -1 & x \end{bmatrix} = x^2 + 1$, so the eigenvalues are $\lambda_1 = i$ and $\lambda_2 = -i$. The augmented matrix of the system $(\lambda_1 I - A)X = 0$ is reduced as follows:

$$
\begin{bmatrix} i & 1 & 0 \\ -1 & i & 0 \end{bmatrix} \rightarrow \begin{bmatrix} -1 & i & 0 \\ 0 & 0 & 0 \end{bmatrix} \rightarrow \begin{bmatrix} 1 & -i & 0 \\ 0 & 0 & 0 \end{bmatrix}.
$$

Hence an eigenvector corresponding to $\lambda_1 = i$ is $X_1 = \begin{bmatrix} i \\ 1 \end{bmatrix}$. Similarly, $X_2 = \begin{bmatrix} -i \\ 1 \end{bmatrix}$ is an eigenvector for $\lambda_2 = -i$. Hence the complex version of Theorem 3 §2.3 shows that $P = [X_1 \ X_2] = \begin{bmatrix} i & -i \\ 1 & 1 \end{bmatrix}$ is invertible and

$$
P^{-1}AP = \begin{bmatrix} \lambda_1 & 0 \\ 0 & \lambda_2 \end{bmatrix} = \begin{bmatrix} i & 0 \\ 0 & -i \end{bmatrix}.
$$

As these examples illustrate, calculations in complex linear algebra are really not much different from their real counterparts, except for the fact that the arithmetic uses complex numbers.

2.5.4 Roots of Polynomials

There is, however, one major advantage of the complex case. As we have seen, real matrices can have no real eigenvalues. Perhaps the most important reason for the study of complex linear algebra is that this situation does not arise: Every complex matrix has an eigenvalue (possibly complex). This is a consequence of the following remarkable theorem. (We omit the proof.)

Fundamental Theorem of Algebra[14]. Every nonconstant polynomial with complex coefficients has a complex root.

If $f(x)$ is a polynomial with complex coefficients of degree $n \geq 1$, and if λ_1 is a root, then the factor theorem[15] asserts that

$$f(x) = (x - \lambda_1)\, g(x) \text{ where } g(x) \text{ is a polynomial of degree } n - 1.$$

Suppose that λ_2 is a root of $g(x)$, again by the fundamental theorem. Then $g(x) = (x - \lambda_2)\, h(x)$, so

$$f(x) = (x - \lambda_1)(x - \lambda_2)\, h(x).$$

This process continues until the last polynomial to appear is linear. This last factor can be written in the form $u \cdot (x - \lambda_n)$, so the fundamental theorem takes the following form:

THEOREM ❶   Every complex polynomial $f(x)$ of degree $n \geq 1$ has the form

$$f(x) = u \cdot (x - \lambda_1)(x - \lambda_2) \cdots (x - \lambda_n)$$

where the complex numbers $\lambda_1, \ \lambda_2, \ \cdots \ \lambda_n$ are the roots of $f(x)$ and need not be all distinct, and $u \neq 0$ is the coefficient of x^n in $f(x)$.

In the case of a quadratic polynomial $f(x)$, the degree is 2 and the quadratic formula provides the two roots λ_1 and λ_2. For polynomials of higher degree it is not so simple to find the roots, but computer programs exist to do the calculations.

Of course, the characteristic polynomial $c_A(x)$ of any complex matrix A factors completely as in Theorem 1. Since the roots of $c_A(x)$ are just the eigenvalues of A, we obtain

---

THEOREM ❷   Every $n \times n$ complex matrix A has n complex eigenvalues (possibly with some repeated).

We have seen several illustrations of Theorem 2 (with real eigenvalues) in Section 2.3.

2.5.5   Symmetric Matrices

Most of the applications of linear algebra involve a real matrix A and, while A will have complex eigenvalues by Theorem 2, it is always of interest to know when the eigenvalues are in fact real. This turns out to be the case whenever A is symmetric:

THEOREM ❸   Let A be a symmetric real matrix. If λ is any eigenvalue of A, then λ is real.

This important theorem will be used extensively in Chapter 4. Surprisingly enough, the theory of *complex* eigenvalues can be used to prove this useful result about *real* eigenvalues. The proof is given at the end of this section; we verify the 2×2 case.

Example 7   Verify Theorem 3 when A is 2×2 real and symmetric.

SOLUTION   If $A = \begin{bmatrix} a & b \\ b & c \end{bmatrix}$ is real, the characteristic polynomial is

$$c_A(x) = (x - a)(x - c) - b^2 = x^2 - (a + c)x + (ac - b^2).$$

---

[14] This theorem was first proved by Gauss at age 20, and was published in his doctoral dissertation in 1799.

[15] See Appendix A.3.

The discriminant of $c_A(x)$ is

$$d = (a + c)^2 - 4(ac - b^2) = (a - c)^2 + 4b^2.$$

Hence $d \geq 0$ because a, b, and c are real, so $c_A(x)$ has real roots (the eigenvalues).

2.5.6 Polar Form[16]

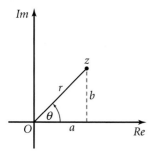

Up to this point we have been describing complex numbers z by writing them in the form $z = a + ib$ where (a, b) are the coordinates of z as a point in the complex plane. However, to describe multiplication of two complex numbers, it is convenient to represent them using polar coordinates in the plane. Write the absolute value of $z = a + ib$ as

$$r = |z| = \sqrt{a^2 + b^2}.$$

If $z \neq 0$, the angle θ shown in the diagram is called an **argument** of z and is denoted

$$\theta = arg(z).$$

The angle θ is not uniquely determined by z and the angle $\theta \pm 2\pi k$ would do equally well for any integer k.[17] The numbers r and θ are related to the real and imaginary parts a and b of z by

$$a = r \cos \theta \quad \text{and} \quad b = r \sin \theta.$$

Hence the complex number $z = a + ib$ has the form

$$z = r(\cos \theta + i \sin \theta).$$

There is a famous expression (called **Euler's formula**[18]) for the complex numbers $\cos \theta + i \sin \theta$:

$$e^{i\theta} = \cos \theta + i \sin \theta \qquad \text{for any angle } \theta.$$

Here $e = 2.71828\cdots$ is the constant familiar from calculus. Then the **polar form** of z is

$$z = re^{i\theta} \text{ where } r = |z| \geq 0 \quad \text{and} \quad \theta = arg(z).$$

Of course it is not unique because the argument of θ can be changed by adding or subtracting multiples of 2π.

Example 8 Find the polar form of $z = -1 + i$ and of $w = \sqrt{3} - i$.

SOLUTION

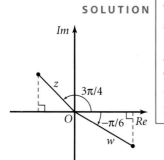

These complex numbers are plotted in the diagram. We have $|z| = \sqrt{(-1)^2 + 1^2} = \sqrt{2}$, and the triangle determined by z and the real axis has sides of length 1 and hypotenuse $\sqrt{2}$. Hence the acute angles in the triangle are both $\frac{\pi}{4} = 45°$, so one argument for z is $arg(z) = \frac{3\pi}{4}$ as can be seen in the diagram. Thus the polar form of z is $z = \sqrt{2}e^{3\pi i/4}$. Turning to w, we see that $|w| = \sqrt{(\sqrt{3})^2 + (-1)^2} = 2$. The triangle determined by w and the real axis has acute angles $\frac{\pi}{6} = 30°$ and $\frac{\pi}{3} = 60°$, so $arg(w) = -\frac{\pi}{6}$. Hence the polar form of w is $w = 2 e^{-\pi i/6}$.

---

[16] This material is not required elsewhere in this book.

[17] Recall that 2π radians represents one full circle, so the angle $\theta \pm 2\pi k$ is obtained from θ by adding (or subtracting) k full revolutions. For a review of the properties of a general angle θ and of $\cos \theta$ and $\sin \theta$, see Appendix A.1.

[18] Named after the great Swiss mathematician Leonhard Euler (1707–1783). We have the Maclaurin expansion $e^x = 1 + x + \frac{1}{2!}x^2 + \frac{1}{3!}x^3 + \cdots$, and substituting $x = i\theta$ gives Euler's formula when we remember that $\sin x = x - \frac{1}{3!}x^3 + \frac{1}{5!}x^5 - \cdots$ and $\cos x = 1 - \frac{1}{2!}x^2 + \frac{1}{4!}x^4 - \cdots$.

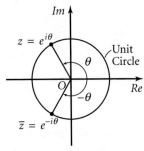

Because $\cos^2 \theta + \sin^2 \theta = 1$ for any angle θ, the numbers $e^{i\theta} = \cos \theta + i \sin \theta$ all have absolute value 1:

$$\left| e^{i\theta} \right| = 1 \text{ for any angle } \theta.$$

In other words, each $e^{i\theta}$ lies on the **unit circle** (centre at the origin and radius 1). On the other hand, every complex number z on the unit circle has the form $z = e^{i\theta}$ for some angle θ (see the diagram):

$$|z| = 1 \text{ if and only if } z = e^{i\theta} \text{ for some angle } \theta.$$

Furthermore, if $|z| = 1$, then $z\bar{z} = |z|^2 = 1$, so $\bar{z} = 1/z$. The diagram also shows that:

$$\text{If } z = e^{i\theta}, \text{ then } \quad \bar{z} = e^{-i\theta} = 1/z.$$

Our main purpose for introducing the polar form is to clearly describe the product of two complex numbers. This is achieved in the following result.

THEOREM 4

Multiplication Rule. If $z = re^{i\theta}$ and $w = se^{i\varphi}$ in polar form, then
$$re^{i\theta} se^{i\varphi} = rs\, e^{i(\theta + \varphi)}.$$

Thus, to multiply two complex numbers, simply multiply the absolute values and add the angles.

PROOF   Since $re^{i\theta}se^{i\varphi} = rs\, e^{i\theta}e^{i\varphi}$, it suffices to show that $e^{i\theta}e^{i\varphi} = e^{i(\theta + \varphi)}$. This is a consequence of the trigonometric identities for $\cos(\theta + \varphi)$ and $\sin(\theta + \varphi)$:

$$\begin{aligned}
e^{i\theta}e^{i\varphi} &= (\cos \theta + i \sin \theta)(\cos \varphi + i \sin \varphi) \\
&= (\cos \theta \cos \varphi - \sin \theta \sin \varphi) + i(\cos \theta \sin \varphi + \sin \theta \cos \varphi) \\
&= \cos(\theta + \varphi) + i \sin(\theta + \varphi) \\
&= e^{i(\theta + \varphi)}.
\end{aligned}$$

Example 9   Multiply $(-1 + i)(\sqrt{3} - i)$ using the multiplication rule.

SOLUTION   In Example 8 we found that polar forms for these numbers are $-1 + i = \sqrt{2}\, e^{3\pi i/4}$ and $\sqrt{3} - i = 2\, e^{-\pi i/6}$. Hence the multiplication rule gives

$$\begin{aligned}
(-1 + i)(\sqrt{3} - i) &= \sqrt{2}e^{(3\pi/4)i}\, 2\, e^{-\pi i/6} = 2\sqrt{2}\, e^{(3\pi/4 - \pi/6)i} \\
&= 2\sqrt{2}\, e^{7\pi i/12} = 2\sqrt{2} \left(\cos \tfrac{7\pi}{12} + i \sin \tfrac{7\pi}{12} \right)
\end{aligned}$$

in polar form. Of course, we also can multiply the left side in Cartesian form to obtain $(1 - \sqrt{3}) + (1 + \sqrt{3})i = 2\sqrt{2} \left(\cos \tfrac{7\pi}{12} + i \sin \tfrac{7\pi}{12} \right)$. Equating real and imaginary parts gives the (somewhat unexpected) formulas $\cos \tfrac{7\pi}{12} = \tfrac{1 - \sqrt{3}}{2\sqrt{2}}$ and $\sin \tfrac{7\pi}{12} = \tfrac{1 + \sqrt{3}}{2\sqrt{2}}$.

The multiplication rule takes a particularly nice form when we use it to compute powers of a complex number. If $z = re^{i\theta}$ in polar form, then

$$z^2 = (re^{i\theta})(re^{i\theta}) = r^2 e^{i2\theta}.$$

Next compute z^3 as $z^3 = zz^2$ to get

$$z^3 = zz^2 = (re^{i\theta})(r^2 e^{i2\theta}) = r^3 e^{i3\theta},$$

again by the multiplication rule. The pattern is clear:

THEOREM 5   **DeMoivre's Theorem**[19]. If $z = re^{i\theta}$ in polar form, then

$$z^n = r^n e^{in\theta} \text{ for } n = 0, \pm 1, \pm 2, \cdots.$$

PROOF   The above argument proves it for $n = 1, 2, \cdots$, and it is clear if $n = 0$. If n is negative, write $n = -m$ where $m > 0$. Then

$$z^n = \frac{1}{z^m} = \frac{1}{r^m e^{im\theta}} = r^{-m}(e^{im\theta})^{-1} = r^{-m}e^{-(im\theta)} = r^{-m}e^{i(-m)\theta} = r^n e^{in\theta}.$$

Example 10   Compute $(1 - i)^{27}$.

SOLUTION   We have $1 - i = \sqrt{2}e^{-\pi i/4}$, so DeMoivre's theorem gives

$$(1 - i)^{27} = (\sqrt{2})^{27}e^{-27\pi i/4}.$$

Since $(\sqrt{2})^2 = 2$, we have $(\sqrt{2})^{27} = 2^{13}\sqrt{2}$. We can simplify the expression $e^{-\frac{27\pi}{4}i}$ by using the fact that $e^{2\pi ki} = 1$ for all integers k (even negative values). Observe that $-\frac{27\pi}{4} = -\frac{3\pi}{4} - 6\pi$. Hence

$$e^{-27\pi i/4} = e^{-3\pi i/4}e^{-6\pi i} = e^{-3\pi i/4} \cdot 1 = e^{-3\pi i/4} = -\frac{1}{\sqrt{2}}(1 + i).$$

Finally $(1 - i)^{27} = (\sqrt{2})^{27}e^{-27\pi i/4i} = 2^{13}\sqrt{2}\{-\frac{1}{\sqrt{2}}(1 + i)\} = -2^{13}(1 + i)$.

DeMoivre's theorem also allows us to take roots of complex numbers. Here is an example.

Example 11   Find all fourth roots of $8(1 + \sqrt{3}i)$; that is, find all complex numbers z such that $z^4 = 8(1 + \sqrt{3}i)$.

SOLUTION   The idea is to write $z = re^{i\theta}$, and find all possibilities for r and θ. We have $8(1 + \sqrt{3}i) = 8(2e^{\pi i/3})$, so the condition that $z^4 = 8(1 + \sqrt{3}i)$ becomes

$$r^4 e^{4\theta i} = 16e^{\pi i/3} \tag{$*$}$$

Equating absolute values gives $r^4 = 16$, so $r = \sqrt[4]{16} = 2$ because $r > 0$. Even though the complex numbers in $(*)$ are equal, their angles may differ by a multiple of 2π:

$$4\theta = \frac{\pi}{3} + 2\pi k \text{ for some } k = 0, \pm 1, \pm 2, \pm 3, \cdots.$$

Hence $\theta = \frac{\pi}{12} + \frac{\pi}{2}k$ for any integer k, and it appears that there are infinitely many possibilities for θ, one for each choice of k. However, the various possibilities for θ are obtained from $\frac{\pi}{12}$ by adding multiples of $\frac{\pi}{2}$. Hence the distinct ones correspond to $k = 0, 1, 2,$ and 3; all the others differ from one of these by a multiple of 2π and so yield nothing new (see the diagram).

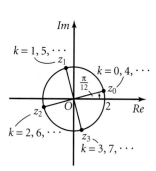

So the four possibilities for z are

$$z_0 = 2e^{\pi i/12}, \quad z_1 = 2e^{7\pi i/12}, \quad z_2 = 2e^{13\pi i/12}, \quad z_3 = 2e^{19\pi i/12}.$$

These are plotted in the diagram. They are equally spaced around the circle $|z| = 2$, starting at $\theta = \frac{\pi}{12}$.

The technique in Example 11 works to find all n^{th} roots of any complex number w; that is, all complex numbers z such that $z^n = w$. It turns out that there are n of them, equally spaced on a circle of radius $\sqrt[n]{|w|}$ so the angle between consecutive values is $\frac{2\pi}{n}$.

---

[19] Abraham DeMoivre (1667–1754) was a French mathematician and statistician.

Possibly the most important case is that of the complex numbers z such that $z^n = 1$, the so-called n^{th} **roots of unity**. Here, if we write $z = re^{i\theta}$, we obtain $r^n e^{n\theta i} = 1e^{0i}$, so equating absolute values gives $r = 1$, and equating angles gives $n\theta = 0 + 2\pi k$ for $k = 0, \pm 1, \pm 2, \pm 3, \cdots$. Thus $\theta = \frac{2\pi}{n}k$, so the roots are all given by taking $k = 0, 1, 2, \cdots, n - 1$.

THEOREM 6   The nth roots of unity (that is the solutions to $z^n = 1$) are the complex numbers
$$e^{2\pi k i/n} \text{ where } k = 0, 1, 2, 3, \cdots, n - 1.$$

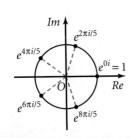

These n^{th} roots of unity are equally spaced on the unit circle. Every value of k yields a value of $\theta = \frac{2\pi}{n}k$ that differs from one of these by a multiple of 2π. Of course $k = 0$ gives the root $z = 1$, so all the roots are obtained by dividing the unit circle into n equal sectors, starting at $z = 1$. The 5th roots of unity are plotted in the diagram.

2.5.7   Proof of Theorem 3

If Z is a complex matrix, the **conjugate matrix** $\overline{Z}$ is defined to be the matrix obtained from Z by conjugating every entry. Thus, if $Z = [z_{ij}]$, then $\overline{Z} = [\overline{z}_{ij}]$. For example, if

$$Z = \begin{bmatrix} -i+2 & 5 \\ i & 3+4i \end{bmatrix}, \text{ then } \overline{Z} = \begin{bmatrix} i+2 & 5 \\ -i & 3-4i \end{bmatrix}.$$

It follows from C1 and C2 in §2.5.1 above that, if Z and W are two complex matrices and λ is a complex number, then

$$\overline{Z + W} = \overline{Z} + \overline{W}$$
$$\overline{ZW} = \overline{Z}\,\overline{W}$$
$$\overline{(\lambda Z)} = \overline{\lambda}\,\overline{Z}$$

Now suppose that A is a real symmetric matrix. Observe that $\overline{A} = A$ because A is real (using C4 in §2.5.1 above). If λ is an eigenvalue of A, we show that λ is real by showing that $\overline{\lambda} = \lambda$ (again by C4). Let X be a (possibly complex) eigenvector corresponding to λ, so that $X \neq 0$ and $AX = \lambda X$. Define $c = X^T \overline{X}$. If we write $X = [z_1 \ z_2 \ \cdots \ z_n]^T$ where the z_i are complex numbers, we have

$$c = X^T \overline{X} = [z_1 \ z_2 \ \cdots \ z_n] \begin{bmatrix} \overline{z}_1 \\ \overline{z}_2 \\ \vdots \\ \overline{z}_n \end{bmatrix}$$
$$= z_1\overline{z}_1 + z_2\overline{z}_2 + \cdots + z_n\overline{z}_n$$
$$= |z_1|^2 + |z_2|^2 + \cdots + |z_n|^2.$$

Thus c is a real number, and $c > 0$ because at least one of the $z_i \neq 0$ (as $X \neq 0$). We show that $\overline{\lambda} = \lambda$ by verifying that $\lambda c = \overline{\lambda} c$. We have

$$\lambda c = \lambda(X^T \overline{X}) = (\lambda X)^T \overline{X} = (AX)^T \overline{X} = X^T A^T \overline{X}.$$

At this point we use the hypothesis that A is symmetric and real. This means $A^T = A = \overline{A}$, so we continue

$$\lambda c = X^T A^T \overline{X} = X^T (\overline{A}\,\overline{X}) = X^T \overline{(AX)} = X^T \overline{(\lambda X)} = X^T (\overline{\lambda}\,\overline{X}) = \overline{\lambda} X^T \overline{X} = \overline{\lambda} c$$

as required. The technique in this proof will be used again in Chapter 4.

Exercises 2.5

Throughout these exercises, z and w denote complex numbers.

1. Write each of the following in the form $a + bi$.
  a) $(2 - 3i) - 3(5 + 7i) + 4$ **b)** $(4 - i)(2i - 5) + |3 - 2i|$
  c) i^{11}
  d) $(2 - 3i)^3$
  e) $\frac{3-i}{2i+5}$
  f) $\frac{3-5i}{7-i}$
  g) $\frac{1-i}{2-3i} - \frac{1+2i}{5+i}$
  h) $\frac{3-i}{2-i} + 3\frac{5i}{2i+1}$
  i) $\frac{|2-3i|}{|2+3i|}$
  j) $\left|\frac{3+4i}{|3+4i|}\right|$

2. In each case solve for the real number x.
  a) $(2 + xi)(3 - 2i) = 12 + 5i$
  b) $(2 + xi)^2 = 4$

3. In each case solve for the complex number z.
  a) $iz + (1 - i)^2 = 5 - 2i$ **b)** $(i + z) - 3i(2 - z) = iz + 1$
  c) $z(1 + i) = \overline{z} - (3 + 2i)$ **d)** $z(2 - i) = (\overline{z} + 1)(1 + i)$

4. Find all complex numbers z such that $|z| = 1$ and $z/\overline{z} = -1$.

5. **a)** Show that $z + \overline{z}$ is a real number for each complex number z.
  b) What can you say about $z - \overline{z}$?

6. Let $z = a + bi$ and $w = a' + b'i$ be arbitrary complex numbers. In each case verify the identity by computing each side separately and comparing.
  a) C1. $\overline{(z \pm w)} = \overline{z} \pm \overline{w}$
  b) C2. $\overline{(zw)} = \overline{z}\,\overline{w}$
  c) C3. $\overline{(\overline{z})} = z$

7. In each case either show that the statement is true or give an example showing that it is false.
  a) If $a^2 + b^2 = 0$ where a and b are real numbers, then $a = 0$ and $b = 0$.
  b) If $z^2 + w^2 = 0$ where z and w are complex numbers, then $z = 0$ and $w = 0$.
  c) If $z = 1/z$, then $z = \pm 1$.
  d) If $|z| = 1$, then $z = 1, -1, i$ or $-i$.
  e) If $|z| = |w|$, then $z = \pm w$.
  f) If $\overline{z} = -z$, then z is pure imaginary.

8. Find the roots of the following quadratic polynomials:
  a) $x^2 - 1$
  b) $x^2 + 1$
  c) $3x^2 - 5x + 10$
  d) $3x^2 + 5x + 10$
  e) $-3x^2 - 5x - 10$
  f) $-3x^2 + 5x + 10$

9. In each case find a real irreducible quadratic with λ as a root:
  a) $\lambda = 1 - 2i$
  b) $\lambda = 3i$
  c) $\lambda = -2i$
  d) $\lambda = 2 - 5i$

10. Solve each of the following systems of equations.
  a)
  $$x + \quad iy - iz = 3 + i$$
  $$-ix + \quad 2y + iz = 2$$
  $$(i - 1)x - (1 + 2i)y + 2z = i - 1$$
  b)
  $$x + (1 + i)y - \quad iz = 2$$
  $$(1 + i)x + \quad + (1 - i)z = 3 + i$$
  $$-x + (1 - i)y + \quad iz = i - 1$$

11. Find the inverse of the following matrices, if possible.
  a) $\begin{bmatrix} 1+i & -2 \\ 2i & -1-i \end{bmatrix}$
  b) $\begin{bmatrix} 1 & 1-i \\ 2+i & 3+i \end{bmatrix}$
  c) $\begin{bmatrix} 1+2i & -i & 3+5i \\ 2 & 1+4i & 3-i \\ -i & 5+i & 4-2i \end{bmatrix}$
  d) $\begin{bmatrix} 1-i & 1-i & 1+i \\ 2+i & 3+i & 4+i \\ -3i & 2-i & 5+5i \end{bmatrix}$

12. In each case find, if possible, an invertible matrix P such that $P^{-1}AP = D$ is diagonal.
  a) $\begin{bmatrix} -2 & -1 \\ 5 & 2 \end{bmatrix}$
  b) $\begin{bmatrix} 1 & i \\ -i & 1 \end{bmatrix}$
  c) $\begin{bmatrix} -3 & 5 & 4 \\ -2 & 3 & 2 \\ 0 & 0 & 1 \end{bmatrix}$
  d) $\begin{bmatrix} -5 & 6 & 2 \\ -3 & 4 & 1 \\ -5 & 5 & 2 \end{bmatrix}$
  e) $\begin{bmatrix} 2 & 51 & -53 \\ 10 & -32 & -24 \\ -11 & 19 & -78 \end{bmatrix}$
  f) $\begin{bmatrix} -91 & 70 & -23 \\ 32 & 14 & 16 \\ 25 & 19 & -19 \end{bmatrix}$
  g) $\begin{bmatrix} -1-i & -3+i & -2+2i \\ 1+i & -3+2i & -i \\ -3+5i & 2+3i & 3+5i \end{bmatrix}$
  h) $\begin{bmatrix} 2+i & 2-i & -4+i \\ 3-i & 1+2i & 6+5i \\ 5-i & 6+i & 2+7i \end{bmatrix}$

13. Let $A\begin{bmatrix} \cos\theta & -\sin\theta \\ \sin\theta & \cos\theta \end{bmatrix}$ where θ is any angle.
  a) Show that the characteristic polynomial of A is $c_A(x) = x^2 - 2\cos\theta\,x + 1$.
  b) Show that the eigenvalues of A are $\lambda_1 = \cos\theta + i\sin\theta$ and $\lambda_2 = \cos\theta - i\sin\theta$.
  c) Find an invertible matrix P such that $P^{-1}AP = \begin{bmatrix} \lambda_1 & 0 \\ 0 & \lambda_2 \end{bmatrix}$.

14. If Z and W are complex matrices, show that $\overline{ZW} = \overline{Z}\,\overline{W}$.

15. If λ is an eigenvalue (possibly not real) of a real matrix A, show that $\overline{\lambda}$ is also an eigenvalue.

16. If λ is a root of a real polynomial $f(x)$, show that $\overline{\lambda}$ is also a root.

17. Show that $|\overline{z}| = |z|$ for any complex number z.

18. Describe the set of all complex numbers z such that $|z| = 1$.

19. Show that $\left|\frac{z}{w}\right| = \frac{|z|}{|w|}$ whenever $w \neq 0$.

20. Express each of the following in polar form.
   a) $2 - 2i$ **b)** $-2i$
   c) $-\sqrt{3} + i$ **d)** $-3 - \sqrt{3}i$
   e) $5i$ **f)** $5(1 + i)$

21. Express each of the following in the form $a + bi$.
   a) $3\,e^{\pi i}$ **b)** $e^{5\pi i/3}$
   c) $2\,e^{\pi i/4}$ **d)** $\sqrt{2}\,e^{-\pi i/4}$
   e) $e^{15\pi/4}$ **f)** $2\sqrt{3}\,e^{-\pi i/3}$

22. Express each of the following in the form $a + bi$.
   a) $(1 - \sqrt{3}i)^5$ **b)** $(\sqrt{3} + i)^{-4}$
   c) $(1 + i)^{12}$ **d)** $(1 - i)^{10}$
   e) $(1 - i)^6(\sqrt{3} + i)^3$ **f)** $(\sqrt{3} - i)^9(2 - 2i)^5$

23. Find all:
   a) fourth roots of unity.   **b)** cube roots of unity.

24. Find all complex numbers z such that:
   a) $z^4 = -1$ **b)** $z^4 = 2(\sqrt{3}i - 1)$
   c) $z^3 = -27i$ **d)** $z^6 = -64$

25. Use DeMoivre's theorem to show that:
   a) $\cos(2\theta) = \cos^2\theta - \sin^2\theta$ and
      $\sin(2\theta) = 2\cos\theta\sin\theta$.
   b) $\cos(3\theta) = \cos^3\theta - 3\cos\theta\sin^2\theta$ and
      $\sin(2\theta) = 3\cos^2\theta\sin\theta - \sin^3\theta$.

26. Show that $\cos\theta = \frac{1}{2}(e^{i\theta} + e^{-i\theta})$ and $\sin\theta = \frac{1}{2i}(e^{i\theta} - e^{-i\theta})$ for any angle θ.

2.6   LINEAR RECURRENCES

A sequence $x_0, x_1, \cdots$ of numbers is said to be given **recursively** if each number in the sequence is completely determined by those that come before it. Such sequences arise frequently in mathematics and computer science and in various parts of the natural and social sciences. Here is an example.

Example 1   An urban planner wants to determine the number x_k of ways that a row of k parking spaces can be filled with cars and trucks if trucks take up two spaces each. Find x_{12}.

SOLUTION   Clearly $x_0 = 1$ and $x_1 = 1$, while $x_2 = 2$ because there can be only two cars or one truck. We have $x_3 = 3$ (the 3 configurations are ccc, cT and Tc), and $x_4 = 5$ ($cccc$, ccT, cTc, Tcc and TT). However, enumerating the possibilities in this way becomes difficult if the number k of parking spaces is large. Some other method is needed. In this case (and many others) it turns out that the numbers x_k are given recursively, and this solves the problem. In fact, we claim that

$$x_{k+2} = x_k + x_{k+1}   \text{ for every } k \geq 0.$$

This determines x_k for every $k \geq 2$ since x_0 and x_1 are given. Indeed, the first few possibilities are

$$x_0 = 1$$
$$x_1 = 1$$
$$x_2 = x_0 + x_1 = 2$$
$$x_3 = x_1 + x_2 = 3$$
$$x_4 = x_2 + x_3 = 5$$
$$x_5 = x_3 + x_4 = 8$$
$$x_6 = x_4 + x_5 = 13$$
$$\vdots \qquad \vdots \qquad \vdots$$

Continuing in this way we obtain $x_{12} = 233$ as the reader can verify. While this method can be used with a computer to quickly calculate x_k for large values of k, it would be nice to have a "formula" for x_k in terms of k to get an approximate idea of the size of x_k as k increases (for example $x_{30} = 832\,040$). This can be done using diagonalization, as we shall see.

2.6.1   Linear Recurrences

The equation $x_{k+2} = x_k + x_{k+1}$ that occurs in Example 1 is called a **linear recurrence relation** for the numbers $x_0, x_1, x_2, \cdots$. We begin our discussion with a recurrence that is somewhat easier to solve than this one (we return to it in Example 3).

Suppose the numbers $x_0, x_1, x_2, \cdots$ are given by

$$x_{k+2} = x_{k+1} + 2x_k \quad \text{for } k \geq 0$$

where x_0 and x_1 are specified. If $x_0 = 1$ and $x_1 = 2$, the sequence is uniquely determined:

$$x_0 = 1$$
$$x_1 = 2$$
$$x_2 = x_1 + 2x_0 = 4$$
$$x_3 = x_2 + 2x_1 = 8$$
$$x_4 = x_3 + 2x_2 = 16$$
$$\vdots \qquad \vdots \qquad \vdots$$

It is clear that $x_k = 2^k$ holds for $k = 0, 1, 2, 3,$ and 4, and this formula satisfies the recurrence $x_{k+2} = x_{k+1} + 2x_k$ as is readily checked.

However if we take $x_0 = 1$ and $x_1 = 1$ instead, the sequence continues $x_2 = 3$, $x_3 = 5$, $x_4 = 11$, $x_5 = 21, \cdots$. In this case, the sequence is uniquely determined but no formula is apparent. Nonetheless, a simple device transforms the recurrence into a matrix recurrence, which we can solve easily.

Example 2   Suppose the sequence $x_0, x_1, x_2, \cdots$ is given recursively by $x_0 = 1$, $x_1 = 1$, and $x_{k+2} = x_{k+1} + 2x_k$ for each $k \geq 0$. Find a formula for x_k in terms of k.

SOLUTION   The idea is to consider the sequence $V_0, V_1, V_2, \cdots$ instead of $x_0, x_1, x_2, \cdots$ where

$$V_k = \begin{bmatrix} x_k \\ x_{k+1} \end{bmatrix}.$$

Then $V_0 = \begin{bmatrix} x_0 \\ x_1 \end{bmatrix} = \begin{bmatrix} 1 \\ 1 \end{bmatrix}$ is specified, and the numerical recurrence $x_{k+2} = x_{k+1} + 2x_k$ transforms into a matrix recurrence as follows:

$$V_{k+1} = \begin{bmatrix} x_{k+1} \\ x_{k+2} \end{bmatrix} = \begin{bmatrix} x_{k+1} \\ x_{k+1} + 2x_k \end{bmatrix} = \begin{bmatrix} 0 & 1 \\ 2 & 1 \end{bmatrix} \begin{bmatrix} x_k \\ x_{k+1} \end{bmatrix} = AV_k$$

where $A = \begin{bmatrix} 0 & 1 \\ 2 & 1 \end{bmatrix}$. Hence $V_0, V_1, \cdots$ is a dynamical system, so Theorem 1 §2.4 applies if the matrix A is diagonalizable. We have

$$c_A(x) = det \begin{bmatrix} x & -1 \\ -2 & x-1 \end{bmatrix} = x(x-1) - 2 = (x-2)(x+1).$$

Hence the eigenvalues $\lambda_1 = 2$ and $\lambda_2 = -1$ are distinct, so A is indeed diagonalizable. Corresponding eigenvectors are $X_1 = \begin{bmatrix} 1 \\ 2 \end{bmatrix}$ and $X_2 = \begin{bmatrix} 1 \\ -1 \end{bmatrix}$ as the reader can check, so $P = \begin{bmatrix} 1 & 1 \\ 2 & -1 \end{bmatrix}$ is a diagonalizing matrix for A. We compute the coefficients b_i in Theorem 1 §2.4:

$$\begin{bmatrix} b_1 \\ b_2 \end{bmatrix} = P^{-1}V_0 = -\frac{1}{3}\begin{bmatrix} -1 & -1 \\ -2 & 1 \end{bmatrix}\begin{bmatrix} 1 \\ 1 \end{bmatrix} = \begin{bmatrix} \frac{2}{3} \\ \frac{1}{3} \end{bmatrix}.$$

Thus Theorem 1 §2.4 gives

$$\begin{bmatrix} x_k \\ x_{k+1} \end{bmatrix} = V_k = b_1\lambda_1^k X_1 + b_2\lambda_2^k X_2 = \tfrac{2}{3}2^k\begin{bmatrix} 1 \\ 2 \end{bmatrix} + \tfrac{1}{3}(-1)^k\begin{bmatrix} 1 \\ -1 \end{bmatrix}.$$

Equating top entries yields

$$x_k = \tfrac{1}{3}\left(2^{k+1} + (-1)^k\right) \quad \text{for } k \geq 0$$

which is the desired formula for the x_k.

Note that we can write $x_k = \tfrac{1}{3}2^{k+1}\left(1 + \tfrac{1}{2}(\tfrac{-1}{2})^k\right) \approx \tfrac{1}{3}2^{k+1}$ for large k. (This amounts to the observation that $\lambda_1 = 2$ is the dominant eigenvalue here.) This formula is quite useful in this case because the approximation is good even for small k. For example, we get $x_6 \approx \tfrac{1}{3}2^{6+1} = \tfrac{128}{3} = 42.67$, which compares favourably with the true value $x_6 = 43$. In fact, for large k, x_k is the integer nearest to $\tfrac{1}{3}2^{k+1}$.

We now apply this diagonalization technique to the combinatorial problem in Example 1.

Example 3   An urban planner wants to determine the number x_k of ways that a row of k parking spaces can be filled with cars and trucks if trucks take up two spaces each. Find a formula for x_k and estimate it for large k.

SOLUTION   We saw in Example 1 that $x_0 = 1$, $x_1 = 1$, and

$$x_{k+2} = x_k + x_{k+1} \quad \text{for every } k \geq 0. \tag{$*$}$$

If we write $V_k = \begin{bmatrix} x_k \\ x_{k+1} \end{bmatrix}$, the recurrence $(*)$ becomes a matrix recursion for the V_k:

$$\begin{aligned} V_{k+1} = \begin{bmatrix} x_{k+1} \\ x_{k+2} \end{bmatrix} &= \begin{bmatrix} x_{k+1} \\ x_k + x_{k+1} \end{bmatrix} \\ &= \begin{bmatrix} 0 & 1 \\ 1 & 1 \end{bmatrix}\begin{bmatrix} x_k \\ x_{k+1} \end{bmatrix} \\ &= A\,V_k \quad \text{for all } k \geq 0 \end{aligned}$$

where $A = \begin{bmatrix} 0 & 1 \\ 1 & 1 \end{bmatrix}$. Moreover A is diagonalizable here. The characteristic polynomial is

$$c_A(x) = det\begin{bmatrix} x & -1 \\ -1 & x-1 \end{bmatrix} = x^2 - x - 1.$$ This has roots $\tfrac{1}{2}[1 \pm \sqrt{5}]$ by the quadratic formula, so A has distinct eigenvalues

$$\lambda_1 = \tfrac{1}{2}[1 + \sqrt{5}] \quad \text{and} \quad \lambda_2 = \tfrac{1}{2}[1 - \sqrt{5}].$$

Since $\lambda_i^2 = \lambda_i + 1$ for each i, corresponding eigenvectors are $X_1 = \begin{bmatrix} 1 \\ \lambda_1 \end{bmatrix}$ and $X_2 = \begin{bmatrix} 1 \\ \lambda_2 \end{bmatrix}$ respectively as the reader can verify. Hence $P = \begin{bmatrix} 1 & 1 \\ \lambda_1 & \lambda_2 \end{bmatrix}$ is a diagonalizing matrix, so we compute the coefficients b_1 and b_2 (in Theorem 1 §2.4) as follows

$$\begin{bmatrix} b_1 \\ b_2 \end{bmatrix} = P^{-1}V_0 = \frac{1}{-\sqrt{5}}\begin{bmatrix} \lambda_2 & -1 \\ -\lambda_1 & 1 \end{bmatrix}\begin{bmatrix} 1 \\ 1 \end{bmatrix} = \frac{1}{\sqrt{5}}\begin{bmatrix} \lambda_1 \\ -\lambda_2 \end{bmatrix}$$

where we used the fact that $\lambda_1 + \lambda_2 = 1$. Thus Theorem 1 §2.4 gives

$$\begin{bmatrix} x_k \\ x_{k+1} \end{bmatrix} = V_k = b_1\lambda_1^k X_1 + b_2\lambda_2^k X_2 = \frac{\lambda_1}{\sqrt{5}}\lambda_1^k\begin{bmatrix} 1 \\ \lambda_1 \end{bmatrix} - \frac{\lambda_2}{\sqrt{5}}\lambda_2^k\begin{bmatrix} 1 \\ \lambda_2 \end{bmatrix}.$$

Comparing first entries gives an exact formula for the numbers x_k:

$$x_k = \frac{1}{\sqrt{5}}[\lambda_1^{k+1} - \lambda_2^{k+1}] \quad \text{for each } k \geq 0.$$

Finally, observe that λ_1 is dominant here (in fact, $\lambda_1 = 1.618$ and $\lambda_2 = -0.618$ to three figures) so λ_2^{k+1} is negligible compared with λ_1^{k+1} if k is large. Thus

$$x_k \approx \tfrac{1}{\sqrt{5}} \lambda_1^{k+1} \quad \text{for each } k \geq 0.$$

(This also follows from Theorem 1 §2.4.) This is a good approximation, even for as small a value as $k = 12$. Indeed, repeated use of the recurrence $x_{k+2} = x_k + x_{k+1}$ gives the exact value $x_{12} = 233$, while the approximation is $x_{12} \approx \frac{(1.618)^{13}}{\sqrt{5}} = 232.94$.

The sequence $x_0, x_1, x_2, \cdots$ in Example 3 was first discussed in 1202 by Leonardo Pisano of Pisa, also known as Fibonacci, and is now called the **Fibonacci sequence**. It is completely determined by the conditions $x_0 = 1$, $x_1 = 1$ and the recurrence $x_{k+2} = x_k + x_{k+1}$ for each $k \geq 0$. These numbers have been studied for centuries, and have many interesting properties (there is even a journal devoted exclusively to them). For example, biologists have discovered that the arrangement of leaves around the stems of some plants follow a Fibonacci pattern.

We conclude with an example showing that nonlinear recurrences can be complicated.

Example 4   Suppose a sequence $x_0, x_1, x_2, \cdots$ satisfies the following recurrence:

$$x_{k+1} = \begin{cases} \tfrac{1}{2}x_k & \text{if } x_k \text{ is even} \\ 3x_k + 1 & \text{if } x_k \text{ is odd} \end{cases}$$

If $x_0 = 1$, the sequence is $1, 4, 2, 1, 4, 2, 1, \cdots$ and so continues to cycle indefinitely. The same thing happens if $x_0 = 7$. Then the sequence is

$$7, 22, 11, 34, 17, 52, 26, 13, 40, 20, 10, 5, 16, 8, 4, 2, 1, \cdots$$

and it again cycles. However, it is not known whether every choice of x_0 will lead eventually to 1. It is quite possible that, for some x_0, the sequence will continue to produce different values indefinitely, or will repeat a value and cycle without reaching 1. No one knows for sure.

Exercises 2.6

1. Consider a sequence $x_0, x_1, x_2, \cdots$ satisfying the recurrence $x_{k+2} = 6x_k + x_{k+1}$.
   a) If $x_0 = 1$ and $x_1 = 3$, compute the first five terms of the sequence and guess a formula for x_k.
   b) If $x_0 = 1$ and $x_1 = 1$, find a formula for x_k.

2. Solve the following linear recurrences.
   a) $x_{k+2} = 3x_k + 2x_{k+1}$, where $x_0 = 1$ and $x_1 = 1$.
   b) $x_{k+2} = 2x_k - x_{k+1}$, where $x_0 = 1$ and $x_1 = 2$.
   c) $x_{k+2} = 2x_k + x_{k+1}$, where $x_0 = 0$ and $x_1 = 1$.
   d) $x_{k+2} = 6x_k - x_{k+1}$, where $x_0 = 1$ and $x_1 = 1$.

3. Solve the following linear recurrences.
   a) $x_{k+3} = 6x_{k+2} - 11x_{k+1} + 6x_k$, where $x_0 = 1$, $x_1 = 0$, and $x_2 = 1$.
   b) $x_{k+3} = -2x_{k+2} + x_{k+1} + 2x_k$, where $x_0 = 1$, $x_1 = 0$, and $x_2 = 1$.

4.[†] Solve the following linear recurrences.
   a) $x_{k+3} = x_{k+2} + x_{k+1} + x_k$, where $x_0 = 1$, $x_1 = 1$, and $x_2 = 1$.
   b) $x_{k+3} = 2x_{k+2} - x_{k+1} - 2x_k$, where $x_0 = 1$, $x_1 = 1$, and $x_2 = 1$.
   c) $x_{k+5} = 2x_{k+4} - x_{k+3} - 2x_{k+2} - x_{k+1} - x_k$, where $x_0 = 1$, $x_1 = 0$, $x_2 = 1$, $x_3 = 1$, and $x_4 = 1$.

5. A man must climb a flight of k steps. He always takes one or two steps at a time. Thus he can climb 3 steps in the following ways: 111, 12, or 21. Find the number s_k of ways he can climb the flight of k steps. [Hint: Examples 1 and 3.]

6. How many "words" of k letters can be made from the letters $\{a, b\}$ if there are no adjacent a's?

7. How many sequences of k flips of a coin are there with no HH (where $H = $ heads)?

[†] Requires computer assistance (e.g., Matlab).

8. Find the number x_k of ways to make a stack of k poker chips if only red, blue, and gold chips are used and no two gold chips are adjacent.

9. A nuclear reactor contains α- and β-particles. In every second each α-particle splits into three β-particles, and each β-particle splits into an α-particle and two β-particles. If there is a single α-particle in the reactor at time $t = 0$, how many α-particles are there at $t = 20$ seconds?

10. The annual yield of wheat in a certain country has been found to equal the average of the yield in the previous two years. If the yields in 1990 and 1991 were 10 and 12 million tons respectively, find a formula for the yield k years after 1990. What is the long-term average yield?

11. Suppose a sequence $x_0, x_1, x_2, \cdots$ is given recursively by $x_{k+1} = ax_k$ for all $k \geq 0$, where a is a fixed number. If $x_0 = b$, find x_k in terms of k.

12. **a)** Consider the recurrence $x_{k+2} = ax_k + bx_{k+1}$. Show that the corresponding matrix A has characteristic polynomial $x^2 - bx - a$, eigenvalues $\lambda_1 = \frac{1}{2}\left[b + \sqrt{b^2 + 4a}\right]$ and $\lambda_2 = \frac{1}{2}\left[b - \sqrt{b^2 + 4a}\right]$, and corresponding eigenvectors $X_i = \begin{bmatrix} 1 \\ \lambda_i \end{bmatrix}$ for each i.

   b) If $x_0 = 0, x_1 = 1$, use the diagonalizing matrix $P = [X_1 \; X_2]$ for A to get $V_k = \frac{1}{\sqrt{b^2+4a}}\left[\lambda_1^k X_1 - \lambda_2^k X_2\right]$, and hence $x_k = \frac{1}{\sqrt{b^2+4a}}\left[\lambda_1^k - \lambda_2^k\right]$ for all $k \geq 0$.

13. Consider $x_{k+2} = -5x_k + 2x_{k+1}$; $x_0 = 0$, $x_1 = 1$. Show that the eigenvalues are $\lambda_1 = 1 + 2i$ and $\lambda_2 = 1 - 2i$, with eigenvectors $X_1 = \begin{bmatrix} 1 \\ 1+2i \end{bmatrix}$ and $X_2 = \begin{bmatrix} 1 \\ 1-2i \end{bmatrix}$. Use Exercise 12 to get the formula
$$x_k = \frac{i}{4}\left[(1-2i)^k - (1+2i)^k\right] \text{ for } k \geq 0.$$

14. Find the general solution to the recurrence $x_{k+1} = rx_k + c$ where r and c are constants.

15. Consider a linear recurrence $x_{k+2} = ax_{k+1} + bx_k + c$ where c may not be zero.
   a) If $a + b \neq 1$, show that p can be found such that, if we set $y_k = x_k + p$, then $y_{k+2} = ay_{k+1} + by_k$. [Hence the sequence x_k can be found provided y_k can be found by the methods of this section (or otherwise).]
   b) Use **a)** to solve the recurrence $x_{k+2} = x_{k+1} + 6x_k + 5$ where $x_0 = 1$ and $x_1 = 1$.

16. Consider the linear recurrence
$$x_{k+2} = ax_{k+1} + bx_k + c(k) \qquad (*)$$
where $c(k)$ is a function of k. Also consider the related recurrence
$$x_{k+2} = ax_{k+1} + bx_k. \qquad (**)$$
Suppose that $x_k = p_k$ is a particular solution of $(*)$.
   a) If q_k is any solution of $(**)$, show that $q_k + p_k$ is a solution of $(*)$.
   b) Show that every solution of $(*)$ arises as in **a)** as the sum of a solution of $(**)$ plus the particular solution p_k of $(*)$.

2.7   POLYNOMIAL INTERPOLATION

In experimental science it is frequently necessary to use known data to estimate some quantity. There are many methods of doing this. In this section, we present the method of polynomial interpolation.

2.7.1   Polynomial Interpolation

Example 1

Deflection

An engineer wants to estimate the deflection of a wooden beam under a load of 2200 kg. He knows the data in the following table:

Load (kg)	1000	2000	3000
Deflection (mm)	1.5	2.1	3.4

and wants to "interpolate" to find the estimate he needs. A common way to do this is to find a quadratic $p(x)$ which fits the data exactly in the sense that

$$p(1000) = 1.5$$
$$p(2000) = 2.1$$
$$p(3000) = 3.4$$

Then the estimate would be $p(2200)$. If $p(x) = r_0 + r_1x + r_2x^2$, these conditions become three equations in the unknown coefficients r_0, r_1, and r_2:

$$r_0 + 1000\,r_1 + 1000^2 r_2 = 1.5$$
$$r_0 + 2000\,r_1 + 2000^2 r_2 = 2.1$$
$$r_0 + 3000\,r_1 + 3000^2 r_2 = 3.4$$

The solution is $r_0 = 1.6$, $r_1 = -0.000\,45$, and $r_2 = 0.000\,000\,35$, so the polynomial is

$$p(x) = 1.6 - 0.000\,45x + 0.000\,000\,35x^2.$$

The engineer uses $p(2200) = 2.304$ as the estimate of the deflection.

It often happens that two variables x and y are known to be related but the actual function $y = f(x)$ relating them is not known. Suppose that for certain values $x_1, x_2, \cdots, x_n$ of x, the corresponding values $y_1, y_2, \cdots, y_n$ are known (say from tables or experimental measurements), and it is desired to estimate the value of y corresponding to some other value of x. As in Example 1, one way to do this is to find a polynomial $p(x)$ that "fits" the data in the sense that $p(x_i) = y_i$ for each $i = 1, 2, \cdots, n$. Then the estimate for y is $p(x)$. Such a polynomial always exists if the x_i are distinct.

THEOREM 1

Suppose n data pairs (x_1, y_1), (x_2, y_2), $\cdots$, (x_n, y_n) are given where the x_i are distinct. Then there exists a unique polynomial

$$p(x) = r_0 + r_1x + r_2x^2 + \cdots + r_{n-1}x^{n-1}$$

such that $p(x_i) = y_i$ for each $i = 1, 2, \cdots, n$.

PROOF

We consider the case $n = 4$; the general case is entirely similar. The given conditions that $p(x_i) = y_i$ for each $i = 1, 2, 3$, and 4 give equations

$$r_0 + r_1x_1 + r_2x_1^2 + r_3x_1^3 = y_1$$
$$r_0 + r_1x_2 + r_2x_2^2 + r_3x_2^3 = y_2$$
$$r_0 + r_1x_3 + r_2x_3^2 + r_3x_3^3 = y_3$$
$$r_0 + r_1x_4 + r_2x_4^2 + r_3x_4^3 = y_4$$

In matrix form this system can be written as $AR = Y$ where

$$A = \begin{bmatrix} 1 & x_1 & x_1^2 & x_1^3 \\ 1 & x_2 & x_2^2 & x_2^3 \\ 1 & x_3 & x_3^2 & x_3^3 \\ 1 & x_4 & x_4^2 & x_4^3 \end{bmatrix}, \quad R = \begin{bmatrix} r_0 \\ r_1 \\ r_2 \\ r_3 \end{bmatrix}, \text{ and } Y = \begin{bmatrix} y_1 \\ y_2 \\ y_3 \\ y_4 \end{bmatrix}.$$

Hence it suffices to show that the matrix A is invertible when the x_i are distinct (then $R = A^{-1}Y$ is the column of coefficients of the polynomial we want).

We show that A is invertible by verifying that the only solution to the homogeneous system $AX = 0$ is the trivial solution $X = 0$ (Theorem 5 §1.5). If we write $X = [t_0 \quad t_1 \quad t_2 \quad t_3]^T$, consider the polynomial $f(x) = t_0 + t_1x + t_2x^2 + t_3x^3$ with the entries of X as coefficients. Then we have

$$AX = \begin{bmatrix} 1 & x_1 & x_1^2 & x_1^3 \\ 1 & x_2 & x_2^2 & x_2^3 \\ 1 & x_3 & x_3^2 & x_3^3 \\ 1 & x_4 & x_4^2 & x_4^3 \end{bmatrix} \begin{bmatrix} t_0 \\ t_1 \\ t_2 \\ t_3 \end{bmatrix} = \begin{bmatrix} f(x_1) \\ f(x_2) \\ f(x_3) \\ f(x_4) \end{bmatrix}$$

Hence the requirement that $AX = 0$ means $f(x_i) = 0$ for each $i = 1, 2, 3,$ and 4. In other words, $f(x)$ is a polynomial of degree at most 3 which has 4 distinct roots $x_1, x_2, x_3,$ and x_4. This can happen only if $f(x)$ is identically zero[20] that is if $t_0 = t_1 = t_2 = t_3 = 0$. This means that $X = 0$ as required.

The polynomial $p(x)$ in Theorem 1 is called the **interpolating polynomial** for the data $(x_1, y_1), (x_2, y_2), \cdots, (x_n, y_n)$. It is an exact fit in the sense that $p(x_i) = y_i$ holds for each i. Finding $p(x)$ may not be feasible if n is large, and polynomials of lower degree which "best fit" the data can be found, for example, by the method of least squares (see Section 4.6.5).

Matrices like A in the proof of Theorem 1 and their determinants, arise in other contexts and so have independent interest. Given numbers $x_1, x_2, \cdots, x_n$, the matrix

$$\begin{bmatrix} 1 & x_1 & x_1^2 & \cdots & x_1^{n-1} \\ 1 & x_2 & x_2^2 & \cdots & x_2^{n-1} \\ 1 & x_3 & x_3^2 & \cdots & x_3^{n-1} \\ \vdots & \vdots & \vdots & & \vdots \\ 1 & x_n & x_n^2 & \cdots & x_n^{n-1} \end{bmatrix}$$

(or its transpose) is called the **Vandermonde matrix**[21] corresponding to the numbers $x_1, x_2, \cdots, x_n$, and its determinant is called the **Vandermonde determinant**. There is a simple formula for this determinant. The following example treats the case $n = 3$.

Example 2   Show that $det \begin{bmatrix} 1 & x_1 & x_1^2 \\ 1 & x_2 & x_2^2 \\ 1 & x_3 & x_3^2 \end{bmatrix} = (x_2 - x_1)(x_3 - x_1)(x_3 - x_2)$.

SOLUTION   We begin by using row operations to introduce zeros into column 1:

$$det \begin{bmatrix} 1 & x_1 & x_1^2 \\ 1 & x_2 & x_2^2 \\ 1 & x_3 & x_3^2 \end{bmatrix} = det \begin{bmatrix} 1 & x_1 & x_1^2 \\ 0 & x_2-x_1 & x_2^2-x_1^2 \\ 0 & x_3-x_1 & x_3^2-x_1^2 \end{bmatrix}$$

$$= det \begin{bmatrix} 1 & x_1 & x_1^2 \\ 0 & x_2-x_1 & (x_2-x_1)(x_2+x_1) \\ 0 & x_3-x_1 & (x_3-x_1)(x_3+x_1) \end{bmatrix}$$

Now take the common factor out of each of rows 2 and 3:

$$det \begin{bmatrix} 1 & x_1 & x_1^2 \\ 1 & x_2 & x_2^2 \\ 1 & x_3 & x_3^2 \end{bmatrix} = (x_2 - x_1)(x_3 - x_1) \, det \begin{bmatrix} 1 & x_1 & x_1^2 \\ 0 & 1 & x_2+x_1 \\ 0 & 1 & x_3+x_1 \end{bmatrix}$$

$$= (x_2 - x_1)(x_3 - x_1) \, det \begin{bmatrix} 1 & x_2+x_1 \\ 1 & x_3+x_1 \end{bmatrix}$$

$$= (x_2 - x_1)(x_3 - x_1)(x_3 - x_2).$$

The result in Example 2 is typical of what happens for any Vandermonde determinant. The result is stated in full generality in the following theorem.

---

[20] Since $f(x_1) = 0$, the factor theorem asserts that $f(x) = (x - x_1)g(x)$ where $g(x)$ is another polynomial. Since $f(x)$ has *four* distinct roots, continuing this process means that all four terms $(x - x_1), (x - x_2), (x - x_3),$ and $(x - x_4)$ are factors of $f(x)$, contrary to the fact that $f(x)$ has degree at most 3. See Appendix A.3.

[21] After A.T. Vandermonde (1735–1796), a French mathematician.

THEOREM **2** **Vandermonde Determinant.** Let x_1, $x_2, \cdots, x_n$ be real numbers where $n \geq 2$. Then the corresponding Vandermonde determinant is given by

$$\begin{bmatrix} 1 & x_1 & x_1{}^2 & \cdots & x_1{}^{n-1} \\ 1 & x_2 & x_2{}^2 & \cdots & x_2{}^{n-1} \\ 1 & x_3 & x_3{}^2 & \cdots & x_3{}^{n-1} \\ \vdots & \vdots & \vdots & & \vdots \\ 1 & x_n & x_n{}^2 & \cdots & x_n{}^{n-1} \end{bmatrix} = \prod_{1 \leq j < i \leq n} (x_i - x_j)$$

where $\prod_{1 \leq j < i \leq n}(x_i - x_j)$ means the product of all factors $(x_i - x_j)$ where $j < i$ and both i and j are between 1 and n.

We omit the proof. To illustrate the theorem we state the expansion of the 4×4 Vandermonde determinant:

$$det \begin{bmatrix} 1 & x_1 & x_1{}^2 & x_1{}^3 \\ 1 & x_2 & x_2{}^2 & x_2{}^3 \\ 1 & x_3 & x_3{}^2 & x_3{}^3 \\ 1 & x_4 & x_4{}^2 & x_4{}^3 \end{bmatrix} = (x_2 - x_1)(x_3 - x_1)(x_3 - x_2)(x_4 - x_1)(x_4 - x_2)(x_4 - x_3).$$

Exercises 2.7

1. In each case find the interpolating polynomial for the given data, and use the polynomial to estimate the value of y corresponding to the given value of x.
   a) $(0, 2)$, $(1, 3)$, $(3, 8)$; $x = 2$.
   b) $(0, 5)$, $(1, 3)$, $(2, 5)$; $x = 1.5$.
   c) $(0, 1)$, $(1, 1)$, $(-1, 4)$, $(2, 5)$; $x = \frac{1}{2}$.
   d) $(0, 1)$, $(1, 1)$, $(-1, 2)$, $(-2, -3)$; $x = -\frac{1}{2}$.

2. Some observations of the growth of a stock are given in the following table:

Week	1	2	3
Value ($)	1.22	1.49	2.45

   a) Use polynomial interpolation to estimate the value of the stock in weeks 4 and 10.
   b)[†] The value turned out to be $3.75 in week 4; now use polynomial interpolation again to estimate the value of the stock in weeks 5 and 10.
   c) Argue whether this method provides valuable information or not.

3. Consider a ski jump starting at a height of 40 m, finishing at a height of 5 m, covering from start to finish a horizontal distance of 35 m.
   a) Using polynomial interpolation, design the jump so that, 30 horizontal metres from the top, the skier is 7.5 m high.
   b) If you know a bit of calculus, design the jump so that the angle at takeoff is 0° with the horizontal.

c) Specify now that the jump forms a straight line descent for the first 25 horizontal and 20 vertical metres. Design the jump so that the line segment and the remaining curve have the same first derivative (tangent) at the point of intersection.
d) Do as in c), but require also that the second derivatives also match at the point of intersection.

4. Let A denote the Vandermonde matrix corresponding to the numbers $x_1, x_2, \cdots, x_n$. In the proof of Theorem 1 it was shown that A is invertible if the x_i are distinct. Show, conversely, that if A is invertible, then the x_i must be distinct.

5.[†] *Cubic Spline* In some applications, a better choice of a curve through several points is obtained by joining cubic (i.e., degree 3) polynomials through consecutive points with matching first and second derivatives at the given points.

So a *cubic spline* through data points $(0, 1)$, $(1, 3)$, and $(3, 2)$ for example, is formed by 2 cubic polynomials of the form

$s_1 = a_1x^3 + b_1x^2 + c_1x + d_1$ and $s_2 = a_2x^3 + b_2x^2 + c_2x + d_2$

satisfying the 6 equations (in the 8 unknowns a_1, a_2, b_1, b_2, c_1, c_2, d_1, d_2):

$$s_1(0) = 1, \ s_1(1) = 3, \ s_2(1) = 3, \ s_2(3) = 2,$$
$$s_1'(1) = s_2'(1), \ s_1''(1) = s_2''(1)$$

[†] Requires computer assistance (e.g., Matlab).

To uniquely determine the two cubics, we also require some conditions at the endpoints; for example, a vanishing second derivative:

$$s_1''(0) = 0 \text{ and } s_2''(2) = 0$$

a) Solve the above system of 8 equations in 8 unknowns to find the two required cubic polynomials.

b) Find the cubic spline through the data points of Example 1, and use it to estimate the deflection of the beam under a load of 2200 kg. Compare with the results of polynomial interpolation and argue why there is a difference.

2.8   SYSTEMS OF DIFFERENTIAL EQUATIONS

Many problems in Science and Engineering come down to solving differential equations. In this brief section we sketch how diagonalization can be used to solve certain systems of first order, ordinary differential equations. Of course some familiarity with calculus is required.

Recall that a real valued function f is a rule assigning a uniquely determined real number $f(x)$ to every real number x. Sometimes $f(x)$ is specified by a formula, for example $f(x) = 2x^2 + 3$ for all x. But more elaborate functions also arise such as the exponential function $f(x) = e^x$, or the cosine function $f(x) = \cos x$. Note that two functions f and g are *equal* if they have the same effect on every real number x, that is if $f(x) = g(x)$ holds for all real x. The *sum* $f + g$ and the *scalar product* af (where a is a number) are new functions defined by

$$(f + g)(x) = f(x) + g(x) \quad \text{for all } x,$$
$$af(x) = af(x) \quad \text{for all } x.$$

These are called **pointwise** addition and scalar multiplication, respectively; they are the usual operations that occur in calculus and algebra.

A function f is called **differentiable** if its derivative f' exists; we refer the reader to calculus texts for the precise definition of the derivative. All we need is the fact that, if f and g are both differentiable, so also are $f + g$ and af (for any constant a), and the derivatives are given by

$$(f + g)' = f' + g' \quad \text{and} \quad (af)' = af'.$$

These facts are proved in every calculus text.

2.8.1   The Diagonalization Method

Let f denote a differentiable function of a real variable x. The simplest first order[22] differential equation is

$$f' = af \text{ where } a \text{ is a constant.}$$

The chain rule of differentiation shows that $f(x) = e^{ax}$ satisfies this equation, and some elementary calculus shows that every solution is a multiple of e^{ax}.

LEMMA ①   Every solution of the differential equation $f' = af$ is given by

$$f(x) = ce^{ax} \text{ for some constant } c.$$

PROOF   If f is any solution, define a function g by $g(x) = f(x)e^{-ax}$. The product rule of differentiation shows that $g'(x) = f'(x)e^{-ax} - af(x)e^{-ax} = 0$, so $g(x) = c$ is a constant function. Hence $f(x) = ce^{ax}$.

---

[22] A *first order* differential equation is one involving only the function and its derivative, and no second or higher derivatives occur.

The problem we want to address here is how to use Lemma 1 to find all solutions of a *system* of first order differential equations. More precisely, if $f_1, f_2, \cdots, f_n$, are differentiable functions, we want to solve the system

$$
\begin{aligned}
f'_1 &= a_{11}f_1 + a_{12}f_2 + \cdots + a_{1n}f_n \\
f'_2 &= a_{21}f_1 + a_{22}f_2 + \cdots + a_{2n}f_n \\
&\vdots \qquad\qquad\qquad \vdots \\
f'_n &= a_{n1}f_1 + a_{n2}f_2 + \cdots + a_{nn}f_n
\end{aligned}
\tag{$*$}
$$

where the a_{ij} are constants. That is we want to describe all differentiable functions $f_1, f_2, \cdots, f_n$ that satisfy these equations. This system can easily be written in matrix form. Let

$$
\mathbf{f} = \begin{bmatrix} f_1 \\ f_2 \\ \vdots \\ f_n \end{bmatrix} \quad \mathbf{f}' = \begin{bmatrix} f'_1 \\ f'_2 \\ \vdots \\ f'_n \end{bmatrix} \quad \text{and} \quad A = \begin{bmatrix} a_{11} & a_{12} & \cdots & a_{1n} \\ a_{21} & a_{22} & \cdots & a_{2n} \\ \vdots & \vdots & & \vdots \\ a_{n1} & a_{n2} & \cdots & a_{nn} \end{bmatrix}.
$$

Then the system ($*$) of differential equations becomes the single matrix equation

$$
\mathbf{f}' = A\mathbf{f}. \tag{$**$}
$$

Given the matrix A we ask for all columns $\mathbf{f}$ of functions that satisfy ($**$). A variation on the technique used on dynamical systems will solve the problem if A is a diagonalizable matrix. We illustrate the method with an example where $n = 2$.

Example 1

Find all solutions to the system

$$
\begin{aligned}
f'_1 &= 2f_1 - f_2 \\
f'_2 &= 6f_1 - 5f_2
\end{aligned}.
$$

Then find a solution that satisfies $f_1(0) = 2$ and $f_2(0) = 3$.

SOLUTION

This system has the form $\mathbf{f}' = A\mathbf{f}$ where $A = \begin{bmatrix} 2 & -1 \\ 6 & -5 \end{bmatrix}$ and $\mathbf{f} = \begin{bmatrix} f_1 \\ f_2 \end{bmatrix}$. The characteristic polynomial of A is $c_A(x) = (x - 1)(x + 4)$, so the eigenvalues are $\lambda_1 = 1$ and $\lambda_2 = -4$, with corresponding eigenvectors $X_1 = \begin{bmatrix} 1 \\ 1 \end{bmatrix}$ and $X_2 = \begin{bmatrix} 1 \\ 6 \end{bmatrix}$ as is easily verified. Hence the matrix $P = [X_1 \ \ X_2] = \begin{bmatrix} 1 & 1 \\ 1 & 6 \end{bmatrix}$ diagonalizes A, that is

$$
P^{-1}AP = D = diag(\lambda_1, \ \lambda_2) = \begin{bmatrix} \lambda_1 & 0 \\ 0 & \lambda_2 \end{bmatrix}.
$$

The key to our method is to consider new functions $\mathbf{g} = \begin{bmatrix} g_1 \\ g_2 \end{bmatrix}$ given by

$$
\mathbf{f} = P\mathbf{g}, \text{ equivalently } \mathbf{g} = P^{-1}\mathbf{f}.
$$

In other words,

$$
\begin{bmatrix} f_1 \\ f_2 \end{bmatrix} = \begin{bmatrix} 1 & 1 \\ 1 & 6 \end{bmatrix}\begin{bmatrix} g_1 \\ g_2 \end{bmatrix}, \text{ that is } \begin{cases} f_1 = g_1 + g_2 \\ f_2 = g_1 + 6g_2 \end{cases}.
$$

It follows that $f'_1 = g'_1 + g'_2$ and $f'_2 = g'_1 + 6g'_2$, and in matrix form this is

$$
\mathbf{f}' = \begin{bmatrix} f'_1 \\ f'_2 \end{bmatrix} = \begin{bmatrix} g'_1 + g'_2 \\ g'_1 + 6g'_2 \end{bmatrix} = \begin{bmatrix} 1 & 1 \\ 1 & 6 \end{bmatrix}\begin{bmatrix} g'_1 \\ g'_2 \end{bmatrix} = P\mathbf{g}'.
$$

Theorem 3 has a geometric interpretation in $\mathbb{R}^3$ which clarifies the notion of linear independence. Let $\vec{v}$ and $\vec{w}$ be two nonzero vectors in $\mathbb{R}^3$. Then Theorem 3 asserts that the set $\{\vec{v},\ \vec{w}\}$ is linearly dependent if and only if one of $\vec{v}$ and $\vec{w}$ is a scalar multiple of the other; that is, if and only if they are parallel. Hence we have

COROLLARY   Let $\vec{v}$ and $\vec{w}$ be nonzero vectors in $\mathbb{R}^3$.

(1) $\{\vec{v},\ \vec{w}\}$ is linearly dependent if and only if $\vec{v}$ and $\vec{w}$ are parallel.
(2) $\{\vec{v},\ \vec{w}\}$ is linearly independent if and only if $\vec{v}$ and $\vec{w}$ are not parallel.

Now we can give a complete geometrical description of the span of two nonzero vectors in $\mathbb{R}^3$.

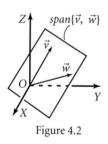

Figure 4.1

Assume that $\vec{v}$ and $\vec{w}$ are two nonzero vectors in $\mathbb{R}^3$. There are two cases:

Case 1. If $\vec{v}$ and $\vec{w}$ are parallel (that is, $\{\vec{v},\ \vec{w}\}$ is linearly dependent in $\mathbb{R}^3$) then $span\{\vec{v},\ \vec{w}\}$ is the line through the origin with direction vector $\vec{v}$ (or $\vec{w}$). This is illustrated in Figure 4.1.

Case 2. If $\vec{v}$ and $\vec{w}$ are not parallel (that is, $\{\vec{v},\ \vec{w}\}$ is linearly independent in $\mathbb{R}^3$) then $span\{\vec{v},\ \vec{w}\}$ is the plane through the origin with normal $\vec{n} = \vec{v} \times \vec{w}$. In this case $span\{\vec{v},\ \vec{w}\}$ is the unique plane through the origin containing $\vec{v}$ and $\vec{w}$. This is illustrated in Figure 4.2.

PROOF   **Case 1.** In this case, each of $\vec{v}$ and $\vec{w}$ is a scalar multiple of the other by Theorem 3, and so $span\{\vec{v},\ \vec{w}\} = span\{\vec{v}\} = span\{\vec{w}\}$ is the line through the origin with direction vector $\vec{v}$ (or $\vec{w}$).

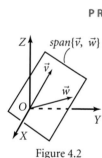

Figure 4.2

Case 2. We have $\vec{n} = \vec{v} \times \vec{w} \neq \vec{0}$ because $\vec{v}$ and $\vec{w}$ are not parallel (Theorem 2 §3.3). For convenience, write $U = span\{\vec{v},\ \vec{w}\}$ and let P denote the plane through the origin with normal $\vec{n}$. Then $P = \{\vec{p} \mid \vec{n} \cdot \vec{p} = 0\}$, so P is a subspace of $\mathbb{R}^3$ (verify). Moreover, $\vec{v}$ and $\vec{w}$ are in P by Theorem 2 §3.3 so $U \subseteq P$ by Theorem 1 §4.1. It remains to show that $P \subseteq U$. Let $\vec{p}$ be a vector in P; we must show that $\vec{p}$ is in U. If $[\vec{p}\ \ \vec{v}\ \ \vec{w}]$ denotes the matrix with $\vec{p}$, $\vec{v}$, and $\vec{w}$ as its columns, then Theorem 1 §3.5 gives

$$det[\vec{p}\ \ \vec{v}\ \ \vec{w}] = \vec{p} \cdot (\vec{v} \times \vec{w}) = \vec{p} \cdot \vec{n} = 0.$$

Hence $[\vec{p}\ \ \vec{v}\ \ \vec{w}]$ is not an invertible matrix, so $\{\vec{p},\ \vec{v},\ \vec{w}\}$ is linearly dependent by Theorem 2. This means that there is a linear combination $a\vec{p} + b\vec{v} + c\vec{w} = \vec{0}$ where a, b, and c are not all zero. But $a \neq 0$ because $\{\vec{v},\ \vec{w}\}$ is linearly independent, so $\vec{p} = \frac{-b}{a}\vec{v} + \frac{-c}{a}\vec{w}$ is in U. This shows that $P \subseteq U$, as required.

Exercises 4.2

1. Show that each of the following sets of vectors is independent.
   a) $\{[-1\ \ 2]^T,\ [3\ \ 4]^T\}$ in $\mathbb{R}^2$.
   b) $\{[1\ \ 1\ \ 1]^T,\ [2\ \ 1\ \ 0]^T\}$ in $\mathbb{R}^3$.
   c) $\{[3\ \ 1\ \ -2]^T,\ [-2\ \ -3\ \ -1]^T,\ [1\ \ 3\ \ 3]^T\}$ in $\mathbb{R}^3$.
   d) $\{[1\ \ 0\ \ 1\ \ 0]^T,\ [0\ \ 1\ \ 0\ \ 1]^T,\ [3\ \ -1\ \ 2\ \ -1]^T\}$ in $\mathbb{R}^4$.

2. Which of the following subsets are independent? If the set is dependent, give an example of a nontrivial linear combination that equals zero.

a) $\{[1\ \ 5]^T,\ [0\ \ -2]^T\}$ in $\mathbb{R}^2$.
b) $\{[2\ \ -6]^T,\ [-1\ \ 3]^T\}$ in $\mathbb{R}^2$.
c) $\{[1\ \ -1\ \ 0]^T,\ [3\ \ 2\ \ -1]^T,\ [5\ \ 0\ \ -1]^T\}$ in $\mathbb{R}^3$.
d) $\{[3\ \ 0\ \ -1]^T,\ [2\ \ 1\ \ -1]^T\}$ in $\mathbb{R}^3$.
e) $\{[1\ \ -1\ \ 1\ \ -1]^T,\ [2\ \ 0\ \ 1\ \ 0]^T,\ [0\ \ -2\ \ 1\ \ -2]^T\}$ in $\mathbb{R}^4$.
f) $\{[1\ \ 2\ \ 3\ \ 4]^T,\ [-1\ \ 0\ \ 2\ \ 2]^T,\ [-4\ \ 2\ \ 0\ \ -1]^T\}$ in $\mathbb{R}^4$.
g) $\{[1\ \ 1\ \ 0\ \ 0]^T,\ [1\ \ 0\ \ 1\ \ 0]^T,\ [0\ \ 0\ \ 1\ \ 1]^T,\ [0\ \ 1\ \ 0\ \ 1]^T\}$ in $\mathbb{R}^4$.

3. Use Theorem 2 to determine if A is invertible.

a) $A = \begin{bmatrix} 5 & 10 \\ 1 & 2 \end{bmatrix}$
   b) $A = \begin{bmatrix} 1 & 1 & 0 \\ 0 & -2 & 5 \\ 3 & 0 & 4 \end{bmatrix}$

c) $A = \begin{bmatrix} 3 & 4 & -1 & 1 \\ -3 & -3 & 0 & 0 \\ 2 & -2 & 1 & -2 \\ 1 & -8 & -6 & 1 \end{bmatrix}$
   d) $A = \begin{bmatrix} 3 & -1 & 4 & -1 & -4 \\ 5 & 6 & 6 & 13 & 1 \\ 6 & 6 & -6 & 0 & 0 \\ 3 & 0 & 0 & -3 & -3 \\ 2 & 0 & 9 & 7 & -2 \end{bmatrix}$

4. Use Theorem 2 to determine whether or not these sets of vectors are independent.
   a) $\{[3 \ 1]^T, [-2 \ 2]^T\}$ in $\mathbb{R}^2$.
   b) $\{[1 \ 1 \ -1]^T, [1 \ -1 \ 1]^T, [0 \ 0 \ 1]^T\}$ in $\mathbb{R}^3$.
   c) $\{[5 \ -2 \ 1]^T, [-5 \ 0 \ -5]^T, [4 \ -2 \ 0]^T\}$ in $\mathbb{R}^3$.
   d) $\{[1 \ 0 \ -2 \ 5]^T, [4 \ 4 \ -3 \ 2]^T, [0 \ 1 \ 0 \ -3]^T, [1 \ 3 \ 3 \ 1]^T\}$ in $\mathbb{R}^4$.

5. Using Theorem 2, determine if the following sets of vectors span the indicated space.
   a) $\{[4 \ -7]^T, [2 \ -5]^T\}, \mathbb{R}^2$.
   b) $\{[0 \ -6 \ -6]^T, [8 \ -3 \ 5]^T, [-9 \ 7 \ -2]^T\}, \mathbb{R}^3$.
   c) $\{[-8 \ -1 \ 3 \ 6]^T, [-5 \ -5 \ 4 \ -9]^T, [7 \ 5 \ 9 \ 0]^T, [6 \ 1 \ -16 \ 3]^T\}, \mathbb{R}^4$.
   d) $\{[2 \ 1 \ 7 \ -2]^T, [3 \ 5 \ 4 \ 5]^T, [4 \ -4 \ -3 \ -3]^T, [-5 \ 0 \ 6 \ -4]^T\}, \mathbb{R}^4$.

6. For which sets of vectors in Exercises 1 and 2 could you use Theorem 2 to determine their independence?

7. In each case either show that the statement is true or give an example showing that it is false. Throughout, $X, Y, Z, X_1, X_2, \cdots, X_n$ denote vectors in $\mathbb{R}^n$.
   a) If $\{X, Y\}$ is independent, then $\{X, Y, X + Y\}$ is independent.
   b) If $\{X, Y, Z\}$ is independent, then $\{X, Y\}$ is independent.
   c) If $\{X, Y\}$ is dependent, then $\{X, Y, Z\}$ is dependent.
   d) If all of $X_1, X_2, \cdots, X_n$ are nonzero, then $\{X_1, X_2, \cdots, X_n\}$ is independent.
   e) If one of $X_1, X_2, \cdots, X_n$ is zero, then $\{X_1, X_2, \cdots, X_n\}$ is dependent.
   f) If $aX + bY + cZ = 0$ where $a, b,$ and c are in $\mathbb{R}$, then $\{X, Y, Z\}$ is independent.
   g) If $\{X, Y, Z\}$ is independent, then $aX + bY + cZ = 0$ for some $a, b,$ and c in $\mathbb{R}$.

h) If $\{X_1, X_2, \cdots, X_n\}$ is dependent, then $t_1X_1 + t_2X_2 + \cdots + t_nX_n = 0$ for t_i in $\mathbb{R}$ not all zero.
   i) If $\{X_1, X_2, \cdots, X_n\}$ is independent, then $t_1X_1 + t_2X_2 + \cdots + t_nX_n = 0$ for some t_i in $\mathbb{R}$.

8. Suppose that $\vec{u}, \vec{v},$ and $\vec{w}$ are nonzero vectors in $\mathbb{R}^3$ with the property that $\vec{u} \cdot \vec{v} = \vec{u} \cdot \vec{w} = \vec{v} \cdot \vec{w} = 0$. Show that $\{\vec{u}, \vec{v}, \vec{w}\}$ is linearly independent.

9. Let $\{X, Y, Z, W\}$ be an independent set in $\mathbb{R}^n$. Which of the following sets is independent? Support your answer.
   a) $\{X - Y, Y - Z, Z - X\}$
   b) $\{X + Y, Y + Z, Z + X\}$
   c) $\{X - Y, Y - Z, Z - W, W - X\}$
   d) $\{X + Y, Y + Z, Z + W, W + X\}$

10. If A is an $n \times n$ matrix, show that $det A = 0$ if and only if some column of A is a linear combination of the other columns.

11. Let A be any $m \times n$ matrix, and let $B_1, B_2, B_3, \cdots, B_k$ be columns in $\mathbb{R}^m$ such that the system $AX_i = B_i$ has a solution X_i for each i. If $\{B_1, B_2, B_3, \cdots, B_k\}$ is independent in $\mathbb{R}^m$, show that $\{X_1, X_2, X_3, \cdots, X_k\}$ is independent in $\mathbb{R}^n$.

12. If $\{X_1, X_2, X_3, \cdots, X_k\}$ is independent, show that $\{X_1, X_1 + X_2, X_1 + X_2 + X_3, \cdots, X_1 + X_2 + \cdots + X_k\}$ is also independent.

13. If $\{Y, X_1, X_2, X_3, \cdots, X_k\}$ is independent, show that $\{Y + X_1, Y + X_2, Y + X_3, \cdots, Y + X_k\}$ is also independent.

14. Suppose $\{X_1, X_2, X_3, \cdots, X_k\}$ is independent in $\mathbb{R}^n$. If Y is not in $span\{X_1, X_2, X_3, \cdots, X_k\}$, show that $\{Y, X_1, X_2, X_3, \cdots, X_k\}$ is independent.

15. a) If $\{X_1, X_2, X_3, X_4, X_5, X_6\}$ is an independent set of vectors, show that the subset $\{X_2, X_3, X_5\}$ is also independent.
   b) If $\mathcal{X}$ is any independent set in $\mathbb{R}^n$, show that any nonempty subset $\mathcal{Y} \subseteq \mathcal{X}$ is also independent.

16. a) If $\{X_1, X_2, X_3, X_4\}$ is a dependent set of vectors, show that any superset $\{X_1, X_2, X_3, X_4, Y, Z\}$ is also dependent.
   b) If $\mathcal{X}$ is any dependent set in $\mathbb{R}^n$, show that any superset $\mathcal{Y} \supseteq \mathcal{X}$ is also dependent.

4.3 DIMENSION

Consider the following four classes of subspaces of $\mathbb{R}^3$:

The zero subspace $\{0\}$.

The lines through the origin.

The planes through the origin.

The space $\mathbb{R}^3$ itself.

It is common geometrical language to say that $\mathbb{R}^3$ is 3-dimensional, that planes are all 2-dimensional, and that lines are all 1-dimensional. Thus the idea of "dimension" gives a measure of the "size" of a subspace of $\mathbb{R}^3$. In this section we show how to define the dimension of any subspace of $\mathbb{R}^n$ and, as a byproduct, show that the above list contains *all* the subspaces of $\mathbb{R}^3$. In doing so, we introduce one of the most important concepts in linear algebra—the idea of a basis of a subspace.

4.3.1 Fundamental Theorem

The notion of a basis rests on the following remarkable relationship between the sizes of spanning and independent sets: *The number of independent vectors in a subspace U cannot exceed the number of vectors in a spanning set for U.* The importance of this theorem is difficult to exaggerate.

THEOREM 1

Fundamental Theorem. Let U be a subspace of $\mathbb{R}^n$.

If U is spanned by m vectors and U contains k linearly independent vectors, then $k \leq m$.

Because of its importance, we give two proofs of this theorem at the end of this section.

As its name suggests, the Fundamental theorem has a wide variety of applications. Since $\mathbb{R}^n$ can be spanned by the columns of the identity matrix (Example 10 §4.1) and these columns are independent (Example 2 §4.2), taking $U = \mathbb{R}^n$ in Theorem 1 gives:

COROLLARY

No linearly independent set in $\mathbb{R}^n$ can contain more than n vectors.
No spanning set for $\mathbb{R}^n$ can contain fewer than n vectors.

Our main use of Theorem 1 depends on the following concept. If U is a subspace of $\mathbb{R}^n$, a set $\{X_1, X_2, \cdots, X_k\}$ of vectors in U is called a **basis** of U if:

(1) $\{X_1, X_2, \cdots, X_k\}$ is linearly independent.

(2) $U = span\{X_1, X_2, \cdots, X_k\}$.

Possibly the most important consequence of the Fundamental theorem is the following important result: Any two bases[3] of a subspace must have the same number of elements.

THEOREM 2

Invariance Theorem. If $\{X_1, X_2, \cdots, X_k\}$ and $\{Y_1, Y_2, \cdots, Y_m\}$ are two bases of a subspace U of $\mathbb{R}^n$, then $k = m$.

PROOF

We have $k \leq m$ by the Fundamental theorem because $\{X_1, X_2, \cdots, X_k\}$ is independent in U and $\{Y_1, Y_2, \cdots, Y_m\}$ spans U. Similarly, $m \leq k$, whence $m = k$.

The whole point of Theorem 2 is that it allows us to make the following definition: If U is a subspace of $\mathbb{R}^n$, the number of vectors in a basis of U is called the **dimension** of U, and is denoted $dim U$. The remarkable thing about the dimension is that (by Theorem 2) it can be determined by counting the number of vectors in *any* basis of U. Because of this, the dimension is called an **invariant** of the subspace U.

---

[3] The plural of "basis" is "bases".

If $\{E_1, E_2, \cdots, E_n\}$ is the set of columns of the $n \times n$ identity matrix, then $\mathbb{R}^n = span\{E_1, E_2, \cdots, E_n\}$ by Example 10 §4.1, and $\{E_1, E_2, \cdots, E_n\}$ is linearly independent by Example 2 §4.2. Hence $\{E_1, E_2, \cdots, E_n\}$ is a basis of $\mathbb{R}^n$, called the **standard basis** of $\mathbb{R}^n$. In particular, this shows:

Example 1 $dim(\mathbb{R}^n) = n$ for each $n \geq 1$, and $\{E_1, E_2, \cdots, E_n\}$ is a basis.

For $n = 2$ and $n = 3$ this is compatible with our sense that the plane $\mathbb{R}^2$ is two-dimensional and space $\mathbb{R}^3$ is three-dimensional. Note that if $n = 1$ it says that $dim\mathbb{R} = 1$. In other words, the line $\mathbb{R}$ has dimension 1, and the standard basis is $\{1\}$.

Returning to subspaces of $\mathbb{R}^n$, we define the dimension of the zero subspace $\{0\}$ to be zero:

$$dim\{0\} = 0.$$

This amounts to saying that $\{0\}$ has an empty basis, that is a basis containing no vectors. (This makes sense because the zero vector 0 cannot belong to *any* linearly independent set by Example 5 §4.2.)

Example 2 Show that the lines through the origin in $\mathbb{R}^3$ are precisely the subspaces of dimension 1.

SOLUTION   If L is the line through the origin with direction vector $\vec{d}$, then $L = \{t\vec{d} \mid t$ in $\mathbb{R}\} = span\{\vec{d}\}$. Since $\vec{d} \neq \vec{0}$, the set $\{\vec{d}\}$ is linearly independent, and so is a basis of L. Thus $dimL = 1$. Conversely, if $U \subseteq \mathbb{R}^3$ is a subspace of dimension 1, let $\{\vec{v}\}$ be a basis. Then $U = span\{\vec{v}\} = \{t\vec{v} \mid t$ in $\mathbb{R}\}$, and so U is the line through the origin with direction vector $\vec{v}$.

We will see below (Example 8) that the planes through the origin are precisely the subspaces of $\mathbb{R}^3$ of dimension 2.

Note that the argument in Example 2 also shows more generally that the 1-dimensional subspaces U of $\mathbb{R}^n$ are precisely the subspaces of the form $U = span\{X\} = \{tX \mid t$ in $\mathbb{R}\}$ for some $X \neq 0$ in $\mathbb{R}^n$.

When working with a subspace U, it is often convenient to simplify a basis by multiplying some of the basis vectors by nonzero scalars. The next example shows that this will always produce another basis.

Example 3 Assume that $\{X_1, X_2, \cdots, X_k\}$ is a basis of a subspace U of $\mathbb{R}^n$. If $a_1, a_2, \cdots, a_k$ are nonzero scalars, show that $\{a_1X_1, a_2X_2, \cdots, a_kX_k\}$ is also a basis of U.

SOLUTION   Suppose that a linear combination of the new set of vectors vanishes:

$$t_1(a_1X_1) + t_2(a_2X_2) + \cdots + t_k(a_kX_k) = 0.$$

Then $t_1a_1 = t_2a_2 = \cdots = t_ka_k = 0$ because $\{X_1, X_2, \cdots, X_k\}$ is independent. Since each $a_i \neq 0$, this forces $t_1 = t_2 = \cdots = t_k = 0$. Hence $\{a_1X_1, a_2X_2, \cdots, a_kX_k\}$ is linearly independent.

It remains to show that $U = span\{a_1X_1, a_2X_2, \cdots, a_kX_k\}$.
Write $V = span\{a_1X_1, a_2X_2, \cdots, a_kX_k\}$ for convenience. Then $V \subseteq U$ by Theorem 1 §4.1 because each a_iX_i is in U. Moreover, the same theorem shows that $U \subseteq V$ because $X_i = \frac{1}{a_i}(a_iX_i)$ is in V for each i. Hence $U = V$ and we are done.

4.3.2 | Existence of Bases

In order to calculate the dimension of a nonzero subspace U of $\mathbb{R}^n$ it is necessary to find a basis of U. However, at this point we do not know whether U *has* a basis. In fact it does, and one way to verify this is to find a way to create larger and larger linearly independent sets in U until a basis is reached. The next result contains the key idea.

LEMMA

Independent Lemma. Suppose $\{X_1, X_2, \cdots, X_k\}$ is a linearly independent set of vectors in $\mathbb{R}^n$. If Y is any vector of $\mathbb{R}^n$ which is not in $span\{X_1, X_2, \cdots, X_k\}$, then the larger set $\{Y, X_1, X_2, \cdots, X_k\}$ is also linearly independent.

PROOF

Suppose that

$$tY + t_1X_1 + t_2X_2 + \cdots + t_kX_k = 0 \tag{$*$}$$

is a linear combination from $\{Y, X_1, X_2, \cdots, X_k\}$ that vanishes; we must show that $t = t_1 = t_2 = \cdots = t_k = 0$. First we have $t = 0$ because, otherwise, $Y = \frac{-1}{t}(t_1X_1 + t_2X_2 + \cdots + t_kX_k)$ is in $span\{X_1, X_2, \cdots, X_k\}$, contrary to our assumption. Hence $t = 0$ and $(*)$ becomes $t_1X_1 + t_2X_2 + \cdots + t_kX_k = 0$. But then $t_1 = t_2 = \cdots = t_k = 0$ because $\{X_1, X_2, \cdots, X_k\}$ is independent.

The Independent lemma gives a geometrical interpretation of what it means for three vectors $\vec{u}, \vec{v},$ and $\vec{w}$ in $\mathbb{R}^3$ to be linearly independent.

Example 4

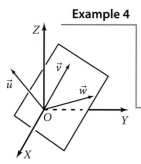

Observe first that if $\{\vec{u}, \vec{v}, \vec{w}\}$ is any linearly independent set of vectors, then $\{\vec{v}, \vec{w}\}$ must also be linearly independent (Exercise 15 §4.2). Hence $\vec{v}$ and $\vec{w}$ are nonparallel vectors in $\mathbb{R}^3$ as in the diagram. Then $span\{\vec{v}, \vec{w}\}$ is the plane through the origin containing $\vec{v}$ and $\vec{w}$ (by Theorem 4 §4.2). Hence the Independent lemma asserts that if $\vec{u}$ is any vector not in the plane containing $\vec{v}$ and $\vec{w}$, then $\{\vec{u}, \vec{v}, \vec{w}\}$ is a linearly independent set of vectors.

With the Independent lemma in hand, we can show that every nonzero subspace of $\mathbb{R}^n$ does indeed have a basis.

THEOREM 3

Let $U \neq \{0\}$ be any nonzero subspace of $\mathbb{R}^n$.

(1) U has a basis, and $dim\,U \leq n$.

(2) Any linearly independent subset of U can be enlarged to a basis of U.

(3) Any spanning set of U contains a basis of U.

PROOF

We first prove (2), then (1) and (3).

(2) Suppose that $\{X_1, X_2, \cdots, X_k\}$ is any independent subset of U; we must show that it is part of a basis of U. If $U = span\{X_1, X_2, \cdots, X_k\}$, we are done because $\{X_1, X_2, \cdots, X_k\}$ is itself a basis. Otherwise, choose a vector X_{k+1} in U which is not in $span\{X_1, X_2, \cdots, X_k\}$. Then $\{X_1, X_2, \cdots, X_k, X_{k+1}\}$ is a larger independent subset of U by the Independent lemma. Now repeat the process.

If $U = span\{X_1, X_2, \cdots, X_k, X_{k+1}\}$, we are done. Otherwise, enlarge it again. Since the Corollary of the Fundamental theorem shows that U contains no independent set with more than n vectors, this enlarging process cannot continue indefinitely. So at some stage we reach an independent set which spans U; that is, we reach a basis of U. This proves (2).

(1) As $U \neq \{0\}$, it contains at least one linearly independent subset (for example, $\{X\}$ where X is any nonzero vector in U). Hence U has a basis by (2), and this basis cannot contain more than n vectors by the Corollary of the Fundamental theorem. In other words, $dimU \leq n$.

(3) Let $U = span\{X_1, X_2, \cdots, X_k\}$. If $\{X_1, X_2, \cdots, X_k\}$ is independent, it is a basis of U and we are done. Otherwise, one of the X_i is a linear combination of the others by Theorem 3 §4.2. After possible relabelling, assume that X_1 is in $span\{X_2, X_3, \cdots, X_k\}$. Hence $U = span\{X_2, X_3, \cdots, X_k\}$ by Theorem 1 §4.1. Again, if $\{X_2, X_3, \cdots, X_k\}$ is independent, we are done. If not, continue the process. Either we are done at some stage or, after possible relabelling, we reach $U = span\{X_k\}$. But then $\{X_k\}$ is a basis because $X_k \neq 0$ (since $U \neq \{0\}$).

Example 5   If $\{C_1, C_2, \cdots, C_k\}$ is a linearly independent set of columns in $\mathbb{R}^n$, show that the C_i are the first k columns of some invertible $n \times n$ matrix.

SOLUTION   Observe that $k \leq n$ by the Corollary to Theorem 1. Since $\{C_1, C_2, \cdots, C_k\}$ is independent in $\mathbb{R}^n$, (2) of Theorem 3 shows that it can be enlarged to a basis $\{C_1, C_2, \cdots, C_k, C_{k+1}, \cdots, C_n\}$ of $\mathbb{R}^n$. Hence the matrix $A = [C_1 \quad C_2 \quad \cdots \quad C_k \quad C_{k+1} \quad \cdots \quad C_n]$ is invertible by Theorem 2 §4.2, as required.

Note that, apart from the Independent lemma, Theorem 3 does not specify how to construct the new columns $C_{k+1}, \cdots, C_n$ in Example 5. In fact there are many choices. Theorem 3 asserts only the existence of such columns.

In the following sections we will make frequent use of the next result, each part of which is an easy consequence of Theorem 3.

THEOREM 4   Let U and V denote subspaces of $\mathbb{R}^n$.

(1) If $U \subseteq V$, then $dimU \leq dimV$.

(2) If $U \subseteq V$ and $dimU = dimV$, then $U = V$.

(3) If $dimU = d$, then any set of d linearly independent vectors in U is automatically a basis of U.

(4) If $dimU = d$, then any spanning set for U containing d vectors is automatically a basis of U.

PROOF   (1) If $U = \{0\}$, then $dimU = 0 \leq dimV$. Otherwise, any basis of U is an independent set in V, and so (by the Fundamental theorem) contains no more vectors than a basis of V. In other words, $dimU \leq dimV$.

(2) Write $d = dimU = dimV$, and let $\{X_1, X_2, \cdots, X_d\}$ be a basis of U. If $U \neq V$, choose Y in V such that Y is not in $U = span\{X_1, X_2, \cdots, X_d\}$. By the Independent lemma the set $\{X_1, X_2, \cdots, X_d, Y\}$ is a linearly independent set in V containing $d + 1$ vectors. But this contradicts the Fundamental theorem because V has a spanning set (in fact a basis) of d vectors. Hence $U \neq V$ is impossible, so $U = V$ after all.

(3) Let $\{X_1, X_2, \cdots, X_d\}$ be an independent set in U; we must show that it spans U. Write $W = span\{X_1, X_2, \cdots, X_d\}$. Then $W \subseteq U$ by Theorem 1 §4.1 because each X_i is in U, and $dimW = d$ because $\{X_1, X_2, \cdots, X_d\}$ is a basis of W. Hence $W = U$ by (2). Thus $U = W = span\{X_1, X_2, \cdots, X_d\}$, so $\{X_1, X_2, \cdots, X_d\}$ is a basis of U.

(4) If $U = span\{X_1, X_2, \cdots, X_d\}$, then $\{X_1, X_2, \cdots, X_d\}$ contains a basis of U by Theorem 3. This basis contains $d = dimU$ vectors, and so must be all of $\{X_1, X_2, \cdots, X_d\}$. In other words, $\{X_1, X_2, \cdots, X_d\}$ is a basis of U.

Parts (3) and (4) of Theorem 4 are "laboursaving" results since they show that it is sufficient to verify either independence or spanning in order to verify that a set of d vectors (in a subspace U of dimension d) is a basis; the other is then automatic. Of course it is necessary that the number of vectors in the set equals $dimU$.

Example 6 Show that $\{[2 \ \ 0 \ \ -1]^T, [1 \ \ 4 \ \ 9]^T, [-1 \ \ 5 \ \ 6]^T\}$ is a basis of $\mathbb{R}^3$.

SOLUTION By Theorem 4 it suffices to show that $\{[2 \ \ 0 \ \ -1]^T, [1 \ \ 4 \ \ 9]^T, [-1 \ \ 5 \ \ 6]^T\}$ is linearly independent (spanning would do as well). This follows from Theorem 2 §4.2 if we can show that the matrix A with these vectors as columns is invertible. But, using row operations as in Chapter 2,

$$detA = det\begin{bmatrix} 2 & 1 & -1 \\ 0 & 4 & 5 \\ -1 & 9 & 6 \end{bmatrix} = det\begin{bmatrix} 0 & 19 & 11 \\ 0 & 4 & 5 \\ -1 & 9 & 6 \end{bmatrix} = -51 \neq 0.$$

Hence A is indeed invertible.

Part (2) of Theorem 4 is also a "laboursaving" result, and is frequently the easiest way to show that two subspaces of the same dimension are equal: Simply show that one is contained in the other. This is illustrated in the following example (where we give a different proof of part of Theorem 4 §4.2).

Example 7 Let $\vec{v}$ and $\vec{w}$ be linearly independent (that is, nonparallel) vectors in $\mathbb{R}^3$, and let $P = span\{\vec{v}, \vec{w}\}$ denote the plane spanned by $\vec{v}$ and $\vec{w}$. Show that P is the plane (through the origin) with normal $\vec{n} = \vec{v} \times \vec{w}$.

SOLUTION Note first that $\vec{n} \neq \vec{0}$ by Theorem 2 §3.3 because $\vec{v}$ and $\vec{w}$ are not parallel. Let Q denote the plane through the origin with $\vec{n}$ as normal, and write $\vec{n} = [a \ \ b \ \ c]^T$. Then Q has equation $ax + by + cz = 0$, that is

$$Q = \left\{[x \ y \ z]^T \mid ax + by + cz = 0\right\} = \left\{\vec{x} \mid \vec{n} \cdot \vec{x} = 0\right\}$$

where we denote $\vec{x} = [x \ \ y \ \ z]^T$. Since $\vec{n}$ is orthogonal to both $\vec{v}$ and $\vec{w}$ (Theorem 2 §3.3), we have $\vec{n} \cdot \vec{v} = 0$ and $\vec{n} \cdot \vec{w} = 0$. This means that both $\vec{v}$ and $\vec{w}$ are in Q, and hence that $P \subseteq Q \subseteq \mathbb{R}^3$. Since $dimP = 2$, Theorem 4 gives

$$dimP \leq dimQ \leq dim\mathbb{R}^3, \text{ that is, } 2 \leq dimQ \leq 3.$$

Now observe that $dimQ$ is an integer, so this means that $dimQ = 2$ or $dimQ = 3$, whence $Q = P$ or $Q = \mathbb{R}^3$ by (2) of Theorem 4. But $Q \neq \mathbb{R}^3$ because $\vec{n}$ is not in Q (as $\vec{n} \neq \vec{0}$), so $Q = P$ as required.

We conclude with a characterization (mentioned earlier) of all subspaces of $\mathbb{R}^3$.

Example 8   Show that the only subspaces of $\mathbb{R}^3$ are the zero space $\{0\}$, lines through the origin, planes through the origin, and $\mathbb{R}^3$ itself.

SOLUTION   Let U denote a subspace of $\mathbb{R}^3$. Then $dim U \leq dim(\mathbb{R}^3) = 3$ so, since $dim U$ is a nonnegative integer, $dim U$ is one of 0, 1, 2, or 3. We examine each case separately:

$dim U = 0$.   Then $U = \{0\}$.

$dim U = 1$.   If $\{\vec{d}\}$ is a basis of U, then $U = span\{\vec{d}\} = \{t\vec{d} \mid t$ a real number$\}$ is the line through the origin with direction vector $\vec{d}$.

$dim U = 2$.   If $\{\vec{v}, \vec{w}\}$ is a basis of U, then U is the plane through the origin with normal $\vec{v} \times \vec{w}$ containing $\vec{v}$ and $\vec{w}$ by Example 7.

$dim U = 3$.   Since $U \subseteq \mathbb{R}^3$ and $dim U = 3 = dim(\mathbb{R}^3)$, we have $U = \mathbb{R}^3$ by (2) of Theorem 4.

4.3.3   Proof of the Fundamental Theorem

If U is a subspace of $\mathbb{R}^n$ which is spanned by m vectors, and if U contains k linearly independent vectors, we must show that $k \leq m$. Let $U = span\{X_1, X_2, \cdots, X_m\}$, and let $\{Y_1, Y_2, \cdots, Y_k\}$ be an independent set in U.

PROOF 1   Since each Y_j in $span\{X_1, X_2, \cdots, X_m\}$, it is a linear combination of $X_1, X_2, \cdots, X_m$, say[4]

$$Y_j = a_{1j}X_1 + a_{2j}X_2 + \cdots + a_{mj}X_m = \sum_{i=1}^{m} a_{ij}X_i \text{ for each } j = 1, 2, \cdots, k.$$

The coefficients here form an $m \times k$ matrix $A = [a_{ij}]$. We must show that $k \leq m$; we do so by showing that $k > m$ leads to a contradiction. Indeed, if $k > m$ the system $AX = 0$ has a nontrivial solution $X = [x_1 \quad x_2 \quad \cdots \quad x_k]^T \neq 0$ by Theorem 1 §1.3. Using the entries x_j of X as coefficients, we compute the following linear combination of the Y_j:

$$\sum_{j=1}^{k} x_j Y_j = \sum_{j=1}^{k} x_j \left(\sum_{i=1}^{m} a_{ij}X_i \right)$$

$$= \sum_{j=1}^{k} \sum_{i=1}^{m} a_{ij}x_j X_i$$

$$= \sum_{i=1}^{m} \left(\sum_{j=1}^{k} a_{ij}x_j \right) X_i$$

$$= \sum_{i=1}^{m} (0)X_i = 0$$

where the sum $\Sigma_{j=1}^{k} a_{ij}x_j = 0$ for each i because it is entry i of $AX = 0$. Thus $\Sigma_{j=1}^{k} x_j Y_j = 0$, a contradiction because the Y_j are independent and not all the x_j are zero (since $X \neq 0$).

PROOF 2   We assume that $k > m$ and show that this leads to a contradiction.
As $U = span\{X_1, X_2, \cdots, X_m\}$, let $Y_1 = a_1X_1 + a_2X_2 + \cdots + a_mX_m$. As $Y_1 \neq 0$ not all of the a_i are zero, say $a_1 \neq 0$ (after relabelling the X_i). Then $U = span\{Y_1, X_2, X_3, \cdots, X_m\}$ as the reader can verify. Now write $Y_2 = b_1Y_1 + c_2X_2 + c_3X_3 + \cdots + c_mX_m$. Then some $c_i \neq 0$ because $\{Y_1, Y_2\}$ is independent so, as before, $U = span\{Y_1, Y_2, X_3, \cdots, X_m\}$ after possible relabelling of the X_i. As $k > m$ this procedure continues until all

---

[4] We again use summation notation for convenience. For example $a_1 + a_2 + a_3 + a_4 = \Sigma_{i=1}^{4} a_i$ and $a_3X_3 + a_4X_4 + a_5X_5 = \Sigma_{i=3}^{5} a_iX_i$.

the vectors X_1, X_2, $\cdots$, X_m are replaced by Y_1, Y_2, $\cdots$, Y_m. In particular $U = span\{Y_1, Y_2, \cdots, Y_m\}$. But then Y_{m+1} is a linear combination of Y_1, Y_2, $\cdots$, Y_m contrary to the independence of the Y_j.

The second proof above gives even more. If $U = span\{X_1, X_2, \cdots, X_m\}$, and if $\{Y_1, Y_2, \cdots, Y_k\}$ is independent in U, Proof 2 shows not only that $k \leq m$ but also that k of the (spanning) vectors X_1, X_2, $\cdots$, X_m can be replaced by the (independent) vectors Y_1, Y_2, $\cdots$, Y_k and the resulting set will still span U. In this form the result is called the **Steinitz Exchange Lemma**.

Exercises 4.3

1. The following sets of vectors are all bases of the subspace they span. Give the dimension of each subspace.
   a) $\{[8\ \ 4\ \ 0]^T, [-7\ \ 7\ \ 3]^T\}$.
   b) $\{[3\ \ 0\ \ -5]^T, [2\ \ -1\ \ 0]^T, [-2\ \ 4\ \ -9]^T\}$.
   c) $\{[-9\ \ 0\ \ -1\ \ 6]^T, [5\ \ 7\ \ -3\ \ -2]^T\}$.
   d) $\{[-1\ \ 6\ \ 2\ \ 6]^T, [-2\ \ 4\ \ 0\ \ -4]^T, [-6\ \ 5\ \ 0\ \ 1]^T\}$.
   e) $\{[1\ \ 0\ \ 0\ \ 0]^T, [0\ \ 0\ \ 1\ \ 0]^T, [0\ \ 1\ \ 0\ \ 0]^T,$
      $[0\ \ 0\ \ 0\ \ 1]^T\}$.

2. Show that the following sets of vectors are bases of the indicated space.
   a) $\{[1\ \ 1\ \ 0]^T, [1\ \ 0\ \ 1]^T, [0\ \ 1\ \ 1]^T\}$ in $\mathbb{R}^3$.
   b) $\{[-1\ \ 1\ \ 1]^T, [1\ \ -1\ \ 1]^T, [1\ \ 1\ \ -1]^T\}$ in $\mathbb{R}^3$.
   c) $\{[1\ \ 2\ \ 1\ \ 2]^T, [-1\ \ 0\ \ 2\ \ 1]^T, [0\ \ 0\ \ 1\ \ 1]^T,$
      $[0\ \ 1\ \ -1\ \ 1]^T\}$ in $\mathbb{R}^4$.
   d) $\{[1\ \ 1\ \ 0\ \ 0]^T, [1\ \ 0\ \ 0\ \ 1]^T, [0\ \ 1\ \ 1\ \ 0]^T,$
      $[0\ \ 1\ \ 0\ \ 1]^T\}$ in $\mathbb{R}^4$.

3. Verify that the following sets of vectors span the given space. Could they form a basis for the space? Support your answer.
   a) $\{[-5\ \ -2\ \ -2]^T, [7\ \ -9\ \ 3]^T, [4\ \ -8\ \ 9]^T, [8\ \ 4\ \ 7]^T\}$ in $\mathbb{R}^3$.
   b) $\{[2\ \ 3\ \ 5\ \ -4]^T, [6\ \ 1\ \ -4\ \ -7]^T, [3\ \ 6\ \ 3\ \ 2]^T,$
      $[1\ \ 0\ \ 0\ \ 0]^T, [6\ \ -3\ \ -2\ \ 0]^T, [7\ \ -4\ \ 2\ \ 9]^T\}$ in $\mathbb{R}^4$.
   c) $\{[-4\ \ 3\ \ 2]^T, [-1\ \ 1\ \ 11]^T, [-3\ \ 2\ \ -9]^T\}$ in $\mathbb{R}^3$.
   d) $\{[1\ \ -6\ \ 3\ \ -7]^T, [5\ \ 1\ \ 5\ \ 9]^T, [3\ \ 9\ \ 0\ \ 2]^T,$
      $[2\ \ 0\ \ 3\ \ 0]^T\}$ in $\mathbb{R}^4$.

4. The following pairs of vector sets claim to be two bases of the same subspace. Can you determine if this is false without doing any calculations?
   a) $\{[3\ \ -1]\}$ and $\{[2\ \ 0], [-5\ \ 3]\}$ of a subspace in $\mathbb{R}^2$.
   b) $\{[6\ \ 0\ \ -9], [-4\ \ 2\ \ 3], [-3\ \ 8\ \ 7]\}$ and $\{[6\ \ 4\ \ 3],$
      $[2\ \ 9\ \ -1]\}$ of a subspace in $\mathbb{R}^3$.
   c) $\{[2\ \ 1\ \ 0], [-3\ \ -7\ \ 3]\}$ and $\{[1\ \ 6\ \ -3], [5\ \ 8\ \ -3]\}$ of a subspace in $\mathbb{R}^3$.
   d) $\{[6\ \ -2\ \ -8\ \ 0], [7\ \ 0\ \ 9\ \ 0]\}$ and $\{[-2\ \ -5\ \ -4\ \ 6],$
      $[6\ \ 3\ \ 7\ \ -8], [9\ \ 9\ \ 0\ \ 2], [-7\ \ -1\ \ 0\ \ 9]\}$
      of a subspace in $\mathbb{R}^4$.

5. Generate the standard basis for the given space.
   a) $\mathbb{R}^2$.   b) $\mathbb{R}^3$.   c) $\mathbb{R}^5$.   d) $\mathbb{R}$.

6. Find a basis and calculate the dimension of the following subspaces of $\mathbb{R}^4$. Can you find more than one basis for each subspace?
   a) $span\{[1\ \ -1\ \ 2\ \ 0]^T, [2\ \ 3\ \ 0\ \ 3]^T, [1\ \ 9\ \ -6\ \ 6]^T\}$.
   b) $span\{[2\ \ 1\ \ 0\ \ -1]^T, [-1\ \ 1\ \ 1\ \ 2]^T, [2\ \ 7\ \ 4\ \ 5]^T\}$.
   c) $span\{[-1\ \ 2\ \ 1\ \ 0]^T, [2\ \ 0\ \ 3\ \ -1]^T, [4\ \ 4\ \ 11\ \ -3]^T,$
      $[3\ \ -2\ \ 2\ \ -1]^T\}$.
   d) $span\{[-2\ \ 0\ \ 3\ \ 1]^T, [1\ \ 2\ \ -1\ \ 0]^T, [-2\ \ 8\ \ 5\ \ 3]^T,$
      $[1\ \ 2\ \ 2\ \ 1]^T\}$.

7. Find a basis and calculate the dimension of the following subspaces of $\mathbb{R}^4$.
   a) $U = \{[a\ \ a+b\ \ a-b\ \ b]^T \mid a \text{ and } b \text{ in } \mathbb{R}\}$.
   b) $U = \{[a+b\ \ a-b\ \ b\ \ a]^T \mid a \text{ and } b \text{ in } \mathbb{R}\}$.
   c) $U = \{[a\ \ b\ \ c+a\ \ c]^T \mid a, b, \text{ and } c \text{ in } \mathbb{R}\}$.
   d) $U = \{[a-b\ \ b+c\ \ a\ \ b+c]^T \mid a, b, \text{ and } c \text{ in } \mathbb{R}\}$.
   e) $U = \{[a\ \ b\ \ c\ \ d]^T \mid a+b-c+d = 0 \text{ in } \mathbb{R}\}$.

8. In each case find a basis for and calculate the dimension of $nullA$:
   a) $A = \begin{bmatrix} 1 & 2 & -3 & 4 & 0 \\ -1 & 0 & 2 & -4 & 1 \\ -1 & 4 & 0 & -4 & 3 \end{bmatrix}$

   b) $A = \begin{bmatrix} 1 & 1 & -2 & 0 & 4 \\ 2 & 1 & 0 & 1 & -5 \\ 7 & 2 & 6 & -10 & -7 \end{bmatrix}$

9. In each case show that U is a subspace of $\mathbb{R}^4$, find a basis of U and calculate the dimension of U.
   a) $U = \{X \text{ in } \mathbb{R}^4 \mid X^T A = 0\}$ where $A = \begin{bmatrix} 1 & 1 & 0 & 3 \\ -1 & 2 & 2 & -1 \end{bmatrix}^T$.
   b) $U = \{X \text{ in } \mathbb{R}^4 \mid X^T A = 0\}$ where $A = \begin{bmatrix} 0 & 1 & 2 & -1 \\ 1 & -1 & 0 & 3 \end{bmatrix}^T$.
   c) $U = \{X \text{ in } \mathbb{R}^4 \mid X^T A = (BX)^T\}$ where
      $A = \begin{bmatrix} 1 & 0 & 1 & 0 \\ 0 & 1 & 0 & 1 \end{bmatrix}^T$ and $B = \begin{bmatrix} 1 & 2 & 3 & 4 \\ 0 & 1 & 1 & -1 \end{bmatrix}$.
   d) $U = \{X \text{ in } \mathbb{R}^4 \mid X^T A = (BX)^T\}$ where
      $A = \begin{bmatrix} 2 & 0 & 1 & -3 \\ -1 & 1 & 1 & 0 \end{bmatrix}^T$ and $B = \begin{bmatrix} 2 & 1 & 0 & -1 \\ 1 & 1 & -1 & -1 \end{bmatrix}$.

10. In each case either show that the statement is true or give an example showing that it is false.
   a) Every set of four nonzero vectors in $\mathbb{R}^4$ is a basis.
   b) No basis of $\mathbb{R}^3$ can contain a vector with a component 0.
   c) $\mathbb{R}^3$ has a basis of the form $\{X, X + Y, Y\}$ where X and Y are vectors.
   d) Every basis of $\mathbb{R}^5$ contains one column of I_5.
   e) Every nonempty subset of a basis of $\mathbb{R}^3$ is again a basis of $\mathbb{R}^3$.
   f) If $\{X_1, X_2, X_3, X_4\}$ and $\{Y_1, Y_2, Y_3, Y_4\}$ are bases of $\mathbb{R}^4$, then $\{X_1 + Y_1, X_2 + Y_2, X_3 + Y_3, X_4 + Y_4\}$ is also a basis of $\mathbb{R}^4$.

11. Given that $\{[3 \ -1 \ 2 \ 1], [0 \ 2 \ -1 \ 0], [4 \ -1 \ 3 \ -3]\}$ is a basis for some subspace U of $\mathbb{R}^4$, is $\{[-6 \ 2 \ -4 \ -2], [0 \ -4 \ 2 \ 0], [-8 \ 2 \ -6 \ 6]\}$ also a basis of U?

12. Show that every nonzero vector in $\mathbb{R}^n$ is in some basis of $\mathbb{R}^n$.

13. a) Find a basis of $\mathbb{R}^4$ containing the vector $[11 \ -19 \ 203 \ -131]^T$.
   b) If X is *any* vector in $\mathbb{R}^4$, can you find a basis containing X? Defend your answer.
   c) Find a condition on vectors X and Y in $\mathbb{R}^4$ such that there is a basis of $\mathbb{R}^4$ containing both X and Y if and only if the condition is satisfied. Defend your answer.

14. Let $\{X, Y, Z, W\}$ denote vectors in $\mathbb{R}^3$. Find a condition on this set of vectors such that it contains a basis of $\mathbb{R}^3$ if and only if the condition is satisfied. Defend your answer.

15. a) Find a basis of vectors on $\mathbb{R}^3$ consisting of vectors whose components sum to 1.
   b) Can you find a basis as in **a)** if we ask that the components sum to 0? Defend your answer.

16. Suppose that $\{X, Y, Z, W\}$ is a basis of $\mathbb{R}^4$. Show that:
   a) $\{X + aW, Y, Z, W\}$ is also a basis of $\mathbb{R}^4$ for any choice of the scalar a.
   b) $\{X + W, Y + W, Z + W, W\}$ is also a basis of $\mathbb{R}^4$.
   c) $\{X, X + Y, X + Y + Z, X + Y + Z + W\}$ is also a basis of $\mathbb{R}^4$.

17. Suppose that the columns $\{X, Y\}$ constitute a basis of $\mathbb{R}^2$, and let $A = \begin{bmatrix} a & c \\ b & d \end{bmatrix}$ denote a matrix.
   a) If A is invertible, show that $\{aX + bY, cX + dY\}$ is a basis of $\mathbb{R}^2$.
   b) If $\{aX + bY, cX + dY\}$ is a basis of $\mathbb{R}^2$, show that A is invertible.

18. a) If $\{X, Y\}$ is independent in $\mathbb{R}^4$, show that $\{X, Y, E_l, E_t\}$ is a basis of $\mathbb{R}^4$ for some choice of E_l and E_t in the standard basis of $\mathbb{R}^4$.
   b) If $\{X_1, X_2, \cdots, X_k\}$ is independent in $\mathbb{R}^n$ with $k < n$, show that $\{X_1, X_2, \cdots, X_k, E_{l_{k+1}}, \cdots, E_{l_n}\}$ is a basis of $\mathbb{R}^n$ for some choice of $E_{l_{k+1}}, \cdots, E_{l_n}$ in the standard basis of $\mathbb{R}^n$.

   c) Let $\{F_1, F_2, \cdots, F_m\}$ be a basis of a subspace U of $\mathbb{R}^n$. If $\{X_1, X_2, \cdots, X_k\}$ is independent in U with $k < m$, show that $\{X_1, X_2, \cdots, X_k, F_{l_{k+1}}, \cdots, F_{l_n}\}$ is a basis of U for some choice of $F_{l_{k+1}}, \cdots, F_{l_n}$.

19. Suppose that $\{X_1, X_2, X_3, \cdots, X_n\}$ is a basis of $\mathbb{R}^n$. If A is an invertible matrix, show that $\{AX_1, AX_2, AX_3, \cdots, AX_n\}$ is also a basis of $\mathbb{R}^n$.

20. Let U and W denote subspaces of $\mathbb{R}^n$, and assume that $U \subseteq W$. If $dim W = 1$, show that either $U = \{0\}$ or $U = W$.

21. Let U and W denote subspaces of $\mathbb{R}^n$, and assume that $U \subseteq W$. If $dim U = n - 1$, show that either $W = U$ or $W = \mathbb{R}^n$.

22. Let U and W denote subspaces of $\mathbb{R}^n$, and suppose that $dim U = 2$. Show that either $U \subseteq W$ or $dim(U \cap W) \le 1$. (See Exercise 24 §4.1.) [Hint: $U \cap W$ is a subspace of U. Use Theorem 4.]

23. Let A denote an $m \times n$ matrix. Show that:
   a) $dim(null A) = dim(null(AV))$ for every invertible $n \times n$ matrix V.
   b) $dim(im A) = dim(im(UA))$ for every invertible $m \times m$ matrix U.

24. Let U be a subspace of $\mathbb{R}^n$, and let $\{X_1, X_2, \cdots, X_k\}$ be a maximal independent subset of U (that is, no independent subset of U contains more than k vectors). Show that $\{X_1, X_2, \cdots, X_k\}$ is a basis of U. [Hint: If $span\{X_1, X_2, \cdots, X_k\} \ne U$, choose Y in U which is not in $span\{X_1, X_2, \cdots, X_k\}$, and apply Lemma 1.]

25. Let $U \ne \{0\}$ be a subspace of $\mathbb{R}^n$, and let $\{X_1, X_2, \cdots, X_k\}$ be a minimal spanning subset of U (that is, $U = span\{X_1, X_2, \cdots, X_k\}$ and no spanning set of U contains fewer than k vectors). Show that $\{X_1, X_2, \cdots, X_k\}$ is a basis of U. [Hint: If $\{X_1, X_2, \cdots, X_k\}$ is not independent, apply Theorem 3 §4.2.]

26. Let $A = \begin{bmatrix} B & 0 \\ 0 & C \end{bmatrix}$ where B and C are $n \times n$ and $m \times m$ matrices, respectively.
   a) If B and C are diagonalizable matrices with diagonalizing matrices P and Q respectively, show that $\begin{bmatrix} B & 0 \\ 0 & C \end{bmatrix}$ is diagonalizable with diagonalizing matrix $\begin{bmatrix} P & 0 \\ 0 & Q \end{bmatrix}$.
   b) If $A = \begin{bmatrix} B & 0 \\ 0 & C \end{bmatrix}$ is diagonalizable, show that both B and C are diagonalizable. [Hint: Let $\{X_1, \cdots, X_{n+m}\}$ be a basis of $\mathbb{R}^{n+m}$ consisting of eigenvectors of A, and write $X_i = \begin{bmatrix} Y_i \\ Z_i \end{bmatrix}$ where each Y_i is in $\mathbb{R}^n$ and each Z_i is in $\mathbb{R}^m$. Show that $\{Y_1, \cdots, Y_n\}$ and $\{Z_1, \cdots, Z_m\}$ span $\mathbb{R}^n$ and $\mathbb{R}^m$ respectively, and so contain bases by Theorem 3. Use Theorem 3 §2.3.]

27. Let U and W be any two subspaces of $\mathbb{R}^n$, and consider the subspaces

$U \cap W = \{X \text{ in } \mathbb{R}^n \mid X \text{ is in both } U \text{ and } W\}$

$U + W = \{X \text{ in } \mathbb{R}^n \mid X \text{ is a sum of a vector in } U$ and a vector in $W\}$ as in Exercise 23 §4.1.

Show that $dim(U + W) = dimU + dimW - dim(U \cap W)$.

[Hint: Let $\{X_1, \cdots, X_d\}$ be a basis of $U \cap W$ and, by Theorem 3, extend it to bases $\{X_1, \cdots, X_d, Y_1, \cdots, Y_k\}$ and $\{X_1, \cdots, X_d, Z_1, \cdots, Z_m\}$ of U and W respectively. Show that $\{X_1, \cdots, X_d, Y_1, \cdots, Y_k, Z_1, \cdots, Z_m\}$ is a basis of $U + W$.]

4.4 RANK

In this section we complete some unfinished business from Section 1.2 by giving a precise definition of the rank of an $m \times n$ matrix, and showing that the rank of A equals the rank of A^T. We then relate the rank to the dimensions of the image and null spaces of A.

4.4.1 Row and Column Spaces

If A is an $m \times n$ matrix, we have already discussed the null space, $nullA$, and the image, imA. We are going to find natural bases for both these spaces, and so calculate their dimension. To do this, and for other reasons as well, it is essential to consider two other subspaces associated with A. They are defined as follows:

The **column space**, $colA$, of an $m \times n$ matrix A is the subspace of $\mathbb{R}^m$ spanned by the columns of A.

The **row space**, $rowA$, of an $m \times n$ matrix A is the subspace of $\mathbb{R}^n$ spanned by the rows of A.

Observe that in discussing $rowA$ we are regarding the elements of $\mathbb{R}^n$ as rows.

One reason for the importance of the spaces $rowA$ and $colA$ is that they are unchanged when row (respectively column) operations are performed on the matrix A.

LEMMA 1 Let A denote an $m \times n$ matrix.

(1) If $A \rightarrow B$ using a sequence of row operations, then $rowB = rowA$.

(2) If $A \rightarrow B$ using a sequence of column operations, then $colB = colA$.

PROOF **(1)** It is enough to prove it for a single row operation (since B is obtained from A by a sequence of row operations). We do this for a row operation of type III; a similar argument works for the other types.

Hence, suppose that B is obtained by adding u times row p of A to row q. Then each row of B is a linear combination of the rows of A, so $rowB \subseteq rowA$ by Theorem 1 §4.1. On the other hand we can carry $B \rightarrow A$ by *subtracting* u times row p of B from row q. Hence $rowA \subseteq rowB$ follows in the same way. Thus $rowA = rowB$ as required.

(2) This is proved in the same way using column operations.

In particular, suppose $A \rightarrow R$ by row operations where R is a row-echelon matrix, and suppose further that R has k leading 1's. Then R has k nonzero rows, say $Y_1, Y_2, \cdots, Y_k$, so $rowR = span\{Y_1, Y_2, \cdots, Y_k\}$. Moreover $\{Y_1, Y_2, \cdots, Y_k\}$ is linearly independent by Example 7 §4.2, so it is a basis of $rowR$.

Since $rowR = rowA$ by Lemma 1, we have

$$k = dim(rowR) = dim(rowA).$$

Hence the number k of leading 1's is the same *no matter how A is carried to row-echelon form*[5]. We express this by saying that the number of leading 1's is an *invariant* of A, called the **rank** of A, and denoted $rankA$. This is consistent with the usage in Section 1.2, and the above discussion is summarized in the following theorem.

THEOREM ❶

Let A be an $m \times n$ matrix. Then

$$rankA = dim(rowA).$$

Moreover, if $A \to R$ by row operations where R is a row-echelon matrix, the nonzero rows of R are a basis of $rowA$.

Theorem 1 has an additional virtue: It provides a routine method for finding a basis for any subspace U of $\mathbb{R}^n$ when a spanning set is given. Indeed, if $U = span\{X_1,\ X_2,\ \cdots,\ X_k\}$ where the X_i are written as rows, simply carry the matrix with the X_i as its rows to row-echelon form R. Then the nonzero rows of R are a basis of U.

Example 1

Find a basis of $U = span\{[1\ \ 1\ \ -2\ \ 4],\ [2\ \ 5\ \ 4\ \ -2],\ [1\ \ 7\ \ 14\ \ -16]\}$.

SOLUTION

Observe that $U = rowA$ where $A = \begin{bmatrix} 1 & 1 & -2 & 4 \\ 2 & 5 & 4 & -2 \\ 1 & 7 & 14 & -16 \end{bmatrix}$. The reduction of A to row-echelon form is

$$\begin{bmatrix} 1 & 1 & -2 & 4 \\ 2 & 5 & 4 & -2 \\ 1 & 7 & 14 & -16 \end{bmatrix} \to \begin{bmatrix} 1 & 1 & -2 & 4 \\ 0 & 3 & 8 & -10 \\ 0 & 6 & 16 & -20 \end{bmatrix}$$

$$\to \begin{bmatrix} 1 & 1 & -2 & 4 \\ 0 & 3 & 8 & -10 \\ 0 & 0 & 0 & 0 \end{bmatrix}$$

$$\to \begin{bmatrix} 1 & 1 & -2 & 4 \\ 0 & 1 & \frac{8}{3} & -\frac{10}{3} \\ 0 & 0 & 0 & 0 \end{bmatrix}.$$

Hence $\{[1\ \ 1\ \ -2\ \ 4],\ [0\ \ 1\ \ \frac{8}{3}\ \ -\frac{10}{3}]\}$ is a basis of $rowA = U$. We note that $\{[1\ \ 1\ \ -2\ \ 4],\ [0\ \ 3\ \ 8\ \ -10]\}$ is also a basis (see Example 3 §4.3), possibly more convenient.

4.4.2 The Rank Theorem

Theorem 1 can also be used to find a basis of $colA$: Carry A^T to row-echelon form R and use the transposes of the nonzero rows of R. (Equivalently, carry A to "column-echelon form" C and use the nonzero columns of C.) However, there is an easy way to select a basis of $colA$ directly from the columns of A. This is part of the following very important theorem: If A is any $m \times n$ matrix, the subspace $rowA$ of $\mathbb{R}^n$ has the *same dimension* as the subspace $colA$ of $\mathbb{R}^m$.

---

[5] This was asserted without proof in Section 1.2.

THEOREM 2

Rank Theorem. Let A be an $m \times n$ matrix. Then

$$dim(rowA) = dim(colA) = rankA.$$

Moreover, if $A \to R$ by row operations where R is a row-echelon matrix, and if the leading 1's are in columns $j_1, j_2, \cdots, j_r$ of R, then the corresponding columns $j_1, j_2, \cdots, j_r$ of A are a basis of $colA$.

PROOF

Since $r = rankA$, the displayed equations follow from the last sentence and Theorem 1. To prove the last sentence, write $A = [C_1 \ C_2 \ \cdots \ C_n]$ where C_j denotes column j of A. We use the fact that $R = UA$ for some invertible matrix U (Theorem 1 §1.6). Hence

$$R = UA = U[C_1 \ C_2 \ \cdots \ C_n]$$
$$= [UC_1 \ UC_2 \ \cdots \ UC_n]$$

so UC_j is column j of R. Since R contains r leading 1's, let $UC_{j_1}, UC_{j_2}, \cdots, UC_{j_r}$ be the columns of R that contain a leading 1. Then $\{UC_{j_1}, UC_{j_2}, \cdots, UC_{j_r}\}$ is a basis of $colR$ as the reader can verify. We use this to show that $\{C_{j_1}, C_{j_2}, \cdots, C_{j_r}\}$ is a basis of $colA$, as required.

Independence: Suppose $t_1 C_{j_1} + t_2 C_{j_2} + \cdots + t_r C_{j_r} = 0$ where each t_i is a real number. Left multiplying by U gives

$$0 = U0 = U(t_1 C_{j_1} + t_2 C_{j_2} + \cdots + t_r C_{j_r}) = t_1 UC_{j_1} + t_2 UC_{j_2} + \cdots + t_r UC_{j_r}.$$

Hence each $t_i = 0$ by the independence of $\{UC_{j_1}, UC_{j_2}, \cdots, UC_{j_r}\}$, and we have proved the independence of $\{C_{j_1}, C_{j_2} \cdots, C_{j_r}\}$.

Spanning: Given X in $colA$, write $X = r_1 C_1 + r_2 C_2 + \cdots + r_n C_n$ where each r_j is a real number. Then $UX = r_1 UC_1 + r_2 UC_2 + \cdots + r_n UC_n$ is in $colR$ because each UC_j is in $colR$. But $\{UC_{j_1}, UC_{j_2}, \cdots, UC_{j_r}\}$ spans $colR$, so there exist $t_1, t_2, \cdots, t_r$ such that

$$UX = t_1 UC_{j_1} + t_2 UC_{j_2} + \cdots + t_r UC_{j_r}.$$

Hence $UX = U(t_1 C_{j_1} + t_2 C_{j_2} + \cdots + t_r C_{j_r})$, so left multiplication by U^{-1} gives $X = t_1 C_{j_1} + t_2 C_{j_2} + \cdots + t_r C_{j_r}$. Thus X is in $span\{C_{j_1}, C_{j_2} \cdots, C_{j_r}\}$, as required.

Example 2

If $A = \begin{bmatrix} 1 & -1 & 3 & -2 \\ 2 & -2 & 2 & -1 \\ -1 & 1 & 5 & -4 \end{bmatrix}$, find a basis for $rowA$ and $colA$.

SOLUTION

One reduction of A to row-echelon form is as follows:

$$A = \begin{bmatrix} 1 & -1 & 3 & -2 \\ 2 & -2 & 2 & -1 \\ -1 & 1 & 5 & -4 \end{bmatrix}$$

$$\to \begin{bmatrix} 1 & -1 & 3 & -2 \\ 0 & 0 & -4 & 3 \\ 0 & 0 & 8 & -6 \end{bmatrix}$$

$$\to \begin{bmatrix} 1 & -1 & 3 & -2 \\ 0 & 0 & 1 & -\frac{3}{4} \\ 0 & 0 & 0 & 0 \end{bmatrix} = R.$$

Hence $\{[1 \;\; -1 \;\; 3 \;\; -2], [0 \;\; 0 \;\; 1 \;\; -\frac{3}{4}]\}$ is a basis of *rowA* by Theorem 1. Since the leading ones are in columns 1 and 3 of the row-echelon matrix R, Theorem 2 shows that columns 1 and 3 of A constitute a basis $\left\{ \begin{bmatrix} 1 \\ 2 \\ -1 \end{bmatrix}, \begin{bmatrix} 3 \\ 2 \\ 5 \end{bmatrix} \right\}$ of *colA*. Of course both bases contain $2 = rankA$ vectors as the Rank theorem asserts.

The Rank theorem has many consequences. First, if A is an $m \times n$ matrix, then *rowA* is spanned by the m rows of A, whence $rankA = dim(rowA) \leq m$ because the dimension of a subspace cannot exceed the number of vectors in any spanning set. Similarly, $rankA \leq n$ because $rankA = dim(colA)$. We record this as

COROLLARY 1   If A is an $m \times n$ matrix, then $rankA \leq m$ and $rankA \leq n$.

If A is an $n \times n$ matrix, then *rowA* is spanned by n rows, so $dim(rowA) = n$ if and only if the rows are independent (using Theorem 4 §4.3). But the rows are independent if and only if A is invertible (by Theorem 2 §4.2), so we have

COROLLARY 2   An $n \times n$ matrix A is invertible if and only if $rankA = n$.

The fact that the columns of A are just the transposes of the rows of A^T means that $dim(colA) = dim(row(A^T))$, that is

COROLLARY 3 $rankA^T = rankA$ for any matrix A.

COROLLARY 4   If A is an $m \times n$ matrix, then $rankA = rank(UAV)$ for any invertible matrices U and V.

PROOF   Recall (Lemma 1 §1.6) that doing an elementary row operation to A is the same as left multiplying A by an elementary matrix. Since the invertible matrix U is a product of elementary matrices (Theorem 1 §1.6), it follows that UA is obtained from A by a series of row operations. Hence $rank(UA) = rankA$ by Lemma 1. Now, write $UA = B$ for convenience, and apply Corollary 3 to get

$$rank(UAV) = rank(BV) = rank(BV)^T = rank(V^T B^T).$$

But V^T is invertible so the first part of this proof gives $rank(V^T B^T) = rankB^T = rankB = rankA$. Thus $rank(UAV) = rankA$ as required.

The result in Corollary 4 should be compared to Theorem 3 §1.6.

If A is an $n \times n$ matrix, then A is invertible if and only if $rankA = n$ by Corollary 2. In view of Corollary 1, this asserts that A is invertible if and only if $rankA$ is as large as possible. This raises a natural question about an arbitrary $m \times n$ matrix A: When do the two extreme cases $rankA = n$ and $rankA = m$ arise? The next two theorems show that the cases are naturally related to the independence and spanning properties of the columns of A (and hence to the systems of linear equations with A as coefficient matrix), and also to the invertibility of the (square and symmetric) matrices $A^T A$ and AA^T.

Recall that if $A = [C_1 \quad C_2 \quad \cdots \quad C_n]$ is an $m \times n$ matrix with columns $C_1, C_2, \cdots, C_n$, and if $X = [x_1 \quad x_2 \quad \cdots \quad x_n]^T$ is a column of scalars, then

$$AX = [C_1 \quad C_2 \quad \cdots \quad C_n] \begin{bmatrix} x_1 \\ x_2 \\ \vdots \\ x_n \end{bmatrix} = x_1 C_1 + x_2 C_2 + \cdots + x_n C_n. \tag{$*$}$$

We will refer to this several times.

THEOREM 3 Let A be an $m \times n$ matrix. The following are equivalent:

(1) $AX = 0$, X a column, has only the trivial solution $X = 0$.
(2) The columns of A are linearly independent.
(3) $rankA = n$.
(4) $A^T A$ is an invertible $n \times n$ matrix.

PROOF Let $C_1, C_2, \cdots, C_n$ denote the columns of A.

$(1) \Rightarrow (2)$. If $x_1 C_1 + x_2 C_2 + \cdots + x_n C_n = 0$, then $AX = 0$ by $(*)$, so each $x_i = 0$ by (1).

$(2) \Rightarrow (3)$. Since $colA = span\{C_1, C_2, \cdots, C_n\}$, (2) implies that $n = dim(colA) = rankA$.

$(3) \Rightarrow (4)$. To prove (4) we verify that $(A^T A)X = 0$ implies that $X = 0$ (by Theorem 5 §1.5). So assume that $A^T AX = 0$, write $AX = [y_1 \quad y_2 \quad \cdots \quad y_m]^T$, and compute:

$$y_1^2 + y_2^2 + \cdots + y_m^2 = (AX)^T(AX) = X^T(A^T AX) = X^T 0 = 0.$$

It follows that each $y_j = 0$; that is, $AX = 0$. If $X = [x_1 \quad x_2 \quad \cdots \quad x_n]^T$, this means that $x_1 C_1 + x_2 C_2 + \cdots + x_n C_n = 0$ by $(*)$. But $\{C_1, C_2, \cdots, C_n\}$ is independent by Theorem 4 §4.3 (because $span\{C_1, C_2, \cdots, C_n\} = colA$ has dimension n by (3)). Hence every $x_i = 0$, whence $X = 0$. This is what we wanted.

$(4) \Rightarrow (1)$. If $AX = 0$, then $A^T AX = 0$, so $X = 0$ by (4).

Theorem 3 describes what happens when an $m \times n$ matrix has rank n. The following companion theorem discusses the situation when the rank is m.

THEOREM 4 The following are equivalent for an $m \times n$ matrix A:

(1) $AX = B$ has a solution for every column B in $\mathbb{R}^m$.
(2) The columns of A span $\mathbb{R}^m$.
(3) $rankA = m$.
(4) AA^T is an invertible $m \times m$ matrix.

PROOF Again let $C_1, C_2, \cdots, C_n$ denote the columns of A.

$(1) \Rightarrow (2)$. If B is in $\mathbb{R}^m$, then (1) and equation $(*)$ (preceding Theorem 3) give $B = AX = x_1 C_1 + x_2 C_2 + \cdots + x_n C_n$ for scalars x_i, so B is in $colA$.

$(2) \Rightarrow (3)$. $colA = \mathbb{R}^m$ by (2), so $rankA = dim(colA) = dim(\mathbb{R}^m) = m$.

$(3) \Rightarrow (1)$. Since $colA \subseteq \mathbb{R}^m$ and $dim(colA) = m$ by (3), we have $colA = \mathbb{R}^m$ by Theorem 4 §4.3. Hence if B is in $\mathbb{R}^m$, then $B = x_1 C_1 + x_2 C_2 + \cdots + x_n C_n$ for scalars x_i, that is $B = AX$ where $X = [x_1 \quad x_2 \quad \cdots \quad x_n]^T$. This proves (1).

$(3) \Leftrightarrow (4)$. Write $M = A^T$. If we apply $(3) \Leftrightarrow (4)$ in Theorem 3 to the $n \times m$ matrix M, we obtain $M^T M$ is invertible if and only if $rankM = m$; that is, AA^T is invertible if and only if $rankA = m$. This is $(3) \Leftrightarrow (4)$ in the present theorem.

It is instructive to compare conditions (1) and (2) in Theorems 3 and 4 with Theorem 5 §1.5. In that earlier theorem these conditions are all equivalent to the square matrix A being invertible, while the present theorems isolate the roles played by these conditions in an arbitrary matrix. Let A be any $m \times n$ matrix. Theorems 3 and 4 relate several important properties of A to the invertibility of the square matrices $A^T A$ and AA^T. Even if the columns of A are not independent or do not span $\mathbb{R}^m$ (as in these theorems), the matrices $A^T A$ and AA^T are both symmetric and as such have real eigenvalues by Theorem 3 §2.5. This focuses our attention on the study of symmetric matrices. In fact the eigenvalues of $A^T A$ and AA^T are all nonnegative, and this leads to the so-called singular value decomposition of A, which provides basic information about A and is important in numerical analysis. We investigate this in Section 4.11.

4.4.3   Null Space and Image

In Section 4.1 we discussed two subspaces associated with an $m \times n$ matrix A, the null space $nullA = \{X \mid X \text{ in } \mathbb{R}^n \text{ and } AX = 0\}$ and the image $imA = \{AX \mid X \text{ in } \mathbb{R}^n\}$. Using the rank, there are simple ways to find bases for these spaces. The next theorem does this for imA because the Rank theorem does it for $colA$.

THEOREM 5   If A is any $m \times n$ matrix of rank r, then
$$colA = imA = \{AX \mid X \text{ in } \mathbb{R}^n\}.$$
Hence the Rank theorem provides a basis for imA. In particular,
$$dim(imA) = rankA.$$

PROOF   Equation (*) preceding Theorem 3 shows that the vectors AX in imA are just the linear combinations of the columns of A, that is $imA = colA$.[6] In particular, $dim(imA) = dim(colA) = rankA$.

Turning to the null space, a natural basis can be found using the Gaussian algorithm. We first discuss a specific example which exhibits most of the salient features of the situation.

Example 3   If $A = \begin{bmatrix} 1 & -2 & 1 & 1 \\ -1 & 2 & 0 & 1 \\ 2 & -4 & 1 & 0 \end{bmatrix}$, find a basis of $nullA$ and so find its dimension.

SOLUTION   If X is in $nullA$, then $AX = 0$, so X is given by solving the system $AX = 0$. Using Gaussian elimination, the augmented matrix is carried to reduced row-echelon form as follows:

$$\begin{bmatrix} 1 & -2 & 1 & 1 & 0 \\ -1 & 2 & 0 & 1 & 0 \\ 2 & -4 & 1 & 0 & 0 \end{bmatrix} \rightarrow \begin{bmatrix} 1 & -2 & 1 & 1 & 0 \\ 0 & 0 & 1 & 2 & 0 \\ 0 & 0 & -1 & -2 & 0 \end{bmatrix}$$
$$\rightarrow \begin{bmatrix} 1 & -2 & 0 & -1 & 0 \\ 0 & 0 & 1 & 2 & 0 \\ 0 & 0 & 0 & 0 & 0 \end{bmatrix}.$$

Hence, writing $X = [x_1 \ x_2 \ x_3 \ x_4]^T$, the leading variables are x_1 and x_3, and the non-leading variables x_2 and x_4 become parameters: $x_2 = s$ and $x_4 = t$. Then the equations corresponding to the reduced matrix determine the leading variables in terms of the parameters:

---

[6] This observation was made earlier in Example 12 §4.1.

$$x_1 = 2s + t \quad \text{and} \quad x_3 = -2t.$$

This means that the general solution is

$$X = [2s + t \quad s \quad -2t \quad t]^T = s[2 \quad 1 \quad 0 \quad 0]^T + t[1 \quad 0 \quad -2 \quad 1]^T. \tag{$**$}$$

Hence X is in $span\{X_1, X_2\}$ where $X_1 = [2 \quad 1 \quad 0 \quad 0]^T$ and $X_2 = [1 \quad 0 \quad -2 \quad 1]^T$ are the basic solutions, and we have shown that $null(A) \subseteq span\{X_1, X_2\}$. But each of X_1 and X_2 are in $nullA$ (they are solutions of the system $AX = 0$), so we have

$$nullA = span\{X_1, X_2\}$$

by Theorem 1 §4.1. We claim further that $\{X_1, X_2\}$ is linearly independent. To see this, let $sX_1 + tX_2 = 0$ be a linear combination that vanishes. Then ($**$) shows that $[2s + t \quad s \quad -2t \quad t]^T = 0$, whence $s = t = 0$. Thus $\{X_1, X_2\}$ is a basis of $null(A)$, and so $dim(nullA) = 2$.

The calculation in Example 3 is typical of what happens in general. If A is an $m \times n$ matrix, it was shown in Theorem 2 §1.3 that the system $AX = 0$ has exactly $n - r$ basic solutions $X_1, X_2, \cdots, X_{n-r}$ where $r = rankA$, and that

$$nullA = span\{X_1, X_2, \cdots, X_{n-r}\}.$$

Moreover, the general solution is a linear combination $X = t_1X_1 + t_2X_2 + \cdots + t_{n-r}X_{n-r}$ where each coefficient t_i is a parameter equal to a nonleading variable. Thus if this linear combination vanishes, that is, if $X = 0$, then each $t_i = 0$ (as for s and t in Example 3, each t_i is a coefficient when X is expressed as a linear combination of the standard basis of $\mathbb{R}^n$). This proves that $\{X_1, X_2, \cdots, X_{n-r}\}$ is linearly independent, and so is a basis of $nullA$. Theorem 6 summarizes this discussion.

THEOREM 6

Let A denote an $m \times n$ matrix of rank r, and let $X_1, X_2, \cdots, X_{n-r}$ be the basic solutions of the homogeneous system $AX = 0$ that are produced by the Gaussian algorithm. Then $\{X_1, X_2, \cdots, X_{n-r}\}$ is a basis of $nullA$. In particular,

$$dim(nullA) = n - r.$$

Combining Theorems 5 and 6, we obtain a useful equation relating the dimensions of the image and null space of a matrix.

COROLLARY

If A is any $m \times n$ matrix, then

$$dim(imA) + dim(nullA) = n.$$

Exercises 4.4

1. Give the row space and column space of the following matrices.

a) $A = \begin{bmatrix} 4 & -6 \\ 7 & 6 \end{bmatrix}$
b) $A = \begin{bmatrix} -5 & -4 \\ 8 & 0 \\ -1 & -3 \end{bmatrix}$

c) $A = \begin{bmatrix} 0 & -4 & -8 & -4 \\ 8 & 2 & -8 & 0 \\ -3 & 1 & -1 & -2 \end{bmatrix}$
d) $A = \begin{bmatrix} 9 & -5 & 1 & -1 \\ 8 & -5 & -3 & 1 \\ 0 & 4 & 7 & 6 \\ 0 & 2 & -7 & 7 \end{bmatrix}$

2. Match each matrix on the left with a matrix on the right sharing the same row or column space.

a) $A = \begin{bmatrix} 0 & 1 & -3 & 2 \\ 0 & 2 & 1 & -3 \\ 2 & -5 & 0 & 5 \end{bmatrix}$
b) $A = \begin{bmatrix} 1 & 0 & 0 & 0 \\ 0 & 1 & 0 & 0 \\ 2 & 1 & 0 & 0 \end{bmatrix}$

c) $A = \begin{bmatrix} 1 & 0 & 1 & 1 \\ 0 & 1 & 1 & -1 \\ 2 & 1 & 3 & 1 \end{bmatrix}$
d) $A = \begin{bmatrix} 0 & -2 & 6 & -4 \\ 2 & -3 & 1 & 2 \\ 2 & -5 & 0 & 5 \end{bmatrix}$

e) $A = \begin{bmatrix} 0 & 0 & 1 & 1 \\ -1 & 1 & 0 & 2 \\ -1 & 1 & 2 & 4 \end{bmatrix}$
f) $A = \begin{bmatrix} 1 & -1 & 0 & -2 \\ 0 & 0 & 1 & 1 \\ 0 & 0 & 0 & 0 \end{bmatrix}$

3. Given *rowA* for some matrix A, what is the rank of A?
   a) $rowA = span\{[1 \quad 0 \quad 0 \quad 1], [0 \quad 1 \quad 1 \quad 0], [0 \quad 0 \quad 0 \quad 1]\}$.
   b) $rowA = span\{[1 \quad 2 \quad -1 \quad 3], [2 \quad -3 \quad 1 \quad 4],$
   $[4 \quad -13 \quad 5 \quad 6]\}$.
   c) $rowA = span\{[-1 \quad 0 \quad 3 \quad 2], [3 \quad 2 \quad 0 \quad -4],$
   $[9 \quad 8 \quad 9 \quad -10], [4 \quad 2 \quad -3 \quad -6]\}$.

4. In each case find a basis of the subspace U.
   a) $U = span\{[1 \quad 2 \quad -1 \quad 3]^T, [2 \quad -3 \quad 1 \quad 4]^T,$
   $[4 \quad -13 \quad 5 \quad 6]^T\}$.
   b) $U = span\{[1 \quad 2 \quad -1 \quad 0 \quad 4]^T, [-3 \quad 1 \quad 0 \quad 2 \quad 5]^T,$
   $[-7 \quad 7 \quad -2 \quad 6 \quad 13]^T, [-2 \quad 3 \quad -1 \quad 2 \quad 9]^T\}$.
   c) $U = span\{[-1 \quad 0 \quad 3 \quad 2]^T, [3 \quad 2 \quad 0 \quad -4]^T,$
   $[9 \quad 8 \quad 9 \quad -10]^T, [4 \quad 2 \quad -3 \quad -6]^T\}$.

5. In each case find bases for the row and column spaces of A and determine the rank of A.

a) $A = \begin{bmatrix} 1 & -1 & 3 & 2 & 1 \\ -2 & 3 & 1 & 1 & 1 \\ -4 & 7 & 9 & 7 & 5 \\ 3 & -4 & 2 & 1 & 0 \end{bmatrix}$ **b)** $A = \begin{bmatrix} 1 & 2 & 0 & 5 & 7 & 1 \\ 2 & 1 & 1 & -1 & 0 & 3 \\ -5 & 2 & -4 & 19 & 21 & 9 \\ 1 & -1 & 1 & -6 & -7 & 2 \end{bmatrix}$

6. In each case find a basis of the nullspace of A, compute *rankA*, and verify Theorem 6.

a) $A = \begin{bmatrix} 3 & 1 & 1 \\ 2 & 0 & 1 \\ 4 & 2 & 1 \\ 1 & -1 & 1 \end{bmatrix}$ **b)** $A = \begin{bmatrix} 3 & 5 & 5 & 2 & 0 \\ 1 & 0 & 2 & 2 & 1 \\ 1 & 1 & 1 & -2 & -2 \\ 2 & 0 & 4 & 4 & 2 \end{bmatrix}$

7. In each case either show that the statement is true or give an example showing that it is false. Throughout let A denote an $m \times n$ matrix.
   a) If A has a row of zeros, then $rowA = \{0\}$.
   b) If the rows of A are linearly independent, then $rowA = \mathbb{R}^n$.
   c) If the rows of A span $\mathbb{R}^n$, then $rowA = \mathbb{R}^n$.
   d) If A has a row of zeros, then $rankA = 0$.
   e) If A has a row of zeros, then $rankA < m$.
   f) If B is $m \times n$ and $rankB = r = rankA$, then $rank(A + B) = r$.

8. Can a 3×4 matrix have independent rows? Independent columns? Explain.

9. If A is 4×3 and $rankA = 2$, can A have independent columns? Independent rows? Explain.

10. Can a nonsquare matrix A have its rows independent and its columns independent? Explain.

11. Can the null space of a 3×6 matrix have dimension 2? Explain.

12. If a matrix A is not square, show that either the rows or the columns of A are dependent.

13. If A is an $m \times n$ matrix and $rankA = m$, show that $m \leq n$.

14. Let A and B denote matrices of size $k \times m$ and $m \times n$ respectively.
   a) Show that each column of AB is a linear combination of the columns of A. [Hint: Equation (*) preceding Theorem 3].
   b) Show that $rank(AB) \leq rankA$.
   c) Show that $rank(AB) \leq rankB$. [Hint: Corollary 3 of Theorem 2.]

15. Let A and B denote matrices of sizes $m \times n$ and $n \times k$ respectively.
   a) If $AB = 0$, show that $colB \subseteq nullA$. [Hint: Theorem 3 §1.4 (2).]
   b) If $colB \subseteq nullA$, show that $AB = 0$. [Hint: Theorem 3 §1.4 (1).]

16. Consider the system of equations $AX = B$ where A is $m \times n$ and B is $m \times 1$.
   a) Show that the system $AX = B$ has a solution if and only if B is in *colA*. [Hint: Equation (*) preceding Theorem 3.]
   b) Show that the system $AX = B$ has a solution if and only if $rankA = rank[A \quad B]$, where $[A \quad B]$ is the augmented matrix of the system.

17. If I is the $m \times m$ identity matrix, show that $I + ZZ^T$ is invertible for every $m \times k$ matrix Z. [Hint: Factor
$$I + ZZ^T = [I \quad Z]\begin{bmatrix} I \\ Z^T \end{bmatrix}$$ in block form and use Theorem 4.]

18. Let A denote an $m \times n$ matrix.
   a) If $rankA = m$, show that $AB = I_m$ for some $n \times m$ matrix B. [Hint: Theorem 4 (4).]
   b) If $AB = I_m$ for some $n \times m$ matrix B, show that $rankA = m$. [Hint: Exercise 14 **b)**.]

19. Let A denote an $m \times n$ matrix.
   a) Show that $null(A^TA) = null(A)$. [Hint: Use the proof of $(3) \Rightarrow (4)$ in Theorem 3.]
   b) Conclude that $rank(A^TA) = rankA$.
   c) Show that $im(A^T) = im(A^TA)$. [Hint: Show that $im(A^TA) \subseteq im(A^T)$, and apply Theorem 4 §4.3.]

20. If A is an $m \times n$ matrix, it can be proved that there exists a unique $n \times m$ matrix $A^\#$ such that $AA^\#A = A$, $A^\#AA^\# = A^\#$, and both $AA^\#$ and $A^\#A$ are symmetric. The matrix $A^\#$ is called the **Moore-Penrose** inverse of A.
   a) If A is square and invertible, show that $A^\# = A^{-1}$.
   b) If $rankA = m$, show that $A^\# = A^T(AA^T)^{-1}$.
   c) If $rankA = n$, show that $A^\# = (A^TA)^{-1}A^T$.

4.5 ORTHOGONALITY

Length and orthogonality are two of the most important concepts in geometry. In $\mathbb{R}^2$ and $\mathbb{R}^3$ these notions can both be defined using the dot product, and this observation is exploited in this section to extend these concepts to $\mathbb{R}^n$. This in turn leads to a natural extension of the notion of distance to $\mathbb{R}^n$, to an extension of Pythagoras' theorem, and to the idea of an orthogonal basis—one of the most useful concepts in linear algebra.

4.5.1 Dot Product, Length, and Distance

Recall that, given $\vec{v} = [x_1 \ \ x_2 \ \ x_3]^T$ and $\vec{w} = [y_1 \ \ y_2 \ \ y_3]^T$ in $\mathbb{R}^3$, their dot product $\vec{v} \cdot \vec{w}$ and the length $\|\vec{v}\|$ of $\vec{v}$ are defined by

$$\vec{v} \cdot \vec{w} = x_1y_1 + x_2y_2 + x_3y_3 \quad \text{and} \quad \|\vec{v}\| = \sqrt{x_1^2 + x_2^2 + x_3^2}.$$

These formulas extend in the obvious way to columns in $\mathbb{R}^n$. Accordingly, given columns $X = [x_1 \ \ x_2 \ \ \cdots \ \ x_n]^T$ and $Y = [y_1 \ \ y_2 \ \ \cdots \ \ y_n]^T$ in $\mathbb{R}^n$, we define their **dot product** $X \cdot Y$ as follows:

$$X \cdot Y = x_1y_1 + x_2y_2 + \cdots + x_ny_n = X^TY.$$

Note that X^TY is technically a 1×1 matrix, which we take to be a number.[7] The **length** of the column vector $X = [x_1 \ \ x_2 \ \ \cdots \ \ x_n]^T$ is defined to be

$$\|X\| = \sqrt{X \cdot X} = \sqrt{x_1^2 + x_2^2 + \cdots + x_n^2}$$

where $\sqrt{(\ \ )}$ indicates the positive square root.[8]

Example 1

Given $X = [3 \ \ {-2} \ \ 0 \ \ 4 \ \ {-1}]$ and $Y = [1 \ \ 1 \ \ {-1} \ \ 0 \ \ 6]$ in $\mathbb{R}^5$, we have $X \cdot Y = 3 - 2 + 0 + 0 - 6 = -5$, and $\|X\| = \sqrt{9 + 4 + 0 + 16 + 1} = \sqrt{30}$.

The following facts will be used frequently below.

THEOREM 1

Let X, Y, and Z denote columns in $\mathbb{R}^n$. Then:

(1) $X \cdot Y = Y \cdot X$.

(2) $X \cdot (Y + Z) = X \cdot Y + X \cdot Z$.

(3) $(aX) \cdot Y = a(X \cdot Y) = X \cdot (aY)$ for all scalars a.

(4) $\|X\|^2 = X \cdot X$.

(5) $\|X\| \geq 0$, and $\|X\| = 0$ if and only if $X = 0$.

(6) $\|aX\| = |a| \ \|X\|$ for all scalars a.

PROOF

Let $X = [x_1 \ \ x_2 \ \ \cdots \ \ x_n]^T$ and $Y = [y_1 \ \ y_2 \ \ \cdots \ \ y_n]^T$ be columns in $\mathbb{R}^n$. Then (1) follows from $X \cdot Y = x_1y_1 + x_2y_2 + \cdots + x_ny_n$, (2) and (3) follow from matrix arithmetic because $X \cdot Y = X^TY$, (4) is clear from the definition, and (6) follows because $|a| = \sqrt{a^2}$ for all real numbers a. As for (5), $\|X\| \geq 0$ is clear, as is $\|0\| = 0$; finally, if $\|X\| = 0$, then $x_1^2 + x_2^2 + \cdots + x_n^2 = 0$, so each $x_i = 0$ because the x_i are real numbers. Thus $X = 0$.

---

[7] If X and Y are written as rows rather than columns, this becomes $X \cdot Y = XY^T$.

[8] Since $X \cdot X = x_1^2 + x_2^2 + \cdots + x_n^2 \geq 0$ for all choices of the real numbers x_i, the length $\|X\|$ is a nonnegative real number for every column X in $\mathbb{R}^n$.

Because of Theorem 1, computations with dot products in $\mathbb{R}^n$ are similar to those in $\mathbb{R}^3$. In particular it follows from (1) and (2) that the dot product of two sums $X_1 + \cdots + X_k$ and $Y_1 + \cdots + Y_m$ in $\mathbb{R}^n$ is the sum of the dot products of every X_i with every Y_j:

$$(X_1 + \cdots + X_k) \cdot (Y_1 + \cdots + Y_m)$$
$$= X_1 \cdot Y_1 + X_1 \cdot Y_2 + X_2 \cdot Y_1 + \cdots + X_k \cdot Y_m$$
$$= \Sigma_{i,j} X_i \cdot Y_j.$$

If this is combined with (3) in Theorem 1, we can do calculations like

$$(2X_1 - 3X_2) \cdot (5Y_1 + 4Y_2)$$
$$= 10(X_1 \cdot Y_1) + 8(X_1 \cdot Y_2) - 15(X_2 \cdot Y_1) - 12(X_2 \cdot Y_2).$$

Such computations will be carried out without comment below.

Example 2   If X and Y are in $\mathbb{R}^n$, show that

$$\|X + Y\|^2 = \|X\|^2 + 2X \cdot Y + \|Y\|^2.$$

SOLUTION   We use Theorem 1 several times:

$$\|X + Y\|^2 = (X + Y) \cdot (X + Y)$$
$$= X \cdot X + X \cdot Y + Y \cdot X + Y \cdot Y$$
$$= \|X\|^2 + 2X \cdot Y + \|Y\|^2.$$

Example 3   Let $\mathbb{R}^n = span\{F_1, F_2, \cdots, F_m\}$. If X in $\mathbb{R}^n$ satisfies $X \cdot F_i = 0$ for each i, show that $X = 0$.

SOLUTION   We show $X = 0$ by showing that $\|X\| = 0$ and applying (5) of Theorem 1. By hypothesis, write $X = t_1 F_1 + t_2 F_2 + \cdots + t_m F_m$ for some t_i in $\mathbb{R}$. Then

$$\|X\|^2 = X \cdot X = X \cdot (t_1 F_1 + t_2 F_2 + \cdots + t_m F_m)$$
$$= t_1(X \cdot F_1) + t_2(X \cdot F_2) + \cdots + t_m(X \cdot F_m)$$
$$= 0$$

by hypothesis. Hence $\|X\| = 0$, and so $X = 0$ by Theorem 1.

A vector E in $\mathbb{R}^n$ is called a **unit vector** if $\|E\| = 1$. Thus if $\{E_1, E_2, \cdots, E_n\}$ is the standard basis of $\mathbb{R}^n$ then each E_i is a unit vector (E_i is column i of the $n \times n$ identity matrix). We will use the following observation several times below.

Example 4   If $X \neq 0$ in $\mathbb{R}^n$, show that $E = \frac{1}{\|X\|}X$ is the unique positive scalar multiple of X that is a unit vector.

SOLUTION   If $E = tX$ where $t > 0$, then $\|E\| = |t| \|X\| = t\|X\|$ by Theorem 1. Hence if $\|E\| = 1$, we have $t\|X\| = 1$, so $t = \frac{1}{\|X\|}$.

If $\vec{v}$ and $\vec{w}$ are nonzero vectors in $\mathbb{R}^3$, we showed (Theorem 2 §3.2) that the angle θ between them is given by $\cos\theta = \frac{\vec{v} \cdot \vec{w}}{\|\vec{v}\|\|\vec{w}\|}$. Since $|\cos\theta| \leq 1$ for any angle θ, it follows that $\|\vec{v} \cdot \vec{w}\| \leq \|\vec{v}\|\|\vec{w}\|$, and this holds even if $\vec{v} = \vec{0}$ or $\vec{w} = \vec{0}$. This inequality has an important analogue in $\mathbb{R}^n$.

THEOREM 2 **Cauchy Inequality.**[9] If X and Y are vectors in $\mathbb{R}^n$, then

$$|X \cdot Y| \leq \|X\|\|Y\|.$$

Moreover, equality holds if and only if one of X and Y is a scalar multiple of the other.

PROOF If either $X = 0$ or $Y = 0$, the inequality holds (in fact, it is equality). Otherwise, write $\|X\| = a$ and $\|Y\| = b$ for convenience. Then $a > 0$ and $b > 0$, and a computation like that in Example 2 gives

$$\|bX - aY\|^2 = 2ab(ab - X \cdot Y) \quad \text{and} \quad \|bX + aY\|^2 = 2ab(ab + X \cdot Y). \quad (*)$$

It follows that $ab - X \cdot Y \geq 0$ and $ab + X \cdot Y \geq 0$, whence $-ab \leq X \cdot Y \leq ab$. This gives the Cauchy inequality. If equality holds, we have $|X \cdot Y| = ab$, so either $X \cdot Y = ab$ or $X \cdot Y = -ab$. Using $(*)$, these imply that $bX - aY = 0$ or $bX + aY = 0$, respectively. Thus one of X and Y is a scalar multiple of the other (even if $a = 0$ or $b = 0$).

The Cauchy inequality is often written in the equivalent form $(X \cdot Y)^2 \leq \|X\|^2\|Y\|^2$. Thus, for example, in $\mathbb{R}^4$ we have

$$(a_1b_1 + a_2b_2 + a_3b_3 + a_4b_4)^2 \leq (a_1^2 + a_2^2 + a_3^2 + a_4^2)(b_1^2 + b_2^2 + b_3^2 + b_4^2)$$

for all choices of the numbers a_i and b_i.

There is an important consequence of the Cauchy inequality. Given X and Y in $\mathbb{R}^n$, we use the inequality and Example 2 to compute

$$\begin{aligned}
\|X + Y\|^2 &= \|X\|^2 + 2X \cdot Y + \|Y\|^2 \\
&\leq \|X\|^2 + 2\|X\|\|Y\| + \|Y\|^2 \\
&= (\|X\| + \|Y\|)^2.
\end{aligned}$$

If we take positive square roots, this gives the

COROLLARY **Triangle Inequality.** If X and Y are vectors in $\mathbb{R}^n$, then $\|X + Y\| \leq \|X\| + \|Y\|$.

The reason for the name will be clear when we have introduced the notion of distance into $\mathbb{R}^n$.

If $\vec{v}$ and $\vec{w}$ denote two vectors in $\mathbb{R}^3$, the distance between $\vec{v}$ and $\vec{w}$ (regarded as points) is $\|\vec{v} - \vec{w}\|$ as in the diagram. The analogue for $\mathbb{R}^n$ is as follows: If X and Y are vectors in $\mathbb{R}^n$, the **distance** between X and Y is defined to be

$$d(X, Y) = \|X - Y\|.$$

This distance function has all the intuitive properties of distance that are familiar from $\mathbb{R}^2$ and $\mathbb{R}^3$, including another version of the triangle inequality.

THEOREM 3 Let X, Y, and Z denote vectors in $\mathbb{R}^n$. Then:

(1) $d(X, Y) \geq 0$ for all X and Y.
(2) $d(X, Y) = 0$ if and only if $X = Y$.
(3) $d(X, Y) = d(Y, X)$.
(4) **Triangle Inequality.** $d(X, Y) \leq d(X, Z) + d(Z, Y)$.

---

[9] Augustin Louis Cauchy (1789–1857) was born in Paris and became a professor at the École Polytechnique at the age of 26. He was one of the great mathematicians and is best remembered for his work in analysis where he established standards of rigour that carry down to today's calculus texts.

PROOF   (1) and (2) are translations of part (5) of Theorem 1, and (3) holds because $\|X\| = \|-X\|$ by part (6) of Theorem 1. To prove (4), we use the Corollary to Theorem 2:

$$d(X, Y) = \|X - Y\|$$
$$= \|(X - Z) + (Z - Y)\| \le \|(X - Z)\| + \|(Z - Y)\|$$
$$= d(X, Z) + d(Z, Y).$$

This proves (4).

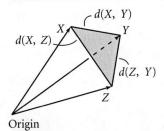

Now the name "Triangle Inequality" in (4) makes sense: Consider the "triangle" in $\mathbb{R}^n$ with vertices X, Y, and Z, as depicted in the diagram. Then the length $d(X, Y)$ of one side of the triangle is smaller than the sum $d(X, Z) + d(Z, Y)$ of the lengths of the other two sides. Note that, as in $\mathbb{R}^3$, we regard a vector X in $\mathbb{R}^n$ as an arrow from the origin to the point X. While not totally accurate, this method of visualizing $\mathbb{R}^n$ does not lead one astray.

4.5.2 Orthogonal Sets and the Expansion Theorem

The concept of orthogonality is a central idea in geometry, occurring as it does in Pythagoras' theorem, in the notion of the normal to a plane, and in the way we find the point on a line that is closest to a given point. Orthogonality turns out to play an even more important role in the geometry of $\mathbb{R}^n$ as we shall see. Moreover, as for length and distance, the definition is a natural extension of the situation in $\mathbb{R}^3$.

As in $\mathbb{R}^3$, two vectors X and Y in $\mathbb{R}^n$ are said to be **orthogonal** if

$$X \cdot Y = 0$$

More generally, a set of vectors $\{X_1, X_2, \cdots, X_k\}$ is called an **orthogonal set** of vectors if

$$X_i \cdot X_j = 0 \quad \text{for all } i \ne j$$
$$X_i \ne 0 \quad \text{for all } i.$$

(The reason for insisting that each X_i is nonzero is that we will be concerned primarily with orthogonal bases.) Note that $\{X\}$ is an orthogonal set for any $X \ne 0$ in $\mathbb{R}^n$. An orthogonal set of vectors $\{X_1, X_2, \cdots, X_k\}$ is called **orthonormal** if $\|X_i\| = 1$ for each i, that is if each X_i is a unit vector.

Example 5   The standard basis of $\mathbb{R}^n$ is an orthonormal set of vectors.

If $\{X_1, X_2, \cdots, X_k\}$ is an orthogonal set in $\mathbb{R}^n$, it is easy to verify that $\{a_1 X_1, a_2 X_2, \cdots, a_k X_k\}$ is also an orthogonal set for any choice of scalars $a_i \ne 0$. In particular, $\left\{ \frac{1}{\|X_1\|} X_1, \frac{1}{\|X_2\|} X_2, \cdots, \frac{1}{\|X_k\|} X_k \right\}$ is an orthonormal set by Example 4, and we say it is the result of **normalizing** the orthogonal set $\{X_1, X_2, \cdots, X_k\}$.

Example 6   The set $\{[1 \ -1 \ 3 \ 0]^T, [-2 \ 1 \ 1 \ 1]^T, [1 \ 1 \ 0 \ 1]^T, [1 \ 10 \ 3 \ -11]^T\}$ is orthogonal in $\mathbb{R}^4$ as is easily verified. After normalizing, the corresponding orthonormal set is $\left\{ \frac{1}{\sqrt{11}}[1 \ -1 \ 3 \ 0]^T, \frac{1}{\sqrt{7}}[-2 \ 1 \ 1 \ 1]^T, \frac{1}{\sqrt{3}}[1 \ 1 \ 0 \ 1]^T, \frac{1}{\sqrt{231}}[1 \ 10 \ 3 \ -11]^T \right\}$.

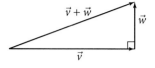

No discussion of geometry can omit mention of the most famous theorem about orthogonality: Pythagoras' theorem. Suppose orthogonal vectors $\vec{v} \neq \vec{0}$ and $\vec{w} \neq \vec{0}$ are given in $\mathbb{R}^3$. Then Pythagoras' theorem asserts that $\|\vec{v} + \vec{w}\|^2 = \|\vec{v}\|^2 + \|\vec{w}\|^2$ (see the diagram). More generally, if $\{X,\ Y\}$ is an orthogonal set in $\mathbb{R}^n$, then $X \cdot Y = 0$ so

$$\|X + Y\|^2 = \|X\|^2 + 2(X \cdot Y) + \|Y\|^2$$
$$= \|X\|^2 + \|Y\|^2.$$

In fact, this works for orthogonal sets of more than two vectors in $\mathbb{R}^n$.

THEOREM 4

Pythagoras' Theorem. Let $\{X_1,\ X_2,\ \cdots,\ X_k\}$ be an orthogonal set[10] of vectors in $\mathbb{R}^n$. Then

$$\|X_1 + X_2 + \cdots + X_k\|^2 = \|X_1\|^2 + \|X_2\|^2 + \cdots + \|X_k\|^2.$$

PROOF

The fact that $X_i \cdot X_j = 0$ whenever $i \neq j$ gives

$$\|X_1 + X_2 + \cdots + X_k\|^2$$
$$= (X_1 + X_2 + \cdots + X_k) \cdot (X_1 + X_2 + \cdots + X_k)$$
$$= X_1 \cdot X_1 + X_2 \cdot X_2 + \cdots + X_k \cdot X_k$$
$$\quad + (X_1 \cdot X_2 + X_1 \cdot X_3 + X_2 \cdot X_3 + \cdots)$$
$$= \|X_1\|^2 + \|X_2\|^2 + \cdots + \|X_k\|^2 + (0 + 0 + 0 + \cdots).$$

This proves the theorem.

If $\{\vec{v},\ \vec{w}\}$ is an orthogonal set in $\mathbb{R}^3$, then $\vec{v}$ and $\vec{w}$ are certainly not parallel (being orthogonal), so $\{\vec{v},\ \vec{w}\}$ is linearly independent by the Corollary of Theorem 3 §4.2. The next theorem shows that this observation holds much more generally.

THEOREM 5

Every orthogonal set of vectors in $\mathbb{R}^n$ is linearly independent.

PROOF

If $\{X_1,\ X_2,\ \cdots,\ X_k\}$ is orthogonal, suppose a linear combination vanishes: $t_1 X_1 + t_2 X_2 + \cdots + t_k X_k = 0$. We must show that each $t_i = 0$. If we take the dot product with X_1, the result is

$$0 = X_1 \cdot 0 = X_1 \cdot (t_1 X_1 + t_2 X_2 + \cdots + t_k X_k)$$
$$= t_1(X_1 \cdot X_1) + t_2(X_1 \cdot X_2) + \cdots + t_k(X_1 \cdot X_k)$$
$$= t_1 \|X_1\|^2 + t_2(0) + \cdots + t_k(0)$$
$$= t_1 \|X_1\|^2.$$

Since $\|X_1\|^2 \neq 0$ (because $X_1 \neq 0$), it follows that $t_1 = 0$. Similarly, $t_i = 0$ for each i.

Theorem 5 points immediately to the consideration of orthogonal bases. These turn out to be much more convenient than ordinary bases for the following reason. If $\{X_1,\ X_2,\ \cdots,\ X_k\}$ is a basis of a subspace U, then $U = span\{X_1,\ X_2,\ \cdots,\ X_k\}$ so every vector X in U can be (uniquely) expressed as a linear combination $X = t_1 X_1 + t_2 X_2 + \cdots + t_k X_k$. The problem is that, in general, it is tedious to compute the coefficients t_i (this requires solving k equations in k variables). However, explicit formulas exist for the coefficients if the basis $\{X_1,\ X_2,\ \cdots,\ X_k\}$ is orthogonal.

---

[10] This is valid even if some of the X_i are zero.

THEOREM 6   **Expansion Theorem.** Let $\{X_1, X_2, \cdots, X_k\}$ be an orthogonal basis of a subspace U of $\mathbb{R}^n$. If X is any vector in U, then

$$X = \frac{X \cdot X_1}{\|X_1\|^2}X_1 + \frac{X \cdot X_2}{\|X_2\|^2}X_2 + \cdots + \frac{X \cdot X_k}{\|X_k\|^2}X_k.$$

PROOF   We have $X = t_1X_1 + t_2X_2 + \cdots + t_kX_k$ for some coefficients t_i because $U = span\{X_1, X_2, \cdots, X_k\}$. Take the dot product of both sides with X_1:

$$\begin{aligned}
X \cdot X_1 &= (t_1X_1 + t_2X_2 + \cdots + t_kX_k) \cdot X_1 \\
&= t_1(X_1 \cdot X_1) + t_2(X_2 \cdot X_1) + \cdots + t_k(X_k \cdot X_1) \\
&= t_1\|X_1\|^2 + t_2(0) + \cdots + t_k(0) \\
&= t_1\|X_1\|^2.
\end{aligned}$$

Since $\|X_1\|^2 \neq 0$, this gives $t_1 = \frac{X \cdot X_1}{\|X_1\|^2}$. Similarly, $t_i = \frac{X \cdot X_i}{\|X_i\|^2}$ for each i.

Example 7   As in Example 6, let $X_1 = [1 \ \ -1 \ \ 3 \ \ 0]^T$, $X_2 = [-2 \ \ 1 \ \ 1 \ \ 1]^T$, $X_3 = [1 \ \ 1 \ \ 0 \ \ 1]^T$, and $X_4 = [1 \ \ 10 \ \ 3 \ \ -11]^T$. Then $\{X_1, X_2, X_3, X_4\}$ is orthogonal in $\mathbb{R}^4$, hence it is independent by Theorem 5, and so it is a basis because $dim(\mathbb{R}^4) = 4$. Given $X = [a \ \ b \ \ c \ \ d]^T$ in $\mathbb{R}^4$, we can express X as a linear combination of X_1, X_2, X_3, and X_4. In fact the Expansion theorem gives $X = t_1X_1 + t_2X_2 + t_3X_3 + t_4X_4$ where

$$t_1 = \frac{X \cdot X_1}{\|X_1\|^2} = \frac{a - b + 3c}{11} \qquad t_2 = \frac{X \cdot X_2}{\|X_2\|^2} = \frac{-2a + b + c + d}{7}$$

$$t_3 = \frac{X \cdot X_3}{\|X_3\|^2} = \frac{a + b + d}{3} \qquad t_4 = \frac{X \cdot X_4}{\|X_4\|^2} = \frac{a + 10b + 3c - 11d}{231}$$

The reader may wish to verify that in fact $X = t_1X_1 + t_2X_2 + t_3X_3 + t_4X_4$.

4.5.3   The Gram-Schmidt Algorithm

The Expansion theorem demonstrates the desirability of orthogonal bases. More evidence will be given in the following section. However, first we must show that every subspace of $\mathbb{R}^n$ *has* an orthogonal basis; we accomplish this by giving a method for converting any basis into an orthogonal basis.

In showing that every subspace of $\mathbb{R}^n$ has a basis, it was essential in Section 4.3 to be able to enlarge any independent set. The key result was the Independent lemma (Lemma 1 §4.3): If $\{X_1, X_2, \cdots, X_m\}$ is independent in $\mathbb{R}^n$ and Y is not in $span\{X_1, X_2, \cdots, X_m\}$, then $\{Y, X_1, X_2, \cdots, X_m\}$ is also an independent set. The analogue for orthogonal sets is

LEMMA 1   **Orthogonal Lemma.** Let $\{F_1, F_2, \cdots, F_k\}$ be an orthogonal set in $\mathbb{R}^n$. Given X in $\mathbb{R}^n$, write

$$F_{k+1} = X - \left(\frac{X \cdot F_1}{\|F_1\|^2}F_1 + \frac{X \cdot F_2}{\|F_2\|^2}F_2 + \cdots + \frac{X \cdot F_k}{\|F_k\|^2}F_k \right).$$

Then:

    (1) F_{k+1} is orthogonal to each of $F_1, F_2, \cdots, F_k$.

    (2) If X is not in $span\{F_1, F_2, \cdots, F_k\}$, then $F_{k+1} \neq 0$ and the larger set $\{F_1, F_2, \cdots, F_k, F_{k+1}\}$ is an orthogonal set.

PROOF For convenience, write $c_i = \frac{X \cdot F_i}{\|F_i\|^2}$ for each i. Given $1 \le i \le k$, we have

$$
\begin{aligned}
F_{k+1} \cdot F_i &= (X - c_1 F_1 - c_2 F_2 - \cdots - c_k F_k) \cdot F_i \\
&= X \cdot F_i - c_1(F_1 \cdot F_i) - c_2(F_2 \cdot F_i) - \cdots - c_k(F_k \cdot F_i) \\
&= X \cdot F_i - c_i \|F_i\|^2 \\
&= 0.
\end{aligned}
$$

This proves (1), and (2) follows because $F_{k+1} \ne 0$ if X is not in $span\{F_1, F_2, \cdots, F_k\}$.

It is worth observing that if X *is* in $span\{F_1, F_2, \cdots, F_k\}$ in Lemma 1, then $F_{k+1} = 0$ by the Expansion theorem.

The Orthogonal lemma gives a method of extending an orthogonal set to a larger orthogonal set. In this way it provides a version, for orthogonal sets, of the fact that every independent subset of a subspace U is part of an basis of U.

THEOREM 7

If U is a nonzero subspace of $\mathbb{R}^n$, then every orthogonal subset $\{F_1, F_2, \cdots, F_k\}$ of U is part of an orthogonal basis of U. In particular, U has an orthogonal basis.

PROOF If $span\{F_1, F_2, \cdots, F_k\} = U$, then $\{F_1, F_2, \cdots, F_k\}$ is already an orthogonal basis. Otherwise, there exists X in U which is not in $span\{F_1, F_2, \cdots, F_k\}$. If F_{k+1} is as in the Orthogonal lemma, then F_{k+1} is in U and $\{F_1, F_2, \cdots, F_k, F_{k+1}\}$ is orthogonal. If $span\{F_1, F_2, \cdots, F_k, F_{k+1}\} = U$, we are done. Otherwise, the process continues to create larger and larger orthogonal subsets of U, each containing $\{F_1, F_2, \cdots, F_k\}$. They are all independent by Theorem 5, so we have an orthogonal basis when we reach such a set containing $dim\, U$ vectors. Finally, as $U \ne 0$, choose $F_1 \ne 0$ in U. Then $\{F_1\}$ is an orthogonal set, so the foregoing procedure produces an orthogonal basis of U (containing the vector F_1).

The method of proof of Theorem 7 actually gives more information. It leads to a procedure by which any basis $\{X_1, X_2, \cdots, X_m\}$ of a subspace U of $\mathbb{R}^n$ can be systematically modified to produce an orthogonal basis $\{F_1, F_2, \cdots, F_m\}$ of U. These new vectors F_i are constructed one at a time from the X_i. To start the process, take

$$F_1 = X_1.$$

Then X_2 is not in $span\{F_1\}$ because $\{X_1, X_2\}$ is independent so, with an eye on the Orthogonal lemma, take

$$F_2 = X_2 - \frac{X_2 \cdot F_1}{\|F_1\|^2} F_1.$$

Thus $\{F_1, F_2\}$ is an orthogonal set by the Orthogonal lemma. Moreover, $span\{F_1, F_2\} = span\{X_1, X_2\}$ as is easily verified. Hence X_3 is not in $span\{F_1, F_2\}$ because $\{X_1, X_2, X_3\}$ is independent. Now another application of the Orthogonal lemma shows that $\{F_1, F_2, F_3\}$ is orthogonal where

$$F_3 = X_3 - \frac{X_3 \cdot F_1}{\|F_1\|^2} F_1 - \frac{X_3 \cdot F_2}{\|F_2\|^2} F_2.$$

Again one verifies that $span\{F_1, F_2, F_3\} = span\{X_1, X_2, X_3\}$, and the process continues. At the mth iteration we construct an orthogonal set $\{F_1, F_2, \cdots, F_m\}$ such that

$$span\{F_1, F_2, \cdots, F_m\} = span\{X_1, X_2, \cdots, X_m\} = U.$$

Hence $\{F_1, F_2, \cdots, F_m\}$ is the desired orthogonal basis of U. The procedure can be summarized as follows.

THEOREM 8

Gram-Schmidt Algorithm.[11] If $\{X_1, X_2, \cdots, X_m\}$ is any basis of a subspace U of $\mathbb{R}^n$, construct $F_1, F_2, \cdots, F_m$ in U successively as follows:

$$F_1 = X_1$$
$$F_2 = X_2 - \frac{X_2 \cdot F_1}{\|F_1\|^2} F_1$$
$$F_3 = X_3 - \frac{X_3 \cdot F_1}{\|F_1\|^2} F_1 - \frac{X_3 \cdot F_2}{\|F_2\|^2} F_2$$
$$\vdots$$
$$F_k = X_k - \frac{X_k \cdot F_1}{\|F_1\|^2} F_1 - \frac{X_k \cdot F_2}{\|F_2\|^2} F_2 - \cdots - \frac{X_k \cdot F_{k-1}}{\|F_{k-1}\|^2} F_{k-1}$$
$$\vdots$$

for each $k = 2, 3, \cdots, m$. Then:

(1) $\{F_1, F_2, \cdots, F_m\}$ is an orthogonal basis of U.
(2) $span\{F_1, F_2, \cdots, F_k\} = span\{X_1, X_2, \cdots, X_k\}$ for each $k = 1, 2, \cdots, m$.

Example 8

Find an orthogonal basis for $span\{[1 \quad 1 \quad 0 \quad 1], [0 \quad 1 \quad -1 \quad 1], [1 \quad 0 \quad 1 \quad 1]\}$.

SOLUTION

Write $X_1 = [1 \quad 1 \quad 0 \quad 1]$, $X_2 = [0 \quad 1 \quad -1 \quad 1]$, and $X_3 = [1 \quad 0 \quad 1 \quad 1]$, and observe that $\{X_1, X_2, X_3\}$ is linearly independent. The Gram-Schmidt Algorithm gives:

$$F_1 = X_1 = [1 \quad 1 \quad 0 \quad 1].$$
$$F_2 = X_2 - \frac{X_2 \cdot F_1}{\|F_1\|^2} F_1 = [0 \quad 1 \quad -1 \quad 1] - \tfrac{2}{3}[1 \quad 1 \quad 0 \quad 1]$$
$$= \tfrac{1}{3}[-2 \quad 1 \quad -3 \quad 1].$$
$$F_3 = X_3 - \frac{X_3 \cdot F_1}{\|F_1\|^2} F_1 - \frac{X_3 \cdot F_2}{\|F_2\|^2} F_2$$
$$= [1 \quad 0 \quad 1 \quad 1] - \tfrac{2}{3}[1 \quad 1 \quad 0 \quad 1] - \frac{(-4/3)}{(15/9)}\tfrac{1}{3}[-2 \quad 1 \quad -3 \quad 1]$$
$$= \tfrac{1}{5}[-1 \quad -2 \quad 1 \quad 3].$$

Hence the algorithm gives the orthogonal basis $\{[1 \quad 1 \quad 0 \quad 1], \tfrac{1}{3}[-2 \quad 1 \quad -3 \quad 1], \tfrac{1}{5}[-1 \quad -2 \quad 1 \quad 3]\}$. In hand calculations, or for other reasons, it may be convenient to eliminate fractions and common factors, so $\{[1 \quad 1 \quad 0 \quad 1], [-2 \quad 1 \quad -3 \quad 1], [-1 \quad -2 \quad 1 \quad 3]\}$ is also an orthogonal basis. (See the following Note.)

Note on Computation. Observe that the vector $\frac{X \cdot F_i}{\|F_i\|^2} F_i$ in the Gram-Schmidt algorithm is unchanged if F_i is replaced by aF_i for any nonzero scalar a. Hence if a newly constructed F_i is multiplied by a nonzero scalar at some stage of the Gram-Schmidt algorithm, the subsequent F's will be unchanged. This is useful in actual calculations. As an illustration, in Example 8 we could have used $F_2 = [-2 \quad 1 \quad -3 \quad 1]$ at the second stage of the algorithm. This would have made the hand calculation of F_3 easier, but there is another reason: Because computing F_2 involved a division (by 3 in Example 8), a computer would have carried some round-off error into the calculation of F_3. In a large calculation, this round-off error can accumulate and become a serious problem.

---

[11] Erhardt Schmidt (1876–1959) was a German mathematician who first described the algorithm in 1907. Jörgen Pederson Gram (1850–1916) was a Danish actuary.

4.5.4 QR-Factorization

We conclude this section with the matrix version of the Gram-Schmidt process. The result is a factorization of any matrix with independent columns as the product of a matrix with *orthonormal* columns and an invertible upper triangular matrix with positive diagonal entries. This is important in applications, and is particularly useful in calculations because there are computer algorithms that accomplish the decomposition with good control over round-off error.

Suppose $A = [C_1 \ \ C_2 \ \ \cdots, \ C_n]$ is an $m \times n$ matrix with linearly independent columns $C_1, \ C_2, \ \cdots, \ C_n$. The Gram-Schmidt algorithm can be applied to these columns to provide orthogonal columns $F_1, \ F_2, \ \cdots, \ F_n$ where

$$
\begin{aligned}
F_1 &= C_1 \\
F_2 &= C_2 - \frac{C_2 \cdot F_1}{\|F_1\|^2} F_1 \\
F_3 &= C_3 - \frac{C_3 \cdot F_1}{\|F_1\|^2} F_1 - \frac{C_3 \cdot F_2}{\|F_2\|^2} F_2 \\
&\ \ \vdots \\
F_n &= C_n - \frac{C_n \cdot F_1}{\|F_1\|^2} F_1 - \frac{C_n \cdot F_2}{\|F_2\|^2} F_2 - \cdots - \frac{C_n \cdot F_{n-1}}{\|F_{n-1}\|^2} F_{n-1}.
\end{aligned}
$$

Now write $Q_j = \frac{1}{\|F_j\|} F_j$ for each j. Then $Q_1, \ Q_2, \ \cdots, \ Q_n$ are orthonormal columns, and the above equations become

$$
\begin{aligned}
\|F_1\| Q_1 &= C_1 \\
\|F_2\| Q_2 &= C_2 - (C_2 \cdot Q_1) Q_1 \\
\|F_3\| Q_3 &= C_3 - (C_3 \cdot Q_1) Q_1 - (C_3 \cdot Q_2) Q_2 \\
&\ \ \vdots \\
\|F_n\| Q_n &= C_n - (C_n \cdot Q_1) Q_1 - (C_n \cdot Q_2) Q_2 - \cdots - (C_n \cdot Q_{n-1}) Q_{n-1}.
\end{aligned}
$$

Finally, use these equations to express each C_k as a linear combination of $Q_1, \ Q_2, \ \cdots, \ Q_n$:

$$
\begin{aligned}
C_1 &= \|F_1\| Q_1 \\
C_2 &= (C_2 \cdot Q_1) Q_1 + \|F_2\| Q_2 \\
C_3 &= (C_3 \cdot Q_1) Q_1 + (C_3 \cdot Q_2) Q_2 + \|F_3\| Q_3 \\
&\ \ \vdots \\
C_n &= (C_n \cdot Q_1) Q_1 + (C_n \cdot Q_2) Q_2 + (C_n \cdot Q_3) Q_3 + \cdots + \|F_n\| Q_n.
\end{aligned}
$$

Using block multiplication (Theorem 3 §1.4), these equations have a matrix form that gives the required factorization:

$$
\begin{aligned}
A &= [C_1 \ \ C_2 \ \ C_3 \ \ \cdots \ \ C_n] \\
&= [Q_1 \ \ Q_2 \ \ Q_3 \ \ \cdots \ \ Q_n]
\begin{bmatrix}
\|F_1\| & C_2 \cdot Q_1 & C_3 \cdot Q_1 & \cdots & C_n \cdot Q_1 \\
0 & \|F_2\| & C_3 \cdot Q_2 & \cdots & C_n \cdot Q_2 \\
0 & 0 & \|F_3\| & \cdots & C_n \cdot Q_3 \\
\vdots & \vdots & \vdots & \ddots & \vdots \\
0 & 0 & 0 & \cdots & \|F_n\|
\end{bmatrix}
\end{aligned} \qquad (*)
$$

Here the first factor $Q = [Q_1 \ \ Q_2 \ \ Q_3 \ \ \cdots \ \ Q_n]$ has orthonormal columns, and the second factor is an $n \times n$ upper triangular matrix R with positive diagonal entries (and so is invertible). We record this in the following theorem (the proof of uniqueness is deferred to the end of this section).

THEOREM 9 **QR-Factorization.** If A is an $m \times n$ matrix with linearly independent columns, then A can be factored as

$$A = QR$$

where Q is an $m \times n$ matrix with orthonormal columns, and R is an invertible, upper triangular matrix with positive entries on the main diagonal. Furthermore, this factorization is unique in the sense that if $A = Q_1 R_1$ is another such factorization, then $Q_1 = Q$ and $R_1 = R$.

If a matrix A has independent rows and we apply QR-factorization to A^T, the result is:

COROLLARY If A has independent rows, then $A = LP$ where P has orthonormal rows and L is an invertible lower triangular matrix with positive main diagonal entries.

Example 9 Find the QR-factorization of $A = \begin{bmatrix} 1 & 1 & 0 \\ -1 & 0 & 1 \\ 0 & 1 & 1 \\ 0 & 0 & 1 \end{bmatrix}$.

SOLUTION The columns of A are $C_1 = [1 \ -1 \ 0 \ 0]^T$, $C_2 = [1 \ 0 \ 1 \ 0]^T$, and $C_3 = [0 \ 1 \ 1 \ 1]^T$. It is easy to verify that $\{C_1, C_2, C_3\}$ is independent so, if we apply the Gram-Schmidt algorithm to these columns C_i, the result is

$$\begin{aligned} F_1 &= C_1 & &= [1 \ -1 \ 0 \ 0]^T \\ F_2 &= C_2 - \tfrac{1}{2}F_1 & &= [\tfrac{1}{2} \ \tfrac{1}{2} \ 1 \ 0]^T \\ F_3 &= C_3 + \tfrac{1}{2}F_1 - F_2 & &= [0 \ 0 \ 0 \ 1]^T \end{aligned}$$

Hence let $Q_j = \frac{1}{\|F_j\|} F_j$ for each j. Then equation $(*)$ preceding Theorem 9 gives $A = QR$ where

$$Q = [Q_1 \ \ Q_2 \ \ Q_2] = \begin{bmatrix} \frac{1}{\sqrt{2}} & \frac{1}{\sqrt{6}} & 0 \\ \frac{-1}{\sqrt{2}} & \frac{1}{\sqrt{6}} & 0 \\ 0 & \frac{2}{\sqrt{6}} & 0 \\ 0 & 0 & 1 \end{bmatrix} = \frac{1}{\sqrt{6}} \begin{bmatrix} \sqrt{3} & 1 & 0 \\ -\sqrt{3} & 1 & 0 \\ 0 & 2 & 0 \\ 0 & 0 & \sqrt{6} \end{bmatrix},$$

$$R = \begin{bmatrix} \|F_1\| & C_2 \cdot Q_1 & C_3 \cdot Q_1 \\ 0 & \|F_2\| & C_3 \cdot Q_2 \\ 0 & 0 & \|F_3\| \end{bmatrix} = \begin{bmatrix} \sqrt{2} & \frac{1}{\sqrt{2}} & \frac{-1}{\sqrt{2}} \\ 0 & \frac{\sqrt{3}}{\sqrt{2}} & \frac{\sqrt{3}}{\sqrt{2}} \\ 0 & 0 & 1 \end{bmatrix}$$

$$= \frac{1}{\sqrt{2}} \begin{bmatrix} 2 & 1 & -1 \\ 0 & \sqrt{3} & \sqrt{3} \\ 0 & 0 & \sqrt{2} \end{bmatrix}.$$

The reader can verify that indeed $A = QR$.

Remark. If an $m \times n$ matrix A has independent columns, then $A^T A$ is invertible (by Theorem 3 §4.4), and it is often desirable to compute the inverse of $A^T A$ (see Section 4.6 for example). This is simplified if we have a QR-factorization of A (and is one of the main reasons for the importance of Theorem 9). For if $A = QR$ is such a factorization, then $Q^T Q = I_n$ because Q has orthonormal columns (verify), so we obtain

$$A^T A = R^T Q^T Q R = R^T R.$$

Hence computing $(A^T A)^{-1}$ amounts to finding R^{-1}, and this is a routine matter because R is upper triangular. Thus the difficulty in computing $(A^T A)^{-1}$ lies in obtaining the QR-factorization of A.

A major virtue of orthogonal matrices is that they are easy to invert—simply take the transpose. This makes the $n \times n$ version of the QR-factorization (Theorem 9 §4.5) even more useful. We restate it here for reference.

THEOREM 4

QR-Factorization. Every invertible matrix A can be factored as
$$A = QR$$
where Q is an orthogonal matrix and R is an invertible, upper triangular matrix with positive entries on the main diagonal. Furthermore, this factorization is unique in the sense that if $A = Q_1 R_1$ is another such factorization then $Q_1 = Q$ and $R_1 = R$.

It is important to note that a systematic procedure for finding QR-factorizations is available using the Gram-Schmidt algorithm—see the discussion preceding Theorem 9 §4.5, and other good numerical algorithms which are available.

4.7.2 The Principal Axis Theorem

Recall that an $n \times n$ matrix A is said to be diagonalizable if $P^{-1}AP$ is a diagonal matrix for some invertible matrix P. By analogy, A is called **orthogonally diagonalizable** if an orthogonal matrix P can be found such that
$$P^{-1}AP = P^T AP \text{ is a diagonal matrix.}$$

The Principal Axis theorem asserts that every symmetric matrix is orthogonally diagonalizable (and conversely). The proof requires an important lemma which formalizes a technique that is basic to diagonalization, and which will be used three times below.

LEMMA 1

Let $\{X_1, X_2, \cdots, X_k\}$ be a linearly independent set of eigenvectors of an $n \times n$ matrix A, extend it to a basis $\{X_1, X_2, \cdots, X_k, \cdots, X_n\}$ of $\mathbb{R}^n$, and let
$$P = [X_1 \ X_2 \ \cdots \ X_n]$$
be the (invertible) matrix with the X_i as its columns. If $\lambda_1, \lambda_2, \cdots, \lambda_k$ are the (not necessarily distinct) eigenvalues of A corresponding to $X_1, X_2, \cdots, X_k$ respectively, then $P^{-1}AP$ has block form
$$P^{-1}AP = \begin{bmatrix} diag(\lambda_1, \lambda_2, \cdots, \lambda_k) & B \\ 0 & A_1 \end{bmatrix}$$
where B and A_1 are matrices of size $k \times (n-k)$ and $(n-k) \times (n-k)$ respectively.

PROOF

If $\{E_1, E_2, \cdots, E_n\}$ is the standard basis of $\mathbb{R}^n$, note that PE_i is column i of P for each i, that is $PE_i = X_i$. Hence $P^{-1}X_i = E_i$ for each $1 \le i \le n$. On the other hand, observe that
$$P^{-1}AP = P^{-1}A[X_1 \ X_2 \ \cdots \ X_n] = [P^{-1}AX_1 \ P^{-1}AX_2 \ \cdots \ P^{-1}AX_n].$$
Hence, if $1 \le i \le k$, column i of $P^{-1}AP$ is
$$(P^{-1}A)X_i = P^{-1}(\lambda_i X_i) = \lambda_i(P^{-1}X_i) = \lambda_i E_i.$$
This describes the first k columns of $P^{-1}AP$, and Lemma 1 follows.

Note that Lemma 1 (with $k = n$) shows that an $n \times n$ matrix A is diagonalizable if $\mathbb{R}^n$ has a basis of eigenvectors of A, as in part (1) of Theorem 1.

We can now prove one of the most useful results in linear algebra.

THEOREM 5   **Principal Axis Theorem**. The following are equivalent for an $n \times n$ matrix A:

(1) A is orthogonally diagonalizable.

(2) A has an orthonormal set of n eigenvectors.

(3) A is symmetric.

PROOF $(1) \Leftrightarrow (2)$. Let $P = [X_1 \ \cdots \ X_n]$ be an invertible $n \times n$ matrix with columns X_i. As in the discussion preceeding Theorem 3 §2.3, $(1) \Leftrightarrow (2)$ follows from the following statements: P is orthogonal if and only if $\{X_1, \ \cdots, \ X_n\}$ is an orthonormal set in $\mathbb{R}^n$; and $P^{-1}AP$ is diagonal if and only if $\{X_1, \ \cdots, \ X_n\}$ is a basis of eigenvectors of A.

$(1) \Rightarrow (3)$. Let $P^TAP = D$ where D is diagonal and $P^{-1} = P^T$. Then $A = PDP^T$ so, since D is symmetric, we have $A^T = P^{TT}D^TP^T = PDP^T = A$. This proves (3).

$(3) \Rightarrow (1)$. Let A be an $n \times n$ symmetric matrix; we prove (1) by induction on n. If $n = 1$, then (1) is clear. In general, since A is symmetric let λ_1 be a real eigenvalue of A (Theorem 3 §2.5), and let $AX_1 = \lambda_1 X_1$ for some eigenvector X_1 in $\mathbb{R}^n$ which we may assume satisfies $\|X_1\| = 1$. Use the Gram-Schmidt algorithm to find an orthonormal basis $\{X_1, X_2, \cdots, X_n\}$ of $\mathbb{R}^n$ containing this eigenvector X_1. Then $P_1 = [X_1 \ \ X_2 \ \cdots \ X_n]$ is an orthogonal matrix and

$$P_1^TAP_1 = P_1^{-1}AP_1 = \begin{bmatrix} \lambda_1 & B \\ 0 & A_1 \end{bmatrix}$$

in block form by Lemma 1. But $P_1^TAP_1$ is symmetric (because A is), so it follows that $B = 0$ and A_1 is symmetric of size $(n-1) \times (n-1)$. Hence, by induction, there exists an orthogonal $(n-1) \times (n-1)$ matrix Q such that $Q^TA_1Q = D_1$ is diagonal. But then $P_2 = \begin{bmatrix} 1 & 0 \\ 0 & Q \end{bmatrix}$ is an orthogonal matrix, and

$$(P_1P_2)^TA(P_1P_2) = P_2^T(P_1^TAP_1)P_2$$
$$= \begin{bmatrix} 1 & 0 \\ 0 & Q^T \end{bmatrix}\begin{bmatrix} \lambda_1 & 0 \\ 0 & A_1 \end{bmatrix}\begin{bmatrix} 1 & 0 \\ 0 & Q \end{bmatrix}$$
$$= \begin{bmatrix} \lambda_1 & 0 \\ 0 & D_1 \end{bmatrix}$$

is diagonal. Since P_1P_2 is orthogonal (Corollary to Theorem 2), this proves (1).

A set of n orthonormal eigenvectors for a symmetric matrix A is is called a set of **principal axes** for A. The name comes from geometry, and will be clarified in Section 4.8 when we discuss quadratic forms.

Example 3   If $A = \begin{bmatrix} 1 & 0 & 2 \\ 0 & 1 & -1 \\ 2 & -1 & 5 \end{bmatrix}$, find an orthogonal matrix P such that P^TAP is diagonal.

SOLUTION   The procedure is exactly the same as for diagonalizing A. The characteristic polynomial of A is $c_A(x) = x(x-1)(x-6)$, so A has eigenvalues $\lambda_1 = 0$, $\lambda_2 = 1$ and $\lambda_3 = 6$, with corresponding eigenvectors $X_1 = [-2 \ \ 1 \ \ 1]^T$, $X_2 = [1 \ \ 2 \ \ 0]^T$ and $X_3 = [2 \ \ -1 \ \ 5]^T$. Surprisingly, these eigenvectors are orthogonal. Hence, after normalizing, we obtain a set $\left\{ \frac{1}{\sqrt{6}}X_1, \ \frac{1}{\sqrt{5}}X_2, \ \frac{1}{\sqrt{30}}X_3 \right\}$ of principal axes for A. These yield the orthogonal matrix

$$P = \begin{bmatrix} \frac{1}{\sqrt{6}}X_1 & \frac{1}{\sqrt{5}}X_2 & \frac{1}{\sqrt{30}}X_3 \end{bmatrix} = \frac{1}{\sqrt{30}}\begin{bmatrix} -2\sqrt{5} & \sqrt{6} & 2 \\ \sqrt{5} & 2\sqrt{6} & -1 \\ \sqrt{5} & 0 & 5 \end{bmatrix}.$$

This matrix P is a diagonalizing matrix for A (which happens to be orthogonal), and so $P^TAP = P^{-1}AP = diag(\lambda_1, \ \lambda_2, \ \lambda_3) = diag(0, \ 1, \ 6)$.

The fact that the eigenvectors in Example 3 were orthogonal is no coincidence: The fact that the matrix is *symmetric* forces them to be orthogonal. To see why, we need the following fact about symmetric matrices.

LEMMA 2

If A is a symmetric $n \times n$ matrix in $\mathbb{R}^n$, then $(AX) \cdot Y = X \cdot (AY)$ for all columns X and Y in $\mathbb{R}^n$.

PROOF

We have $A^T = A$ so $(AX) \cdot Y = (AX)^T Y = X^T A^T Y = X^T (AY) = X \cdot (AY)$.

THEOREM 6

If A is a symmetric matrix, then eigenvectors of A corresponding to distinct eigenvalues are orthogonal.

PROOF

Suppose that $AX = \lambda X$ and $AY = \mu Y$ where $\lambda \neq \mu$ are distinct eigenvalues. Then Lemma 2 gives

$$\lambda(X \cdot Y) = (\lambda X) \cdot Y = (AX) \cdot Y = X \cdot (AY) = X \cdot (\mu Y) = \mu(X \cdot Y).$$

Hence $(\lambda - \mu)(X \cdot Y) = 0$, so $X \cdot Y = 0$ because $\lambda \neq \mu$.

If λ is an eigenvalue of an $n \times n$ matrix A, write

$$E_\lambda(A) = \{X \ in \ \mathbb{R}^n | \ AX = \lambda X\}.$$

This is a subspace of $\mathbb{R}^n$ called the eigenspace of A corresponding to λ, and the eigenvectors corresponding to λ are just the nonzero members of $E_\lambda(A)$.[16] In fact, $E_\lambda(A)$ is the null space of the matrix $\lambda I - A$:

$$E_\lambda(A) = \{X \ in \ \mathbb{R}^n | \ (\lambda I - A)X = 0\} = null(\lambda I - A),$$

so (by Theorem 6 §4.4) the basic solutions of the linear system $(\lambda I - A)X = 0$ form a basis of $E_\lambda(A)$. Of course the eigenvalues λ of A are the roots of the characteristic polynomial $c_A(x)$ of A, defined by

$$c_A(x) = det(xI - A).$$

With this and Theorem 6, the process for orthogonally diagonalizing a symmetric $n \times n$ matrix is a straightforward extension of the diagonalization procedure given in Section 2.3.

Orthogonal Diagonalization Algorithm

To diagonalize an $n \times n$ symmetric matrix A:

Step 1. Find the distinct eigenvalues λ.

Step 2. Obtain a basis for each eigenspace $E_\lambda(A)$ as the basic solutions of $(\lambda I - A)X = 0$.

Step 3. Obtain an orthonormal basis of each $E_\lambda(A)$ using the Gram-Schmidt procedure if necessary.

Step 4. The set of all the eigenvectors obtained in Step 3 is an orthonormal basis of $\mathbb{R}^n$ by Theorem 5.

Step 5. If P is the orthogonal matrix with the basis in Step 4 as its columns, then $P^T AP$ is diagonal.

Example 4

Orthogonally diagonalize the symmetric matrix

$$A = \begin{bmatrix} 5 & -2 & 4 \\ -2 & 8 & 2 \\ 4 & 2 & 5 \end{bmatrix}.$$

SOLUTION

The characteristic polynomial is $c_A(x) = x(x - 9)^2$, so the eigenvalues are $\lambda_1 = 0$ and $\lambda_2 = 9$. Bases for the eigenspaces are

---

[16] Note that $E_\lambda(A)$ is a subspace for *any* number λ; the eigenvalues are the numbers λ for which $E_\lambda(A) \neq 0$.

$E_{\lambda_1}(A) = span\{[2 \ \ 1 \ \ -2]^T\}$ and $E_{\lambda_2}(A) = span\{[1 \ \ -2 \ \ 0]^T, \ [1 \ \ 0 \ \ 1]^T\}$.

Note that $[2 \ \ 1 \ \ -2]^T$ from $E_{\lambda_1}(A)$ is orthogonal to both vectors $[1 \ \ -2 \ \ 0]^T$ and $[1 \ \ 0 \ \ 1]^T$ in $E_{\lambda_2}(A)$, as Theorem 6 guarantees, but this basis of $E_{\lambda_2}(A)$ is not orthogonal. Applying the Gram-Schmidt algorithm yields an orthogonal basis: $E_{\lambda_2}(A) = span\{[1 \ \ -2 \ \ 0]^T, \ [4 \ \ 2 \ \ 5]^T\}$. Hence $\{[2 \ \ 1 \ \ -2]^T, \ [1 \ \ -2 \ \ 0]^T, \ [4 \ \ 2 \ \ 5]^T\}$ is an orthogonal basis of $\mathbb{R}^3$ consisting of eigenvectors of A, whence normalization gives the orthonormal basis (principal axes for A)

$$\left\{\tfrac{1}{3}[2 \ \ 1 \ \ -2]^T, \ \tfrac{1}{\sqrt{5}}[1 \ \ -2 \ \ 0]^T, \ \tfrac{1}{3\sqrt{5}}[4 \ \ 2 \ \ 5]^T\right\}.$$

Hence $P = \begin{bmatrix} \frac{2}{3} & \frac{1}{\sqrt{5}} & \frac{4}{3\sqrt{5}} \\ \frac{1}{3} & \frac{-2}{\sqrt{5}} & \frac{2}{3\sqrt{5}} \\ \frac{-2}{3} & 0 & \frac{5}{3\sqrt{5}} \end{bmatrix} = \frac{1}{3\sqrt{5}}\begin{bmatrix} 2\sqrt{5} & 3 & 4 \\ \sqrt{5} & -6 & 2 \\ -2\sqrt{5} & 0 & 5 \end{bmatrix}$ is an orthogonal matrix such that

$P^T A P = P^{-1} A P = diag(0, \ 9, \ 9)$.

4.7.3   Triangulation

If we substitute "*upper triangular*" for "*diagonal*" in the Principal Axis theorem, we can weaken the requirement that A is symmetric to asking only that all the eigenvalues are real. The proof is virtually the same.

THEOREM 7

Triangulation Theorem. If A is a square matrix with real eigenvalues, there exists an orthogonal matrix P such that $P^T A P$ is upper triangular.

PROOF

If A is an $n \times n$ matrix with real eigenvalues, the proof of $(3) \Rightarrow (1)$ of Theorem 5 goes through except that B need not be zero and D_1 is upper triangular, not diagonal. We leave the details to the reader.

Unfortunately, Theorem 7 provides no systematic way to find the matrix P. An algorithm exists which is a refinement of the method for orthogonal diagonalization.[17] Even so, the theorem is useful as it stands and reveals important information about the determinant and trace of a matrix.

Here the **trace** trA of an $n \times n$ matrix A is defined to be the sum of the main diagonal elements of A, in other words:

If $A = [a_{ij}]$, then $trA = a_{11} + a_{22} + \cdots + a_{nn}$.

It is evident that $tr(A + B) = trA + trB$ and that $tr(cA) = c \, trA$ holds for all $n \times n$ matrices A and B, and all scalars c. The following fact is more surprising.

LEMMA 3

Let A and B be $n \times n$ matrices. Then:

(1) $tr(AB) = tr(BA)$.

(2) If P is an invertible matrix, then $tr(P^{-1}AP) = trA$.

PROOF

Write $A = [a_{ij}]$ and $B = [b_{ij}]$. Then the $(i, \ i)$-entry of AB is $d_i = a_{i1}b_{1i} + a_{i2}b_{2i} + \cdots + a_{in}b_{ni} = \Sigma_j a_{ij}b_{ji}$. Hence

$$tr(AB) = d_1 + d_2 + \cdots + d_n = \Sigma_i d_i = \Sigma_i(\Sigma_j a_{ij}b_{ji}).$$

Similarly we have $tr(BA) = \Sigma_i(\Sigma_j b_{ij}a_{ji})$. Since these two double sums are the same, this proves (1). Then (2) follows from (1) because $tr(P^{-1}AP) = tr[P^{-1}(AP)] = tr[(AP)P^{-1}] = trA$.

---

[17] See W.K. Nicholson, *Linear Algebra with Applications*, 4th ed., McGraw-Hill Ryerson, Section 8.7.

Our reason for looking at Lemma 3 here is that it gives the first part of

THEOREM 8 Let A be an $n \times n$ matrix with real eigenvalues $\lambda_1, \lambda_2, \cdots, \lambda_n$ (possibly not all distinct). Then
$$tr A = \lambda_1 + \lambda_2 + \cdots + \lambda_n \quad \text{and} \quad det A = \lambda_1 \lambda_2 \cdots \lambda_n.$$

PROOF By Theorem 7, let P be a matrix (in fact, orthogonal) such that $P^{-1}AP = U$ is upper triangular. Then $tr A = tr U$ (by Lemma 3) and $det A = det U$. The result now follows because U has the same eigenvalues as A (Theorem 6 §2.3), so they appear on the main diagonal of U.

4.7.4 Diagonalization Revisited

There are two results in Section 2.3 (Theorems 4 and 5) that could not be proved using the methods available there. In this concluding section we use our present techniques to derive (and, in one case, extend) these theorems.

Theorem 4 §2.3 asserts (without proof) that an $n \times n$ matrix A is diagonalizable if it has n distinct eigenvalues. The next result explains (and extends) this by revealing an important connection between eigenvalues and linear independence: Eigenvectors corresponding to distinct eigenvalues are necessarily linearly independent.

THEOREM 9 Let $X_1, X_2, \cdots, X_k$ be eigenvectors corresponding to distinct eigenvalues $\lambda_1, \lambda_2, \cdots, \lambda_k$ of an $n \times n$ matrix A. Then $\{X_1, X_2, \cdots, X_k\}$ is a linearly independent set.

PROOF We use induction on k. If $k = 1$, then $\{X_1\}$ is independent because $X_1 \neq 0$. In general, suppose the theorem is true for some $k > 0$. Given eigenvectors $\{X_1, X_2, \cdots, X_{k+1}\}$, suppose a linear combination vanishes:
$$t_1 X_1 + t_2 X_2 + \cdots + t_{k+1} X_{k+1} = 0. \tag{$*$}$$
We must show that each $t_i = 0$. Left multiply $(*)$ by A and use the fact that $AX_i = \lambda_i X_i$ to get
$$t_1 \lambda_1 X_1 + t_2 \lambda_2 X_2 + \cdots + t_{k+1} \lambda_{k+1} X_{k+1} = 0. \tag{$**$}$$
If we multiply $(*)$ by λ_1 and subtract the result from $(**)$, the first terms cancel and we obtain
$$t_2(\lambda_2 - \lambda_1)X_2 + t_3(\lambda_3 - \lambda_1)X_3 + \cdots + t_{k+1}(\lambda_{k+1} - \lambda_1)X_{k+1} = 0.$$
Since $\{X_2, X_3, \cdots, X_{k+1}\}$ is independent by the induction hypothesis, this gives
$$t_2(\lambda_2 - \lambda_1) = 0, \ t_3(\lambda_3 - \lambda_1) = 0, \ \cdots, \ t_{k+1}(\lambda_{k+1} - \lambda_1) = 0,$$
and so $t_2 = t_3 = \cdots = t_{k+1} = 0$ because the λ_i are distinct. Hence $(*)$ becomes $t_1 X_1 = 0$, which implies that $t_1 = 0$ because $X_1 \neq 0$. This is what we wanted.

Theorem 9 completes some unfinished business from Section 2.3.

COROLLARY **(Theorem 4, Section 2.3.)** If A is an $n \times n$ matrix with n distinct eigenvalues, then A is diagonalizable.

PROOF Choose one eigenvector for each of the n distinct eigenvalues. Then these eigenvectors are independent by Theorem 9, and so are a basis of $\mathbb{R}^n$ by Theorem 3 §4.3. Now use Theorem 1.

Recall that the *multiplicity* of an eigenvalue λ of A is the number of times λ occurs as a root of the characteristic polynomial $c_A(x)$. In other words,[18] the multiplicity of λ is

---
[18] See Appendix A.3.

the largest integer $m \geq 1$ such that $c_A(x) = (x - \lambda)^m g(x)$ for some polynomial $g(x)$. The assertion (without proof) in Theorem 5 §2.3 is that a square matrix is diagonalizable if and only if the multiplicity of each eigenvalue λ equals $dim[E_\lambda(A)]$. We are going to prove this, and the proof requires the following result which is valid for *any* square matrix, diagonalizable or not.

LEMMA 4   Let λ be an eigenvalue of multiplicity m of a square matrix A. Then $dim[E_\lambda(A)] \leq m$.

PROOF   Write $dim[E_\lambda(A)] = d$. By the definition of multiplicity, it suffices to show that $c_A(x) = (x - \lambda)^d g(x)$ for some polynomial $g(x)$. To this end, let $\{X_1, X_2, \cdots, X_d\}$ be a basis of $E_\lambda(A)$. Then Lemma 1 shows that an invertible $n \times n$ matrix P exists such that

$$P^{-1}AP = \begin{bmatrix} \lambda I_d & B \\ 0 & A_1 \end{bmatrix}$$

in block form, where I_d denotes the $d \times d$ identity matrix. Now write $A' = P^{-1}AP$ and observe that $c_{A'}(x) = c_A(x)$ by Theorem 6 §2.3. But Theorem 3 §2.2 gives

$$c_{A'}(x) = det(xI_n - A')$$
$$= det\begin{bmatrix} (x-\lambda)I_d & -B \\ 0 & xI_{n-d} - A_1 \end{bmatrix}$$
$$= det[(x - \lambda)I_d] det[xI_{n-d} - A_1]$$
$$= (x - \lambda)^d c_{A_1}(x).$$

Hence $c_A(x) = c_{A'}(x) = (x - \lambda)^d g(x)$ where $g(x) = c_{A_1}(x)$. This is what we wanted.

It is impossible to ignore the question when equality holds in Lemma 4 for each eigenvalue λ. It turns out that this characterizes the diagonalizable matrices. This is the second piece of unfinished business from Section 2.3.

THEOREM 10   (**Theorem 5, Section 2.3.**) The following are equivalent for a square matrix A:

    (**1**) A is diagonalizable.

    (**2**) $dim[E_\lambda(A)]$ equals the multiplicity of λ for every eigenvalue λ of A.

PROOF   Let $\lambda_1, \lambda_2, \cdots, \lambda_k$ be the distinct eigenvalues of A and, for each i, let m_i denote the multiplicity of λ_i and write $d_i = dim[E_{\lambda_i}(A)]$. Then $c_A(x) = (x - \lambda_1)^{m_1}(x - \lambda_2)^{m_2} \cdots (x - \lambda_k)^{m_k}$ so $m_1 + \cdots + m_k = n$. Moreover, $d_i \leq m_i$ for each i by Lemma 4.

(1)$\Rightarrow$(2). By (1), $\mathbb{R}^n$ has a basis of n eigenvectors of A, so let t_i of them lie in $E_{\lambda_i}(A)$ for each i. Then $t_i \leq d_i$ for each i and so

$$n = t_1 + \cdots + t_k \leq d_1 + \cdots + d_k \leq m_1 + \cdots + m_k = n.$$

Hence $d_1 + \cdots + d_k = m_1 + \cdots + m_k$ so, since $d_i \leq m_i$ for each i, we must have $d_i = m_i$. This is (2).

(2)$\Rightarrow$(1). Let B_i denote a basis of $E_{\lambda_i}(A)$ for each i, and let $B = B_1 \cup \cdots \cup B_k$. Since each B_i contains m_i vectors by (2), and since the B_i are pairwise disjoint (the λ_i are distinct), it follows that B contains n vectors. So it suffices to show that B is linearly independent (then B is a basis of $\mathbb{R}^n$). Suppose a linear combination of the vectors in B vanishes, and let Y_i denote the sum of all terms that come from B_i. Then Y_i lies in $E_{\lambda_i}(A)$ for each i, so the nonzero Y_i are independent by Theorem 2 (as the λ_i are distinct). Since the sum of the Y_i is zero, it follows that $Y_i = 0$ for each i. Hence all coefficients of terms in Y_i are zero (because B_i is independent). This shows that B is independent.

Examples of how Theorem 3 is used can be found in Section 2.3.

Exercises 4.7

1. In each case either show that the statement is true or give an example showing that it is false.
   a) Every eigenvalue of a matrix has a unit eigenvector (that is one of length 1).
   b) If P has orthogonal columns and $det\ P = \pm 1$, then P is orthogonal.
   c) Every orthogonal matrix is invertible.
   d) Every orthogonal matrix is symmetric.
   e) Every diagonal matrix is orthogonal.
   f) If A is symmetric, then $P^T A P$ is also symmetric for all matrices P.

2. By normalizing the columns, make each of the following matrices orthogonal.

   a) $\begin{bmatrix} 2 & -2 \\ 1 & 4 \end{bmatrix}$ **b)** $\begin{bmatrix} 3 & 4 \\ -4 & 3 \end{bmatrix}$

   c) $\begin{bmatrix} \cos\theta & -\sin\theta & 0 \\ \sin\theta & \cos\theta & 0 \\ 0 & 0 & 3 \end{bmatrix}$ **d)** $\begin{bmatrix} 1 & 0 & 2 \\ -1 & 1 & 1 \\ 1 & 1 & -1 \end{bmatrix}$

   e) $\begin{bmatrix} -1 & 2 & 2 \\ 2 & -1 & 2 \\ 2 & 2 & -1 \end{bmatrix}$ **f)** $\begin{bmatrix} 2 & 3 & -6 \\ 6 & 2 & 3 \\ -3 & 6 & 2 \end{bmatrix}$

3. If the first two rows of an orthogonal matrix are $\begin{bmatrix} \frac{1}{3} & \frac{2}{3} & \frac{2}{3} \end{bmatrix}$ and $\begin{bmatrix} \frac{2}{3} & \frac{-2}{3} & \frac{1}{3} \end{bmatrix}$, find all possible third rows.

4. If $\{X_1, X_2, \cdots, X_n\}$ is an orthonormal basis of $\mathbb{R}^n$, find all Y in $\mathbb{R}^n$ such that $\{Y, X_2, \cdots, X_n\}$ is an orthonormal basis of $\mathbb{R}^n$. [Hint: Expand Y in terms of $\{X_1, X_2, \cdots, X_n\}$ by the Expansion theorem.]

5. For each matrix A, find an orthogonal matrix P such that $P^T A P$ is diagonal.

   a) $A = \begin{bmatrix} 3 & 0 & 0 \\ 0 & 2 & 2 \\ 0 & 2 & 5 \end{bmatrix}$ **b)** $A = \begin{bmatrix} 3 & 0 & 7 \\ 0 & 5 & 0 \\ 7 & 0 & 3 \end{bmatrix}$

   c) $A = \begin{bmatrix} 3 & 3 & 0 \\ 3 & 3 & 0 \\ 0 & 0 & 6 \end{bmatrix}$ **d)** $A = \begin{bmatrix} 1 & 3 & 0 \\ 3 & 13 & 2 \\ 0 & 2 & 1 \end{bmatrix}$

   e) $A = \begin{bmatrix} 3 & 5 & 0 & 0 \\ 5 & 3 & 0 & 0 \\ 0 & 0 & 1 & 7 \\ 0 & 0 & 7 & 1 \end{bmatrix}$ **f)** $A = \begin{bmatrix} 3 & 5 & -1 & 1 \\ 5 & 3 & 1 & -1 \\ -1 & 1 & 3 & 5 \\ 1 & -1 & 5 & 3 \end{bmatrix}$

6. If P is an orthogonal matrix and c is a scalar, show that cP is orthogonal if and only if $c = \pm 1$.

7. If P is a triangular, orthogonal matrix, show that P is diagonal and each diagonal entry is 1 or -1. [Hint: If P is $n \times n$, induct on n. Write $P = \begin{bmatrix} a & X \\ 0 & Q \end{bmatrix}$ in block form.]

8. An $n \times n$ matrix P is called a **permutation matrix** if the columns of P are just the columns of I_n in some order.

   a) Show that every permutation matrix is orthogonal.
   b) Show that the rows of a permutation matrix are the rows of I_n in some order.

9. Show that an $n \times n$ matrix P is orthogonal if and only if $\|PX\| = \|X\|$ for every column X in $\mathbb{R}^n$. [Hint: If $\|PX\| = \|X\|$, replace X by $X + Y$ to show that $(PX) \cdot (PY) = X \cdot Y$ for all X and Y.]

10. Let A be an $m \times n$ matrix with columns $C_1, C_2, \cdots, C_n$. Explain why the (i, j)-entry of $A^T A$ is $C_i \cdot C_j$.

11. Show that the following are equivalent for an $m \times n$ matrix A:
   i) A has orthogonal columns.
   ii) $A = PD$ where P has orthonormal columns and D is diagonal and invertible.
   iii) $A^T A$ is invertible and diagonal.
   [Hint: For (i)$\Rightarrow$(ii) take $D = diag(\|C_1\|, \|C_2\|, \cdots, \|C_n\|)$ where C_j is column j of A. Exercise 10 is useful for **iii)**$\Rightarrow$**i)**.]

12. Show that the following are equivalent for a symmetric matrix A:
   i) A is orthogonal.
   ii) $A^2 = I$.
   iii) The only eigenvalues of A are ± 1.
   [Hint: For **iii)**$\Rightarrow$**ii)** use the Principal Axis theorem.]

13. If the columns $C_1, C_2, \cdots, C_n$ of the $n \times n$ matrix $A = [a_{ij}]$ are orthogonal, show that the (i, j)-entry of A^{-1} is $\frac{a_{ji}}{\|C_i\|^2}$. [Hint: Use Exercise 10 to show that $A^T A = D = diag(\|C_1\|^2, \|C_2\|^2, \cdots, \|C_n\|^2).$]

14. If A is symmetric, show that $\lambda \geq 0$ for every eigenvalue of A if and only if $A = B^2$ for some symmetric matrix B. [Hint: If $P^T A P = D = diag(\lambda_1, \cdots, \lambda_n)$ where $P^{-1} = P^T$ and each $\lambda_i > 0$, take $B = P\ diag(\sqrt{\lambda_1}, \cdots, \sqrt{\lambda_n})P^T.$]

15. Extend Theorem 6 as follows: Let λ and μ be distinct eigenvectors of a square matrix A, and hence of A^T. If X is an eigenvector of A corresponding to λ and Y is an eigenvector of A^T corresponding to μ, show that X and Y are orthogonal.

16. Matrices A and B are called **orthogonally similar** (written $A \overset{\circ}{\sim} B$) if $B = P^T A P$ for some orthogonal matrix P. Hence the Principal Axis theorem asserts that a matrix A is symmetric if and only if $A \overset{\circ}{\sim} D$ for some diagonal matrix D.
   a) Show: (i) $A \overset{\circ}{\sim} A$ for all A; (ii) If $A \overset{\circ}{\sim} B$ then $B \overset{\circ}{\sim} A$; (iii) If $A \overset{\circ}{\sim} B$ and $B \overset{\circ}{\sim} C$, then $A \overset{\circ}{\sim} C$.
   b) If $A \overset{\circ}{\sim} B$, show that $A^T \overset{\circ}{\sim} B^T$.
   c) If A and B are invertible and $A \overset{\circ}{\sim} B$, show that $A^{-1} \overset{\circ}{\sim} B^{-1}$.
   d) If $A \overset{\circ}{\sim} B$, show that A and B have the same eigenvalues. [Hint: Theorem 6 §2.3.]
   e) If A and B are symmetric, show that $A \overset{\circ}{\sim} B$ if and only if A and B have the same eigenvalues.

17. Let A be an $n \times n$ matrix. If $(AX) \cdot Y = X \cdot (AY)$ holds for all columns X and Y in $\mathbb{R}^n$, show that A is symmetric. (Converse to Lemma 2.) [Hint: Show that $(AX) \cdot Y = X \cdot (A^T Y)$ holds for all columns X and Y in $\mathbb{R}^n$. If $X^T BY = 0$ for all columns X and Y, show that $B = 0$ by taking X and Y to be various columns of I_n.]

18. A square matrix E is called a projection matrix if $E^2 = E = E^T$. (See Exercise 20 §4.6.)

  a) If E is a projection matrix, show that $P = I - 2E$ is orthogonal and symmetric.

  b) If P is an orthogonal, symmetric matrix, show that $E = \frac{1}{2}(I - P)$ is a projection matrix.

  c) If Q has orthonormal columns, show that $E = QQ^T$ is a projection matrix.

19. Show that every 2×2 orthogonal matrix has the form $\begin{bmatrix} \cos\theta & -\sin\theta \\ \sin\theta & \cos\theta \end{bmatrix}$ or $\begin{bmatrix} \cos\theta & \sin\theta \\ \sin\theta & -\cos\theta \end{bmatrix}$ for some angle θ. [Hint: See the discussion preceding Theorem 7 §3.5.]

20. A square matrix A is said to be **nilpotent** if $A^k = 0$ for some $k \geq 1$.

  a) If N is a square upper triangular matrix with 0's on the main diagonal, show that N is nilpotent. [Hint: Induct on n where A is $n \times n$.]

  b) If A is nilpotent, show that $P^T AP$ has the form in **a)** for some orthogonal matrix P. [Hint: Theorem 7.]

  c) If A is a square matrix with real eigenvalues, show that $A = S + N$ for some symmetric matrix S and some nilpotent matrix N. [Hint: Theorem 7 and **a)**.]

21. a) If A is nilpotent, show that every eigenvalue of A is zero.

  b) If every eigenvalue of A is zero, use Theorem 7 to show that A is nilpotent.

  c) Show that the only nilpotent, diagonalizable matrix A is $A = 0$.

22. If A is a square matrix with real eigenvalues, show that $Q^T AQ$ is lower triangular for some orthogonal matrix Q.

23. Let $P = \begin{bmatrix} a & -b \\ b & a \end{bmatrix}$ and $Q = \begin{bmatrix} a & -b & -c & -d \\ b & a & -d & c \\ c & d & a & -b \\ d & -c & b & a \end{bmatrix}$. Compute $P^T P$ and $Q^T Q$ and, for each of P and Q, give a necessary and sufficient condition that the matrix is orthogonal. (Matrices of the form P are a representation of the complex numbers—identify $a + bi = \begin{bmatrix} a & -b \\ b & a \end{bmatrix}$. Matrices of the form Q are related in the same way to the **quaternions**, an extension of the complex numbers.)

24. If C is an $n \times n$ matrix with its nonzero columns orthogonal, show that $C = PD$ where P is orthogonal and D is diagonal with nonnegative entries.

4.8   QUADRATIC FORMS [19]

The Principal Axis theorem states that every symmetric matrix can be orthogonally diagonalized. This result has far reaching consequences, some of which are investigated in this section. We begin with quadratic forms which provide a geometrical view (and the name!) of the Principal Axis theorem. This leads to the study of positive definite matrices, and to the Cholesky decomposition. Then we look at constrained optimization where a quantity is maximized (or minimized) subject to a condition on the variables.

4.8.1   Quadratic Forms

The equation of a curve in the plane can often be made simpler by a change of coordinates, and the same is true for the equation of a surface in $\mathbb{R}^3$. In this section we show how to use the Principal Axis theorem to accomplish this for graphs of quadratics in n variables.

Example 1   Consider the graph of the equation $x_1 x_2 = 1$ as shown in the diagram. The curve is clearly symmetric about the line $x_2 = x_1$. Hence we are going to look at the equation of this curve in terms of new variables y_1 and y_2, where the Y_1-axis is the line $x_2 = x_1$. To do this, we obtain the Y_1- and Y_2-axes from the X_1- and X_2-axes by a counterclockwise rotation of $\frac{\pi}{4}$. Recall that the matrix of the rotation through an angle θ is $\begin{bmatrix} \cos\theta & -\sin\theta \\ \sin\theta & \cos\theta \end{bmatrix}$

---

[19] This section can be omitted without loss of continuity.

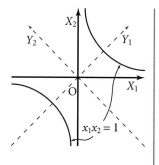

$x_1 x_2 = 1$

by Theorem 3 §3.4. Hence, if the vector $[x_1 \ x_2]^T$ is rotated through $\frac{\pi}{4}$ the resulting vector $[y_1 \ y_2]^T$ is given by

$$\begin{bmatrix} y_1 \\ y_2 \end{bmatrix} = \begin{bmatrix} \cos(\frac{\pi}{4}) & -\sin(\frac{\pi}{4}) \\ \sin(\frac{\pi}{4}) & \cos(\frac{\pi}{4}) \end{bmatrix} \begin{bmatrix} x_1 \\ x_2 \end{bmatrix}$$

$$= \begin{bmatrix} \frac{1}{\sqrt{2}} & -\frac{1}{\sqrt{2}} \\ \frac{1}{\sqrt{2}} & \frac{1}{\sqrt{2}} \end{bmatrix} \begin{bmatrix} x_1 \\ x_2 \end{bmatrix}$$

$$= \frac{1}{\sqrt{2}} \begin{bmatrix} x_1 - x_2 \\ x_1 + x_2 \end{bmatrix}.$$

The matrix $\begin{bmatrix} \frac{1}{\sqrt{2}} & -\frac{1}{\sqrt{2}} \\ \frac{1}{\sqrt{2}} & \frac{1}{\sqrt{2}} \end{bmatrix}$ is orthogonal, so

$$\begin{bmatrix} x_1 \\ x_2 \end{bmatrix} = \begin{bmatrix} \frac{1}{\sqrt{2}} & -\frac{1}{\sqrt{2}} \\ \frac{1}{\sqrt{2}} & \frac{1}{\sqrt{2}} \end{bmatrix}^T \begin{bmatrix} y_1 \\ y_2 \end{bmatrix} = \frac{1}{\sqrt{2}} \begin{bmatrix} y_1 + y_2 \\ -y_1 + y_2 \end{bmatrix}.$$

Hence $x_1 = \frac{1}{\sqrt{2}}(y_1 + y_2)$ and $x_2 = \frac{1}{\sqrt{2}}(-y_1 + y_2)$, so the equation $x_1 x_2 = 1$ becomes $y_2^2 - y_1^2 = 2$ in terms of these new variables. In this form we recognize the equation as that of a hyperbola in the Y_1-Y_2-coordinate system. The new Y_1- and Y_2-axes are called the **principal axes** of the hyperbola. This is the source of the name Principal Axis theorem.

Note that we chose the new Y_1- and Y_2-axes in Example 1 by observing a symmetry of the graph of the original equation $x_1 x_2 = 1$. While this is still possible for equations in three variables (the graph is then a surface in $\mathbb{R}^3$), this type of geometric insight is not available when more than three variables are involved. The approach we adopt is as follows: The change of variables in Example 1 carried the equation $x_1 x_2 = 1$ to the equation $y_2^2 - y_1^2 = 2$ which has no cross term $y_1 y_2$. It is in this form that the Principal Axis theorem applies to a much wider class of equations and actually *reveals* symmetries in their graphs.

An expression like $x_1^2 - x_2^2 + 2x_3^2 + 3x_1 x_2 - x_1 x_3$ is an example of a quadratic form in the variables x_1, x_2 and x_3. In general, a **quadratic form** q in the n variables x_1, x_2, $\cdots$, x_n is a linear combination of the terms x_1^2, x_2^2, $\cdots$, x_n^2, $x_1 x_2$, $x_1 x_3$, $x_2 x_3$, $\cdots$:

$$q = r_1 x_1^2 + r_2 x_2^2 + \cdots + r_n x_n^2 + r_{12} x_1 x_2 + r_{13} x_1 x_3 + r_{23} x_2 x_3 + \cdots$$

where the coefficients r_i and r_{ij} are real numbers. Even though q is not a linear function of the x_i, it can be easily described using matrix multiplication. Indeed if we write $X = [x_1 \ x_2 \ \cdots \ x_n]^T$, q can be written in **matrix form**

$$q = X^T A X \text{ where } A \text{ is a } symmetric \ n \times n \text{ matrix.}$$

In fact, the main diagonal entries of the matrix A are the coefficients (possibly zero) of x_1^2, x_2^2, and x_n^2 in order and, if $i \ne j$, the (i, j)- and (j, i)-entries of A are both equal to half the coefficient of $x_i x_j$. Here is an example.

Example 2 Write $q = x_1^2 + 3x_3^2 + 2x_1 x_2 - x_1 x_3$ in matrix form $q = X^T A X$ where A is symmetric.

SOLUTION Applying the above rule, we get

$$q = [x_1 \ x_2 \ x_3] \begin{bmatrix} 1 & 1 & -\frac{1}{2} \\ 1 & 0 & 0 \\ -\frac{1}{2} & 0 & 3 \end{bmatrix} \begin{bmatrix} x_1 \\ x_2 \\ x_3 \end{bmatrix}.$$

The reader should verify that this really works.

The reason for writing quadratic forms as in Example 2 is that the Principal Axis theorem can be applied to the symmetric matrix A. Suppose that a quadratic form q is written in matrix form as

$$q = X^T A X$$

where A is a symmetric $n \times n$ matrix and $X = [x_1 \ x_2 \ \cdots \ x_n]^T$. We want to find new variables $Y = [y_1 \ y_2 \ \cdots \ y_n]^T$ such that, when q is written in terms of $y_1, \ y_2, \ \cdots, \ y_n$, there are no cross terms $y_i y_j$ where $i \neq j$. This amounts to asking that $q = Y^T D Y$ where D is a *diagonal* matrix. Since A is symmetric, the Principal Axis theorem guarantees the existence of an orthogonal matrix P such that

$$P^T A P = D = \begin{bmatrix} \lambda_1 & 0 & \cdots & 0 \\ 0 & \lambda_2 & \cdots & 0 \\ \vdots & \vdots & \ddots & \vdots \\ 0 & 0 & \cdots & \lambda_n \end{bmatrix}$$

where the λ_i are the (real but not necessarily distinct) eigenvalues of the symmetric matrix A. Note that $P^{-1} = P^T$. Now define the new variables Y by

$$Y = P^T X \quad \text{equivalently} \quad X = PY.$$

Then substitution in the equation $q = X^T A X$ gives

$$q = (PY)^T A (PY) = Y^T (P^T A P) Y = Y^T D Y = \lambda_1 y_1^2 + \lambda_2 y_2^2 + \cdots + \lambda_n y_n^2.$$

Hence this change of variables has produced the desired simplification of q (and we say that the quadratic form q has been **diagonalized**). The following theorem summarizes this discussion.

THEOREM 1

Let $q = X^T A X$ be a quadratic form where A is a symmetric $n \times n$ matrix and $X = [x_1 \ x_2 \ \cdots \ x_n]^T$. Let P be an orthogonal matrix such that $P^T A P = diag(\lambda_1, \ \lambda_2, \ \cdots, \ \lambda_n)$ where the λ_i are the (real) eigenvalues of A repeated according to their multiplicities. Define new variables $Y = [y_1 \ y_2 \ \cdots \ y_n]^T$ by

$$Y = P^T X \quad \text{equivalently} \quad X = PY.$$

Then

$$q = \lambda_1 y_1^2 + \lambda_2 y_2^2 + \cdots + \lambda_n y_n^2$$

in terms of these new variables y_i.

Example 3   The quadratic form $q = x_1 x_2$ in Example 1 has matrix form $q = X^T A X$ where $X = [x_1 \ x_2]^T$ and $A = \begin{bmatrix} 0 & \frac{1}{2} \\ \frac{1}{2} & 0 \end{bmatrix}$. The eigenvalues are $-\frac{1}{2}$ and $\frac{1}{2}$, with corresponding eigenvectors $\begin{bmatrix} 1 \\ -1 \end{bmatrix}$ and $\begin{bmatrix} 1 \\ 1 \end{bmatrix}$, respectively. They are (of course) orthogonal and, after normalizing, the orthogonal matrix P is $P = \frac{1}{\sqrt{2}} \begin{bmatrix} 1 & 1 \\ -1 & 1 \end{bmatrix}$. Hence the new variables are $\begin{bmatrix} y_1 \\ y_2 \end{bmatrix} = Y = P^T X = \frac{1}{\sqrt{2}} \begin{bmatrix} 1 & -1 \\ 1 & 1 \end{bmatrix} \begin{bmatrix} x_1 \\ x_2 \end{bmatrix}$. Thus $y_1 = \frac{1}{\sqrt{2}}(x_1 - x_2)$ and $y_2 = \frac{1}{\sqrt{2}}(x_1 + x_2)$ as in Example 1.

Note that this "diagonalizing" change of variables is not unique. For example, if we take $[-1 \ \ 1]^T$ as the eigenvector corresponding to the eigenvalue $-\frac{1}{2}$, the resulting formulas are $y_1' = \frac{1}{\sqrt{2}}(-x_1 + x_2)$ and $y_2' = \frac{1}{\sqrt{2}}(x_1 + x_2)$. Then y_2' is the same as y_2, but y_1' is the negative of the preceding y_1. Geometrically, this amounts to pointing the y_1-axis in the opposite direction in Example 1.

Example 4 Diagonalize the quadratic form $q = x_1^2 + 2x_2^2 + x_3^2 - 2x_1x_2 - 2x_2x_3$.

SOLUTION Here $q = X^TAX$ where $A = \begin{bmatrix} 1 & -1 & 0 \\ -1 & 2 & -1 \\ 0 & -1 & 1 \end{bmatrix}$ and $X = \begin{bmatrix} x_1 \\ x_2 \\ x_3 \end{bmatrix}$. The eigenvalues of A are $\lambda_1 = 0$,

$\lambda_2 = 1$, and $\lambda_3 = 3$, with (orthogonal) eigenvectors $G_1 = [1 \ \ 1 \ \ 1]^T$, $G_2 = [-1 \ \ 0 \ \ 1]^T$, and $G_3 = [1 \ \ -2 \ \ 1]^T$ respectively. Normalizing gives the principal axes $F_1 = \frac{1}{\sqrt{3}}G_1$, $F_2 = \frac{1}{\sqrt{2}}G_2$, and $F_3 = \frac{1}{\sqrt{6}}G_3$, and so we obtain an orthogonal matrix

$$P = [F_1 \ \ F_2 \ \ F_3] = \begin{bmatrix} \frac{1}{\sqrt{3}} & -\frac{1}{\sqrt{2}} & \frac{1}{\sqrt{6}} \\ \frac{1}{\sqrt{3}} & 0 & -\frac{2}{\sqrt{6}} \\ \frac{1}{\sqrt{3}} & \frac{1}{\sqrt{2}} & \frac{1}{\sqrt{6}} \end{bmatrix}$$

such that $P^TAP = diag(\lambda_1, \lambda_2, \lambda_3) = diag(0, 1, 3)$. Thus the new variables $[y_1 \ y_2 \ y_3]^T = Y = P^TX$ are

$$y_1 = \tfrac{1}{\sqrt{3}}(x_1 + x_2 + x_3), \ \ y_2 = \tfrac{1}{\sqrt{2}}(-x_1 + x_3), \ \text{and} \ y_3 = \tfrac{1}{\sqrt{6}}(x_1 - 2x_2 + x_3).$$

If we compute $X = PY$ and substitute in q, we diagonalize the quadratic form in the sense that $q = \lambda_1 y_1^2 + \lambda_2 y_2^2 + \lambda_3 y_3^2 = y_2^2 + 3y_3^2$.

These methods shed light on graphs of the form $q = 1$ where q is a quadratic form in two variables x_1 and x_2 (as in Example 1). The graph of the equation $rx_1^2 + sx_2^2 = 1$ is called an **ellipse** if $rs > 0$ and a **hyperbola** if $rs < 0$. Our theory guarantees that every equation $ax_1^2 + bx_1x_2 + cx_2^2 = 1$ can be transformed into such a diagonal form by a change of coordinates. The next theorem shows that this can always be achieved by a rotation (as in Example 1), and it also gives a simple way to decide from the coefficients a, b, and c whether it is an ellipse or a hyperbola.

THEOREM 2 Consider the quadratic form $q = ax_1^2 + bx_1x_2 + cx_2^2$.
   (1) There is a counterclockwise rotation of the coordinate axes about the origin such that q has the form $q = ry_1^2 + sy_2^2$ in the new variables y_1 and y_2.
   (2) The graph of the equation $ax_1^2 + bx_1x_2 + cx_2^2 = 1$ is an ellipse if $b^2 - 4ac < 0$ and it is a hyperbola if $b^2 - 4ac > 0$.

PROOF The matrix of q is $A = \begin{bmatrix} a & \frac{1}{2}b \\ \frac{1}{2}b & c \end{bmatrix}$. Let λ_1 and λ_2 be the eigenvalues of A with

orthonormal eigenvectors X_1 and X_2. Hence $P = [X_1 \ \ X_2]$ is an orthogonal matrix and $P^TAP = diag(\lambda_1, \lambda_2)$. We have $detP = \pm1$ so, by interchanging X_1 and X_2 if necessary, we can ensure that $detP = 1$ and hence (by Theorem 7 §3.4) that multiplication by P is a rotation of $\mathbb{R}^2$. Since the new coordinates y_1 and y_2 are given by $[y_1 \ \ y_2]^T = P^T[x_1 \ \ x_2]^T$, the new axes are obtained by a rotation (since P^T is also orthogonal and $det(P^T) = 1$). This proves (1). Furthermore, the fact that $P^T = P^{-1}$ gives

$$\lambda_1\lambda_2 = det\begin{bmatrix} \lambda_1 & 0 \\ 0 & \lambda_2 \end{bmatrix} = det(P^TAP) = detA = -\tfrac{1}{4}(b^2 - 4ac).$$

Since $q = \lambda_1 y_1^2 + \lambda_2 y_2^2$ in the new coordinate system, the graph of the equation $q = 1$ is an ellipse if $\lambda_1\lambda_2 > 0$ (that is $b^2 - 4ac < 0$), and it is a hyperbola if $\lambda_1\lambda_2 < 0$ (that is $b^2 - 4ac > 0$). This proves (2).

There are many ways to diagonalize a given quadratic form q. For example, consider $q = 3x_1^2 + 4x_1x_2 + 2x_2^2$. Then $q = X^TAX$ where $A = \begin{bmatrix} 3 & 2 \\ 2 & 2 \end{bmatrix}$. This matrix has eigenvalues $\lambda_1 = \frac{1}{2}(5 + \sqrt{17})$ and $\lambda_2 = \frac{1}{2}(5 - \sqrt{17})$, and so q can be written in the form $q = \lambda_1 y_1^2 + \lambda_2 y_2^2$ for appropriate new variables y_1 and y_2. On the other hand, q can be written as follows:

$$q = x_1^2 + 2(x_1 + x_2)^2 \quad \text{and} \quad q = 3(x_1 + \tfrac{2}{3}x_2)^2 + \tfrac{2}{3}x_2^2.$$

These formulas reveal two other changes of variables that diagonalize q:

$$\begin{aligned} y'_1 &= x_1 \\ y'_2 &= x_1 + x_2 \end{aligned} \quad \text{and} \quad \begin{aligned} y''_1 &= x_1 + \tfrac{2}{3}x_2 \\ y''_2 &= x_2 \end{aligned}.$$

The general problem of how such changes of variables are related has been studied in great detail; however we shall not pursue this here.

4.8.2   Positive Definite Matrices

If A is an $n \times n$ symmetric matrix, the quadratic form $q = X^TAX$ can be viewed as a function $q : \mathbb{R}^n \to \mathbb{R}$ given by $q(X) = X^TAX$. If $n = 2$ and $X = [x_1 \ x_2]^T$, then $q = q(x_1, x_2)$ is a function of two variables and we can look at the graph of q in $\mathbb{R}^3$. Three examples are shown in the diagram.

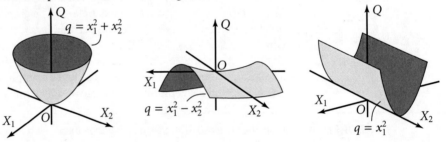

In this section we examine the important special case where the graph stays strictly above the X_1-X_2-plane except at the origin (as in the first example in the diagram). Moreover, we treat the general case where $q = q(x_1, x_2, \cdots, x_n)$ is a function of n variables.

If $q = q(X) = X^TAX$ is a quadratic form on $\mathbb{R}^n$, it is clear that $q(0) = 0$, and q is said to be a **positive definite form** if $q(X) > 0$ whenever $X \neq 0$. For example, it is clear that $q(x_1, x_2) = x_1^2 + 2x_2^2$ is positive definite; however it is sometimes less clear.

Example 5   If $A = \begin{bmatrix} 2 & -1 \\ -1 & 1 \end{bmatrix}$ and $X = \begin{bmatrix} x_1 \\ x_2 \end{bmatrix}$, show that the corresponding form

$q = X^TAX = 2x_1^2 + x_2^2 - 2x_1x_2$ is positive definite.

SOLUTION   We can write $q = x_1^2 + (x_1 - x_2)^2$, so the only way that q can be zero is if $x_1 = 0$ and $x_1 - x_2 = 0$; that is, if $X = 0$.

The Principal Axis theorem provides the following important characterization of these positive definite forms $q = X^TAX$ in terms of the (real) eigenvalues of the symmetric matrix A.

THEOREM 3 If A is a symmetric matrix, the quadratic form $q(X) = X^T A X$ is positive definite if and only if every eigenvalue of A is positive.

PROOF By the Principal Axis theorem let P be an orthogonal matrix such that $P^T A P = D = diag(\lambda_1, \lambda_2, \cdots, \lambda_n)$ where the λ_i are the eigenvalues of A. Suppose $\lambda_i > 0$ for each i. If $X \neq 0$, write $Y = P^T X = [y_1 \ y_2 \ \cdots \ y_n]^T$. Then $Y \neq 0$ because P^T is invertible. Since $X = PY$, this means that

$$q(X) = X^T A X = Y^T (P^T A P) Y = Y^T D Y = \lambda_1 y_1^2 + \lambda_2 y_2^2 + \cdots + \lambda_n y_n^2 > 0$$

because each $\lambda_i > 0$ and some $y_i \neq 0$. Conversely, if $q(X) > 0$ for all $X \neq 0$, let $X_j = PE_j$ where E_j is column j of I_n. Then $0 < q(X_j) = X_j^T A X_j = E_j^T (P^T A P) E_j = E_j^T D E_j = \lambda_j$, as required.

Motivated by Theorem 3, a square matrix is called **positive definite** if it is symmetric and all its eigenvalues are positive. Hence Theorem 3 asserts that a symmetric matrix A is positive definite if and only if the corresponding quadratic form $q(X) = X^T A X$ is a positive definite form. In particular, Example 5 shows that $\begin{bmatrix} 2 & -1 \\ -1 & 1 \end{bmatrix}$ is a positive definite matrix.

COROLLARY Every positive definite matrix A is invertible; indeed, $det A > 0$.

PROOF Since A is symmetric, we have $P^T A P = D = diag(\lambda_1, \lambda_2, \cdots, \lambda_n)$ for some orthogonal matrix P. Hence $det A = det D = \lambda_1 \lambda_2 \cdots \lambda_n$, so $det D > 0$ because each $\lambda_i > 0$.

These positive definite matrices arise frequently when optimization (maximum or minimum) problems are encountered, and so have applications throughout Science and Engineering. They are also used in factor analysis in statistics, and we will encounter them when discussing general inner products in Chapter 5.

Example 6 If U is any invertible $n \times n$ matrix, show that $A = U^T U$ is positive definite.

Let $q(X) = X^T A X$ be the quadratic form associated with A. If $X \neq 0$ in $\mathbb{R}^n$, then $q(X) = X^T A X = X^T (U^T U) X = (UX)^T (UX) = \|UX\|^2 > 0$ because $UX \neq 0$ (U is invertible).

If A is an $m \times n$ matrix, it follows from Theorem 3 §4.4 that the $n \times n$ symmetric matrix $A^T A$ is positive definite if and only if A has linearly independent columns (see Exercise 12).

It is remarkable that the converse to Example 6 is also true. In fact every positive definite matrix A can be factored as $A = U^T U$ where U is an upper triangular matrix with positive elements on the main diagonal. However, before verifying this, we introduce another concept that is central to any discussion of positive definite matrices.

If A is any $n \times n$ matrix, let $^r A$ denote the $r \times r$ submatrix of A in the upper left corner of A; that is $^r A$ is the matrix obtained from A by deleting the last $n - r$ rows and columns. The matrices $^1 A$, $^2 A$, $^3 A$, $\cdots$, $^n A = A$ are called the **principal submatrices** of A.

Example 7 If $A = \begin{bmatrix} 10 & 5 & 2 \\ 5 & 3 & 2 \\ 2 & 2 & 3 \end{bmatrix}$ then $^1 A = [10]$, $^2 A = \begin{bmatrix} 10 & 5 \\ 5 & 3 \end{bmatrix}$ and $^3 A = A$.

LEMMA 1   Let A be $n \times n$. If A is positive definite, so also is each principal submatrix ${}^r A$ for $r = 1, 2, \cdots, n$.

PROOF   Write $A = \begin{bmatrix} {}^r A & P \\ Q & R \end{bmatrix}$ in block form. If $Y \neq 0$ in $\mathbb{R}^r$, write $X = \begin{bmatrix} Y \\ 0 \end{bmatrix}$ in $\mathbb{R}^n$. Then $X \neq 0$ so the fact that A is positive definite gives

$$0 < X^T A X = [Y^T \ 0] \begin{bmatrix} {}^r A & P \\ Q & R \end{bmatrix} \begin{bmatrix} Y \\ 0 \end{bmatrix} = Y^T ({}^r A) \, Y.$$

This shows that ${}^r A$ is positive definite.[20]

If A is positive definite, Lemma 1 and the Corollary to Theorem 3 show that $det({}^r A) > 0$ for every r. This proves part of the following theorem which contains the converse to Example 6, and characterizes the positive definite matrices among the symmetric ones.

THEOREM 4   The following conditions are equivalent for a symmetric $n \times n$ matrix A:

(1) A is positive definite.
(2) $det({}^r A) > 0$ for each $r = 1, 2, \cdots, n$.
(3) $A = U^T U$ where U is an upper triangular matrix with positive entries on the main diagonal.

Furthermore, the factorization in (3) is unique (called the **Cholesky Factorization** of A).

PROOF $(3) \Rightarrow (1)$ is Example 6, and $(1) \Rightarrow (2)$ follows from Lemma 1 and the Corollary to Theorem 3.

$(2) \Rightarrow (3)$. Assume (2) and proceed by induction on n. If $n = 1$, then $A = [a]$ where $a > 0$ by (2), so take $U = [\sqrt{a}]$. If $n > 1$, write $B = {}^{(n-1)} A$. Then B is symmetric and satisfies (2) so, by induction, we have $B = U^T U$ as in (3) where U is of size $(n-1) \times (n-1)$. Then, as A is symmetric, it has block form $A = \begin{bmatrix} B & P \\ P^T & a \end{bmatrix}$ where P is a column in $\mathbb{R}^{n-1}$ and a is in $\mathbb{R}$. If we write $X = (U^T)^{-1} P$ and $b = a - X^T X$, block multiplication gives

$$A = \begin{bmatrix} U^T U & P \\ P^T & a \end{bmatrix} = \begin{bmatrix} U^T & 0 \\ X^T & 1 \end{bmatrix} \begin{bmatrix} U & X \\ 0 & b \end{bmatrix},$$

as the reader can verify. Taking determinants and applying Theorem 3 §2.2 gives $det A = det(U^T) \, det U \cdot b = b(det U)^2$. Hence $b > 0$ because $det A > 0$ by (2). But then the above factorization can be written $A = \begin{bmatrix} U^T & 0 \\ X^T & \sqrt{b} \end{bmatrix} \begin{bmatrix} U & X \\ 0 & \sqrt{b} \end{bmatrix}$. Since U has positive diagonal entries, this is a Cholesky factorization of A. This proves (3).

As to the uniqueness, suppose that $A = U^T U = U_1^T U_1$ are two Cholesky factorizations. Write $D = U U_1^{-1} = (U^T)^{-1} U_1^T$. Then D is upper triangular (because $D = U U_1^{-1}$) and lower triangular (because $D = (U^T)^{-1} U_1^T$) and so is a diagonal matrix. Thus $U = DU_1$ and $U_1 = DU$ (since $U_1^T = U^T D$), so it suffices to show that $D = I$. But eliminating U_1 gives $U = D^2 U$, so $D^2 = I$ because U is invertible. Since the diagonal entries of D are positive (this is true of U and U_1), it follows that $D = I$.

The remarkable thing is that the matrix U in the Cholesky factorization is easy to obtain from A using row operations. The key is that Step 1 of the following algorithm is possible for any positive definite matrix A. A proof of the algorithm is given following Example 8.

---

20 A similar argument shows that, if B is any matrix obtained from a positive definite matrix A by deleting certain rows and deleting the *same* columns, then B is also positive definite.

Algorithm for the Cholesky Factorization. If A is a positive definite matrix, the Cholesky factorization $A = U^T U$ can be obtained as follows:

Step 1. Carry A to an upper triangular matrix U_1 with positive diagonal entries by row operations each of which adds a multiple of a row to a lower row.

Step 2. Obtain U from U_1 by dividing each row of U_1 by the square root of the diagonal entry in that row.

Example 8 Find the Cholesky factorization of $A = \begin{bmatrix} 10 & 5 & 2 \\ 5 & 3 & 2 \\ 2 & 2 & 3 \end{bmatrix}$.

SOLUTION The matrix A is positive definite by Theorem 4 because $det\,^1(A) = 10 > 0$, $det\,^2(A) = 5 > 0$, and $det\,^3(A) = detA = 3 > 0$. Hence Step 1 of the Algorithm is carried out as follows:

$$A = \begin{bmatrix} 10 & 5 & 2 \\ 5 & 3 & 2 \\ 2 & 2 & 3 \end{bmatrix} \rightarrow \begin{bmatrix} 10 & 5 & 2 \\ 0 & \frac{1}{2} & 1 \\ 0 & 1 & \frac{13}{5} \end{bmatrix} \rightarrow \begin{bmatrix} 10 & 5 & 2 \\ 0 & \frac{1}{2} & 1 \\ 0 & 0 & \frac{3}{5} \end{bmatrix} = U_1.$$

Now carry out Step 2 on U_1 to obtain $U = \begin{bmatrix} \sqrt{10} & \frac{5}{\sqrt{10}} & \frac{2}{\sqrt{10}} \\ 0 & \frac{1}{\sqrt{2}} & \sqrt{2} \\ 0 & 0 & \frac{\sqrt{3}}{\sqrt{5}} \end{bmatrix}$. The reader can verify that $U^T U = A$.

Proof of the Cholesky Algorithm

If A is positive definite, let $A = U^T U$ be the Cholesky factorization, and let $D = diag(d_1, \cdots, d_n)$ be the common diagonal of U and U^T. Then $U^T D^{-1}$ is lower triangular with ones on the diagonal (call such matrices LT-1). Hence $L = (U^T D^{-1})^{-1}$ is also LT-1, and so $I_n \rightarrow L$ by a sequence of row operations each of which adds a multiple of a row to a lower row (verify; modify columns right to left). But then $A \rightarrow LA$ by the same sequence of row operations (see the discussion preceding Theorem 1 §1.6). Since $LA = [D(U^T)^{-1}][U^T U] = DU$ is upper triangular with positive entries on the diagonal, this shows that Step 1 of the Algorithm is possible.

Turning to Step 2, let $A \rightarrow U_1$ as in Step 1 so that $U_1 = L_1 A$ where L_1 is LT-1. Since A is symmetric, we get

$$L_1 U_1^T = L_1(L_1 A)^T = L_1 A^T L_1^T = L_1 A L_1^T = U_1 L_1^T. \qquad (*)$$

Let $D_1 = diag(e_1, \cdots, e_n)$ where $e_1, \cdots, e_n$ denote the diagonal entries of U_1. Then $(*)$ gives $L_1(U_1^T D_1^{-1}) = U_1 L_1^T D_1^{-1}$, and this is both upper triangular (right side) and LT-1 (left side), and so must equal I_n. In particular, $U_1^T D_1^{-1} = L_1^{-1}$. Now let $D_2 = diag(\sqrt{e_1}, \cdots, \sqrt{e_n})$, so that $D_2^2 = D_1$. If we write $U = D_2^{-1} U_1$, we have

$$U^T U = (U_1^T D_2^{-1})(D_2^{-1} U_1) = U_1^T (D_2^2)^{-1} U_1 = (U_1^T D_1^{-1}) U_1 = (L_1^{-1}) U_1 = A.$$

This proves Step 2 because $U = D_2^{-1} U_1$ is formed by dividing each row of U_1 by the square root of its diagonal entry (verify).

4.8.3 Constrained Optimization

It is a frequent occurrence in applications that a function $q = q(x_1, x_2, \cdots, x_n)$ of n variables, called an **objective function**, is to be made as large or as small as possible among all vectors $X = [x_1 \; x_2 \; \cdots \; x_n]^T$ lying in a certain region of $\mathbb{R}^n$ called the **feasible region**. A wide variety of objective functions q arise in practice; our primary concern here is to examine one important situation where q is a quadratic form. The next example gives some indication of how such problems arise.

Example 9

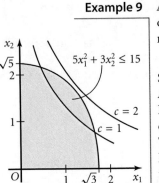

A politician proposes to spend x_1 dollars annually on health care and x_2 dollars annually on education. She is constrained in her spending by various budget pressures, and one model of this is that the expenditures x_1 and x_2 should satisfy a constraint like

$$5x_1^2 + 3x_2^2 \leq 15.$$

Since $x_i \geq 0$ for each i, the feasible region is the shaded area shown in the diagram. Any choice of feasible point $[x_1 \ x_2]^T$ in this region will satisfy the budget constraints. However, these choices have different effects on voters, and the politician wants to choose $X = [x_1 \ x_2]^T$ to maximize some measure $q = q(x_1, x_2)$ of voter satisfaction. Thus the assumption is that, for any value of c, all points on the graph of $q(x_1, x_2) = c$ have the same appeal to voters. Hence the goal is to find the largest value of c for which the graph of $q(x_1, x_2) = c$ contains a feasible point.

The choice of the function q depends upon many factors; we will show how to solve the problem for any quadratic form q (even with more than two variables). In the diagram the function q is given by

$$q(x_1, x_2) = x_1x_2,$$

and the graphs of $q(x_1, x_2) = c$ are shown for $c = 1$ and $c = 2$. As c increases the graph of $q(x_1, x_2) = c$ moves up and to the right. From this it is clear that there will be a solution for some value of c between 1 and 2 (in fact the largest value is $c = \frac{1}{2}\sqrt{15} = 1.94$ to two decimal places).

The constraint $5x_1^2 + 3x_2^2 \leq 15$ in Example 9 can be put in a standard form. If we divide through by 15, it becomes $\left(\frac{x_1}{\sqrt{3}}\right)^2 + \left(\frac{x_2}{\sqrt{5}}\right)^2 \leq 1$. This suggests that we introduce new variables $Y = [y_1 \ y_2]^T$ where $y_1 = \frac{x_1}{\sqrt{3}}$ and $y_2 = \frac{x_2}{\sqrt{5}}$. Then the constraint becomes $\|Y\|^2 \leq 1$, equivalently $\|Y\| \leq 1$. In terms of these new variables, the objective function is $q = \sqrt{15}\,y_1y_2$, and we want to maximize this subject to $\|Y\| \leq 1$. When this is done, the maximizing values of x_1 and x_2 are obtained from $x_1 = \sqrt{3}\,y_1$ and $x_2 = \sqrt{5}\,y_2$.

Hence, for constraints like that in Example 9, there is no real loss in generality in assuming that the constraint takes the form $\|X\| \leq 1$. In this case the Principal Axis theorem solves the problem. Recall that a vector in $\mathbb{R}^n$ of length 1 is called a *unit vector*.

THEOREM 5

Consider the quadratic form $q = q(X) = X^TAX$ where A is an $n \times n$ symmetric matrix, and let λ_1 and λ_n denote the largest and smallest eigenvalues of A, respectively. Then:

(1) $max\{q(X) \mid \|X\| \leq 1\} = \lambda_1$, and $q(F_1) = \lambda_1$ where F_1 is any unit eigenvector corresponding to λ_1.

(2) $min\{q(X) \mid \|X\| \leq 1\} = \lambda_n$, and $q(F_n) = \lambda_n$ where F_n is any unit eigenvector corresponding to λ_n.

PROOF

Since A is symmetric, let the (real) eigenvalues λ_i of A be ordered as to size as follows: $\lambda_1 \geq \lambda_2 \geq \cdots \geq \lambda_n$. By the Principal Axis Theorem, let P be an orthogonal matrix such that $P^TAP = D = diag(\lambda_1, \lambda_2, \cdots, \lambda_n)$. Define $Y = P^TX$, equivalently $X = PY$, and observe that $\|Y\| = \|X\|$ because $\|Y\|^2 = Y^TY = X^T(PP^T)X = X^TX = \|X\|^2$. If we write $Y = [y_1 \ y_2 \ \cdots \ y_n]^T$, then

$$\begin{aligned} q(X) = q(PY) &= (PY)^TA(PY) \\ &= Y^T(P^TAP)Y = Y^TDY \\ &= \lambda_1y_1^2 + \lambda_2y_2^2 + \cdots + \lambda_ny_n^2. \end{aligned} \qquad (**)$$

Now assume that $\|X\| \leq 1$. Since $\lambda_i \leq \lambda_1$ for each i, $(**)$ gives

$$q(X) = \lambda_1 y_1^2 + \lambda_2 y_2^2 + \cdots + \lambda_n y_n^2 \leq \lambda_1 y_1^2 + \lambda_1 y_2^2 + \cdots + \lambda_1 y_n^2 = \lambda_1 \|Y\|^2 \leq \lambda_1$$

because $\|Y\| = \|X\| \leq 1$. This shows that $q(X)$ cannot exceed λ_1 when $\|X\| \leq 1$. To see that this maximum is actually achieved, let F_1 be a unit eigenvector corresponding to λ_1. Then

$$q(F_1) = F_1^T A F_1 = F_1^T(\lambda_1 F_1) = \lambda_1(F_1^T F_1) = \lambda_1 \|F_1\|^2 = \lambda_1.$$

Hence λ_1 is the maximum value of $q(X)$ when $\|X\| \leq 1$, proving (1). The proof of (2) is analogous.

The set of all vectors X in $\mathbb{R}^n$ such that $\|X\| \leq 1$ is called the **unit ball**. If $n = 2$, it is often called the unit disk and consists of the unit circle and its interior; if $n = 3$, it is the unit sphere and its interior. It is worth noting that the maximum value of a quadratic form $q(X)$ as X ranges *throughout* the unit ball is (by Theorem 5) actually attained for a unit vector X on the *boundary* of the unit ball.

Theorem 5 is important for applications involving vibrations in areas as diverse as aerodynamics and particle physics, and the maximum and minimum values in the theorem are often found using advanced calculus to minimize the quadratic form on the unit ball. The algebraic approach using the Principal Axis theorem gives a geometrical interpretation of the optimal values because they are eigenvalues.

Example 10   Maximize and minimize the form $q(X) = 3x_1^2 + 14x_1 x_2 + 3x_2^2$ subject to $\|X\| \leq 1$.

SOLUTION   The matrix of q is $A = \begin{bmatrix} 3 & 7 \\ 7 & 3 \end{bmatrix}$, with eigenvalues $\lambda_1 = 10$ and $\lambda_2 = -4$, and corresponding unit eigenvectors $F_1 = \frac{1}{\sqrt{2}}[1 \ \ 1]^T$ and $F_2 = \frac{1}{\sqrt{2}}[1 \ \ -1]^T$. Hence, among all unit vectors X in $\mathbb{R}^2$, $q(X)$ takes its maximal value 10 at $X = F_1$, and the minimum value of $q(X)$ is -4 when $X = F_2$.

As noted above, the objective function in a constrained optimization problem need not be a quadratic form. We conclude with an example where the objective function is linear, and the feasible region is determined by linear constraints.

Example 11   A manufacturer makes x_1 units of product 1, and x_2 units of product 2, at a profit of $70 and $50 per unit respectively, and wants to choose x_1 and x_2 to maximize the total profit $p(x_1, x_2) = 70x_1 + 50x_2$. However x_1 and x_2 are not arbitrary; for example, $x_1 \geq 0$ and $x_2 \geq 0$. Other conditions also come into play.

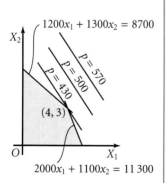

Each unit of product 1 costs $1200 to produce and requires 2000 square metres of warehouse space; each unit of product 2 costs $1300 to produce and requires 1100 square metres of space. If the total warehouse space is 11 300 square metres, and if the total production budget is $8700, x_1 and x_2 must also satisfy the conditions

$$2000x_1 + 1100x_2 \leq 11\ 300,$$
$$1200x_1 + 1300x_2 \leq 8700.$$

The feasible region in the plane satisfying these constraints (and $x_1 \geq 0$, $x_2 \geq 0$) is shaded in the diagram. If the profit equation $70x_1 + 50x_2 = p$ is plotted for various values of p, the resulting lines are parallel, with p increasing with distance from the origin. Hence the best choice occurs for the line $70x_1 + 50x_2 = 430$ that touches the shaded region at the point $(4, 3)$. So the profit p has a maximum of $p = 430$ for $x_1 = 4$ units and $x_2 = 3$ units.

Example 11 is a simple case of the general **linear programming** problem[21] which arises in economic, management, network, and scheduling applications. Here the objective function is a linear combination $q = a_1x_1 + a_2x_2 + \cdots + a_nx_n$ of the variables, and the feasible region consists of the vectors $X = [x_1 \ \ x_2 \ \cdots \ x_n]^T$ in $\mathbb{R}^n$ which satisfy a set of linear inequalities of the form $b_1x_1 + b_2x_2 + \cdots + b_nx_n \leq b$. There is a good method (an extension of the Gaussian algorithm) called the **simplex algorithm** for finding the maximum and minimum values of q when X ranges over such a feasible set. As Example 11 suggests, the optimal values turn out to be vertices of the feasible set. In particular, they are on the boundary of the feasible region, as is the case in Theorem 5.

4.8.4   Statistical Principal Component Analysis

Linear algebra is important in multivariate analysis in statistics, and we conclude with a very short look at one application of diagonalization in this area. A main feature of probability and statistics is the idea of a *random variable X*, that is a real valued function which takes its values according to a probability law (called its *distribution*). Random variables occur in a wide variety of contexts; examples include the number of meteors falling per square kilometre in a given region, the price of a share of Microsoft, or the duration of a long distance telephone call from a certain city.

The values of a random variable X are distributed about a central number μ, called the *mean* of X. The mean can be calculated from the distribution as the *expectation* $E(X) = \mu$ of the random variable X. Functions of a random variable are again random variables. In particular, $(X - \mu)^2$ is a random variable, and the *variance* of the random variable X, denoted $var(X)$, is defined to be the number

$$var(X) = E\{(X - \mu)^2\} \quad \text{where } \mu = E(X).$$

It is not difficult to see that $var(X) \geq 0$ for every random variable X. The number $\sigma = \sqrt{var(X)}$ is called the *standard deviation* of X, and is a measure of how much the values of X are spread about the mean μ of X. A main goal of statistical inference is finding reliable methods for estimating the mean and the standard deviation of a random variable X by sampling the values of X.

If two random variables X and Y are given, and their joint distribution is known, then functions of X and Y are also random variables. In particular, $X + Y$ and aX are random variables for any real number a, and we have

$$E(X + Y) = E(X) + E(Y) \quad \text{and} \quad E(aX) = aE(X). \text{[22]}$$

An important question is how much the random variables X and Y depend on each other. One measure of this is the *covariance* of X and Y, denoted $cov(X, \ Y)$, defined by

$$cov(X, \ Y) = E\{(X - \mu)(Y - v)\} \quad \text{where } \mu = E(X) \text{ and } v = E(Y).$$

Clearly, $cov(X, X) = var(X)$. If $cov(X, Y) = 0$ then X and Y have little relationship to each other and are said to be *uncorrelated*.[23]

Multivariate statistical analysis deals with a family $X_1, \ X_2, \ \cdots, \ X_n$ of random variables with means $\mu_i = E(X_i)$ and variances $\sigma_i^2 = var(X_i)$ for each i. We denote the covariance of X_i and X_j by $\sigma_{ij} = cov(X_i, \ X_j)$. Then the *covariance matrix* of the random variables $X_1, \ X_2, \ \cdots, \ X_n$ is defined to be the $n \times n$ matrix

$$\Sigma = [\sigma_{ij}]$$

---

[21] A good introduction can be found at http://www.mcgrawhill.ca/college/nicholson, and more information is available in "Linear Programming and Extensions" by N. Wu and R. Coppins, McGraw-Hill, 1981.

[22] Because of this we say that $E(\ )$ is a linear transformation from the vector space of all random variables to the space of real numbers. In Section 5.3 we will have more to say about such general linear transformations.

[23] If X and Y are independent in the sense of probability theory, then they are uncorrelated; however, the converse is not true in general.

whose (i, j)-entry is σ_{ij}. The matrix Σ is clearly symmetric; in fact it can be shown that Σ is **positive semidefinite** in the sense that $\lambda \geq 0$ for every eigenvalue λ of Σ. (In reality, Σ is positive definite in most cases of interest.) So suppose that the eigenvalues of Σ are $\lambda_1 \geq \lambda_2 \geq \cdots \geq \lambda_n \geq 0$, with corresponding eigenvectors $\overline{E}_1, \overline{E}_2, \cdots, \overline{E}_n$.[24] If $P = [\overline{E}_1 \ \overline{E}_2 \ \cdots \ \overline{E}_n]$, the Principal Axis theorem shows that P is an orthogonal matrix and

$$P^T \Sigma P = diag(\lambda_1, \lambda_2, \cdots, \lambda_n).$$

If we write $\overline{X} = [X_1 \ X_2 \ \cdots \ X_n]^T$, the procedure for diagonalizing a quadratic form (Theorem 1) gives new variables $\overline{Y} = [Y_1 \ Y_2 \ \cdots \ Y_n]^T$ defined by

$$\overline{Y} = P^T \overline{X}. \tag{$***$}$$

These new random variables $Y_1, Y_2, \cdots, Y_n$ are called the **principal components** of the original random variables X_i, and are linear combinations of the X_i. Furthermore, it can be shown that

$$cov(Y_i, Y_j) = 0 \text{ if } i \neq j \quad \text{and} \quad var(Y_i) = \lambda_i \text{ for each } i.$$

Of course the principal components Y_i point along the principal axes of the quadratic form $q = \overline{X}^T \Sigma \overline{X}$.

The sum of the variances of a set of random variables is called the **total variance** of the variables, and determining the source of this total variance is one of the benefits of principal component analysis. The fact that the matrices Σ and $diag(\lambda_1, \lambda_2, \cdots, \lambda_n)$ are similar means that they have the same trace, that is

$$\sigma_{11} + \sigma_{22} + \cdots + \sigma_{nn} = \lambda_1 + \lambda_2 + \cdots + \lambda_n$$

This means that the principal components Y_i have the same total variance as the original random variables X_i. Moreover, the fact that $\lambda_1 \geq \lambda_2 \geq \cdots \geq \lambda_n \geq 0$ means that most of this variance resides in the first few Y_i. In practice, statisticians find that studying these first few Y_i (and ignoring the rest) gives an accurate analysis of the total system variability. This results in substantial data reduction since often only a few Y_i suffice for all practical purposes. Furthermore, these Y_i are easily obtained as linear combinations of the X_i. Finally, the analysis of the principal components often reveals relationships among the X_i that were not previously suspected, and so results in interpretations that would not otherwise have been made.[25]

Exercises 4.8

1. In each case either show that the statement is true or give an example showing that it is false. Throughout, A denotes a square matrix.

a) Every positive definite matrix is orthogonally diagonalizable.

b) If all eigenvalues of A are positive, then A is symmetric.

c) Every symmetric matrix with positive determinant is positive definite.

d) If A is positive definite and $X^T A X = 0$ where X is in $\mathbb{R}^n$, then $X = 0$.

e) If A is positive definite and $det\ A = 1$, then A is orthogonal.

f) If U is invertible and all its eigenvalues are positive, then U is positive definite.

2. In each case, if $q = X^T B X$ for all X in $\mathbb{R}^n$, find a symmetric matrix A such that $q = X^T A X$ for all X.

a) $B = \begin{bmatrix} 2 & -1 & 1 \\ 1 & -1 & 3 \\ 0 & 2 & 1 \end{bmatrix}$ **b)** $B = \begin{bmatrix} 2 & 2 & 7 \\ 4 & 1 & -2 \\ -1 & 0 & 5 \end{bmatrix}$

3. In each case find a change of variables that will diagonalize the quadratic form q, and express q in terms of these new variables.

a) $q = x_1^2 + 4x_1x_2 + x_2^2.$ **b)** $q = 2x_1^2 + 4x_1x_2 - x_2^2.$

c) $q = x_1^2 + 4x_1x_2 + 3x_2^2.$ **d)** $q = -x_1^2 + 4x_1x_2 + 3x_2^2.$

e) $q = x_1^2 + 2x_2^2 + x_3^2 - 2x_1x_2 - 2x_2x_3.$

f) $q = 5x_1^2 + 8x_2^2 + 5x_3^2 - 4x_1x_2 - 8x_1x_3 - 4x_2x_3.$

---

[24] In probability and statistics random variables are commonly denoted by upper case letters. Although it is in conflict with our usage of upper case letters for *matrices*, we will bow to convention and stay with the upper case notation, and denote column matrices of random variables as $\overline{X}$.

[25] A more detailed analysis of principal components can be found for example in R.A. Johnson and D.W. Wichern, *Applied Multivariate Statistical Analysis*, 4th ed., Prentice-Hall, 1998.

4. In each case decide if the graph of the equation is an ellipse or a hyperbola, and find a change of variables that transforms the equation to one with no cross terms.

   a) $3x_1^2 - 4x_1x_2 = 2.$ **b)** $2x_1^2 + 4x_1x_2 + 5x_2^2 = 1.$

5. In each case find the maximum and minimum of $q(X) = X^TAX$ among all columns X such that $\|X\| \leq 1.$

   a) $q(X) = 3x_1^2 + 4x_1x_2 + x_2^2, X = [x_1 \ x_2]^T.$

   b) $q(X) = 2x_1^2 - 5x_1x_2 - 3x_2^2, X = [x_1 \ x_2]^T.$

   c) $q(X) = 3x_1^2 - x_2^2 - 2x_3^2 - 2x_1x_2 + 8x_2x_3, X = [x_1 \ x_2 \ x_3]^T.$

   d) $q(X) = x_1^2 - 3x_2^2 - x_3^2 - 4x_1x_3 + 4x_2x_3, X = [x_1 \ x_2 \ x_3]^T.$

6. In each case find the Cholesky factorization of the matrix A.

   a) $A = \begin{bmatrix} 2 & 3 \\ 3 & 5 \end{bmatrix}$ **b)** $A = \begin{bmatrix} 3 & -2 \\ -2 & 2 \end{bmatrix}$

   c) $A = \begin{bmatrix} 10 & 4 & 3 \\ 4 & 2 & 2 \\ 3 & 2 & 3 \end{bmatrix}$ **d)** $A = \begin{bmatrix} 5 & 3 & -2 \\ 3 & 2 & -1 \\ -2 & -1 & 4 \end{bmatrix}$

7. If A is positive definite, show that every diagonal entry of A is positive. [Hint: Consider $E_j^TAE_j$ where E_j is column j of the identity matrix.]

8. a) If A is symmetric and invertible, show that A^2 is positive definite. [Hint: Show that $X^TA^2X = \|AX\|^2$ for all X in $\mathbb{R}^n$.]

   b) If $A = \begin{bmatrix} 3 & 2 \\ 2 & 1 \end{bmatrix}$, show that A^2 is positive definite but that A is not.

   c) If A is positive definite, show that A^k is positive definite for all $k \geq 1$. [Hint: A is symmetric and invertible. Use induction on k.]

   d) If A^k is positive definite where k is odd, show that A is positive definite.

9. If A is positive definite, show that A^{-1} is also positive definite. [Hint: Theorem 3.]

10. If A and B are positive definite $n \times n$ matrices, show that $A + B$ is positive definite.

11. If A and B are positive definite matrices (possibly different sizes), show that $\begin{bmatrix} A & 0 \\ 0 & B \end{bmatrix}$ is positive definite. [Hint: See the proof of Lemma 1.]

12. Let A denote an $m \times n$ matrix.
   a) Show that A^TA is positive definite if and only if A has independent columns. [Hint: Theorem 3 §4.4.]
   b) Show that $\lambda \geq 0$ for every eigenvalue λ of A^TA.

13. If A is an $n \times n$ positive definite matrix, and if U is an $n \times m$ matrix of rank m, show that U^TAU is positive definite. [Hint: Theorem 3 §4.4.]

14. If A is positive definite, show that $A = B^2$ where B is positive definite. [Hint: Let $P^TAP = D = diag(\lambda_1, \cdots, \lambda_n), \lambda_i > 0$, and consider $D_0 = diag(\sqrt{\lambda_1}, \cdots, \sqrt{\lambda_n}).$]

15. If A is positive definite, show that $A = CC^T$ for some matrix C with orthogonal columns.
[Hint: Let $P^TAP = D = diag(\lambda_1, \cdots, \lambda_n), \lambda_i > 0$. Write $D_0 = diag(\sqrt{\lambda_1}, \cdots, \sqrt{\lambda_n})$ and take $C = PD_0.$]

16. Call a square matrix **unit triangular** if it is triangular with 1's on the main diagonal.
   a) Suppose that an invertible matrix A can be factored as $A = LDU$ where L is unit lower triangular, U is unit upper triangular, and D is diagonal with positive diagonal entries. Show that this factorization is unique: that is, if $A = L_1D_1U_1$ is another such factorization, show that $L_1 = L, D_1 = D$ and $U_1 = U$. [Hint: If $L_1D_1U_1 = LDU$, scrutinize $L^{-1}L_1D_1 = DUU_1^{-1}.$]
   b) Show that a matrix A is positive definite if and only if it has a factorization of the form $A = U^TDU$, which is a special form of **a)**. [Hint: Cholesky.]

17. Consider the equation $ax_1^2 + bx_1x_2 + cx_2^2 = 1$ where $b \neq 0$. Write $X = [x_1 \ x_2]^T$, and let $Y = [y_1 \ y_2]^T$ denote the new variables obtained by rotating through an angle θ, so that (Theorem 3 §3.5) $Y = RX$ where $R = \begin{bmatrix} \cos\theta & -\sin\theta \\ \sin\theta & \cos\theta \end{bmatrix}$. If θ is an angle such that $\cos 2\theta = \frac{c-a}{\sqrt{b^2+(a-c)^2}}$ and $\sin 2\theta = \frac{b}{\sqrt{b^2+(a-c)^2}}$, show that the resulting equation has no cross term. [Hint: R is orthogonal, so $X = R^TY$. Substitute into the equation $ax_1^2 + bx_1x_2 + cx_2^2 = 1.$]

18. Let $q = X^TAX$ be a quadratic form where A is an $n \times n$ symmetric matrix.
   a) Show that A is uniquely determined by the function q; that is, if $X^TBX = X^TAX$ holds for all columns X in $\mathbb{R}^n$, show that $B = A$. [Hint: If $C = B - A$ show that $X^TCX = 0$ for all X. Replace X by $X + Y$ to conclude that $X^YCY = 0$ for all X and Y. Then consider the columns of the identity matrix.]
   b) If new variables Y are defined by $Y = U^{-1}X$ where U is an invertible matrix, show that q is given in terms of the new variables by $q = Y^TBY$ where $B = U^TAU$.
   c) Two square matrices A and B are said to be **congruent** (written $A \overset{c}{\sim} B$) if $B = U^TAU$ for some invertible matrix U. Show that:
   i) $A \overset{c}{\sim} A$ for all A; If $A \overset{c}{\sim} B$, then $B \overset{c}{\sim} A$; and, If $A \overset{c}{\sim} B$ and $B \overset{c}{\sim} C$, then $A \overset{c}{\sim} C$.
   ii) If $A \overset{c}{\sim} B$, then A is symmetric (invertible) if and only if B is symmetric (invertible).
   iii) A is symmetric if and only $A \overset{c}{\sim} D$ for some diagonal matrix D.
   iv) If $A \overset{c}{\sim} B$, then $rankA = rankB$ and $A^T \overset{c}{\sim} B^T$.

4.9 LINEAR TRANSFORMATIONS

In Section 3.4 we investigated 2×2 matrices by viewing them as transformations of the plane $\mathbb{R}^2$. Not only does this give a graphic interpretation of a matrix which is useful in analyzing the matrix, it also provides a way of studying certain geometrical properties of the plane (for example, we found that rotations about the origin correspond to simple matrices depending on the angle of rotation). In this section we do the same thing for $n \times n$ matrices, and view them as linear transformations of $\mathbb{R}^n$.

4.9.1 Transformations $\mathbb{R}^n \to \mathbb{R}^m$

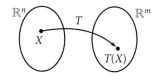

A transformation $T : \mathbb{R}^n \to \mathbb{R}^m$ is a rule[26] that associates with every vector X in $\mathbb{R}^n$ a uniquely determined vector $T(X)$ in $\mathbb{R}^m$. The situation can be visualized as in the diagram. To specify a transformation $T : \mathbb{R}^n \to \mathbb{R}^m$, *every* vector X in $\mathbb{R}^n$ must be assigned to a *uniquely determined* vector $T(X)$ in $\mathbb{R}^m$, called the **image** of X under T. This is referred to as specifying the **action** of the transformation T, or as **defining** T.

Most transformations $\mathbb{R}^n \to \mathbb{R}^m$ are of little interest in linear algebra; the important ones for us are those that preserve addition and scalar multiplication. More precisely, a transformation $T : \mathbb{R}^n \to \mathbb{R}^m$ is called a **linear transformation** if it satisfies the following two properties:

T1. $T(X + Y) = T(X) + T(Y)$ for all X and Y in $\mathbb{R}^n$.
(T preserves addition)

T2. $T(aX) = a\,T(X)$ for all X in $\mathbb{R}^n$ and all scalars a.
(T preserves scalar multiplication)

A linear transformation $\mathbb{R}^n \to \mathbb{R}^n$ is called a **linear operator** on $\mathbb{R}^n$.

Example 1

As we saw in Section 3.4, rotation about the origin, reflection about a line through the origin, and projection on a line through the origin are all examples of linear operators on $\mathbb{R}^2$.

Example 2

The transformation $T : \mathbb{R}^n \to \mathbb{R}^m$ given by $T(X) = 0$ for all X in $\mathbb{R}^n$ is a linear transformation because $0 + 0 = 0$. It is called the **zero transformation**, and is usually denoted $T = 0$.

Example 3

The transformation $1_{\mathbb{R}^n} : \mathbb{R}^n \to \mathbb{R}^n$ defined by $1_{\mathbb{R}^n}(X) = X$ for all X in $\mathbb{R}^n$ is a linear transformation (verify), called the **identity operator** on $\mathbb{R}^n$. More generally, if a is any scalar, the operator $a : \mathbb{R}^n \to \mathbb{R}^n$ defined by $a(X) = aX$ for all X in $\mathbb{R}^n$ is called a **scalar operator**. In this notation, $1_{\mathbb{R}^n} = 1$ and the zero operator is $0 : \mathbb{R}^n \to \mathbb{R}^n$.

Example 4

If U is a subspace of $\mathbb{R}^n$, define the projection operator $T : \mathbb{R}^n \to \mathbb{R}^n$ by $T(X) = proj_U(X)$ for all X in $\mathbb{R}^n$. Show that T is a linear transformation.

SOLUTION

If $\{F_1,\ F_2,\ \cdots\ F_k\}$ is any orthogonal basis of U, we have

$$T(X) = \frac{X \cdot F_1}{\|F_1\|^2}F_1 + \frac{X \cdot F_2}{\|F_2\|^2}F_2 + \cdots + \frac{X \cdot F_k}{\|F_k\|^2}F_k$$

for each X in $\mathbb{R}^n$. As the reader can verify, the result follows because, for each i, we have $(X + Y) \cdot F_i = X \cdot F_i + Y \cdot F_i$ and $(aX) \cdot F_i = a\,(X \cdot F_i)$ for all X and Y in $\mathbb{R}^n$ and all scalars a.

---

[26] Transformations $\mathbb{R} \to \mathbb{R}$ are usually called *functions* or *maps*. However the term "transformation" is commonly used in linear algebra.

Example 5   If Y is a fixed vector in $\mathbb{R}^n$, the transformation $T : \mathbb{R}^n \to \mathbb{R}^n$ defined by $T(X) = X + Y$ for all X in $\mathbb{R}^n$ is called Y-**translation**. Thus $T(0) = 0 + Y = Y$, so the map T is *not* a linear transformation if $Y \neq 0$. (If T were linear, then $T(0) = 0$ by T2.)

We now come to the prototype example of a linear transformation $\mathbb{R}^n \to \mathbb{R}^m$.

Example 6   If A is any $m \times n$ matrix, define a transformation $T : \mathbb{R}^n \to \mathbb{R}^m$ by $T(X) = AX$ for all X in $\mathbb{R}^n$. This is a linear transformation for any choice of A, called the **matrix transformation** induced by A. Indeed, T1 and T2 are basic properties of matrices.

It turns out that *every* linear transformation $\mathbb{R}^n \to \mathbb{R}^m$ is a matrix transformation. This fact depends in part on the following general properties of linear transformations: As well as preserving addition and scalar multiplication, they also preserve the zero vector, negatives, and linear combinations.

THEOREM 1   Let $T : \mathbb{R}^n \to \mathbb{R}^m$ be a linear transformation, let X, X_1, X_2, $\cdots$, X_k denote vectors in $\mathbb{R}^n$, and let a_1, a_2, $\cdots$, a_k denote scalars. Then:

(1) $T(0) = 0$.
(2) $T(-X) = -T(X)$.
(3) $T(a_1X_1 + a_2X_2 + \cdots + a_kX_k) = a_1T(X_1) + a_2T(X_2) + \cdots + a_kT(X_k)$.

PROOF   (1) and (2) follow from $T(aX) = aT(X)$ by taking $a = 0$ and $a = -1$, respectively. We prove (3) by induction on k. If $k = 1$, it is T2. If it holds for some $k \geq 1$, then

$$T(a_1X_1 + a_2X_2 + \cdots + a_kX_k + a_{k+1}X_{k+1})$$
$$= T(a_1X_1 + a_2X_2 + \cdots + a_kX_k) + T(a_{k+1}X_{k+1})$$
$$= [a_1T(X_1) + a_2T(X_2) + \cdots + a_kT(X_k)] + a_{k+1}T(X_{k+1})$$

where we used T1 at step 1, and we used T2 and the induction hypothesis at step 2. This completes the proof.

Example 7   Suppose $T : \mathbb{R}^4 \to \mathbb{R}^3$ is a linear transformation such that

$$T\left([1 \ \ 0 \ \ -1 \ \ 2]^T\right) = [2 \ \ 1 \ \ 0]^T \text{ and } T\left([1 \ \ 1 \ \ -2 \ \ 0]^T\right) = [-1 \ \ 2 \ \ 4]^T.$$

Compute $T\left([-2 \ \ -5 \ \ 7 \ \ 6]^T\right)$.

SOLUTION   For convenience, write $X_1 = [1 \ \ 0 \ \ -1 \ \ 2]^T$, $X_2 = [1 \ \ 1 \ \ -2 \ \ 0]^T$, and $X = [-2 \ \ -5 \ \ 7 \ \ 6]^T$. At first glance the problem seems impossible: We are given $T(X_1)$ and $T(X_2)$, but no way is apparent to find $T(X)$. However, since T is linear, part (3) of Theorem 1 shows that we can find $T(X)$ if X is *any* linear combination of X_1 and X_2. So we try to express X in the form $X = rX_1 + sX_2$. Equating components gives two linear equation for r and s, and the solution is $X = 3X_1 - 5X_2$. Hence Theorem 1 gives

$$T(X) = T(3X_1 - 5X_2)$$
$$= 3T(X_1) - 5T(X_2)$$
$$= 3[2 \ \ 1 \ \ 0]^T - 5[-1 \ \ 2 \ \ 4]^T$$
$$= [11 \ \ -7 \ \ -20]^T.$$

This is what we wanted.

Theorem 1 enables us to show that every linear transformation $\mathbb{R}^n \to \mathbb{R}^m$ is a matrix transformation. The proof requires a fact about matrix multiplication that will be used again later.

LEMMA 1

If A is an $m \times n$ matrix and $AX = 0$ for all X in $\mathbb{R}^n$, then $A = 0$.

PROOF

Write $I_n = [E_1 \ E_2 \ \cdots \ E_n]$ in terms of its columns. Then $AE_i = 0$ for each i by hypothesis, so

$$A = AI_n = A[E_1 \ E_2 \ \cdots \ E_n] = [AE_1 \ AE_2 \ \cdots \ AE_n] = [0 \ 0 \ \cdots \ 0] = 0.$$

THEOREM 2

Let $T : \mathbb{R}^n \to \mathbb{R}^m$ be a linear transformation. Then T is the matrix transformation induced by a uniquely determined $m \times n$ matrix A:

$$T(X) = AX \quad \text{for all } X \text{ in } \mathbb{R}^n.$$

Furthermore, A is given in terms of its columns by

$$A = [T(E_1) \ T(E_2) \ \cdots \ T(E_n)]$$

where $\{E_1, \ E_2, \ \cdots \ E_n\}$ is the standard basis of $\mathbb{R}^n$. The matrix A is called the **standard matrix** of T.

PROOF

Write $X = [x_1 \ x_2 \ \cdots \ x_n]^T$ in $\mathbb{R}^n$, so that $X = x_1E_1 + x_2E_2 + \cdots + x_nE_n$. Hence Theorem 1 and block multiplication (Theorem 3 §1.4) give

$$T(X) = x_1T(E_1) + x_2T(E_2) + \cdots + x_nT(E_n)$$

$$= [T(E_1) \ T(E_2) \ \cdots \ T(E_n)] \begin{bmatrix} x_1 \\ x_2 \\ \vdots \\ x_n \end{bmatrix}$$

$$= AX$$

for every X in $\mathbb{R}^n$. If another $m \times n$ matrix B exists such that $T(X) = BX$ for all X in $\mathbb{R}^n$, then $AX = T(X) = BX$ holds for all X. Thus $(A - B)X = 0$ for all columns X in $\mathbb{R}^n$, whence $A - B = 0$ by Lemma 1.

In other words, Theorem 2 asserts that every linear transformation $\mathbb{R}^n \to \mathbb{R}^m$ is the matrix transformation induced by its standard matrix. Hence, linear transformations $T : \mathbb{R}^n \to \mathbb{R}^m$ and matrix transformations $\mathbb{R}^n \to \mathbb{R}^m$ are different names for the same thing. Both interpretations have virtue depending on the situation.

Example 8

If $T : \mathbb{R}^3 \to \mathbb{R}^2$ is linear and satisfies $T([1 \ 0 \ 1]^T) = [3 \ 2]^T$, $T([0 \ 1 \ 0]^T) = [1 \ 2]^T$, and $T([-1 \ 0 \ 1]^T) = [-2 \ 1]^T$, find $T(X)$ for all $X = [x_1 \ x_2 \ x_3]^T$ in $\mathbb{R}^3$.

SOLUTION

We first find the standard matrix of T. Consequently, let $\{E_1, \ E_2, \ E_3\}$ denote the standard basis of $\mathbb{R}^3$, so we are given $T(E_2) = [1 \ 2]^T$. If we write $P = [1 \ 0 \ 1]^T$ and $Q = [-1 \ 0 \ 1]^T$, then $E_1 = \frac{1}{2}(P - Q)$ and $E_3 = \frac{1}{2}(P + Q)$, so

$$T(E_1) = \tfrac{1}{2}(T(P) - T(Q)) = \tfrac{1}{2}[5 \ 1]^T \quad \text{and} \quad T(E_2) = \tfrac{1}{2}(T(P) + T(Q)) = \tfrac{1}{2}[1 \ 3]^T.$$

Hence the standard matrix of T is $A = [T(E_1) \ T(E_2) \ T(E_3)] = \frac{1}{2}\begin{bmatrix} 5 & 2 & 1 \\ 1 & 4 & 3 \end{bmatrix}$ by Theorem 2, so $T(X) = AX = \frac{1}{2}\begin{bmatrix} 5x_1 + 2x_2 + x_3 \\ x_1 + 4x_2 + 3x_3 \end{bmatrix}$.

Sometimes we can find the standard matrix of a linear transformation without using the formula in Theorem 2. Here is an example.

Example 9   If $U = span\{[2 \ 1 \ 2]^T, \ [1 \ 2 \ -2]^T\}$, find the standard matrix of the projection operator T onto U (that is $T(X) = proj_U(X)$ for all X in $\mathbb{R}^3$).

SOLUTION   Write $F_1 = [2 \ 1 \ 2]^T$, $F_2 = [1 \ 2 \ -2]^T$, and $X = [x_1 \ x_2 \ x_3]^T$. Since $\{F_1, F_2\}$ is an orthogonal basis of U, we have

$$proj_U(X) = \frac{X \cdot F_1}{\|F_1\|^2}F_1 + \frac{X \cdot F_2}{\|F_2\|^2}F_2$$

$$= \frac{2x_1 + x_2 + 2x_3}{9}\begin{bmatrix} 2 \\ 1 \\ 2 \end{bmatrix} + \frac{x_1 + 2x_2 - 2x_3}{9}\begin{bmatrix} 1 \\ 2 \\ -2 \end{bmatrix}$$

$$= \frac{1}{9}\begin{bmatrix} 5 & 4 & 2 \\ 4 & 5 & -2 \\ 2 & -2 & 8 \end{bmatrix}\begin{bmatrix} x_1 \\ x_2 \\ x_3 \end{bmatrix}.$$

The standard matrix of T is now apparent.

Let $T : \mathbb{R}^n \to \mathbb{R}^m$ and $S : \mathbb{R}^m \to \mathbb{R}^k$ be two transformations (not necessarily linear) which link together as follows: $\mathbb{R}^n \xrightarrow{T} \mathbb{R}^m \xrightarrow{S} \mathbb{R}^k$. As in Section 3.4, we define the **composite transformation** $S \circ T : \mathbb{R}^n \to \mathbb{R}^k$ by

$$(S \circ T)(X) = S[T(X)] \quad \text{for all } X \text{ in } \mathbb{R}^n.$$

Thus the action of $S \circ T$ can be described as "first T, then S". Now suppose that S and T are linear transformations with standard matrices A and B respectively. Then

$$(S \circ T)(X) = S[T(X)] = A[B(X)] = (AB)X$$

for all X in $\mathbb{R}^n$. Hence $S \circ T$ is the linear transformation with standard matrix AB. We record this for reference.

THEOREM 3   Let $\mathbb{R}^n \xrightarrow{T} \mathbb{R}^m \xrightarrow{S} \mathbb{R}^k$ be linear transformations. Then the composite $S \circ T : \mathbb{R}^n \to \mathbb{R}^k$ is also a linear transformation. Moreover, if S and T have standard matrices A and B respectively, then $S \circ T$ has standard matrix AB.

As for functions in general, two linear transformations $S : \mathbb{R}^n \to \mathbb{R}^m$ and $T : \mathbb{R}^n \to \mathbb{R}^m$ are said to be **equal**, written $S = T$, if they have the same effect on every vector. In other words

$$S = T \quad \text{if and only if} \quad S(X) = T(X) \text{for every vector } X \text{ in } \mathbb{R}^n.$$

We describe the requirement that $S(X) = T(X)$ for all X by saying that S and T have the same **action**. The next result asserts that a linear transformation $\mathbb{R}^n \to \mathbb{R}^m$ is determined by its effect on any spanning set of $\mathbb{R}^n$. The result is an easy consequence of Theorem 1.

LEMMA 2   Let $S : \mathbb{R}^n \to \mathbb{R}^m$ and $T : \mathbb{R}^n \to \mathbb{R}^m$ be two linear transformations, and suppose that $\mathbb{R}^n = span\{Y_1, Y_2, \cdots, Y_k\}$. If $S(Y_i) = T(Y_i)$ for each i, then $S = T$.

PROOF   Given X in $\mathbb{R}^n$, write $X = a_1Y_1 + a_2Y_2 + \cdots + a_kY_k$ where each a_i is in $\mathbb{R}$. Then Theorem 1 gives

$$
\begin{aligned}
S(X) &= a_1S(Y_1) + a_2S(Y_2) + \cdots + a_kS(Y_k) \\
&= a_1T(Y_1) + a_2T(Y_2) + \cdots + a_kT(Y_k) \\
&= T(X).
\end{aligned}
$$

Since this holds for all X in $\mathbb{R}^n$, we have $S = T$.

Lemma 2 can also be used to *construct* linear transformations. In fact, if a basis of $\mathbb{R}^n$ is given, there is a unique linear transformation $\mathbb{R}^n \to \mathbb{R}^m$ which has *any* desired effect on the basis vectors. More precisely, we have

THEOREM ④   Let $\mathcal{F} = \{F_1,\ F_2,\ \cdots,\ F_n\}$ be any basis of $\mathbb{R}^n$, and select any n vectors $\{Z_1,\ Z_2,\ \cdots,\ Z_n\}$ in $\mathbb{R}^m$, possibly not distinct. Then there is a unique linear transformation $T : \mathbb{R}^n \to \mathbb{R}^m$ such that

$$T(F_i) = Z_i \quad \text{holds for each } i = 1,\ 2,\ \cdots,\ n.$$

In fact T can be defined as follows: If X is any vector in $\mathbb{R}^n$, express X as a linear combination of the vectors in the basis $\mathcal{F}$, say

$$X = a_1F_1 + a_2F_2 + \cdots + a_nF_n.$$

Then $T(X)$ is given by

$$T(X) = a_1Z_1 + a_2Z_2 + \cdots + a_nZ_n. \tag{$*$}$$

PROOF   If $T : \mathbb{R}^n \to \mathbb{R}^m$ is any linear transformation with the property that $T(F_i) = Z_i$ for each i, it is clear from Theorem 1 that $(*)$ holds. Hence Lemma 2 shows that T is uniquely determined *if it exists*. The natural temptation is to define T by $(*)$. That is, if X is any vector in $\mathbb{R}^n$, use the fact that $\mathcal{F}$ spans $\mathbb{R}^n$ to express $X = a_1F_1 + a_2F_2 + \cdots + a_nF_n$, and take

$$T(X) = a_1Z_1 + a_2Z_2 + \cdots + a_nZ_n.$$

However, there is one possible flaw in this definition: If $X = b_1F_1 + b_2F_2 + \cdots + b_nF_n$ is a *possibly different* linear combination for X, we would get

$$T(X) = b_1Z_1 + b_2Z_2 + \cdots + b_nZ_n,$$

and this might be different from $a_1Z_1 + a_2Z_2 + \cdots + a_nZ_n$. However, this is where the assumption that $\mathcal{F}$ is also independent comes in: Since

$$a_1F_1 + a_2F_2 + \cdots + a_nF_n = b_1F_1 + b_2F_2 + \cdots + b_nF_n,$$

the independence of the F_i implies that $a_i = b_i$ for each i (Theorem 1 §4.2). Hence the definition $(*)$ is unambiguous. It is now a routine matter to verify that T is linear, so the theorem is proved.

Theorem 4 is used extensively as a way to define linear transformations by specifying their action on a basis. The definition in $(*)$ is referred to as *extending T linearly* to $\mathbb{R}^n$.

Example 10   Find a linear transformation $T : \mathbb{R}^3 \to \mathbb{R}^2$ such that $T\left([1\ \ 1\ \ 0]^T\right) = [3\ \ {-2}]^T$, $T\left([1\ \ 0\ \ 1]^T\right) = [2\ \ {-1}]^T$, and $T\left([0\ \ 1\ \ 1]^T\right) = [1\ \ 0]^T$.

SOLUTION   For convenience, write $F_1 = [1\ \ 1\ \ 0]^T$, $F_2 = [1\ \ 0\ \ 1]^T$, and $F_3 = [0\ \ 1\ \ 1]^T$. Then $\mathcal{F} = \{F_1, F_2, F_3\}$ is a basis of $\mathbb{R}^3$, so Theorem 4 applies. An arbitrary vector $X = [x_1\ \ x_2\ \ x_3]^T$ in $\mathbb{R}^3$ has the following $\mathcal{F}$-expansion:

$$X = \tfrac{x_1 + x_2 - x_3}{2}F_1 + \tfrac{x_1 - x_2 + x_3}{2}F_2 + \tfrac{-x_1 + x_2 + x_3}{2}F_3.$$

Hence

$$T(X) = \frac{x_1 + x_2 - x_3}{2} T(F_1) + \frac{x_1 - x_2 + x_3}{2} T(F_2) + \frac{-x_1 + x_2 + x_3}{2} T(F_3)$$

$$= \frac{x_1 + x_2 - x_3}{2} \begin{bmatrix} 3 \\ -2 \end{bmatrix} + \frac{x_1 - x_2 + x_3}{2} \begin{bmatrix} 2 \\ -1 \end{bmatrix} + \frac{-x_1 + x_2 + x_3}{2} \begin{bmatrix} 1 \\ 0 \end{bmatrix}$$

$$= \frac{1}{2} \begin{bmatrix} 4x_1 + 2x_2 \\ -3x_1 - x_2 + x_3 \end{bmatrix}.$$

Note that this shows that the standard matrix of T is $\frac{1}{2} \begin{bmatrix} 4 & 2 & 0 \\ -3 & -1 & 1 \end{bmatrix}$.

Let $T : \mathbb{R}^n \rightarrow \mathbb{R}^n$ be a linear operator. A linear operator $S : \mathbb{R}^n \rightarrow \mathbb{R}^n$ is called an **inverse** of T if the action of each of S and T "undoes" the action of the other; that is, if

$$S(T(X)) = X \quad \text{and} \quad T(S(X)) = X \text{ hold for every } X \text{ in } \mathbb{R}^n.$$

In terms of the composition operation, these conditions take the simpler form

$$S \circ T = 1_{\mathbb{R}^n} \quad \text{and} \quad T \circ S = 1_{\mathbb{R}^n}.$$

Thus if R_θ denotes rotation of $\mathbb{R}^2$ about the origin through an angle θ, then $R_{-\theta}$ is an inverse of R_θ because it reverses the action.

An operator T may not have an inverse (see below) but, if an inverse exists, it is uniquely determined by T as the next result shows.

LEMMA 3   If S and S_1 are both inverses of T, then $S = S_1$.

PROOF   We must show that $S(X) = S_1(X)$ for all X in $\mathbb{R}^n$. We are assuming that $T \circ S = 1_{\mathbb{R}^n} = T \circ S_1$ so $T(S(X)) = T(S_1(X))$. Now apply S to get $(S \circ T)(S(X)) = (S \circ T)(S_1(X))$. But $S \circ T = 1_{\mathbb{R}^n}$, so this becomes $S(X) = S_1(X)$, as required.

Hence, if an operator $T : \mathbb{R}^n \rightarrow \mathbb{R}^n$ has an inverse S, then it has exactly one which we denote as $S = T^{-1}$. In this case we say that T is an **invertible** operator. If this all seems a bit like matrix algebra, the next results explains why.

THEOREM 5   Let $T : \mathbb{R}^n \rightarrow \mathbb{R}^n$ be an operator with standard matrix A. Then:
  (1) T has an inverse if and only if A is an invertible matrix.
  (2) In this case A^{-1} is the standard matrix of T^{-1}.

PROOF   If S is an inverse of T, let B denote the standard matrix of S. Then $S \circ T = 1_{\mathbb{R}^n}$, and this operator has standard matrix $BA = I$ by Theorem 3. Similarly, $AB = I$, so A is invertible. Conversely, if A is invertible, let $S : \mathbb{R}^n \rightarrow \mathbb{R}^n$ be the operator with standard matrix A^{-1}. Then $(S \circ T)(X) = S(T(X)) = A^{-1}(AX) = X$ for all X in $\mathbb{R}^n$, so $S \circ T = 1_{\mathbb{R}^n}$. Similarly, $T \circ S = 1_{\mathbb{R}^n}$, so T is invertible with $T^{-1} = S$. This completes the proof of (1), and also proves (2).

4.9.2 Changing Coordinates

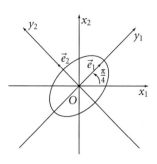

Consider the equation

$$x_1^2 + x_1 x_2 + x_2^2 = 3;$$

its graph is shown in the diagram. If the plane is rotated counterclockwise through $\frac{\pi}{4}$ radians, the variables x_1 and x_2 become

$$y_1 = \tfrac{1}{\sqrt{2}}(x_1 - x_2) \text{ and } y_1 = \tfrac{1}{\sqrt{2}}(x_1 + x_2),$$

respectively. In terms of y_1 and y_2 the equation assumes a much simpler form: $y_1^2 + 3y_1^2 = 6$. The reason is that the curve is symmetric about the new y_1- and y_2-axes. Finding these axes amounts to finding the unit vectors $\vec{e}_1 = \frac{1}{\sqrt{2}}[1\ 1]^T$ and $\vec{e}_2 = \frac{1}{\sqrt{2}}[-1\ 1]^T$ along these axes,[27] that is finding a new basis $\{\vec{e}_1, \vec{e}_2\}$ of $\mathbb{R}^2$ that is compatible with the graph.

More generally, it often happens that one basis of $\mathbb{R}^n$ is more convenient than another. Changing the basis of $\mathbb{R}^n$ amounts to specifying a new "coordinate system" in $\mathbb{R}^n$, and we now investigate how the "coordinates" of a given vector change when the basis is changed. We begin by clarifying the relationship between bases and "coordinates".

Let $\mathcal{F} = \{F_1, F_2, \cdots, F_n\}$ be a basis of $\mathbb{R}^n$. Since $\mathcal{F}$ spans $\mathbb{R}^n$, every vector X in $\mathbb{R}^n$ is a linear combination $X = x_1 F_1 + x_2 F_2 + \cdots + x_n F_n$ where the x_i are real numbers. Moreover, since $\mathcal{F}$ is linearly independent, the numbers x_i are uniquely determined.[28] These numbers x_i are called the $\mathcal{F}$-**coordinates** of X, and the column

$$C_{\mathcal{F}}(X) = [x_1\ \ x_2\ \ \cdots\ \ x_n]^T$$

is called the $\mathcal{F}$-**coordinate vector** of X.

Example 11 If $\mathcal{E} = \{E_1, E_2, \cdots, E_n\}$ is the standard basis of $\mathbb{R}^n$, then $C_{\mathcal{E}}(X) = X$ for every X in $\mathbb{R}^n$. The reason is that if $X = [x_1\ \ x_2\ \ \cdots\ \ x_n]^T$, then $X = x_1 E_1 + x_2 E_2 + \cdots + x_n E_n$.

Example 12 If $\mathcal{F} = \{F_1, F_2, \cdots, F_n\}$ is an orthogonal basis of $\mathbb{R}^n$, then for each X in $\mathbb{R}^n$,

$$C_{\mathcal{F}}(X) = \left[\frac{X \cdot F_1}{\|F_1\|^2}\ \ \frac{X \cdot F_2}{\|F_2\|^2}\ \ \cdots\ \ \frac{X \cdot F_n}{\|F_n\|^2} \right]^T$$

because $X = \frac{X \cdot F_1}{\|F_1\|^2} F_1 + \frac{X \cdot F_2}{\|F_2\|^2} F_2 + \cdots + \frac{X \cdot F_n}{\|F_n\|^2} F_n$ by the Expansion theorem (Theorem 6 §4.5). This formula is particularly simple if $\mathcal{F}$ is an orthonormal basis since then all the denominators $\|F_i\|^2$ equal 1.

The following simple fact about coordinate vectors will be used several times.

LEMMA 4 If $\mathcal{F} = \{F_1, F_2, \cdots, F_n\}$ is a basis of $\mathbb{R}^n$, let $P = [F_1\ \ F_2\ \ \cdots\ \ F_n]$ be the matrix with the F_i as its columns. Then

$$C_{\mathcal{F}}(X) = P^{-1}X \quad \text{for all } X \text{ in } \mathbb{R}^n.$$

In particular, $C_{\mathcal{F}}$ is a linear operator $\mathbb{R}^n \to \mathbb{R}^n$ with standard matrix P^{-1}.

---

[27] These vectors can be *discovered* using diagonalization (see Section 4.8): $\vec{e}_1$ and $\vec{e}_2$ are the principal axes of the quadratic form $q = x_1^2 + x_1 x_2 + x_2^2$.

[28] For the x_i to be unique, the vectors in $\mathcal{F}$ must always be listed in the same order—we then call $\mathcal{F}$ an *ordered* basis. Thus, when working with coordinates, we assume that the bases are ordered.

PROOF   Let $X = x_1F_1 + x_2F_2 + \cdots + x_nF_n$, so that $C_{\mathcal{F}}(X) = [x_1 \ x_2 \ \cdots \ x_n]^T$. Block multiplication gives:

$$PC_{\mathcal{F}}(X) = [F_1 \ F_2 \ \cdots \ F_n]\begin{bmatrix} x_1 \\ x_2 \\ \vdots \\ x_n \end{bmatrix} = x_1F_1 + x_2F_2 + \cdots + x_nF_n = X.$$

The lemma follows because P is invertible (its columns form a basis of $\mathbb{R}^n$).

If $\mathcal{F}$ is a basis of $\mathbb{R}^n$, the operator $C_{\mathcal{F}}: \mathbb{R}^n \to \mathbb{R}^n$ is called the **coordinate operator** corresponding to $\mathcal{F}$. Note that if the basis $\mathcal{F}$ is orthonormal, then P is actually an orthogonal matrix (that is $P^{-1} = P^T$).

Now suppose that $\mathcal{F} = \{F_1, F_2, \cdots, F_n\}$ and $\mathcal{G} = \{G_1, G_2, \cdots, G_n\}$ are two bases of $\mathbb{R}^n$. We want to discover how the coordinate vectors $C_{\mathcal{F}}(X)$ and $C_{\mathcal{G}}(X)$ are related. By Lemma 4, we have

$$C_{\mathcal{F}}(X) = P^{-1}X \quad \text{and} \quad C_{\mathcal{G}}(X) = Q^{-1}X \text{ for all } X \text{ in } \mathbb{R}^n,$$

where $P = [F_1 \ F_2 \ \cdots \ F_n]$ and $Q = [G_1 \ G_2 \ \cdots \ G_n]$. Hence, for all X in $\mathbb{R}^n$, we have

$$\begin{aligned} C_{\mathcal{G}}(X) &= Q^{-1}X = Q^{-1}PC_{\mathcal{F}}(X) \\ &= Q^{-1}[F_1 \ F_2 \ \cdots \ F_n]C_{\mathcal{F}}(X) \\ &= [Q^{-1}F_1 \ Q^{-1}F_2 \ \cdots \ Q^{-1}F_n]C_{\mathcal{F}}(X) \\ &= [C_{\mathcal{G}}(F_1) \ C_{\mathcal{G}}(F_2) \ \cdots \ C_{\mathcal{G}}(F_n)]C_{\mathcal{F}}(X) \end{aligned}$$

With this in mind, if $\mathcal{F}$ and $\mathcal{G}$ are any two bases of $\mathbb{R}^n$ we define the matrix

$$P_{\mathcal{G}\leftarrow\mathcal{F}} = [C_{\mathcal{G}}(F_1) \ C_{\mathcal{G}}(F_2) \ \cdots \ C_{\mathcal{G}}(F_n)].$$

The matrix $P_{\mathcal{G}\leftarrow\mathcal{F}}$ is called the **change** matrix[29] from $\mathcal{F}$ to $\mathcal{G}$. This matrix depends only on the two bases $\mathcal{F}$ and $\mathcal{G}$, and not on the vector X; on the other hand, the above calculation shows that

$$C_{\mathcal{G}}(X) = P_{\mathcal{G}\leftarrow\mathcal{F}}C_{\mathcal{F}}(X)$$

holds for *all* X in $\mathbb{R}^n$. This is the desired relationship between the $\mathcal{F}$- and $\mathcal{G}$-coordinates of X, and we state it as the first part of the following theorem.

THEOREM 6   If $\mathcal{F} = \{F_1, F_2, \cdots, F_n\}$ and $\mathcal{G}$ are (ordered) bases of $\mathbb{R}^n$, then

$$C_{\mathcal{G}}(X) = P_{\mathcal{G}\leftarrow\mathcal{F}}C_{\mathcal{F}}(X) \quad \text{for all } X \text{ in } \mathbb{R}^n.$$

Moreover, if $\mathcal{G} = \{G_1, G_2, \cdots, G_n\}$, then the matrix $P_{\mathcal{G}\leftarrow\mathcal{F}}$ can be computed as follows:

$$\big[[G_1 \ G_2 \ \cdots \ G_n] \ \ [F_1 \ F_2 \ \cdots \ F_n]\big] \to [I_n \ P_{\mathcal{G}\leftarrow\mathcal{F}}].$$

In other words, carry the double matrix on the left to reduced row-echelon form, and $P_{\mathcal{G}\leftarrow\mathcal{F}}$ appears on the right.

PROOF   By the above discussion, it remains to verify the second part of the theorem. Write $P = [F_1 \ F_2 \ \cdots \ F_n]$ and $Q = [G_1 \ G_2 \ \cdots \ G_n]$ as before. Since Q is invertible, we can carry $Q \to I_n = Q^{-1}Q$ by row operations, so the same series of operations carries $P \to Q^{-1}P$ by Theorem 1 §1.6. But

$$\begin{aligned} Q^{-1}P = Q^{-1}[F_1 \ F_2 \ \cdots \ F_n] &= [Q^{-1}F_1 \ Q^{-1}F_2 \ \cdots \ Q^{-1}F_n] \\ &= [C_{\mathcal{G}}(F_1) \ C_{\mathcal{G}}(F_2) \ \cdots \ C_{\mathcal{G}}(F_n)] \\ &= P_{\mathcal{G}\leftarrow\mathcal{F}} \end{aligned}$$

by Lemma 4. Hence doing the operations to the double matrix gives $[Q \ P] \to [I_n \ P_{\mathcal{G}\leftarrow\mathcal{F}}]$, as required.

---

[29] The reason for the notation $P_{\mathcal{G}\leftarrow\mathcal{F}}$ will be apparent shortly.

These change matrices are all invertible; in fact we have the following result which explains the notation $P_{\mathcal{G}\leftarrow\mathcal{F}}$.

COROLLARY

Let $\mathcal{F}$, $\mathcal{G}$, and $\mathcal{H}$ be three ordered bases of $\mathbb{R}^n$. Then:

(1) $P_{\mathcal{F}\leftarrow\mathcal{F}} = I_n$.
(2) $P_{\mathcal{G}\leftarrow\mathcal{F}}$ is invertible, and $(P_{\mathcal{G}\leftarrow\mathcal{F}})^{-1} = P_{\mathcal{F}\leftarrow\mathcal{G}}$.
(3) $P_{\mathcal{H}\leftarrow\mathcal{G}}P_{\mathcal{G}\leftarrow\mathcal{F}} = P_{\mathcal{H}\leftarrow\mathcal{F}}$.

PROOF

(1) is a routine computation, and (1) and (3) together imply (2) (verify). To prove (3), let X be a vector in $\mathbb{R}^n$ and apply Theorem 6 three times:

$$P_{\mathcal{H}\leftarrow\mathcal{G}}\, P_{\mathcal{G}\leftarrow\mathcal{F}}\, C_{\mathcal{F}}(X) = P_{\mathcal{H}\leftarrow\mathcal{G}}\, C_{\mathcal{G}}(X) = C_{\mathcal{H}}(X) = P_{\mathcal{H}\leftarrow\mathcal{F}}\, C_{\mathcal{F}}(X).$$

Since this holds for all X in $\mathbb{R}^n$, (3) follows from Lemmas 1 and 2.

Example 13

Find $P_{\mathcal{G}\leftarrow\mathcal{F}}$ where $\mathcal{F} = \{[2 \;\; -1]^T,\; [1 \;\; 5]^T\}$ and $\mathcal{G} = \{[1 \;\; 3]^T,\; [3 \;\; 4]^T\}$ are two bases of $\mathbb{R}^2$.

SOLUTION

As in the last part of Theorem 6, we compute

$$\begin{bmatrix} 1 & 3 & 2 & 1 \\ 3 & 4 & -1 & 5 \end{bmatrix} \rightarrow \begin{bmatrix} 1 & 0 & -\frac{11}{5} & \frac{11}{5} \\ 0 & 1 & \frac{7}{5} & -\frac{2}{5} \end{bmatrix}, \text{ so } P_{\mathcal{G}\leftarrow\mathcal{F}} = \frac{1}{5}\begin{bmatrix} -11 & 11 \\ 7 & -2 \end{bmatrix}.$$

The reader can verify that the columns of $P_{\mathcal{G}\leftarrow\mathcal{F}}$ are indeed $C_{\mathcal{G}}([2 \;\; -1]^T)$ and $C_{\mathcal{G}}([1 \;\; 5]^T)$.

4.9.3 The $\mathcal{F}$-matrix of a Linear Operator

Suppose T is a rotation about the line L through the origin in $\mathbb{R}^3$. Finding the standard matrix of T is not convenient because the usual coordinate axes bear no relation to the line L. Everything is simpler if we use a new *intrinsic* set of axes, one pointing along the line L and the other two orthogonal to L (that is, in the plane $L^{\perp}$). Choosing such a set of axes amounts to choosing a basis $\mathcal{F}$ for $\mathbb{R}^3$ with one vector in L and the other two vectors in $L^{\perp}$. The idea is to find an "$\mathcal{F}$-matrix" for the rotation that plays the same role relative to $\mathcal{F}$ that the standard matrix plays relative to the standard basis. It turns out that computing this $\mathcal{F}$-matrix is not too difficult because $\mathcal{F}$ is naturally aligned with the line L. Since the $\mathcal{F}$-matrix is intimately related to the basis $\mathcal{F}$, it is not surprising that the $\mathcal{F}$-coordinates $C_{\mathcal{F}}(X)$ will be used to describe each vector X.

To motivate the general situation, recall that if $T : \mathbb{R}^n \to \mathbb{R}^n$ is any operator, we have $T(X) = AX$ for all X in $\mathbb{R}^n$ by Theorem 2 where A is the standard matrix of the operator T. Moreover, if $\mathcal{E}$ is the standard basis of $\mathbb{R}^n$, then $C_{\mathcal{E}}(X) = X$ for every X by Example 11, so the equation $T(X) = AX$ becomes

$$C_{\mathcal{E}}[T(X)] = A\, C_{\mathcal{E}}(X) \quad \text{for all } X \text{ in } \mathbb{R}^n.$$

This formula extends to other bases than $\mathcal{E}$. Hence given an operator $T : \mathbb{R}^n \to \mathbb{R}^n$ and a basis $\mathcal{F}$ of $\mathbb{R}^n$, we look for a matrix B such that

$$C_{\mathcal{F}}[T(X)] = B\, C_{\mathcal{F}}(X) \quad \text{for all } X \text{ in } \mathbb{R}^n. \tag{$**$}$$

Such a matrix B is unique if it exists by Lemmas 1 and 4 (verify). Moreover, B describes the action of T because we can easily compute $T(X)$ from the $\mathcal{F}$-coordinates $C_{\mathcal{F}}[T(X)]$ — see Example 15 below for an illustration.

Furthermore, B exists for *any* choice of basis $\mathcal{F} = \{F_1,\ F_2,\ \cdots,\ F_n\}$. Indeed, let A denote the standard matrix of T, and write $P = [F_1\ \ F_2\ \cdots\ F_n]$ as in Lemma 4. Then, using Lemma 4 twice, we have

$$C_{\mathcal{F}}(T(X)) = P^{-1}(T(X)) = P^{-1}(AX) = P^{-1}A(P\,C_{\mathcal{F}}(X)) = (P^{-1}AP)\,C_{\mathcal{F}}(X).$$

Hence $B = P^{-1}AP$ works in (**). This matrix is called the $\mathcal{F}$-**matrix** of T and is denoted $M_{\mathcal{F}}(T)$. We have shown that $M_{\mathcal{F}}(T)$ is the unique matrix with the property that $C_{\mathcal{F}}[T(X)] = M_{\mathcal{F}}(T)\,C_{\mathcal{F}}(X)$ for all X in $\mathbb{R}^n$. This discussion proves most of the following theorem.

THEOREM 7

Let $T : \mathbb{R}^n \to \mathbb{R}^n$ be a linear operator, and let $\mathcal{F}$ be a basis of $\mathbb{R}^n$. Then a uniquely determined $n \times n$ matrix $M_{\mathcal{F}}(T)$ exists such that

$$C_{\mathcal{F}}[T(X)] = M_{\mathcal{F}}(T)\,C_{\mathcal{F}}(X) \quad \text{for all } X \text{ in } \mathbb{R}^n.$$

Furthermore, if $\mathcal{F} = \{F_1,\ F_2,\ \cdots,\ F_n\}$ and we put $P = [F_1\ \ F_2\ \cdots\ F_n]$, we have:

(1) $M_{\mathcal{F}}(T) = P^{-1}AP$ where A is the standard matrix of T.
(2) $M_{\mathcal{F}}(T) = [C_{\mathcal{F}}(T(F_1))\ \ C_{\mathcal{F}}(T(F_2))\ \cdots\ C_{\mathcal{F}}(T(F_n))]$.
(3) $M_{\mathcal{F}}(T)$ is invertible if and only if T is invertible.

PROOF

(1) is proved above. As to (2), Lemma 4 gives $P\,C_{\mathcal{F}}(T(F_j)) = T(F_j) = AF_j$ for each j. Hence

$$\begin{aligned}
AP &= A[F_1\ \ F_2\ \cdots\ F_n] \\
&= [AF_1\ \ AF_2\ \cdots\ AF_n] \\
&= [P\,C_{\mathcal{F}}(T(F_1))\ \ P\,C_{\mathcal{F}}(T(F_2))\ \cdots\ P\,C_{\mathcal{F}}(T(F_n))] \\
&= P[C_{\mathcal{F}}(T(F_1))\ \ C_{\mathcal{F}}(T(F_2))\ \cdots\ C_{\mathcal{F}}(T(F_n))]
\end{aligned}$$

Now (2) follows using (1). Finally, T is invertible if and only if A is invertible (by Theorem 5), and this holds if and only if $M_{\mathcal{F}}(T)$ is invertible by (1). This is (3).

Example 14

If $\mathcal{E}$ is the standard basis of $\mathbb{R}^n$, then $M_{\mathcal{E}}(T)$ is the standard matrix of T for any linear operator T on $\mathbb{R}^n$. This follows from part (1) of Theorem 7 because $P = I$ when $\mathcal{F} = \mathcal{E}$.

If we know the $\mathcal{F}$-matrix of a linear operator $T : \mathbb{R}^n \to \mathbb{R}^n$ for some basis $\mathcal{F}$ of $\mathbb{R}^n$, it is a routine matter to use Theorem 7 to find the action of T. Here is an example.

Example 15

Find the action of the operator $T : \mathbb{R}^n \to \mathbb{R}^n$ where $M_{\mathcal{F}}(T) = \begin{bmatrix} 1 & 2 & 0 \\ 2 & -1 & 3 \\ 1 & 1 & 1 \end{bmatrix}$ and $\mathcal{F} = \{[1\ \ 0\ \ 0]^T,\ [0\ \ 1\ \ 1]^T,\ [0\ \ -1\ \ 1]^T\}$.

SOLUTION

For convenience let $F_1 = [1\ \ 0\ \ 0]^T, F_2 = [0\ \ 1\ \ 1]^T$, and $F_3 = [0\ \ -1\ \ 1]^T$ denote the vectors in $\mathcal{F}$. By Theorem 7 we know that

$$C_{\mathcal{F}}[T(X)] = M_{\mathcal{F}}(T)\,C_{\mathcal{F}}(X)$$

for any $X = [x_1\ \ x_2\ \ x_3]^T$ in $\mathbb{R}^n$. Since we are given $M_{\mathcal{F}}(T)$, the hard part is to compute $C_{\mathcal{F}}(X)$ since it is necessary to express the vector X as a linear combination of the vectors F_i in $\mathcal{F}$. In this case $\mathcal{F}$ is actually orthogonal, so the Expansion theorem simplifies the work:

$$\begin{aligned}
X &= \frac{X \cdot F_1}{\|F_1\|^2}F_1 + \frac{X \cdot F_2}{\|F_2\|^2}F_2 + \frac{X \cdot F_3}{\|F_3\|^2}F_3 \\
&= \frac{x_1}{1}F_1 + \frac{x_2 + x_3}{2}F_2 + \frac{-x_2 + x_3}{2}F_3.
\end{aligned}$$

It follows that $C_{\mathcal{F}}(X) = \frac{1}{2}[2x_1 \quad x_2 + x_3 \quad x_3 - x_2]^T$, so

$$C_{\mathcal{F}}[T(X)] = M_{\mathcal{F}}(T)\, C_{\mathcal{F}}(X)$$

$$= \begin{bmatrix} 1 & 2 & 0 \\ 2 & -1 & 3 \\ 1 & 1 & 1 \end{bmatrix} \frac{1}{2} \begin{bmatrix} 2x_1 \\ x_2 + x_3 \\ x_3 - x_2 \end{bmatrix}$$

$$= \begin{bmatrix} x_1 + x_2 + x_3 \\ 2x_1 - 2x_2 + x_3 \\ x_1 + x_3 \end{bmatrix}.$$

Finally, this gives

$$T(X) = (x_1 + x_2 + x_3)F_1 + (2x_1 - 2x_2 + x_3)F_2 + (x_1 + x_3)F_3$$

$$= \begin{bmatrix} x_1 + x_2 + x_3 \\ x_1 - 2x_2 \\ 3x_1 - 2x_2 + 2x_3 \end{bmatrix}.$$

This is what we wanted.

The formula in part (2) of Theorem 7 is very useful because it means that we can construct the $\mathcal{F}$-matrix of an operator T without knowing the standard matrix of T. More importantly, it means that we can often *choose* the basis $\mathcal{F}$ in such a way that the matrix $M_{\mathcal{F}}(T)$ has a relatively simple form. This is accomplished by choosing $\mathcal{F}$ so that it is naturally compatible with the action of the operator T. We describe this by saying that it is an **intrinsic** basis. This is a key technique in linear algebra; here are two examples.

Example 16

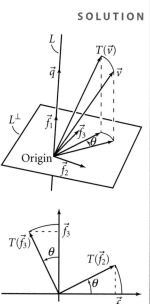

Describe the rotations of $\mathbb{R}^3$ about a line L through the origin by finding an intrinsic basis $\mathcal{F}$ for $\mathbb{R}^3$ and computing $M_{\mathcal{F}}(T)$.

SOLUTION

Let T denote the rotation about L through the angle θ. Choose a unit vector $\vec{f}_1$ in L. Since $dim(L) = 1$, we have $dim(L^{\perp}) = 2$ by Theorem 3 §4.6 so let $\{\vec{f}_2, \vec{f}_3\}$ be an orthonormal basis of $L^{\perp}$. Then $\mathcal{F} = \{\vec{f}_1, \vec{f}_2, \vec{f}_3\}$ is an orthonormal basis of $\mathbb{R}^3$, and it remains to compute $M_{\mathcal{F}}(T)$. The action of T is described in the first diagram. We have

$$T(\vec{f}_1) = \vec{f}_1$$

because $\vec{f}_1$ is in L and T is rotation about L. Moreover, $T(\vec{f}_2)$ and $T(\vec{f}_3)$ lie in the plane $L^{\perp}$ and so are obtained by rotating $\vec{f}_1$ and $\vec{f}_2$ in $L^{\perp}$ through the angle θ. By the second diagram, the results are

$$T(\vec{f}_2) = \cos\theta\, \vec{f}_2 + \sin\theta\, \vec{f}_3$$
$$T(\vec{f}_3) = -\sin\theta\, \vec{f}_2 + \cos\theta\, \vec{f}_3.$$

Hence Theorem 7 gives

$$M_{\mathcal{F}}[T] = \begin{bmatrix} C_{\mathcal{F}}(T(\vec{f}_1)) & C_{\mathcal{F}}(T(\vec{f}_2)) & C_{\mathcal{F}}(T(\vec{f}_3)) \end{bmatrix}$$

$$= \begin{bmatrix} 1 & 0 & 0 \\ 0 & \cos\theta & -\sin\theta \\ 0 & \sin\theta & \cos\theta \end{bmatrix}$$

This describes the operator T. Note that $M_{\mathcal{F}}[T]$ is actually an orthogonal matrix here. We return to this in Theorem 12 below.

Example 17   Describe the reflection T of $\mathbb{R}^3$ in a plane U through the origin by finding an intrinsic basis $\mathcal{F}$ for $\mathbb{R}^3$ and computing $M_{\mathcal{F}}(T)$.

SOLUTION

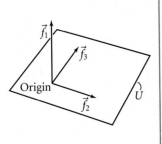

We have $dim\,U = 2$ so $dim(U^{\perp}) = 1$ by Theorem 3 §4.6. So let $\vec{f_1}$ be a unit vector in $U^{\perp}$, and choose an orthonormal basis $\{\vec{f_2}, \vec{f_3}\}$ of U. Then $\mathcal{F} = \{\vec{f_1}, \vec{f_2}, \vec{f_3}\}$ is an orthonormal basis of $\mathbb{R}^3$. If T is reflection in U, it is clear that $T(\vec{f_1}) = -\vec{f_1}$ while $T(\vec{f_2}) = \vec{f_2}$ and $T(\vec{f_3}) = \vec{f_3}$. Hence part (2) of Theorem 7 gives

$$M_{\mathcal{F}}(T) = \begin{bmatrix} C_{\mathcal{F}}[T(\vec{f_1})] & C_{\mathcal{F}}[T(\vec{f_2})] & C_{\mathcal{F}}[T(\vec{f_3})] \end{bmatrix}$$

$$= \begin{bmatrix} -1 & 0 & 0 \\ 0 & 1 & 0 \\ 0 & 0 & 1 \end{bmatrix}.$$

Thus our choice of the basis $\mathcal{F}$ has made $M_{\mathcal{F}}(T)$ into a diagonal matrix.

4.9.4   Similarity

Recall that two $n \times n$ matrices A and B are said to be **similar** if $B = P^{-1}AP$ for some invertible matrix P. In this case we write $A \sim B$. The similarity relation $\sim$ enjoys the following basic properties (see Section 2.3):

    1. $A \sim A$ for all square matrices A.
    2. If $A \sim B$, then $B \sim A$.
    3. If $A \sim B$ and $B \sim C$, then $A \sim C$.

Similar matrices enjoy many of the same features. For example, two similar matrices have the same determinant, trace, characteristic polynomial, and eigenvectors, and if one of them is diagonalizable, so is the other.

It turns out that there is a close connection between similarity and the matrices of a linear operator with respect to various bases. Observe that if $T : \mathbb{R}^n \rightarrow \mathbb{R}^n$ is a linear operator, part (1) of Theorem 7 shows that $M_{\mathcal{F}}(T) \sim M_{\mathcal{G}}(T)$ for any bases $\mathcal{F}$ and $\mathcal{G}$ of $\mathbb{R}^n$ (both are similar to the standard matrix of T). It turns out that the converse is true: If $A \sim B$, there is a linear operator $T : \mathbb{R}^n \rightarrow \mathbb{R}^n$ and bases $\mathcal{F}$ and $\mathcal{G}$ of $\mathbb{R}^n$ such that $A = M_{\mathcal{F}}(T)$ and $B = M_{\mathcal{G}}(T)$. The proof requires a preliminary fact that will be used several times.

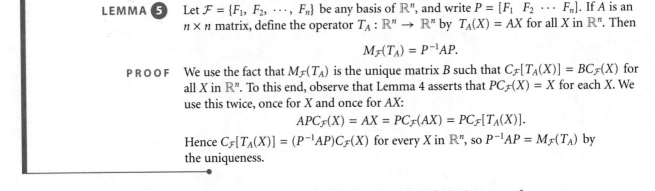

LEMMA 5   Let $\mathcal{F} = \{F_1, F_2, \cdots, F_n\}$ be any basis of $\mathbb{R}^n$, and write $P = [F_1 \; F_2 \; \cdots \; F_n]$. If A is an $n \times n$ matrix, define the operator $T_A : \mathbb{R}^n \rightarrow \mathbb{R}^n$ by $T_A(X) = AX$ for all X in $\mathbb{R}^n$. Then

$$M_{\mathcal{F}}(T_A) = P^{-1}AP.$$

PROOF   We use the fact that $M_{\mathcal{F}}(T_A)$ is the unique matrix B such that $C_{\mathcal{F}}[T_A(X)] = BC_{\mathcal{F}}(X)$ for all X in $\mathbb{R}^n$. To this end, observe that Lemma 4 asserts that $PC_{\mathcal{F}}(X) = X$ for each X. We use this twice, once for X and once for AX:

$$APC_{\mathcal{F}}(X) = AX = PC_{\mathcal{F}}(AX) = PC_{\mathcal{F}}[T_A(X)].$$

Hence $C_{\mathcal{F}}[T_A(X)] = (P^{-1}AP)C_{\mathcal{F}}(X)$ for every X in $\mathbb{R}^n$, so $P^{-1}AP = M_{\mathcal{F}}(T_A)$ by the uniqueness.

Now we can give our characterization of similarity in terms of operators.

THEOREM 8   If A and B are $n \times n$ matrices, then $A \sim B$ if and only if there exists an operator $T : \mathbb{R}^n \to \mathbb{R}^n$ and bases $\mathcal{F}$ and $\mathcal{G}$ of $\mathbb{R}^n$ such that $A = M_{\mathcal{F}}(T)$ and $B = M_{\mathcal{G}}(T)$.

PROOF   If such T, $\mathcal{F}$, and $\mathcal{G}$ exist, then $M_{\mathcal{F}}(T) \sim M_{\mathcal{G}}(T)$ because both matrices are similar to the standard matrix of T by Theorem 7.

Conversely, suppose $A \sim B$, say $B = P^{-1}AP$ where $P = [F_1 \ F_2 \ \cdots \ F_n]$ is invertible. If $\mathcal{F} = \{F_1, F_2, \cdots, F_n\}$ is the basis of $\mathbb{R}^n$ consisting of the columns of P, then $M_{\mathcal{F}}(T_A) = P^{-1}AP = B$ by Lemma 5. On the other hand, if $\mathcal{E}$ is the standard basis of $\mathbb{R}^n$ then $M_{\mathcal{E}}(T_A) = A$ (verify). This proves the theorem.

If A is a square matrix, define the **similarity class** $sim(A)$ of A to be the set of all matrices similar to A. Thus, for example, A is diagonalizable if and only if $sim(A)$ contains a diagonal matrix. In general, even for a nondiagonalizable matrix A, we can ask for the "nicest" matrix in $sim(A)$. Theorem 8 enters into the discussion by providing another description of $sim(A)$. It shows that, given an $n \times n$ matrix A, there exists an operator $T : \mathbb{R}^n \to \mathbb{R}^n$ such that $sim(A)$ is the set of all $\mathcal{F}$-matrices of T. More compactly,

$$sim(A) = \{M_{\mathcal{F}}(T) \mid \mathcal{F} \text{ is some basis of } \mathbb{R}^n\}.$$

Hence the task of finding the "nicest" matrix similar to A becomes: Given an operator $T : \mathbb{R}^n \to \mathbb{R}^n$, find a basis such that $M_{\mathcal{F}}(T)$ is as "nice" as possible. This is illustrated in Examples 16 and 17 and, because operators have a geometric interpretation, this gives new insights into similarity. We return to it in Chapter 5.

4.9.5 Isometries

To illustrate all these concepts, we conclude with a look at a very important class of operators on $\mathbb{R}^n$ called isometries that arise in geometry and in other applications. Using geometrical arguments, it was established in Section 3.4 that rotations about the origin and reflections in a line through the origin are all linear operators on $\mathbb{R}^2$. Similar geometric arguments work in $\mathbb{R}^3$, but we are going to give an algebraic proof that is valid in $\mathbb{R}^n$ for any n. The key observation is that rotations and reflections are distance preserving in the following sense. A transformation $T : \mathbb{R}^n \to \mathbb{R}^n$ (possibly not linear) is said to be **distance preserving** if

$$\|T(X) - T(Y)\| = \|X - Y\| \quad \text{for all } X \text{ and } Y \text{ in } \mathbb{R}^n, \qquad (\ast\ast\ast)$$

that is, the distance between $T(X)$ and $T(Y)$ is the same as the distance between X and Y for all vectors X and Y in $\mathbb{R}^n$. Distance-preserving maps need not be linear: The Y-translations in Example 5 are distance preserving for every choice of Y (verify) but they are not linear if $Y \neq 0$. Surprisingly, the distance-preserving transformations that fix the origin are actually linear.

THEOREM 9   Let $T : \mathbb{R}^n \to \mathbb{R}^n$ be a distance-preserving transformation with the property that $T(0) = 0$. Then T is linear.

PROOF   Let X and Y denote vectors in $\mathbb{R}^n$. Observe first that the equation $\|T(X) - T(Y)\|^2 = \|X - Y\|^2$ (from $(\ast\ast\ast)$) becomes

$$\|T(X)\|^2 - 2\, T(X) \cdot T(Y) + \|T(Y)\|^2.$$

But $\|T(X)\| = \|X\|$ for every X in $\mathbb{R}^n$ (take $Y = 0$ in $(\ast\ast\ast)$), so we obtain

$$T(X) \cdot T(Y) = X \cdot Y \quad \text{for all } X \text{ and } Y \text{ in } \mathbb{R}^n. \qquad (\ast\ast\ast\ast)$$

Now let $\{F_1, F_2, \cdots F_n\}$ be an orthogonal basis of $\mathbb{R}^n$. It follows from (****) that $\{T(F_1), T(F_2), \cdots T(F_n)\}$ is also an orthogonal basis $[T(F_i) \neq 0$ for each i because $\|T(F_i)\| = \|F_i\| \neq 0]$. Hence, to prove that $T(aX) = aT(X)$, it suffices to show that $[T(aX) - aT(X)] \cdot T(F_i) = 0$ for each i (see Example 3 §4.5). But (****) gives

$$[T(aX) - aT(X)] \cdot T(F_i) = T(aX) \cdot T(F_i) - aT(X) \cdot T(F_i)$$
$$= (aX) \cdot F_i - a(X \cdot F_i)$$
$$= 0,$$

as required. A similar argument shows that $T(X + Y) = T(X) + T(Y)$ for all X and Y, so T is linear.

A *linear* operator $T : \mathbb{R}^n \to \mathbb{R}^n$ which is distance preserving is called an **isometry**. This agrees with the definition in Section 3.4 for operators on $\mathbb{R}^2$. The first consequence of Theorem 9 is that, as for $\mathbb{R}^2$, rotations and reflections fixing the origin are all isometries.

COROLLARY ①   In $\mathbb{R}^3$ the following are all isometries:

(**1**) Rotations around a line through the origin.
(**2**) Reflections in a plane through the origin.

PROOF   It is clear geometrically that these transformations are all distance preserving, and they all fix the origin. Hence Theorem 9 shows that they are also linear.

Isometries are distance preserving, and it is easy to verify that translations are also distance preserving. Moreover, the composite of two distance-preserving transformations is again distance preserving (verify). The following corollary shows that *all* distance-preserving transformations arise in this way.

COROLLARY ②   Every distance-preserving transformation $S : \mathbb{R}^n \to \mathbb{R}^n$ is the composite of an isometry followed by a translation. More precisely, there exists a vector Y in $\mathbb{R}^n$ and an isometry T of $\mathbb{R}^n$ such that

$$S(X) = T(X) + Y \text{ for every } X \text{ in } \mathbb{R}^n.$$

PROOF   If $S : \mathbb{R}^n \to \mathbb{R}^n$ is distance preserving, write $S(0) = Y$ and define $T : \mathbb{R}^n \to \mathbb{R}^n$ by $T(X) = S(X) - Y$ for every X in $\mathbb{R}^n$. Then $T(0) = 0$ because $S(0) = Y$ and, for all X and X_1 in $\mathbb{R}^n$,

$$\|T(X) - T(X_1)\| = \|(S(X) - Y) - (S(X_1) - Y)\|$$
$$= \|S(X) - S(X_1)\|$$
$$= \|X - X_1\|$$

because S is distance preserving. Hence T is distance preserving, and so is an isometry by Theorem 9.

We have defined isometries as the linear operators that preserve distance. The next theorem shows that they can also be characterized as the linear operators that preserve length, or dot products, or orthonormal bases.

THEOREM 10

The following are equivalent for a linear operator $T : \mathbb{R}^n \to \mathbb{R}^n$:

(1) T is an isometry.
(2) $\|T(X)\| = \|X\|$ for all X in $\mathbb{R}^n$.
(3) $T(X) \cdot T(Y) = X \cdot Y$ for all X and Y in $\mathbb{R}^n$.
(4) If $\{F_1,\ F_2,\ \cdots,\ F_n\}$ is any orthonormal basis of $\mathbb{R}^n$, so also is $\{T(F_1),\ T(F_2),\ \cdots,\ T(F_n)\}$.
(5) There exists an orthonormal basis $\{F_1,\ F_2,\ \cdots,\ F_n\}$ of $\mathbb{R}^n$ such that $\{T(F_1),\ T(F_2),\ \cdots,\ T(F_n)\}$ is also an orthonormal basis.

PROOF

$(1) \Rightarrow (2)$. We have $T(0) = 0$ because T is linear. If T is an isometry, then $\|T(X)\| = \|T(X) - T(0)\| = \|X - 0\| = \|X\|$ for all X.

$(2) \Rightarrow (3)$. Since T is linear, (2) gives $\|T(X) - T(Y)\| = \|T(X - Y)\| = \|X - Y\|$ for all X and Y. This means that T preserves distance, so (3) follows from the proof of (****) in Theorem 9.

$(3) \Rightarrow (4)$. This is clear when one remembers that $\|T(F_i)\|^2 = T(F_i) \cdot T(F_i) = F_i \cdot F_i = \|F_i\|^2 = 1$ for each i.

$(4) \Rightarrow (5)$. This is clear since $\mathbb{R}^n$ *has* orthonormal bases.

$(5) \Rightarrow (1)$. Given X in $\mathbb{R}^n$, write $X = x_1F_1 + x_2F_2 + \cdots + x_nF_n$ where the x_i are real. Then $T(X) = x_1T(F_1) + x_2T(F_2) + \cdots + x_nT(F_n)$, so Pythagoras' theorem and (5) give $\|T(X)\|^2 = x_1^2 + x_2^2 + \cdots + x_n^2 = \|X\|^2$. It follows that $\|T(X)\| = \|X\|$ for each X. Since T is linear, this gives $\|T(X) - T(Y)\| = \|T(X - Y)\| = \|X - Y\|$ for all X and Y, proving (1).

Condition (5) in Theorem 10 is a useful test that T is an isometry: Simply find an orthonormal basis $\{F_1,\ F_2,\ \cdots,\ F_n\}$ of $\mathbb{R}^n$ (possibly the standard basis) and check whether $\{T(F_1),\ T(F_2),\ \cdots,\ T(F_n)\}$ is also orthonormal.

Example 18

Let $\{F_1,\ F_2,\ F_3,\ F_4\}$ be an orthonormal basis of $\mathbb{R}^4$. Using Theorem 5, let $T : \mathbb{R}^4 \to \mathbb{R}^4$ be the linear operator that satisfies $T(F_1) = F_2$, $T(F_2) = -F_1$, $T(F_3) = F_4$ and $T(F_4) = -F_3$. Then this map T is an isometry by Theorem 10 because $\{T(F_1),\ T(F_2),\ T(F_3),\ T(F_4)\} = \{F_2,\ -F_1,\ F_4,\ -F_3\}$ is another orthonormal basis of $\mathbb{R}^4$.

Example 19

If $\mathcal{F} = \{F_1,\ F_2,\ \cdots,\ F_n\}$ is an orthonormal basis of $\mathbb{R}^n$, the corresponding coordinate operator $C_{\mathcal{F}} : \mathbb{R}^n \to \mathbb{R}^n$ is an isometry by Theorem 10 because $\{C_{\mathcal{F}}(F_1),\ C_{\mathcal{F}}(F_2),\ \cdots,\ C_{\mathcal{F}}(F_n),\}$ is orthonormal (it is the standard basis of $\mathbb{R}^n$).

Isometries are closely related to orthogonal matrices as the next theorem shows.

THEOREM 11

Let $T : \mathbb{R}^n \to \mathbb{R}^n$ be a linear operator with standard matrix A. The following are equivalent:

(1) T is an isometry.
(2) A is an orthogonal matrix.
(3) $M_{\mathcal{F}}(T)$ is an orthogonal matrix for every orthonormal basis $\mathcal{F}$ of $\mathbb{R}^n$.
(4) $M_{\mathcal{F}}(T)$ is an orthogonal matrix for some orthonormal basis $\mathcal{F}$ of $\mathbb{R}^n$.

PROOF $(1) \Rightarrow (2)$. Write $A = [C_1 \quad C_2 \quad \cdots \quad C_n]$ in terms of its columns. If E_i is column i of the identity matrix, then $C_i = AE_i$ for each i and we have

$C_i \cdot C_j = (AE_i) \cdot (AE_j) = T(E_i) \cdot T(E_j) = E_i \cdot E_j$ by Theorem 10. Hence $\{C_1, \ C_2, \ \cdots, \ C_n\}$ is an orthonormal set, and (2) follows.

$(2) \Rightarrow (3)$. If $\mathcal{F} = \{F_1, \ F_2, \ \cdots, \ F_n\}$ is an orthonormal basis of $\mathbb{R}^n$, write $P = [F_1 \quad F_2 \quad \cdots \quad F_n]$—an orthogonal matrix. By Theorem 7, $M_{\mathcal{F}}(T) = P^{-1}AP$, and this is orthogonal being a product of orthogonal matrices by (2).

$(3) \Rightarrow (4)$. This is clear.

$(4) \Rightarrow (1)$. If $\mathcal{F} = \{F_1, \ F_2, \ \cdots, \ F_n\}$ is as in (4) and $P = [F_1 \quad F_2 \quad \cdots \quad F_n]$, then $M_{\mathcal{F}}(T) = P^{-1}AP$ by Theorem 7. But P is an orthogonal matrix, so $A = PM_{\mathcal{F}}(T)P^{-1}$ is also an orthogonal matrix. Hence, for X in $\mathbb{R}^n$, $\|T(X)\|^2 = \|AX\|^2 = (AX)^T(AX) = X^TA^TAX = X^TX = \|X\|^2$. It follows that $\|T(X)\| = \|X\|$ for all X in $\mathbb{R}^n$, so T is an isometry by Theorem 10.

Since orthogonal matrices are invertible, Theorem 5 gives

COROLLARY   Every isometry is invertible.

It was shown in Section 3.4 that every isometry of $\mathbb{R}^2$ is either a rotation about the origin or a reflection in a line through the origin. Moreover, we have seen that rotations about a line through the origin are isometries of $\mathbb{R}^3$, as are reflections in a plane through the origin. It is a remarkable fact that every isometry of $\mathbb{R}^3$ is either a rotation, a reflection, or a composite of two of these.

THEOREM ⑫   Let $T : \mathbb{R}^3 \to \mathbb{R}^3$ be an isometry. Then T is either a rotation about a line through the origin, a reflection in a plane through the origin, or else a composite of two of these where the line is in fact perpendicular to the plane.

PROOF   If A is the standard matrix of T, the characteristic polynomial of A has degree 3 (as A is 3×3) and so has a real root λ_1, an eigenvalue of A. Since A is orthogonal, $\lambda_1 = 1$ or $\lambda_1 = -1$ by Theorem 3 §4.7. Let $\vec{f}_1$ be a unit eigenvector corresponding to λ_1, and let $U = \mathbb{R}\vec{f}_1$ denote the line through the origin parallel to $\vec{f}_1$. Hence $U^{\perp}$ is the plane through the origin perpendicular to U.

Claim. If $\vec{v}$ is in $U^{\perp}$, then $T(\vec{v})$ is also in $U^{\perp}$.

Proof. Let $\vec{u}$ be any vector in U, so that $A\vec{u} = \lambda_1\vec{u}$. If $\vec{v}$ is in $U^{\perp}$ then, since A is an orthogonal matrix by Theorem 11,

$$\lambda_1[(A\vec{v}) \cdot \vec{u}] = (A\vec{v}) \cdot (\lambda_1\vec{u}) = (A\vec{v}) \cdot (A\vec{u}) = \vec{v}^T A^T A \vec{u} = \vec{v}^T\vec{u} = \vec{v} \cdot \vec{u} = 0$$

because $\vec{v}$ is in $U^{\perp}$ and $\vec{u}$ is in U. As $\lambda_1 \neq 0$, we have $(A\vec{v}) \cdot \vec{u} = \vec{0}$ for every $\vec{u}$ in U. Hence $T(\vec{v}) = A\vec{v}$ is in $U^{\perp}$, proving the Claim.

The Claim shows that T induces a transformation

$$T_0 : U^{\perp} \to U^{\perp} \text{ given by } T_0(\vec{v}) = T(\vec{v})$$

for all $\vec{v}$ in $U^{\perp}$. This mapping T_0 is an isometry of the plane $U^{\perp}$ (since T is an isometry) and so is either a rotation or a reflection by Theorem 7 §3.4.[30] In each case, we can choose a convenient orthonormal basis $\{\vec{f}_2, \ \vec{f}_3\}$ of $U^{\perp}$ which will show that the theorem is true.

---

[30] Strictly speaking, Theorem 7 §3.4 refers to isometries of the plane $\mathbb{R}^2$. However, as we will see in Chapter 5, the important thing is that $U^{\perp}$ and $\mathbb{R}^2$ are both *planes*, and so have the same dimension.

Case 1. T_0 is a rotation of $U^\perp$ through an angle θ. In this case choose an orthonormal basis $\{\vec{f_2}, \vec{f_3}\}$ of $U^\perp$ such that θ is counter-clockwise with respect to the axes in the $\vec{f_2}$ and $\vec{f_3}$ directions. Then, as in the solution of Example 16, we have
$T(\vec{f_2}) = \cos\theta\vec{f_2} + \sin\theta\vec{f_3}$ and $T(\vec{f_3}) = -\sin\theta\vec{f_2} + \cos\theta\vec{f_3}$. Moreover $T(\vec{f_1}) = \lambda_1\vec{f_1}$.
Since $\mathcal{F} = \{\vec{f_1}, \vec{f_2}, \vec{f_3}\}$ is an orthonormal basis of $\mathbb{R}^3$, part (2) of Theorem 7 gives

$$M_{\mathcal{F}}(T) = \begin{bmatrix} \lambda_1 & 0 & 0 \\ 0 & \cos\theta & -\sin\theta \\ 0 & \sin\theta & \cos\theta \end{bmatrix}.$$

If $\lambda_1 = 1$, this is the rotation through θ around the line $\mathbb{R}\vec{f_1}$ by Example 16. If $\lambda_1 = -1$, then

$$M_{\mathcal{F}}(T) = \begin{bmatrix} -1 & 0 & 0 \\ 0 & \cos\theta & -\sin\theta \\ 0 & \sin\theta & \cos\theta \end{bmatrix} = \begin{bmatrix} 1 & 0 & 0 \\ 0 & \cos\theta & -\sin\theta \\ 0 & \sin\theta & \cos\theta \end{bmatrix} \begin{bmatrix} -1 & 0 & 0 \\ 0 & 1 & 0 \\ 0 & 0 & 1 \end{bmatrix}$$

which (using Examples 16 and 17) is reflection in the plane $U^\perp$, followed by rotation through the angle θ about the line U. Hence the theorem holds in this case.

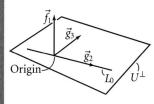

Case 2. T_0 is the reflection of the plane $U^\perp$ in a line L_0 in $U^\perp$ through the origin. In this case choose unit vectors $\vec{g_2}$ and $\vec{g_3}$ in $U^\perp$ where $\vec{g_2}$ is parallel to L_0 and $\vec{g_3}$ is orthogonal to L_0. Hence $T(\vec{g_2}) = \vec{g_2}$ and $T(\vec{g_3}) = -\vec{g_3}$. If $\lambda_1 = 1$, we use the orthonormal basis $\mathcal{G} = \{\vec{g_3}, \vec{f_1}, \vec{g_2}\}$ of $\mathbb{R}^3$. Then Theorem 7 gives

$$M_{\mathcal{G}}(T) = \begin{bmatrix} -1 & 0 & 0 \\ 0 & \lambda_1 & 0 \\ 0 & 0 & 1 \end{bmatrix} = \begin{bmatrix} -1 & 0 & 0 \\ 0 & 1 & 0 \\ 0 & 0 & 1 \end{bmatrix}$$

so T is reflection in the plane $span\{\vec{f_1}, \vec{g_2}\}$ (see Example 17). If $\lambda_1 = -1$, we use $\mathcal{G} = \{\vec{g_2}, \vec{g_3}, \vec{f_1}\}$. Hence

$$M_{\mathcal{G}}(T) = \begin{bmatrix} 1 & 0 & 0 \\ 0 & -1 & 0 \\ 0 & 0 & \lambda_1 \end{bmatrix} = \begin{bmatrix} 1 & 0 & 0 \\ 0 & -1 & 0 \\ 0 & 0 & -1 \end{bmatrix}$$

which is rotation of π around the line $\mathbb{R}\vec{g_2}$ by Example 16.

In fact we have proved that an isometry is either a rotation about a line through the origin, a reflection in a plane through the origin, or else the composite of a reflection in a plane through the origin followed by a rotation about a line through the origin perpendicular to the plane.

Exercises 4.9

1. In each case either show that the statement is true or give an example showing that it is false. Let $\{\vec{e_1}, \vec{e_2}\}$ denote the standard basis of $\mathbb{R}^2$.

a) If $T : \mathbb{R}^n \to \mathbb{R}^m$ is linear and $T(X) = 0$ for some X in $\mathbb{R}^n$, then $X = 0$.

b) There exists a linear transformation $T : \mathbb{R}^2 \to \mathbb{R}^3$ such that $T(\vec{e_1}) = [1\ \ 1\ \ 0]^T$ and $T(\vec{e_2}) = [0\ \ 1\ \ 1]^T$.

c) There exists a linear transformation $T : \mathbb{R}^2 \to \mathbb{R}^4$ such that $T(\vec{e_1}) = [1\ \ -1\ \ 3\ \ -2]^T$ and $T(2\vec{e_1}) = [-1\ \ 1\ \ -3\ \ 2]^T$.

d) If $T : \mathbb{R}^2 \to \mathbb{R}^3$ is linear and $\{X,\ Y\}$ is orthogonal in $\mathbb{R}^2$, then $\{T(X),\ T(Y)\}$ is orthogonal in $\mathbb{R}^3$.

e) If $T : \mathbb{R}^4 \to \mathbb{R}^2$ is defined by $T[x_1\ \ x_2\ \ x_3\ \ x_4]^T = [x_4\ \ x_3]^T$, then T is linear.

f) The composite of two invertible operators is invertible.

g) If $S = 0$ is the zero operator $\mathbb{R}^n \to \mathbb{R}^n$, then $T \circ S = 0$ for all operators T.

2. If Y and Z are vectors in $\mathbb{R}^n$, a vector X is said to be **between** Y and Z if $X = (1 - f)Y + fZ$ for some number f such that $0 \le f \le 1$ [see Exercise 16 §3.1]. If $T : \mathbb{R}^n \to \mathbb{R}^m$ is a linear transformation and X is between Y and Z, show that $T(X)$ is between $T(Y)$ and $T(Z)$.

3. If a is a fixed real number, consider the scalar operator $T : \mathbb{R}^n \to \mathbb{R}^n$ defined by $T(X) = aX$. Show that T is a linear operator, and find the standard matrix of T.

4. If $m < n$ define $T : \mathbb{R}^n \to \mathbb{R}^m$ by $T[x_1 \ x_2 \ \cdots \ x_n]^T = [x_1 \ x_2 \ \cdots \ x_m]^T$. Show that T is a linear transformation, and find its standard matrix.

5. If $m > n$ define $T : \mathbb{R}^n \to \mathbb{R}^m$ by
$$T[x_1 \ x_2 \ \cdots \ x_n]^T = [x_1 \ x_2 \ \cdots \ x_n \ 0 \ \cdots \ 0]^T.$$
Show that T is a linear transformation, and find its standard matrix.

6. a) Find $T([x_1 \ x_2 \ x_3]^T)$ if $T : \mathbb{R}^3 \to \mathbb{R}^3$ is a linear transformation satisfying $T([1 \ 1 \ 0]^T) = [3 \ -1 \ 3]^T$, $T([0 \ 1 \ 1]^T) = [2 \ 1 \ 3]^T$, and $T([0 \ 0 \ 1]^T) = [-1 \ -2 \ 0]^T$.

   b) Find $T([x_1 \ x_2 \ x_3 \ x_4]^T)$ if $T : \mathbb{R}^4 \to \mathbb{R}^2$ is a linear transformation satisfying $T([1 \ 1 \ 0 \ 0]^T) = [2 \ -1]^T$, $T([0 \ 1 \ 0 \ 0]^T) = [-2 \ 3]^T$, $T([0 \ 1 \ 0 \ 2]^T) = [1 \ 0]^T$, and $T([0 \ 0 \ 1 \ 0]^T) = [0 \ -1]^T$.

7. Let $\mathcal{F}$ denote a basis of $\mathbb{R}^3$, and let T be an operator on $\mathbb{R}^3$. In each case find $T([x_1 \ x_2 \ x_3]^T)$.

   a) $\mathcal{F} = \left\{ \begin{bmatrix} 1 \\ 0 \\ 0 \end{bmatrix}, \begin{bmatrix} 1 \\ 1 \\ 0 \end{bmatrix}, \begin{bmatrix} 0 \\ 1 \\ 1 \end{bmatrix} \right\}$ and $M_{\mathcal{F}}(T) = \begin{bmatrix} 1 & 0 & -1 \\ 2 & 1 & 0 \\ -1 & 1 & 4 \end{bmatrix}$.

   b) $\mathcal{F} = \left\{ \begin{bmatrix} 1 \\ 2 \\ 2 \end{bmatrix}, \begin{bmatrix} 2 \\ 1 \\ -2 \end{bmatrix}, \begin{bmatrix} 2 \\ -2 \\ 1 \end{bmatrix} \right\}$ and $M_{\mathcal{F}}(T) = \begin{bmatrix} 3 & -5 & 1 \\ 1 & 1 & 5 \\ -2 & 2 & 7 \end{bmatrix}$.

8. If $X \neq 0$ and Y are vectors in $\mathbb{R}^n$ and $\mathbb{R}^m$ respectively, show that there is a linear transformation $T : \mathbb{R}^n \to \mathbb{R}^m$ such that $T(X) = Y$. [Hint: Part (2) of Theorem 3 §4.3.]

9. A linear transformation $T : \mathbb{R}^n \to \mathbb{R}^1 = \mathbb{R}$ is called a **linear functional** on $\mathbb{R}^n$.

   a) If X_0 is a fixed column in $\mathbb{R}^n$, show that $T(X) = X_0 \cdot X$ defines a linear functional T on $\mathbb{R}^n$.

   b) Show that every linear functional on $\mathbb{R}^n$ arises as in **a)** for some X_0 in $\mathbb{R}^n$. [Hint: Let $X_0 = [a_1, \cdots, a_n]^T$ where $a_i = T(E_i)$ and $\{E_1, \cdots, E_n\}$ is the standard basis.]

10. Suppose that $\mathbb{R}^n = span\{Y_1, Y_2, \cdots, Y_k\}$. If $T : \mathbb{R}^n \to \mathbb{R}^m$ is a linear transformation and $T(Y_i) = 0$ for each i, show that $T = 0$ is the zero transformation.

11. a) If X_0 is a fixed column in $\mathbb{R}^n$, show that $T(r) = rX_0$ defines a linear transformation $\mathbb{R} \to \mathbb{R}^n$.

   b) Show that every linear transformation $\mathbb{R} \to \mathbb{R}^n$ arises as in **a)** for some X_0 in $\mathbb{R}^n$. [Hint: Take $X_0 = T(1)$.]

12. If $T : \mathbb{R}^n \to \mathbb{R}^m$ is a linear transformation, define the **kernel** of T (denoted $kerT$) by $kerT = \{X \text{ in } \mathbb{R}^n \mid T(X) = 0\}$.

   a) Show that $kerT$ is a subspace of $\mathbb{R}^n$.

   b) If $S \circ T = 1_{\mathbb{R}^n}$ for some $S : \mathbb{R}^m \to \mathbb{R}^n$, show that $kerT = 0$.

13. If $T : \mathbb{R}^n \to \mathbb{R}^m$ is a linear transformation, define the **image** of T (denoted imT) by $imT = \{T(X) \mid X \text{ in } \mathbb{R}^n\}$.

   a) Show that imT is a subspace of $\mathbb{R}^m$.

   b) If $T \circ S = 1_{\mathbb{R}^n}$ for some $S : \mathbb{R}^n \to \mathbb{R}^m$, show that $imT = \mathbb{R}^m$.

14. Let $T : \mathbb{R}^n \to \mathbb{R}^m$ be a linear transformation, and let $X_1, X_2, \cdots, X_k$ denote vectors in $\mathbb{R}^n$.

   a) If $\{T(X_1), T(X_2), \cdots, T(X_k)\}$ is independent in $\mathbb{R}^m$, show that $\{X_1, X_2, \cdots, X_k\}$ is independent in $\mathbb{R}^n$.

   b) If $\{X_1, X_2, \cdots, X_k\}$ spans $\mathbb{R}^n$, show that $\{T(X_1), T(X_2), \cdots, T(X_k)\}$ spans imT. (See the preceding exercise.)

15. Given bases $\mathcal{F} = \{[1 \ 1]^T, [0 \ 1]^T\}$ and $\mathcal{G} = \{[2 \ 3]^T, [1 \ 2]^T\}$ of $\mathbb{R}^2$, compute the change matrices $P_{\mathcal{G} \leftarrow \mathcal{F}}$ and $P_{\mathcal{F} \leftarrow \mathcal{G}}$. Verify that they are inverses of each other, and that $C_{\mathcal{G}}(X) = P_{\mathcal{G} \leftarrow \mathcal{F}} C_{\mathcal{F}}(X)$ holds for all X in $\mathbb{R}^2$.

16. In Theorem 9, prove that $T(X + Y) = T(X) + T(Y)$ for all X and Y in $\mathbb{R}^n$.

17. If $\mathcal{F}$ is a basis of $\mathbb{R}^n$, find a specific formula for $C_{\mathcal{F}}^{-1} : \mathbb{R}^n \to \mathbb{R}^n$. What is the matrix of $C_{\mathcal{F}}^{-1}$?

18. a) If $T : \mathbb{R}^n \to \mathbb{R}^n$ is invertible, show that T^{-1} is also invertible.

   b) If $S : \mathbb{R}^n \to \mathbb{R}^n$ and $T : \mathbb{R}^n \to \mathbb{R}^n$ are both invertible, show that $S \circ T$ is also invertible.

19. Let $\mathcal{F} = \{F_1, \cdots, F_n\}$ be a basis of $\mathbb{R}^n$, and write $P = [F_1 \ \cdots \ F_n]$. Show that:

   a) $P_{\mathcal{F} \leftarrow \mathcal{E}} = P^{-1}$;   **b)** $P_{\mathcal{E} \leftarrow \mathcal{F}} = P$.

20. If $T : \mathbb{R}^n \to \mathbb{R}^n$ has standard matrix A and $A^2 = A$, show that $T \circ T = T$.

21. Show that the composite of two distance-preserving isometries of $\mathbb{R}^n$ is again distance preserving.

22. If Y is a fixed vector in $\mathbb{R}^n$, let $Q_Y : \mathbb{R}^n \to \mathbb{R}^n$ denote translation by Y, that is $Q_Y(X) = X + Y$ for all X in $\mathbb{R}^n$. Show that $T \circ Q_Y = Q_{T(Y)} \circ T$ holds for every linear operator $T : \mathbb{R}^n \to \mathbb{R}^n$.

23. Let U denote any subspace of $\mathbb{R}^n$ and write $P(X) = proj_U(X)$ for all X in $\mathbb{R}^n$. Define $T : \mathbb{R}^n \to \mathbb{R}^n$ by $T(X) = 2P(X) - X$ for all X in $\mathbb{R}^n$. We call T a **reflection** in the subspace U by analogy with the case when $n = 3$ and U is a plane in $\mathbb{R}^n$ (see Theorem 1 §3.4). Show that T is an isometry of $\mathbb{R}^n$. [Hint: We have $T(X) = P(X) + [P(X) - X]$ and $X = P(X) + [X - P(X)]$. Use the Projection theorem and Pythagoras' theorem.]

24. If T is the reflection of $\mathbb{R}^3$ in a plane through the origin (see the preceding exercise), show that the standard matrix of T is diagonalizable.

25. If A is an $n \times n$ matrix, define $T_A : \mathbb{R}^n \to \mathbb{R}^n$ by $T_A(X) = AX$ for all X in $\mathbb{R}^n$.
   a) If there exists a basis $\mathcal{F} = \{F_1, F_2, \cdots, F_n\}$ of $\mathbb{R}^n$ such that $M_{\mathcal{F}}(T_A)$ is diagonal, show that A is diagonalizable.
   b) If A is diagonalizable, show that a basis $\mathcal{F} = \{F_1, F_2, \cdots, F_n\}$ of $\mathbb{R}^n$ exists such that $M_{\mathcal{F}}(T_A)$ is diagonal. [Hint: A has a basis of eigenvectors.]

26. Let $\mathcal{F}$ be a basis of $\mathbb{R}^n$. If A and B are $m \times n$ matrices and $A\, C_{\mathcal{F}}(X) = B\, C_{\mathcal{F}}(X)$ for all X in $\mathbb{R}^n$, show that $A = B$.

27. Let $\mathcal{F}$ be a basis of $\mathbb{R}^n$, and let $S : \mathbb{R}^n \to \mathbb{R}^n$ and $T : \mathbb{R}^n \to \mathbb{R}^n$ be operators.
   a) Show that $M_{\mathcal{F}}(S \circ T) = M_{\mathcal{F}}(S)M_{\mathcal{F}}(T)$. [Hint: For each X in $\mathbb{R}^n$, right multiply by $C_{\mathcal{F}}(X)$ and use Theorem 7 and the preceding exercise.]
   b) If T is invertible, show that $M_{\mathcal{F}}(T)$ is invertible and $[M_{\mathcal{F}}(T)]^{-1} = M_{\mathcal{F}}(T^{-1})$. [Hint: Use **a)**.]

28. If $T : \mathbb{R}^n \to \mathbb{R}^n$ is an operator and a is a scalar, define $aT : \mathbb{R}^n \to \mathbb{R}^n$ by $(aT)(X) = aT(X)$ for all X in $\mathbb{R}^n$.
   a) Show that aT is an operator (called the **scalar multiple** of T by a).
   b) If T is an isometry, show that aT is an isometry if and only if $a = \pm 1$.
   We say that an operator S **preserves orthogonality** if $X \cdot Y = 0$ in $\mathbb{R}^n$ implies that $T(X) \cdot T(Y) = 0$.
   c) Show that a linear operator $S : \mathbb{R}^n \to \mathbb{R}^n$ preserves orthogonality if and only if it is a scalar multiple of an isometry. [Hint: If S preserves orthogonality, show that $\|S(E)\| = \|S(F)\|$ for any unit vectors using the fact that $(E + F) \cdot (E - F) = 0$. If $\{F_1, \cdots, F_n\}$ is an orthonormal basis of $\mathbb{R}^n$, let $\|S(F_i)\| = a$ for all i. If $a = 0$, then $S = a1_{\mathbb{R}^n}$; if $a \neq 0$, show that $T = \frac{1}{a}S$ is an isometry.]

29. If Y is a point in $\mathbb{R}^2$, let $S : \mathbb{R}^n \to \mathbb{R}^n$ denote rotation about Y through an angle θ. S is clearly distance preserving. Exhibit S as a rotation followed by a translation (as guaranteed by Corollary 2 of Theorem 9).

30. Show that the isometries of $\mathbb{R}^n$ enjoy the following properties:
   1) $1_{\mathbb{R}^n}$ is an isometry.
   2) If T is an isometry, so is T^{-1}.
   3) If S and T are isometries, so is the composite $S \circ T$.
   By virtue of these properties, the set of all isometries is called a *group* of operators.

31. a) If T is an isometry of $\mathbb{R}^n$, show that $det(M_{\mathcal{F}}(T)) = \pm 1$ for any basis $\mathcal{F}$ of $\mathbb{R}^n$.
   b) If T is an isometry of $\mathbb{R}^3$ with standard matrix A, show that: T is a rotation if and only if $det(M_{\mathcal{F}}(T)) = 1$ for any $\mathcal{F}$; and T is a reflection if and only if $det(M_{\mathcal{F}}(T)) = -1$ for any $\mathcal{F}$. [Hint: Theorem 12 and Exercise 23.]

32. Let $\mathcal{F} = \{F_1, \cdots, F_n\}$ and $\mathcal{G} = \{G_1, \cdots, G_n\}$ be bases of $\mathbb{R}^n$, and write $P_{\mathcal{G} \leftarrow \mathcal{F}} = P$. If $T : \mathbb{R}^n \to \mathbb{R}^n$ is a linear operator, show that $PM_{\mathcal{F}}(T)P^{-1} = M_{\mathcal{G}}(T)$. [Hint: Show that $P M_{\mathcal{F}}(T) = M_{\mathcal{G}}(T) P$ by right multiplying by $C_{\mathcal{F}}(X)$ for all X and applying Exercise 26.]

33. Extend Theorem 7 as follows: Let $T : \mathbb{R}^n \to \mathbb{R}^m$ be a linear transformation with standard matrix A. If $\mathcal{F} = \{F_1, \cdots, F_n\}$ and $\mathcal{G} = \{G_1, \cdots, G_m\}$ are bases of $\mathbb{R}^n$ and $\mathbb{R}^m$ respectively, write $P = [F_1 \cdots F_n]$ and $Q = [G_1 \cdots G_m]$.
   a) Show that $C_{\mathcal{G}}(T(X)) = Q^{-1}AP\, C_{\mathcal{F}}(X)$ for all X in $\mathbb{R}^n$.
   b) Show that $Q^{-1}AP = [C_{\mathcal{G}}(T(F_1))\ \ C_{\mathcal{G}}(T(F_2))\ \cdots\ C_{\mathcal{G}}(T(F_n))]$. [Hint: Proceed as in the proof of Theorem 7 and the paragraph preceding it.]

4.10 COMPLEX MATRICES [31]

Ever since we introduced eigenvalues, it has been clear that complex numbers play an important role in linear algebra. Even such a simple matrix as $A = \begin{bmatrix} 0 & -1 \\ 1 & 0 \end{bmatrix}$ has characteristic polynomial $x^2 + 1$, and so has nonreal eigenvalues i and $-i$. On the other hand, many of the applications of linear algebra involve only real numbers, so we have focused on $\mathbb{R}^n$ and on real matrices throughout this book. However, there is much to be gained by looking at $\mathbb{C}^n$ and at complex matrices, where $\mathbb{C}$ denotes the set of complex numbers. While a brief discussion of the complex numbers was given in Section 2.5, we give a more comprehensive discussion of complex matrices in this section, and extend several of our earlier results about real matrices. Only the basic properties of complex numbers will be needed—mainly complex arithmetic, conjugation, and absolute value.

---

[31] This section is not needed elsewhere in the book.

4.10.1 Complex Inner Products

Most of what we have done in Chapters 1 and 2 remains valid if the phrase "real number" is replaced by "complex number" wherever it occurs. The Gaussian algorithm works to solve systems of linear equations with complex coefficients, and the properties of matrix arithmetic and determinants remain the same. Furthermore, the proofs of theorems in the real case carry over unchanged to complex matrices. Consequently, we will not repeat those arguments again here.

The set of all n-tuples of complex numbers is denoted $\mathbb{C}^n$ and, as for $\mathbb{R}^n$, we denote them as columns (sometimes as rows) and refer to them as vectors. The addition and scalar multiplication of vectors in $\mathbb{C}^n$ is entirely analogous to $\mathbb{R}^n$. However, one important difference arises when the length of a complex vector is considered. For example, using the formula from $\mathbb{R}^n$ on the vector $Z = [1 \quad i]^T$ in $\mathbb{C}^2$, we find that Z has length $\sqrt{1^2 + i^2} = \sqrt{1 + (-1)} = 0$. Since it is important to retain the property that the length of a nonzero vector is positive, we see that the obvious extension of the length formula from $\mathbb{R}^n$ to $\mathbb{C}^n$ does not work. Fortunately, there is a satisfactory way to define the length of a vector in $\mathbb{C}^n$ which reduces to the usual length for vectors in $\mathbb{R}^n$. In fact, we can suitably extend the dot product.

Given $Z = [z_1 \quad z_2 \quad \cdots \quad z_n]^T$ and $W = [w_1 \quad w_2 \quad \cdots \quad w_n]^T$ in $\mathbb{C}^n$, define their **standard inner product** $\langle Z, W \rangle$ to be the complex number given by the formula

$$\langle Z, W \rangle = z_1\overline{w}_1 + z_2\overline{w}_2 + \cdots + z_n\overline{w}_n.$$

Here $\overline{w}$ denotes the conjugate of the complex number w. This reduces to the dot product on $\mathbb{R}^n$ since, if Z and W are actually in $\mathbb{R}^n$, then $\overline{w}_i = w_i$ for each i, so $\langle Z, W \rangle = Z \cdot W$. Moreover, this leads to a satisfactory notion of length in $\mathbb{C}^n$. Indeed,

$$\langle Z, Z \rangle = z_1\overline{z}_1 + z_2\overline{z}_2 + \cdots + z_n\overline{z}_n = |z_1|^2 + |z_2|^2 + \cdots + |z_n|^2$$

where $|z|$ denotes the absolute value of the complex number z. Hence $\langle Z, Z \rangle > 0$ if $Z \neq 0$ so, as in $\mathbb{R}^n$, we define the **length** $\|Z\|$ of Z in $\mathbb{C}^n$ to be

$$\|Z\| = \sqrt{\langle Z, Z \rangle} = \sqrt{|z_1|^2 + |z_2|^2 + \cdots + |z_n|^2}.$$

Hence $\|Z\| = 0$ if and only if $Z = 0$ because $|z_1|^2 + |z_2|^2 + \cdots + |z_n|^2$ is a nonnegative real number which is zero if and only if every $z_i = 0$. This explains why the coefficients of W are conjugated in the definition of $\langle Z, W \rangle$, and it also proves (4) of the following theorem.

THEOREM ❶   Let Z, Z_1, W, and W_1 denote vectors in $\mathbb{C}^n$, and let λ denote a complex number.

    (1) $\langle Z + Z_1, W \rangle = \langle Z, W \rangle + \langle Z_1, W \rangle$ and $\langle Z, W + W_1 \rangle = \langle Z, W \rangle + \langle Z, W_1 \rangle$.

    (2) $\langle \lambda Z, W \rangle = \lambda \langle Z, W \rangle$ and $\langle Z, \lambda W \rangle = \overline{\lambda} \langle Z, W \rangle$.

    (3) $\langle Z, W \rangle = \overline{\langle W, Z \rangle}$.

    (4) $\|Z\| \geq 0$ and $\|Z\| = 0$ if and only if $Z = 0$.

    (5) $\|\lambda Z\| = |\lambda| \, \|Z\|$.

PROOF   We verified (4) above, and we leave (1), (2), and (5) to the reader. To prove (3) let $Z = [z_1 \quad z_2 \quad \cdots \quad z_n]^T$ and $W = [w_1 \quad w_2 \quad \cdots \quad w_n]^T$. Since $\overline{z + w} = \overline{z} + \overline{w}$, $\overline{(zw)} = \overline{z}\,\overline{w}$, and $\overline{\overline{z}} = z$ hold for all complex numbers z and w, we have

$$\overline{\langle W, Z \rangle} = \overline{w_1\overline{z}_1 + \cdots + w_n\overline{z}_n}$$
$$= \overline{w}_1(\overline{\overline{z}_1}) + \cdots + \overline{w}_n(\overline{\overline{z}_n})$$
$$= \overline{w}_1 z_1 + \cdots + \overline{w}_n z_n$$
$$= \langle Z, W \rangle.$$

This proves (3).

The properties in Theorem 1 will be used frequently in what follows, usually without comment.

As for $\mathbb{R}^n$, a vector U in $\mathbb{C}^n$ is called a **unit vector** if $\|U\| = 1$. With this, property (5) in Theorem 1 shows that if $Z \neq 0$ in $\mathbb{C}^n$, then $\frac{1}{\|Z\|}Z$ is a unit vector.

Example 1 | If $Z = [i \ \ 1-i \ \ -3 \ \ 2+3i]^T$ and $W = [2-i \ \ 1 \ \ 1+i \ \ -i]^T$, compute: (1) $\|Z\|$; (2) A unit vector that is a positive scalar multiple of Z; (3) $\langle Z, \ W \rangle$.

SOLUTION | (1). $\|Z\|^2 = |i|^2 + |1-i|^2 + |-3|^2 + |2+3i|^2 = 1 + 2 + 9 + 13 = 25$, so $\|Z\| = 5$.

(2). Using (1), $U = \frac{1}{\|Z\|}Z = \frac{1}{5}Z$ does it.

(3). $\langle Z, \ W \rangle = (i)\overline{(2-i)} + (1-i)\overline{(1)} + (-3)\overline{(1+i)} + (2+3i)\overline{(-i)}$
$\qquad = i(2+i) + (1-i) - 3(1-i) + (2+3i)i$
$\qquad = -6 + 6i.$

4.10.2 Complex Matrices

Matrix multiplication, addition, transposition, and scalar multiplication (by complex scalars) are defined exactly as for real matrices, and the algebraic properties developed in Chapter 1 remain valid. However, the conjugation operation for complex numbers introduces another matrix operation. If $G = [g_{ij}]$ is a complex matrix, the **conjugate** $\overline{G}$ of G is defined to be the matrix

$$\overline{G} = [\overline{g}_{ij}]$$

obtained from G by conjugating every entry. It is a routine exercise to verify the following properties of matrix conjugation.

THEOREM 2 | Let G and K denote complex matrices, and let λ be a complex number.
(1) $\overline{G+K} = \overline{G} + \overline{K}$.
(2) $\overline{GK} = \overline{G}\,\overline{K}$.
(3) $\overline{(\lambda G)} = \overline{\lambda}\,\overline{G}$.
(4) $(\overline{G})^T = \overline{(G^T)}$.
(5) $\langle Z, \ W \rangle = Z^T \overline{W}$ for all columns Z and W in $\mathbb{C}^n$.

As for Theorem 1, these properties will be used repeatedly in what follows.

Matrix conjugation enables us to define the following notion which is essential in discussing complex analogues of the symmetric and orthogonal real matrices. If G is a complex matrix, the **conjugate transpose** G^* of G is defined by

$$G^* = (\overline{G})^T = \overline{(G^T)}.$$

Observe that $A^* = A^T$ when A is a real matrix.

Example 2 | If $G = \begin{bmatrix} -1 & 2-i & -2i \\ 3+4i & i & 7 \end{bmatrix}$ then $G^* = \begin{bmatrix} -1 & 3-4i \\ 2+i & -i \\ 2i & 7 \end{bmatrix}$.

The following properties of the conjugate transpose follow easily from the definition of G^* and the rules governing transposition. As before these properties will be used several times below.

h) If $\{\mathbf{u},\ \mathbf{v},\ \mathbf{w}\}$ is dependent, so is $\{\mathbf{u},\ \mathbf{v}\}$.

i) $\mathbb{P}_2$ has a basis of polynomials $p(x)$ such that $p(0) = 0$.

j) $\mathbb{P}_2$ has a basis of polynomials $p(x)$ such that $p(0) = 1$.

k) Every basis of $\mathbb{M}_{2,2}$ contains an invertible matrix.

l) No basis of $\mathbb{M}_{2,2}$ contains a matrix A such that $A^2 = 0$.

m) No basis of $\mathbb{M}_{2,2}$ consists of matrices A such that $A\,[1\ \ 0]^T = 0$.

2. In each case determine if the set of vectors is independent in V.

a) $V = \mathbb{P}_2;\ \{1 + x,\ 2 - x^2,\ x^2 + 2x\}$

b) $V = \mathbb{P}_2;\ \{2 + x,\ 1 + x^2,\ 1 + x + x^2\}$

c) $V = \mathbb{M}_{2,2};\ \left\{\begin{bmatrix} 1 & 0 \\ 0 & 0 \end{bmatrix},\ \begin{bmatrix} 0 & 1 \\ 1 & 0 \end{bmatrix},\ \begin{bmatrix} 0 & 1 \\ 1 & 1 \end{bmatrix},\ \begin{bmatrix} 1 & 0 \\ 0 & -1 \end{bmatrix}\right\}$

d) $V = \mathbb{M}_{2,2};\ \left\{\begin{bmatrix} 1 & 1 \\ 0 & 0 \end{bmatrix},\ \begin{bmatrix} 1 & 0 \\ 1 & 0 \end{bmatrix},\ \begin{bmatrix} 0 & 0 \\ 1 & 1 \end{bmatrix},\ \begin{bmatrix} 0 & 1 \\ 0 & 1 \end{bmatrix}\right\}$

e) $V = \mathbb{F}[0,\ 1];\ \left\{\frac{1}{x^2-4},\ \frac{1}{x^2+3x+2},\ \frac{1}{x^2-x-2}\right\}$

f) $V = \mathbb{F}[1,\ 2];\ \left\{\frac{1}{x},\ \frac{1}{x^2},\ \frac{1}{x^3}\right\}$

g) $V = \mathbb{F}[0,\ 2\pi];\ \{1,\ \cos^2 x,\ \sin^2 x\}$

h) $V = \mathbb{F}[0,\ 2\pi];\ \{x,\ \cos^2 x,\ \sin^2 x\}$

3. In each case find a basis and calculate the dimension of the subspace U of V.

a) $V = \mathbb{P}_2;\ U = span\{1 - 2x,\ 3x - x^2,\ 3 - 2x^2\}$

b) $V = \mathbb{P}_2;\ U = \{p(x)\ |\ p(1) = 0\}$

c) $V = \mathbb{P}_2;\ U = \{p(x)\ |\ p(x) = p(-x)\}$

d) $V = \mathbb{P}_2;\ U = span\{x - 2,\ x^2 + 2x,\ 4 - x^2\}$

e) $V = \mathbb{M}_{2,2};\ U = span\left\{\begin{bmatrix} 1 & 2 \\ -1 & 0 \end{bmatrix},\ \begin{bmatrix} 2 & 0 \\ 1 & 3 \end{bmatrix},\ \begin{bmatrix} 1 & -6 \\ 5 & 6 \end{bmatrix}\right\}$

f) $V = \mathbb{M}_{2,2};\ U = \{A\ |\ AB = BA\}$ where $B = \begin{bmatrix} 1 & 1 \\ 0 & 0 \end{bmatrix}$

g) $V = \mathbb{M}_{2,2};\ U = \{A\ |\ AB = CA\},\ B = \begin{bmatrix} 1 & 0 \\ 0 & 0 \end{bmatrix},\ C = \begin{bmatrix} 0 & 1 \\ 1 & 0 \end{bmatrix}$

h) $V = \mathbb{M}_{2,2};\ U = \{A\ |\ \text{the columns of } A \text{ have equal sums}\}$

i) $V = \mathbb{M}_{3,3};\ U = \{A\ |\ A^T = -A\}$

j) $V = \mathbb{R}^4;\ U = \{X\ |\ X^T A = 0\}$ where $A = \begin{bmatrix} 1 & -1 & 0 & 2 \\ -2 & 3 & -1 & 4 \end{bmatrix}^T$

k) $V = \mathbb{R}^4;\ U = \{[a\ b\ c\ d]^T\ |\ a + b + c + d = 0\}$

l) $V = span\{\mathbf{u},\ \mathbf{v},\ \mathbf{w},\ \mathbf{z}\}$ where $\{\mathbf{u},\ \mathbf{v},\ \mathbf{w},\ \mathbf{z}\}$ is independent; $U = span\{\mathbf{u} + \mathbf{v},\ \mathbf{v} + \mathbf{w},\ \mathbf{w} + \mathbf{z},\ \mathbf{z} + \mathbf{u}\}$

4. a) Find a basis of $\mathbb{P}_3$ consisting of polynomials whose coefficients sum to 2.

b) What if the coefficients sum to 0?

5. a) Show that any (nonempty) subset of an independent set is independent.

b) Show that any set of vectors that contains a dependent set is itself dependent.

6. Consider the space $\mathbb{C}$ of complex numbers, and let z denote an element of $\mathbb{C}$.

a) If z is not real, show that $\{z,\ z^2\}$ is a basis of $\mathbb{C}$.

b) If z is not real or pure imaginary, show that $\{z,\ \overline{z}\}$ is a basis of $\mathbb{C}$.

7. Show that if $\mathcal{B} = \{p_0(x),\ p_1(x),\ p_2(x),\ \cdots,\ p_n(x)\}$ are polynomials in $\mathbb{P}_n$ of distinct degrees, then $\mathcal{B}$ is a basis of $\mathbb{P}_n$.

8. If V is finite dimensional, show that every (possibly infinite) spanning set $\mathcal{S}$ contains a basis. [Hint: Show first that $\mathcal{S}$ contains a finite spanning set.]

9. Suppose that A is an $n \times n$ matrix such that $A^3 = 0$ but $A^2 \neq 0$. Show that $\{I,\ A,\ A^2\}$ is independent in $\mathbb{M}_{n,n}$. Generalize.

10. Let A and B be nonzero matrices in $\mathbb{M}_{n,n}$. If A is symmetric and B is skew-symmetric (that is $B^T = -B$), show that $\{A,\ B\}$ is independent.

11. Let f and g be functions in $\mathbb{F}[0,\ 1]$ such that $f(0) = 0$ and $g(0) = 1$, and $f(1) = 1$ and $g(1) = 0$. Show that $\{f,\ g\}$ is independent.

12. Let $\{A_1,\ A_2,\ \cdots,\ A_k\}$ be a set of matrices in $\mathbb{M}_{m,n}$, and let P and Q be invertible matrices of sizes $m \times m$ and $n \times n$, respectively.

a) If $\{A_1,\ A_2,\ \cdots,\ A_k\}$ is independent, show that $\{PA_1Q,\ PA_2Q,\ \cdots,\ PA_kQ\}$ is independent.

b) If $\{A_1,\ A_2,\ \cdots,\ A_k\}$ spans $\mathbb{M}_{m,n}$, show that $\{PA_1Q,\ PA_2Q,\ \cdots,\ PA_kQ\}$ spans $\mathbb{M}_{m,n}$.

13. Let A be an $m \times n$ matrix, and let $\{B_1,\ B_2,\ \cdots,\ B_k\}$ be independent columns in $\mathbb{R}^m$. If $X_1,\ X_2,\ \cdots,\ X_k$ are solutions to the equations $AX_i = B_i$ for each $i = 1,\ 2,\ \cdots,\ k$, show that $\{X_1,\ X_2,\ \cdots,\ X_k\}$ is independent in $\mathbb{R}^n$.

14. Let $p(x)$ and $q(x)$ be polynomials of degree at least 1. If $\{p(x),\ q(x)\}$ is independent, show that $\{p(x),\ q(x),\ p(x)q(x)\}$ is also independent.

15. Call a function f in $\mathbb{F}[a,\ b]$ a **constant function** if there exists a constant c such that $f(x) = c$ for all x. Show that the set of all constant functions is a subspace of $\mathbb{F}[a,\ b]$ of dimension 1.

16. a) If $\{a + bx,\ a_1 + b_1x\}$ is a basis of $\mathbb{P}_1$, show that $\{[a\ \ b]^T,\ [a_1\ \ b_1]^T\}$ is a basis of $\mathbb{R}^2$.

b) If $\{[a\ \ b]^T,\ [a_1\ \ b_1]^T\}$ is a basis of $\mathbb{R}^2$, show that $\{a + bx,\ a_1 + b_1x\}$ is a basis of $\mathbb{P}_1$.

17. Find the dimension of the subspace $U = span\{1,\ \cos^2 \theta,\ \cos(2\theta)\}$ of $\mathbb{F}[-\pi,\ \pi]$. Support your answer.

18. Find a basis of $\mathbb{M}_{2,2}$ consisting of matrices A with the property that $A^2 = A$.

19. If A is a 2×2 matrix and $U = \{B \text{ in } \mathbb{M}_{2,2}\ |\ AB = BA\}$, show that $dim\,U \geq 2$. [Hint: I and A are in U. Consider separately the case that $A = aI$ for some a in $\mathbb{R}$.]

20. A polynomial $p(x)$ is called **even** if $p(x) = p(-x)$, and $p(x)$ is called **odd** if $p(x) = -p(-x)$. Let E_n and O_n denote the sets of even and odd polynomials in $\mathbb{P}_n$.

a) Show E_n is a subspace of $\mathbb{P}_n$, and find its dimension.

b) Show O_n is a subspace of $\mathbb{P}_n$, and find its dimension.

21. If $\mathbf{v} \neq \mathbf{0}$ in V, show that the only subspaces of $\mathbb{R}\mathbf{v}$ are $\{\mathbf{0}\}$ and $\mathbb{R}\mathbf{v}$.

22. If $dim V = 2$ and U is any subspace of V other than $\{\mathbf{0}\}$ and V, show that $U = \mathbb{R}\mathbf{v}$ for some nonzero vector $\mathbf{v}$ in V. What does this say about the plane $\mathbb{R}^2$?

23. If U is a subspace of $\mathbb{P}_1$, show that $U = \{\mathbf{0}\}$, $U = \mathbb{P}_1$, $U = \mathbb{R}$, or $U = \mathbb{R}(a + x)$ for some a in $\mathbb{R}$.

24. If $\{\mathbf{u}, \mathbf{v}, \mathbf{w}, \mathbf{z}\}$ is independent, which of the following are independent? Support your answer.

a) $\{\mathbf{u} - \mathbf{v}, \mathbf{v} - \mathbf{w}, \mathbf{w} - \mathbf{u}\}$

b) $\{\mathbf{u} + \mathbf{v}, \mathbf{v} + \mathbf{w}, \mathbf{w} + \mathbf{u}\}$

c) $\{\mathbf{u} - \mathbf{v}, \mathbf{v} - \mathbf{w}, \mathbf{w} - \mathbf{z}, \mathbf{z} - \mathbf{u}\}$

d) $\{\mathbf{u} + \mathbf{v}, \mathbf{v} + \mathbf{w}, \mathbf{w} + \mathbf{u}, \mathbf{z} + \mathbf{u}\}$

25. Show that $\{\mathbf{u}, \mathbf{v}\}$ is dependent if and only if one of $\mathbf{u}$ and $\mathbf{v}$ is a scalar multiple of the other.

26. If $\mathbf{v} \neq \mathbf{0}$ is a vector in a vector space V, show that there exists a basis of V containing $\mathbf{v}$.

27. If $\{\mathbf{v}_1, \mathbf{v}_2, \mathbf{v}_3, \mathbf{v}_4\}$ is independent in V, show that $\{\mathbf{v}_1, \mathbf{v}_2 + a\mathbf{v}_1, \mathbf{v}_3 + c\mathbf{v}_2 + d\mathbf{v}_1, \mathbf{v}_4 + e\mathbf{v}_3 + f\mathbf{v}_2 + g\mathbf{v}_1\}$ is also independent. Generalize.

28. If $\{\mathbf{v}_1, \mathbf{v}_2, \cdots, \mathbf{v}_k\}$ is independent in V, and if $\mathbf{w}$ is not in $span\{\mathbf{v}_1, \mathbf{v}_2, \cdots, \mathbf{v}_k\}$, show that the set $\{\mathbf{w} + \mathbf{v}_1, \mathbf{w} + \mathbf{v}_2, \cdots, \mathbf{w} + \mathbf{v}_k\}$ is also independent.

29. Suppose that $\{\mathbf{v}_1, \mathbf{v}_2, \cdots, \mathbf{v}_k\}$ is a minimal spanning set for a vector space V, that is no spanning set of V contains fewer than k vectors. Show that $\{\mathbf{v}_1, \mathbf{v}_2, \cdots, \mathbf{v}_k\}$ is a basis of V.

30. Suppose that $\{\mathbf{v}_1, \mathbf{v}_2, \cdots, \mathbf{v}_k\}$ is a maximal independent set in a vector space V, that is no independent set in V contains more than k vectors. Show that $\{\mathbf{v}_1, \mathbf{v}_2, \cdots, \mathbf{v}_k\}$ is a basis of V.

31. Show that $\mathbb{F}[0, 1]$ is infinite dimensional. [Hint: Fundamental theorem.]

32. Let $U \subseteq W$ be subspaces of V, and suppose that $dim U = k$ and $dim W = m$ where $k < m$. If l is any integer such that $k \leq l \leq m$, show that there is a subspace X such that $U \subseteq X \subseteq W$ and $dim X = l$. [Hint: Theorem 3.]

33. Let $\mathbb{S}$ denote the set of all infinite sequences $(a_0, a_1, a_2, \cdots)$ of real numbers a_i. Define equality, addition, and scalar multiplication on $\mathbb{S}$ as follows:

$(a_0, a_1, a_2, \cdots) = (b_0, b_1, b_2, \cdots)$
if and only if $a_i = b_i$ for all i.
$(a_0, a_1, a_2, \cdots) + (b_0, b_1, b_2, \cdots) =$
$$(a_0 + b_0, a_1 + b_1, a_2 + b_2, \cdots).$$
$r(a_0, a_1, a_2, \cdots) = (ra_0, ra_1, ra_2, \cdots)$ for all real numbers r.

a) Show that $\mathbb{S}$ is a vector space and that $\mathbb{S}$ is infinite dimensional.

b) Show that $P = \{(a_0, a_1, a_2, \cdots) \mid a_i = 0 \text{ for all but finitely many } i\}$ is a subspace of $\mathbb{S}$. Is $dim P$ infinite? Support your answer.

c) Show that the set $C = \{(a, a, a, \cdots) \mid a \text{ in } \mathbb{R}\}$ is a subspace of $\mathbb{S}$. What is $dim C$?

d) Show that the convergent sequences are an infinite dimensional subspace of $\mathbb{S}$ (requires calculus).

34. Let $\mathbb{S}$ be the space of sequences in the preceding exercise, and define $U = \{(x_0, x_1, x_2, \cdots) \text{ in } \mathbb{S} \mid x_{k+2} = ax_k + bx_{k+1} \text{ for all } k \geq 0\}$ where a and b are fixed real numbers. Let $\mathbf{e} = (e_0, e_1, e_2, \cdots)$ be the sequence in U starting with $e_0 = 1$ and $e_1 = 0$, and let $\mathbf{f} = (f_0, f_1, f_2, \cdots)$ be the sequence in U starting with $f_0 = 0$ and $f_1 = 1$.

a) Show that U is a subspace of S.

b) If $\mathbf{x} = (x_0, x_1, x_2, \cdots)$ is in U, show that $x_k = x_0 e_k + x_1 f_k$ for all $k \geq 0$.

c) Show that $dim U = 2$.

35. If U and W are subspaces of V, define their **intersection** $U \cap W$ and **sum** $U + W$ by $U \cap W = \{\mathbf{v} \text{ in } V \mid \mathbf{v} \text{ is in both } U \text{ and } W\}$ and
$$U + W = \{\mathbf{u} + \mathbf{w} \mid \mathbf{u} \text{ is in } U \text{ and } \mathbf{w} \text{ is in } W\}$$

a) Show that $U \cap W$ and $U + W$ are subspaces of V.

b) If U and W have bases $\{\mathbf{u}_1, \mathbf{u}_2\}$ and $\{\mathbf{v}_1, \mathbf{v}_2, \mathbf{v}_3\}$ respectively, and if $U \cap W = \{\mathbf{0}\}$, show that $\{\mathbf{u}_1, \mathbf{u}_2, \mathbf{v}_1, \mathbf{v}_2, \mathbf{v}_3\}$ is independent.

c) If U and W are both finite dimensional, show that $U + W$ is also finite dimensional (even though V may not be finite dimensional). [Hint: If C and D are (finite) bases of U and W respectively, show that $C \cup D = \{\mathbf{v} \text{ in } V \mid \mathbf{v} \text{ is in } C \text{ or } \mathbf{v} \text{ is in } D\}$ spans $U + W$.]

d) If V is finite dimensional, show that $dim(U + W) = dim U + dim W - dim(U \cap W)$. [Hint: If $\mathcal{B}$ is a basis of $U \cap W$, let (by Theorem 3) $\mathcal{C}$ and $\mathcal{D}$ be bases of U and W respectively, each containing $\mathcal{B}$. Show that $\mathcal{C} \cup \mathcal{D}$ is a basis of $U + W$.]

5.3 LINEAR TRANSFORMATIONS

In Section 3.4 we studied transformations of $\mathbb{R}^2$ such as rotations, reflections, and projections, and we found that they are all given by multiplication by certain 2×2 matrices. The key idea that connects a geometrical transformation $T : \mathbb{R}^2 \to \mathbb{R}^2$ like rotation with a matrix is that T is *linear*, that is, T preserves addition and scalar multiplication in the sense that

$$T(\vec{v} + \vec{w}) = T(\vec{v}) + T(\vec{w}) \quad \text{and} \quad T(r\,\vec{v}) = r\,T(\vec{v}) \qquad (*)$$

for all vectors $\vec{v}$ and $\vec{w}$ in $\mathbb{R}^2$ and all scalars r. In Section 4.9 we applied this to linear transformations $T : \mathbb{R}^n \to \mathbb{R}^m$ and found that these too are given by matrix multiplication. This connection between the abstract concept of linearity and the more concrete, computational notion of matrix multiplication is very useful (one example is our analysis of the isometries of $\mathbb{R}^3$).

The reason for recalling all this here is that the conditions in $(*)$ make sense much more generally, and lead to the general idea of a linear transformation $T : V \to W$ where V and W are arbitrary vector spaces. This is the main theme of this section (and the next). It reveals a new perspective on matrices and provides a whole new way to view similarity. It also increases the applicability of linear algebra since, once one knows what they are, linear transformations appear everywhere.

5.3.1   Linear Transformations

If V and W are two vector spaces, a transformation[10] $T : V \to W$ is a rule that associates with every vector $\mathbf{v}$ in V a uniquely determined vector $T(\mathbf{v})$ in W. A transformation $T : V \to W$ is called a **linear transformation** if it preserves addition and scalar multiplication according to the following axioms:

T1. $T(\mathbf{v} + \mathbf{v}_1) = T(\mathbf{v}) + T(\mathbf{v}_1)$ for all vectors $\mathbf{v}$ and $\mathbf{v}_1$ in V.
T2. $T(r\,\mathbf{v}) = r\,T(\mathbf{v})$ for all vectors $\mathbf{v}$ in V and all scalars r.

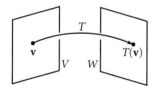

A linear transformation $T : V \to V$ is called a **linear operator** on the vector space V.

The action of a linear transformation $T : V \to W$ can be visualized as in the diagram. The vector space V is called the **domain** of T, and W is the **codomain** of T. If $\mathbf{v}$ is a vector in V, the vector $T(\mathbf{v})$ is called the **image** of $\mathbf{v}$ under T.

Example 1   Every $m \times n$ matrix A induces a linear transformation $T : \mathbb{R}^n \to \mathbb{R}^m$ given by

$$T(X) = AX \text{ for all } X \text{ in } \mathbb{R}^n.$$

In this case Axioms T1 and T2 are simple properties of matrix multiplication. Moreover, *every* linear transformation $\mathbb{R}^n \to \mathbb{R}^m$ is induced by some $m \times n$ matrix A (Theorem 2 §4.9).

---

[10] Another word for transformation is "function", but the word "transformation" is well-established in linear algebra.

Example 2 Transposition is a linear transformation. That is, the map
$$T : \mathbb{M}_{m,n} \to \mathbb{M}_{n,m} \quad \text{given by} \quad T(A) = A^T \text{ for all } A \text{ in } \mathbb{M}_{m,n}$$
is a linear transformation. In this case Axioms T1 and T2 are basic properties of transposition:
$$T(A + B) = (A + B)^T = A^T + B^T = T(A) + T(B)$$
and
$$T(rA) = (rA)^T = rA^T = rT(A)$$
for all A and B in $\mathbb{M}_{m,n}$ and all r in $\mathbb{R}$.

Example 3 If a is a fixed real number, define a transformation $E_a : \mathbb{P}_n \to \mathbb{R}$ by $E_a[p(x)] = p(a)$ for all polynomials $p(x)$ in $\mathbb{P}_n$. Then E_a is linear. Indeed, Axioms T1 and T2 are routine observations:
$$E_a[p(x) + q(x)] = p(a) + q(a) = E_a[p(x)] + E_a[q(x)]$$
and
$$E_a[rp(x)] = rp(a) = rE_a[p(x)]$$
for all $p(x)$ and $q(x)$ in $\mathbb{P}_n$ and all r in $\mathbb{R}$. The transformation E_a is called **evaluation** at a.

The next example is important in analysis.

Example 4 Differentiation is a linear transformation. Let V denote the subspace of $\mathbb{F}[\mathbb{R}]$ consisting of all differentiable real-valued functions defined on $\mathbb{R}$ (see Example 12 §5.1). If we denote the derivative of a function f by f', define
$$T : V \to \mathbb{F}[\mathbb{R}] \text{ by } T(f) = f'.$$
Then T is a linear transformation. In fact Axioms T1 and T2 read $(f + g)' = f' + g'$ and $(rf)' = rf'$ for all r in $\mathbb{R}$, and these are basic facts about differentiation.

Example 5 If V and W are vector spaces, the following are linear transformations.

$1_V : V \to V$ given by $1_V(\mathbf{v}) = \mathbf{v}$ for all $\mathbf{v}$ in V.   **(Identity operator)**
$0 : V \to W$ given by $0(\mathbf{v}) = \mathbf{0}$ for all $\mathbf{v}$ in V.   **(Zero transformation)**
For a in $\mathbb{R}, a : V \to V$ given by $a(\mathbf{v}) = a\mathbf{v}$ for all $\mathbf{v}$ in V.   **(Scalar operator)**

In addition to preserving sums and scalar products, linear transformations preserve the zero vector, negatives and linear combinations. These useful properties are recorded next.

THEOREM 1 Let $T : V \to W$ be a linear transformation. Then:

   (1) $T(\mathbf{0}) = \mathbf{0}$.[11]
   (2) $T(-\mathbf{v}) = -T(\mathbf{v})$ for all $\mathbf{v}$ in V.
   (3) $T(r_1\mathbf{v}_1 + r_2\mathbf{v}_2 + \cdots + r_k\mathbf{v}_k) = r_1T(\mathbf{v}_1) + r_2T(\mathbf{v}_2) + \cdots + r_kT(\mathbf{v}_k)$ for all r_i in $\mathbb{R}$ and all $\mathbf{v}_i$ in V.

---

[11] Note that $\mathbf{0}$ is playing two roles here. On the left side it is the zero vector in V, and it is the zero vector in W on the right side. This is a common abuse of notation, and is harmless once everyone knows it is going on.

PROOF

(1) $T(\mathbf{0}) = T(0\mathbf{v}) = 0\,T(\mathbf{v}) = \mathbf{0}$ for any $\mathbf{v}$ in V by Axiom T2.

(2) $T(-\mathbf{v}) = T((-1)\mathbf{v}) = (-1)T(\mathbf{v}) = -T(\mathbf{v})$, again by Axiom T2.

(3) If $k = 1$, this is Axiom T2. If $k > 1$, we use induction on k.

If it holds for k vectors, then

$$T(r_1\mathbf{v}_1 + r_2\mathbf{v}_2 + \cdots + r_k\mathbf{v}_k + r_{k+1}\mathbf{v}_{k+1})$$
$$= T(r_1\mathbf{v}_1 + r_2\mathbf{v}_2 + \cdots + r_k\mathbf{v}_k) + T(r_{k+1}\mathbf{v}_{k+1})$$
$$= r_1 T(\mathbf{v}_1) + r_2 T(\mathbf{v}_2) + \cdots + r_k T(\mathbf{v}_k) + r_{k+1} T(\mathbf{v}_{k+1})$$

by the induction assumption and Axioms T1 and T2. Hence it holds for $k + 1$ vectors, and the induction goes through.

The next two examples illustrate the importance of the fact that linear transformations preserve linear combinations (property (3) in Theorem 1).

Example 6

Suppose that $T : V \rightarrow W$ is a linear transformation. If $T(\mathbf{v} + 2\mathbf{v}_1) = \mathbf{w}$ and $T(3\mathbf{v} - 5\mathbf{v}_1) = \mathbf{w}_1$, find $T(\mathbf{v})$ and $T(\mathbf{v}_1)$ in terms of $\mathbf{w}$ and $\mathbf{w}_1$.

SOLUTION

Because T is linear, the given equations imply that

$$T(\mathbf{v}) + 2\,T(\mathbf{v}_1) = \mathbf{w}$$
$$3\,T(\mathbf{v}) - 5\,T(\mathbf{v}_1) = \mathbf{w}_1 \cdot$$

If we subtract 3 times the first equation from the second, we get $-11T(\mathbf{v}_1) = \mathbf{w}_1 - 3\mathbf{w}$. Thus $T(\mathbf{v}_1) = \frac{3}{11}\mathbf{w} - \frac{1}{11}\mathbf{w}_1$. Substitution in the first equation gives $T(\mathbf{v}) = \frac{5}{11}\mathbf{w} + \frac{2}{11}\mathbf{w}_1$.

Example 7

Suppose that $T(3 - 5x) = 2$ and $T(1 - x + 2x^2) = 1 + x$ where $T : \mathbb{P}_2 \rightarrow \mathbb{P}_2$ is a linear transformation. Find $T(6 - 11x - 3x^2)$.

SOLUTION

This seems difficult until we realize that (using Theorem 1) we can find $T[p(x)]$ for any polynomial $p(x)$ that is a linear combination of $3 - 5x$ and $1 - x + 2x^2$. So we look for scalars r and s such that

$$6 - 11x - 3x^2 = r(3 - 5x) + s(1 - x + 2x^2).$$

Equating coefficients gives linear equations for r and s: $6 = 3r + s$, $-11 = -5r - s$, and $-3 = 2s$. These equations have the unique solution $r = \frac{5}{2}$ and $s = -\frac{3}{2}$. Then

$$T(6 - 11x - 3x^2) = r\,T(3 - 5x) + s\,T(1 - x + 2x^2)$$
$$= \frac{5}{2}\,T(3 - 5x) - \frac{3}{2}\,T(1 - x + 2x^2)$$
$$= \frac{5}{2}2 - \frac{3}{2}(1 + x)$$
$$= \frac{7}{2} - \frac{3}{2}x.$$

This is what we wanted.

If $T : V \rightarrow W$ is a linear transformation and $T(\mathbf{v}_1)$, $T(\mathbf{v}_2)$, $\cdots$, $T(\mathbf{v}_k)$, are known, property (3) in Theorem 1 shows that $T(r_1\mathbf{v}_1 + r_2\mathbf{v}_2 + \cdots + r_k\mathbf{v}_k)$ can be computed for any choice of the scalars r_i. In particular, if $V = span\{\mathbf{v}_1, \mathbf{v}_2, \cdots, \mathbf{v}_k\}$ then $T(\mathbf{v})$ is determined for every $\mathbf{v}$ in V by the choice of $T(\mathbf{v}_1)$, $T(\mathbf{v}_2)$, $\cdots$, $T(\mathbf{v}_k)$ in W. The next theorem states this differently. Recall that two transformations $S : V \rightarrow W$ and $T : V \rightarrow W$ are **equal** (written $S = T$) if $S(\mathbf{v}) = T(\mathbf{v})$ for all $\mathbf{v}$ in V.

THEOREM 2   Let $S : V \to W$ and $T : V \to W$ be two linear transformations, and assume that $V = span\{\mathbf{v}_1, \mathbf{v}_2, \cdots, \mathbf{v}_k\}$. If $S(\mathbf{v}_i) = T(\mathbf{v}_i)$ for each i, then $S = T$.

PROOF   Given $\mathbf{v}$ in V, write $\mathbf{v} = r_1\mathbf{v}_1 + r_2\mathbf{v}_2 + \cdots + r_k\mathbf{v}_k$ where r_i is in $\mathbb{R}$ for each i. Since $S(\mathbf{v}_i) = T(\mathbf{v}_i)$ for each i, Theorem 1 gives

$$S(\mathbf{v}) = r_1 S(\mathbf{v}_1) + r_2 S(\mathbf{v}_2) + \cdots + r_k S(\mathbf{v}_k)$$
$$= r_1 T(\mathbf{v}_1) + r_2 T(\mathbf{v}_2) + \cdots + r_k T(\mathbf{v}_k)$$
$$= T(\mathbf{v}).$$

Since $\mathbf{v}$ was arbitrary in V, this shows that $S = T$.

Thus a linear transformation $T : V \to W$ is determined by its effect on a spanning set of V. If the spanning set is actually a basis, we can say more. The following lemma will be needed.

LEMMA 1   If $\{\mathbf{b}_1, \mathbf{b}_2, \cdots, \mathbf{b}_n\}$ is a basis of a vector space V, every vector $\mathbf{v}$ in V can be uniquely represented as a linear combination

$$\mathbf{v} = r_1\mathbf{b}_1 + r_2\mathbf{b}_2 + \cdots + r_n\mathbf{b}_n \quad \text{where the } r_i \text{ are in } \mathbb{R}.$$

That is, if $\mathbf{v} = s_1\mathbf{b}_1 + s_2\mathbf{b}_2 + \cdots + s_n\mathbf{b}_n$ is another such representation, s_i in $\mathbb{R}$, then $s_i = r_i$ for each i.

PROOF   Since $V = span\{\mathbf{b}_1, \mathbf{b}_2, \cdots, \mathbf{b}_n\}$, the vector $\mathbf{v}$ has at least one such representation. If

$$r_1\mathbf{b}_1 + r_2\mathbf{b}_2 + \cdots + r_n\mathbf{b}_n = \mathbf{v} = s_1\mathbf{b}_1 + s_2\mathbf{b}_2 + \cdots + s_n\mathbf{b}_n$$

are two such representations, then $(r_1 - s_1)\mathbf{b}_1 + (r_2 - s_2)\mathbf{b}_2 + \cdots + (r_n - s_n)\mathbf{b}_n = \mathbf{0}$. Hence $r_i - s_i = 0$ for each i because $\{\mathbf{b}_1, \mathbf{b}_2, \cdots, \mathbf{b}_n\}$ is linearly independent.

THEOREM 3   Let $\{\mathbf{b}_1, \mathbf{b}_2, \cdots, \mathbf{b}_n\}$ be a basis of a vector space V, and let $\{\mathbf{w}_1, \mathbf{w}_2, \cdots, \mathbf{w}_n\}$ be arbitrary vectors in W (possibly not distinct). Then there exists a unique linear transformation $T : V \to W$ such that

$$T(\mathbf{b}_i) = \mathbf{w}_i \text{ for each } i = 1, 2, \cdots, n.$$

Furthermore, the action of T is given as follows: If

$$\mathbf{v} = r_1\mathbf{b}_1 + r_2\mathbf{b}_2 + \cdots + r_n\mathbf{b}_n$$

is in V where each r_i is in $\mathbb{R}$, then

$$T(\mathbf{v}) = r_1\mathbf{w}_1 + r_2\mathbf{w}_2 + \cdots + r_n\mathbf{w}_n. \qquad (**)$$

PROOF   If T exists, it is unique by Theorem 2 because $\{\mathbf{b}_1, \mathbf{b}_2, \cdots, \mathbf{b}_n\}$ spans V. But if we write $\mathbf{v} = r_1\mathbf{b}_1 + r_2\mathbf{b}_2 + \cdots + r_n\mathbf{b}_n, r_i$ in $\mathbb{R}$, then the r_i are uniquely determined by $\mathbf{v}$ and so $T(\mathbf{v}) = r_1\mathbf{w}_1 + r_2\mathbf{w}_2 + \cdots + r_n\mathbf{w}_n$ is also uniquely determined by $\mathbf{v}$. Hence the formula $(**)$ defines a transformation $T : V \to W$ which clearly satisfies $T(\mathbf{b}_i) = \mathbf{w}_i$ for each i. The verification that this transformation T is linear is left to the reader.

Example 8   Find a linear transformation $T : \mathbb{P}_2 \to \mathbb{P}_4$ such that

$$T(1) = x^4, \ T(1 + x) = 1 + x^3, \text{ and } T(1 + x^2) = 1 - x^2.$$

SOLUTION   The set $\{1, \ 1 + x, \ 1 + x^2\} \subseteq \mathbb{P}_2$ is independent because the polynomials have distinct degrees, and so it is a basis of $\mathbb{P}_2$ because $dim(\mathbb{P}_2) = 3$. By comparing coefficients, the expansion of an arbitrary polynomial in $\mathbb{P}_2$ in terms of this basis is

$$r_0 + r_1 x + r_2 x^2 = (r_0 - r_1 - r_2) \cdot 1 + r_1(1 + x) + r_2(1 + x^2).$$

Hence the required linear transformation is given by

$$T(r_0 + r_1 x + r_2 x^2) = (r_0 - r_1 - r_2) \cdot T(1) + r_1 \cdot T(1 + x) + r_2 \cdot T(1 + x^2)$$
$$= (r_0 - r_1 - r_2)x^4 + r_1(1 + x^3) + r_2(1 - x^2)$$
$$= (r_1 + r_2) - r_2 x^2 + r_1 x^3 + (r_0 - r_1 - r_2)x^4.$$

In practice, linear transformations $T : V \to W$ are usually described by simply giving the action of T on some convenient basis of V; a complete description of $T(\mathbf{v})$ for every vector $\mathbf{v}$ in V as in Example 8 is usually not provided (or needed).

5.3.2 Kernel and Image

Every linear transformation $T : V \to W$ gives rise to two subspaces, called the kernel and image of T, which encode a lot of information about T. The **kernel** of T, denoted $kerT$, is the subspace of V consisting of all vectors that T carries to $\mathbf{0}$; more formally,

$$kerT = \{\mathbf{v} \text{ in } V \mid T(\mathbf{v}) = \mathbf{0}\}.$$

The **image** of T, denoted imT, is the subspace of W consisting of all images under T of vectors in V:

$$imT = \{T(\mathbf{v}) \mid \mathbf{v} \text{ in } V\}.$$

We begin by verifying that $kerT$ and imT are indeed subspaces of V and W.

LEMMA 2

Let $T : V \to W$ be a linear transformation. Then $kerT$ is a subspace of V and imT is a subspace of W.

PROOF

The fact that $T(\mathbf{0}) = \mathbf{0}$ shows that both $kerT$ and imT contain the zero vector. If $\mathbf{v}_1$ and $\mathbf{v}_2$ are both in $kerT$, then $T(\mathbf{v}_1) = \mathbf{0}$ and $T(\mathbf{v}_2) = \mathbf{0}$, so

$$T(\mathbf{v}_1 + \mathbf{v}_2) = T(\mathbf{v}_1) + T(\mathbf{v}_2) = \mathbf{0} + \mathbf{0} = \mathbf{0} \quad \text{and} \quad T(r\mathbf{v}_1) = r\,T(\mathbf{v}_1) = r\mathbf{0} = \mathbf{0}$$

for all r in $\mathbb{R}$. Hence $\mathbf{v}_1 + \mathbf{v}_2$ and $r\mathbf{v}_1$ are both in $kerT$, which shows that $kerT$ is a subspace of V.

If $\mathbf{w}_1$ and $\mathbf{w}_2$ are both in imT, write $\mathbf{w}_1 = T(\mathbf{v}_1)$ and $\mathbf{w}_2 = T(\mathbf{v}_2)$ where $\mathbf{v}_1$ and $\mathbf{v}_2$ are in V. Then

$$\mathbf{w}_1 + \mathbf{w}_2 = T(\mathbf{v}_1) + T(\mathbf{v}_2) = T(\mathbf{v}_1 + \mathbf{v}_2) \quad \text{and} \quad r\mathbf{w}_1 = r\,T(\mathbf{v}_1) = T(r\mathbf{v}_1)$$

show that $\mathbf{w}_1 + \mathbf{w}_2$ and $r\mathbf{w}_1$ are both in imT for all r in $\mathbb{R}$. Hence imT is a subspace of W.

The subspaces $kerT$ and imT, with their relationship to T, are depicted in the diagram.

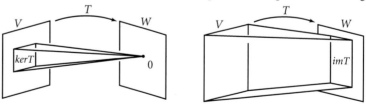

Familiar subspaces of $\mathbb{R}^n$ and $\mathbb{M}_{n,n}$ often occur in a natural way as images or kernels of linear transformations. Here are three examples.

Example 9

If A is an $m \times n$ matrix, let $T : \mathbb{R}^n \to \mathbb{R}^m$ be the matrix transformation given by $T(X) = AX$ for all X in $\mathbb{R}^n$. The subspaces $nullA$ and imA arise as follows:

$$kerT = \{X \mid AX = 0\} = nullA \quad \text{and} \quad imT = \{AX \mid X \text{ in } \mathbb{R}^n\} = imA.$$

Example 10

If U is a subspace of $\mathbb{R}^n$, let $T : \mathbb{R}^n \to \mathbb{R}^n$ be the projection on U, that is define $T(X) = proj_U(X)$ for all X in $\mathbb{R}^n$. Show that

$$im\,T = U \quad \text{and} \quad ker\,T = U^{\perp}.$$

SOLUTION

Note first that T is a linear transformation by Example 4 §4.9. The Projection theorem (Theorem 2 §4.6) asserts that

$$T(X) \text{ is in } U \quad \text{and} \quad X - T(X) \text{ is in } U^{\perp} \quad \text{for all } X \text{ in } \mathbb{R}^n. \qquad (\ast\ast\ast)$$

Since $T(X)$ is in U for all X, we have $im\,T \subseteq U$. On the other hand, if X is in U, then $(\ast\ast\ast)$ shows that $X - T(X)$ is in $U \cap U^{\perp} = \{0\}$ for all X, so $X = T(X)$ is in $im\,T$. This proves that $im\,T = U$.

Similarly, $(\ast\ast\ast)$ shows that $X - T(X)$ is in $U^{\perp}$ for all X, so $ker\,T \subseteq U^{\perp}$. But if X is in $U^{\perp}$, then $(\ast\ast\ast)$ shows that $T(X) = X - (X - T(X))$ is in $U \cap U^{\perp} = \{0\}$, and it follows that X is in $ker\,T$. This shows that $ker\,T = U^{\perp}$.

Recall that a matrix S is called **skew-symmetric** if $S^T = -S$.

Example 11

Let $T : \mathbb{M}_{n,n} \to \mathbb{M}_{n,n}$ be defined by $T(A) = A - A^T$ for all matrices A in $\mathbb{M}_{n,n}$. Show that T is linear,

$$ker\,T = \{A \text{ in } \mathbb{M}_{n,n} \mid A \text{ is symmetric}\},$$

and

$$im\,T = \{S \text{ in } \mathbb{M}_{n,n} \mid S \text{ is skew-symmetric}\}.$$

SOLUTION

The reader can verify that T is linear. Clearly, $ker\,T = \{A \mid A^T = A\}$ is the set of symmetric matrices. On the other hand, $T(A) = A - A^T$ is skew-symmetric for all A (verify), and every skew-symmetric matrix S has the form $S = A - A^T$ where $A = \frac{1}{2}S$ (verify). This proves the second assertion.

Example 12

As in Example 3, if a is a number, let $E_a : \mathbb{P}_n \to \mathbb{R}$ be evaluation at a, that is $E_a[p(x)] = p(a)$ for all polynomials $p(x)$ in $\mathbb{P}_n$. Then

$$ker(E_a) = \{p(x) \mid p(a) = 0\}$$

consists of the polynomials having a as a root. On the other hand,

$$im(E_a) = \{p(a) \mid p(x) \text{ in } \mathbb{P}_n\} = \mathbb{R}$$

because every real number b equals $p(a)$ for some polynomial $p(x)$ (for example, $p(x) = b$, the constant polynomial).

Example 13[12]

Let $T : \mathbb{P}_n \to \mathbb{P}_n$ be the differentiation operator: $T[p(x)] = p'(x)$ for all $p(x)$ in $\mathbb{P}_n$. Then T is linear (see Example 4) and

$$ker\,T = \{p(x) \mid p'(x) = 0\} \text{ consists of the constant polynomials}$$

because they are the only ones whose derivative is identically zero. On the other hand,

$$im\,T = \{p'(x) \mid p(x) \text{ in } \mathbb{P}_n\} = \mathbb{P}_{n-1}.$$

Indeed, $im\,T \subseteq \mathbb{P}_{n-1}$ because $p'(x)$ is always 0 or of degree one less than $p(x)$, and $\mathbb{P}_{n-1} \subseteq im\,T$ because every polynomial in $\mathbb{P}_{n-1}$ has degree at most $n - 1$ and so is the derivative of some polynomial $p(x)$ in $\mathbb{P}_n$.

The kernel and image of a linear transformation T are closely related to two other properties of T. If $T : V \to W$ is a linear transformation, we say that:

---

[12] Requires polynomial calculus.

T is **onto** if $imT = W$.

T is **one-to-one** if $T(\mathbf{v}_1) = T(\mathbf{v}_2)$ implies that $\mathbf{v}_1 = \mathbf{v}_2$.

Thus $T : V \to W$ is onto if every vector $\mathbf{w}$ in W is the image of some vector in V, and T is one-to-one if no vector $\mathbf{w}$ in W is the image of two distinct vectors in V.

Example 14

The linear transformation $T : \mathbb{R}^2 \to \mathbb{R}$ given by $T([r \ \ s]^T) = r$ is onto but not one-to-one. In fact, T is onto because every r in $\mathbb{R}$ is the image of some vector in $\mathbb{R}^2$ (say $T([r \ \ 0]^T) = r$). But T is not one-to-one. For example, $T([1 \ \ 0]^T) = T([1 \ \ 1]^T)$ but $[1 \ \ 0]^T \neq [1 \ \ 1]^T$.

Example 15

The linear transformation $T : \mathbb{R} \to \mathbb{R}^2$ given by $T(r) = [r \ \ 0]^T$ is one-to-one but not onto. Indeed, T is one-to-one because $T(r_1) = T(r_2)$ means $[r_1 \ \ 0]^T = [r_2 \ \ 0]^T$, whence $r_1 = r_2$. But T is not onto because, for example, the vector $[0 \ \ 1]^T$ in $\mathbb{R}^2$ is not the image under T of any vector r in $\mathbb{R}$.

The onto transformations $T : V \to W$ are the ones for which the subspace imT of W is as *large* as possible (namely $imT = W$). By contrast, the next result shows that the one-to-one transformations are those for which the subspace $kerT$ of V is as *small* as possible in V (namely $kerT = \{\mathbf{0}\}$). This is a useful test for when T is one-to-one.

THEOREM 4

Let $T : V \to W$ be a linear transformation. Then

T is one-to-one   if and only if $kerT = \{\mathbf{0}\}$.

PROOF

If T is one-to-one, let $\mathbf{v}$ be a vector in $kerT$, that is $T(\mathbf{v}) = \mathbf{0}$. Hence $T(\mathbf{v}) = T(\mathbf{0})$ by Theorem 1, so $\mathbf{v} = \mathbf{0}$ by the one-to-one condition. It follows that $kerT = \{\mathbf{0}\}$. Conversely, assume that $kerT = \{\mathbf{0}\}$. To show that T is one-to-one, let $T(\mathbf{v}_1) = T(\mathbf{v}_2)$; we must show that $\mathbf{v}_1 = \mathbf{v}_2$. But the linearity of T gives $T(\mathbf{v}_1 - \mathbf{v}_2) = T(\mathbf{v}_1) - T(\mathbf{v}_2) = \mathbf{0}$, so $\mathbf{v}_1 - \mathbf{v}_2$ is in $kerT = \{\mathbf{0}\}$. Thus $\mathbf{v}_1 = \mathbf{v}_2$, as required.

Example 16

If A is an $m \times n$ matrix, consider the matrix transformation $T : \mathbb{R}^n \to \mathbb{R}^m$ given by $T(X) = AX$ for all X in $\mathbb{R}^n$. Theorem 3 §4.4 asserts that $rankA = n$ if and only if the system $AX = 0$ has only the trivial solution $X = 0$. In our present language, this is:

T is one-to-one   if and only if $rankA = n$.

Similarly, Theorem 4 §4.4 shows that $rankA = m$ if and only if the system $AX = B$ has a solution for every column B in $\mathbb{R}^m$. This gives:

T is one-to-one   if and only if $rankA = m$.

5.3.3   The Dimension Theorem

If A is an $m \times n$ matrix, the corollary of Theorem 6 §4.4 asserts that

$$n = dim(imA) + dim(nullA).$$

This equation is important in matrix theory because $nullA$ is the set of all solutions X to the system $AX = 0$ of linear equations, and $dim(imA) = dim(colA) = rankA$ (see Theorem 5 §4.4). If $T : \mathbb{R}^n \to \mathbb{R}^m$ is given by $T(X) = AX$ for all X in $\mathbb{R}^n$, then Example 9 shows that $imA = imT$ and $nullA = kerT$. Consequently, the following theorem is a profound extension of the above equation.

THEOREM 5

Dimension Theorem. Let $T : V \to W$ be a linear transformation. If both $kerT$ and imT are finite dimensional, then V is also finite dimensional and

$$dimV = dim(imT) + dim(kerT).$$

PROOF

Let $\{\mathbf{b}_1, \mathbf{b}_2, \cdots, \mathbf{b}_k\}$ be a basis of $kerT$ and, since $imT = \{T(\mathbf{v}) \mid \mathbf{v} \text{ in } V\}$, let $\{T(\mathbf{d}_1), T(\mathbf{d}_2), \cdots, T(\mathbf{d}_r)\}$ be a basis of imT where each $\mathbf{d}_j$ is in V. Then $dim(kerT) = k$ and $dim(imT) = r$, so it suffices to show that

$$\mathcal{B} = \{\mathbf{b}_1, \mathbf{b}_2, \cdots, \mathbf{b}_k, \mathbf{d}_1, \mathbf{d}_2, \cdots, \mathbf{d}_r\}$$

is a basis of V.

$\mathcal{B}$ *spans* V. If $\mathbf{v}$ is in V, then $T(\mathbf{v})$ is in imT, so write $T(\mathbf{v}) = s_1T(\mathbf{d}_1) + s_2T(\mathbf{d}_2) + \cdots + s_rT(\mathbf{d}_r)$ where each s_j is in $\mathbb{R}$. Then $T(\mathbf{v}) = T(s_1\mathbf{d}_1 + s_2\mathbf{d}_2 + \cdots + s_r\mathbf{d}_r)$ by Theorem 1. Since T is linear, this means that $\mathbf{v} - (s_1\mathbf{d}_1 + s_2\mathbf{d}_2 + \cdots + s_r\mathbf{d}_r)$ lies in $kerT$, and so is a linear combination of $\{\mathbf{b}_1, \mathbf{b}_2, \cdots, \mathbf{b}_k\}$. It follows that $\mathbf{v}$ is in $span\mathcal{B}$, as required.

$\mathcal{B}$ *is linearly independent.* Suppose that t_i and s_j in $\mathbb{R}$ exist such that

$$t_1\mathbf{b}_1 + t_2\mathbf{b}_2 + \cdots + t_k\mathbf{b}_k + s_1\mathbf{d}_1 + s_2\mathbf{d}_2 + \cdots + s_r\mathbf{d}_r = \mathbf{0}. \qquad (****)$$

Since each $\mathbf{b}_i$ is in $kerT$, applying T gives $s_1T(\mathbf{d}_1) + s_2T(\mathbf{d}_2) + \cdots + s_rT(\mathbf{d}_r) = \mathbf{0}$. It follows that each $s_j = 0$, whence $(****)$ becomes $t_1\mathbf{b}_1 + t_2\mathbf{b}_2 + \cdots + t_k\mathbf{b}_k = \mathbf{0}$. Hence each $t_i = 0$, and we are done.

As noted above, the Dimension theorem provides another proof of the important fact that the dimension of the space of solutions of a system $AX = 0$ equals $n - r$ where A is an $m \times n$ matrix of rank r. Another illustration: The result that $dimU + dimU^{\perp} = n$ for all subspaces U of $\mathbb{R}^n$ (Theorem 3 §4.6) follows immediately from the Dimension theorem and Example 10.

The following consequence of the Dimension theorem will be referred to later.

COROLLARY

Let $T : V \to W$ be a linear transformation. If $dimV = dimW$ is finite, then T is one-to-one if and only if T is onto.

PROOF

The Dimension theorem gives $dim(imT) + dim(kerT) = dimV$. If T is one-to-one, then $kerT = \{\mathbf{0}\}$ by Theorem 4, so $dim(kerT) = 0$. Hence $dim(imT) = dimV = dimW$, whence $imT = W$ by Theorem 5 §5.2, and T is onto. Conversely, if T is onto, then $imT = W$ so $dim(imT) = dimW = dimV$. It follows from the Dimension theorem that $dim(kerT) = 0$, so $kerT = \{\mathbf{0}\}$ and T is one-to-one.

If $T : V \to W$ is a linear transformation where $dimV = n$ is finite, and if either of $dim(kerT)$ or $dim(imT)$ is known, then the Dimension theorem provides the other. This can be useful because one of these dimensions can be easier to compute than the other. Applications of this often depends on *defining* an appropriate linear transformation. This is illustrated in the following example which gives a different proof of an important result from Section 1.5.

Example 17

If $BC = I$ where B and C are $n \times n$ matrices, show that also $CB = I$.

SOLUTION

Define $T : \mathbb{M}_{n,n} \to \mathbb{M}_{n,n}$ by $T(A) = CA$ for all A in $\mathbb{M}_{n,n}$. Then T is linear (verify). If A is in $kerT$, then $0 = T(A) = CA$, so $A = IA = BCA = B0 = 0$. This shows that $kerT = \{0\}$, so that T is one-to-one. But then T is onto by the Corollary to the Dimension theorem. In particular $T(D) = I$ for some matrix D, that is $CD = I$. Hence $D = ID = BCD = BI = B$, and so $CB = CD = I$, as asserted.

Exercises 5.3

Throughout these exercises, V always denotes a vector space.

1. True or False?
   a) $T : \mathbb{R} \rightarrow \mathbb{R}$ is a linear transformation where $T(r) = r^2$ for all r in $\mathbb{R}$.
   b) $T : \mathbb{R} \rightarrow \mathbb{R}$ is a linear transformation where $T(r) = |r|$ for all r in $\mathbb{R}$.
   c) $T(X) = AX$ defines a linear transformation $\mathbb{R}^6 \rightarrow \mathbb{R}^5$ for every 5×6 matrix A.
   d) If $T : V \rightarrow W$ is a linear transformation and $T(\mathbf{v}_1) = T(\mathbf{v}_2)$, then $\mathbf{v}_1 - \mathbf{v}_2$ is in $ker T$.
   e) If $T : V \rightarrow W$ is a linear transformation and $T(\mathbf{v}) = \mathbf{0}$ for some $\mathbf{v} \neq \mathbf{0}$, then $T = 0$ is the zero transformation.
   f) If $T : V \rightarrow W$ is linear and $ker T = V$, then $W = 0$.
   g) If $T : V \rightarrow W$ is linear and $im T = 0$, then $T = 0$ is the zero transformation.
   h) If $T : \mathbb{R}^n \rightarrow \mathbb{R}^n$ is defined by $T(X) = proj_{\mathbb{R}^n}(X)$ for all X in $\mathbb{R}^n$ then $T = 1_{\mathbb{R}^n}$.
   i) A linear transformation $\mathbb{R}^n \rightarrow \mathbb{R}^m$ cannot be both one-to-one and onto.
   j) If $T : V \rightarrow W$ is one-to-one and $dim V = dim W = n$, then $im T = W$.
   k) Every linear transformation $T : \mathbb{R}^6 \rightarrow \mathbb{R}^5$ is onto.
   l) There exists a linear transformation T such that $T(\mathbf{v}_1)$ is in $\mathbb{F}[0, 1]$ and $T(\mathbf{v}_2)$ is in $\mathbb{R}^3$.

2. Let $T : V \rightarrow W$ denote a linear transformation. In each case either prove the statement or give an example showing that it is false.
   a) If $dim V = 6$, $dim W = 4$ and $dim(ker T) = 2$, then T is onto.
   b) If $dim V = 4$ and $dim W = 3$, then T is one-to-one.
   c) If $\{\mathbf{e}_1, \mathbf{e}_2, \mathbf{e}_3, \mathbf{e}_4\}$ is a basis of V and $T(\mathbf{e}_2) = \mathbf{0} = T(\mathbf{e}_4)$, then $dim(im T) \leq 2$.
   d) If $dim(ker T) \leq dim W$, then $dim W \geq \frac{1}{2} dim V$.
   e) If T is one-to-one, then $dim V \leq dim W$.
   f) If $dim V \leq dim W$, then T is one-to-one.
   g) If T is onto, then $dim V \geq dim W$.
   h) If $dim V \geq dim W$, then T is onto.

3. Show that the following are linear transformations.
   a) $T : \mathbb{C} \rightarrow \mathbb{C}$ where $T(z) = \bar{z}$, where $\bar{z}$ denotes the conjugate of the complex number z.
   b) $T : \mathbb{M}_{m,n} \rightarrow \mathbb{M}_{k,l}$ where $T(A) = PAQ$ where P and Q are fixed $k \times m$ and $n \times l$ matrices.
   c) $T : \mathbb{P}_n \rightarrow \mathbb{R}$ where $T(a_0 + a_1 x + \cdots + a_n x^n) = a_n$.
   d) $T : \mathbb{R}^n \rightarrow \mathbb{R}$ where $T(X) = Y \cdot X$, where Y is a fixed vector in $\mathbb{R}^n$.
   e) $T : \mathbb{P}_n \rightarrow \mathbb{P}_n$ where $T[p(x)] = p(x + 1)$ for all polynomials $p(x)$ in $\mathbb{P}_n$.
   f) $T : V \rightarrow \mathbb{R}$ where $T(r_1 \mathbf{e}_1 + \cdots + r_n \mathbf{e}_n) = r_1$, where $\{\mathbf{e}_1, \cdots, \mathbf{e}_n\}$ is a fixed basis of V.

   g) $T : \mathbb{M}_{n,n} \rightarrow \mathbb{R}$ where $T(A) = trA$, where trA denotes the trace of the matrix A.
   h) $T : \mathbb{M}_{m,n} \rightarrow \mathbb{R}^m$ where $T(A)$ is column 2 of A and $n \geq 2$.
   i) $T : \mathbb{R} \rightarrow \mathbb{F}[D]$, where $T(a) = f_a$ is the constant function defined by $f_a(x) = a$ for all x in D. (See Exercise 20 §5.1.)

4. Decide whether the following transformations $T : \mathbb{M}_{n,n} \rightarrow \mathbb{R}$ are linear. Support your answer.
   a) $T : \mathbb{M}_{n,n} \rightarrow \mathbb{R}$ where $T(A) = detA$
   b) $T : \mathbb{M}_{n,n} \rightarrow \mathbb{R}$ where $T(A) = rankA$

5. In each case find a linear transformation T with the given properties, and compute $T(\mathbf{v})$.
   a) $T : \mathbb{P}_2 \rightarrow \mathbb{P}_4$, $T(1) = x^4$, $T(x + x^2) = 1$, $T(x - x^2) = x + x^3$; $\mathbf{v} = a + bx + cx^2$
   b) $T : \mathbb{M}_{2,2} \rightarrow \mathbb{R}^2$, $T\begin{bmatrix} 1 & 0 \\ 0 & 1 \end{bmatrix} = \begin{bmatrix} 1 \\ 2 \end{bmatrix}$, $T\begin{bmatrix} 0 & 1 \\ 0 & 0 \end{bmatrix} = \begin{bmatrix} 0 \\ 1 \end{bmatrix}$, $T\begin{bmatrix} 0 & 0 \\ 1 & 0 \end{bmatrix} = \begin{bmatrix} 1 \\ 0 \end{bmatrix}$, $T\begin{bmatrix} 0 & 0 \\ 0 & 1 \end{bmatrix} = \begin{bmatrix} 0 \\ 0 \end{bmatrix}$; $\mathbf{v} = \begin{bmatrix} a & b \\ c & d \end{bmatrix}$

6. If $T : V \rightarrow V$ is linear and $\mathbf{e}$ and $\mathbf{f}$ are in V, find $T(3\mathbf{e} + \mathbf{f})$ and $T(\mathbf{f})$ in terms of $\mathbf{e}$ and $\mathbf{f}$ if $T(\mathbf{e} - \mathbf{f}) = 2\mathbf{e} - \mathbf{f}$ and $T(2\mathbf{f} - \mathbf{e}) = \mathbf{e} + \mathbf{f}$.

7. Let $T : V \rightarrow V$ be a linear transformation, and let $\{\mathbf{b}_1, \mathbf{b}_2, \cdots, \mathbf{b}_n\}$ be a basis of V.
   a) If $T(\mathbf{b}_i) = \mathbf{b}_i$ for each i, show that $T = 1_V$ is the identity transformation.
   b) If $T(\mathbf{b}_i) = \mathbf{0}$ for each i, show that $T = 0$ is the zero transformation.

8. Let $T : V \rightarrow W$ be a linear transformation. Give a careful proof of the fact that $T(\mathbf{v} - \mathbf{v}_1) = T(\mathbf{v}) - T(\mathbf{v}_1)$ for all $\mathbf{v}$ and $\mathbf{v}_1$ in V. Cite every axiom or theorem used.

9. Describe all linear transformations $T : \mathbb{R} \rightarrow V$. [Hint: $r = r \, 1$ for all r in $\mathbb{R}$.]

10. A linear transformation $T : V \rightarrow \mathbb{R}$ is called a **linear functional**.
    a) Let $T : V \rightarrow \mathbb{R}$ be a linear functional where $dim V = n$. If $\mathcal{B}$ is a basis of V, show that there exists a vector Y in $\mathbb{R}^n$ such that $T(\mathbf{v}) = Y \cdot C_{\mathcal{B}}(\mathbf{v})$ for all $\mathbf{v}$ in V. Compare with Exercise 9 §4.9.
    b) If V is the set of all integrable functions in $\mathbb{F}[0, 1]$, show that $T(f) = \int_0^1 f(t)dt$ defines a linear functional $\mathbb{F}[0, 1] \rightarrow \mathbb{R}$.

11. Let V be a finite dimensional vector space. Given $\mathbf{v} \neq \mathbf{0}$ in V and $\mathbf{w}$ in a space W, show that there exists a linear transformation $T : V \rightarrow W$ such that $T(\mathbf{v}) = \mathbf{w}$. What happens if $\mathbf{v} = \mathbf{0}$?

12. Show that the following are equivalent for a linear transformation $T : V \rightarrow W$.
    (a) $ker T = V$ (b) $im T = \{\mathbf{0}\}$ (c) $T = 0$

13. Let $T : V \to W$ be a linear transformation, let $\mathcal{B} = \{\mathbf{b}_1, \mathbf{b}_2, \cdots, \mathbf{b}_n\}$ be vectors in V, and write $\mathcal{C} = \{T(\mathbf{b}_1), T(\mathbf{b}_2), \cdots, T(\mathbf{b}_n)\}$.
 a) If $\mathcal{C}$ is independent, show that $\mathcal{B}$ is independent.
 b) If T is one-to-one and $\mathcal{B}$ is independent, show that $\mathcal{C}$ is independent.
 c) If $W = span\,\mathcal{C}$, show that T is onto.
 d) If $V = span\,\mathcal{B}$, show that $im\,T = span\,\mathcal{C}$.

14. Given vectors $\mathbf{v}_1, \mathbf{v}_2, \cdots, \mathbf{v}_n$ in a vector space V, define $T : \mathbb{R}^n \to V$ by $T[r_1\ r_2\ \cdots\ r_n]^T = r_1\mathbf{v}_1 + r_2\mathbf{v}_2 + \cdots + r_n\mathbf{v}_n$.
 a) Show that T is one-to-one if and only if $\{\mathbf{v}_1, \mathbf{v}_2, \cdots, \mathbf{v}_n\}$ is linearly independent.
 b) Show that T is onto if and only if $\{\mathbf{v}_1, \mathbf{v}_2, \cdots, \mathbf{v}_n\}$ spans V.

15. Let U be a subspace of a finite dimensional vector space V.
 a) Show that $U = ker\,T$ for some linear operator $T : V \to V$. [Hint: Theorem 3.]
 b) Show that $U = im\,S$ for some linear operator $S : V \to V$. [Hint: Theorem 3.]

16. Let $T : \mathbb{M}_{n,n} \to \mathbb{R}$ be the trace map: $T(A) = tr\,A$ for all A in $\mathbb{M}_{n,n}$. Show that $dim(ker\,T) = n^2 - 1$.

17. If A is an $n \times n$ matrix, let $U = \{B \text{ in } \mathbb{M}_{m,n} \mid BA = 0\}$ and let $W = \{BA \mid B \text{ in } \mathbb{M}_{m,n}\}$. Use the Dimension theorem to show that U and W are both subspaces of $\mathbb{M}_{m,n}$, and that $dim\,U + dim\,W = mn$.

18. Use the Dimension theorem to prove Theorem 1 §1.3: A homogeneous system of linear equations that has more variables than equations must have nontrivial solutions.

19. Let U and W denote the spaces of even and odd polynomials in $\mathbb{P}_n$ (see Exercise 20 §5.2). Use the Dimension theorem to show that $dim\,U + dim\,W = n + 1$. [Hint: Consider $T : \mathbb{P}_n \to \mathbb{P}_n$ where $T[p(x)] = p(x) - p(-x)$.]

20. Let U and W denote the spaces of symmetric and skew-symmetric $n \times n$ matrices, respectively. Show that $dim\,U + dim\,W = n^2$. [Hint: Example 11.]

21. Consider the subspace $W = \{p(x) \text{ in } \mathbb{P}_n \mid p(a) = 0\}$ of $\mathbb{P}_n$. Use the Dimension theorem to prove that $\{(x - a), (x - a)^2, (x - a)^3, \cdots, (x - a)^n\}$ is a basis of W.

[Hint: Use the evaluation map $E_a : \mathbb{P}_n \to \mathbb{R}$, Example 2 §5.2 and Theorem 4 §5.2.]

22. Use the Dimension theorem to show that every matrix A in $\mathbb{M}_{n,n}$ has the form $A = B^T - 3B$ for some B in $\mathbb{M}_{n,n}$.

23. Use the Dimension theorem to show that every polynomial $p(x)$ in $\mathbb{P}_{n-1}$ can be written in the form $p(x) = q(x + 1) - q(x)$ for some polynomial $q(x)$ in $\mathbb{P}_n$.

24. Show that differentiation is the only linear transformation $\mathbb{P}_n \to \mathbb{P}_{n-1}$ that satisfies $T(x^k) = kx^{k-1}$ for all $k = 0, 1, 2, \cdots, n$.

25. If a and b are real numbers, define $T_{a,b} : \mathbb{C} \to \mathbb{C}$ by $T_{a,b}(r + si) = ar + bsi$.
 a) Show that $T_{a,b}$ is linear and $T_{a,b}(\bar{z}) = \overline{T_{a,b}(z)}$ for all z in $\mathbb{C}$. Here $\bar{z}$ denotes conjugation.
 b) If $T : \mathbb{C} \to \mathbb{C}$ is linear and satisfies $T(\bar{z}) = \overline{T(z)}$ for all z in $\mathbb{C}$, show that $T = T_{a,b}$ for some a and b. [Hint: Show that $T(1)$ is real and $T(i)$ is pure imaginary.]

26. If a is in $\mathbb{R}$, consider the evaluation transformation $E_a : \mathbb{P}_n \to \mathbb{R}$ where $E_a[p(x)] = p(a)$.
 a) Show that $E_a(x^k) = [E_a(x)]^k$ for each $k = 0, 1, 2, \cdots, n$. (Note that $x^0 = 1$.)
 b) If $T : \mathbb{P}_n \to \mathbb{R}$ is linear and satisfies $T(x^k) = [T(x)]^k$ for each $k = 0, 1, 2, \cdots, n$, show that $T = E_a$ for some a in $\mathbb{R}$. [Hint: If $T = E_a$ for some a, what is $T(x)$?]

27. If $T : \mathbb{M}_{n,n} \to \mathbb{R}$ is linear and satisfies $T(AB) = T(BA)$ for all A and B in $\mathbb{M}_{n,n}$, show that there exists a constant k such that $T(A) = k\,tr(A)$ for all A in $\mathbb{M}_{n,n}$, where tr denotes the trace map (See Lemma 3 §4.7). [Hint: If E_{ij} denote the matrix units in $\mathbb{M}_{n,n}$ (see Example 16 §5.1), take $k = T(E_{11})$. Use the fact that
$$E_{ij}E_{km} = \begin{cases} 0 & \text{if } j \neq k \\ E_{im} & \text{if } j = k \end{cases}$$

28. Let V and W denote finite dimensional vector spaces. Using Theorems 3 and 5:
 a) Show that $dim\,V \leq dim\,W$ if and only if there exists a one-to-one linear transformation $T : V \to W$.
 b) Show that $dim\,V \geq dim\,W$ if and only if there exists an onto linear transformation $T : V \to W$.

5.4 ISOMORPHISMS AND MATRICES

Two vector spaces can appear to be quite different but, on closer examination, be the same underlying space expressed with different symbols. In this case we say that the spaces are isomorphic. This concept is investigated in this section, and is described in two ways using linear transformations: one using the one-to-one and onto properties and the other using composition. The notion of composition leads naturally to a way of introducing the matrix of any linear transformation T and using it to describe the action of T.

5.4.1 Isomorphisms

If V and W are vector spaces, a linear transformation $T : V \to W$ is called an **isomorphism** if it is both one-to-one and onto. If an isomorphism $V \to W$ exists, we say that V and W are **isomorphic**[13] vector spaces and write

$$V \cong W.$$

Example 1 $V \cong V$ for every vector space V because $1_V : V \to V$ is an isomorphism.

Example 2 $\mathbb{M}_{m,n} \cong \mathbb{M}_{n,m}$ because transposition: $\mathbb{M}_{m,n} \to \mathbb{M}_{n,m}$ is an isomorphism.

An isomorphism $T : V \to W$ induces a *pairing*

$$\mathbf{v} \longleftrightarrow T(\mathbf{v})$$

between the vectors $\mathbf{v}$ in V and the vectors $T(\mathbf{v})$ in W. Every vector in each space is paired with exactly one vector in the other space. Moreover, this pairing preserves vector addition and scalar multiplication, and hence preserves all vector space properties. The change of notation $\mathbf{v} \longmapsto T(\mathbf{v})$ changes the vector space V into W. Hence, roughly speaking, isomorphic spaces are the same except for notation. The following example illustrates this.

Example 3   We have $\mathbb{R}^2 \cong \mathbb{C}$ because, for example, the map $T : \mathbb{R}^2 \to \mathbb{C}$ given by $T([x\ y]^T) = x + iy$ is an isomorphism (verify). The pairing T turns $\mathbb{R}^2$ into the complex plane $\mathbb{C}$. $\mathbb{C}$ is the same vector space as $\mathbb{R}^2$, but with a different interpretation: The ordered pair $[x\ y]^T$ is now viewed as the complex number $x + iy$. We obtain one from the other by changing symbols.

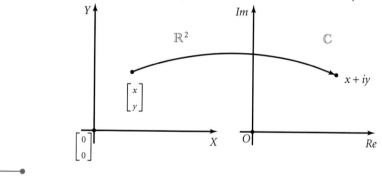

The following theorem is surprising because it shows that, up to isomorphism, there is *only one* n-dimensional vector space.

THEOREM 1   If V has dimension n, then $V \cong \mathbb{R}^n$.

PROOF   Choose a basis $\mathcal{B} = \{\mathbf{b}_1,\ \mathbf{b}_2,\ \cdots,\ \mathbf{b}_n\}$ of V and define $T : \mathbb{R}^n \to V$ by $T([r_1,\ r_2,\ \cdots,\ r_n]^T) = r_1\mathbf{b}_1 + r_2\mathbf{b}_2 + \cdots + r_n\mathbf{b}_n$. Then T is one-to-one because $\mathcal{B}$ is independent, and T is onto because $\mathcal{B}$ spans V (verify). Thus T is an isomorphism, so $V \cong \mathbb{R}^n$.

Because of Theorem 1, it seems at first glance that the study of an abstract n-dimensional vector space V is a waste of time: Since V is just $\mathbb{R}^n$ except for a change of symbols, simply study $\mathbb{R}^n$ and be done with it! But the meaning is in the interpretation. Viewing $\mathbb{R}^2$ as

---

[13] The word comes from two Greek words: *iso* meaning "same" and *morphos* meaning "form".

$\mathbb{C}$ casts a whole new light on the plane — for example the geometrical interpretation of complex multiplication adds new life to $\mathbb{R}^2$ and provides an important new way to study rotations in the plane, while orthogonality and projections are more naturally studied in $\mathbb{R}^2$. Similarly, one verifies that $\mathbb{R}^{n+1} \cong \mathbb{P}_n$, and interpreting vectors in $\mathbb{R}^{n+1}$ as polynomials greatly enriches the structure of $\mathbb{R}^{n+1}$ because polynomials can be multiplied and composed. Another example is $\mathbb{R}^{n^2} \cong \mathbb{M}_{n,n}$ (verify) with the attendant view of vectors in $\mathbb{R}^{n^2}$ as $n \times n$ matrices.

On the other hand, revealing the underlying vector space nature of $\mathbb{C}$, $\mathbb{P}_n$, and $\mathbb{M}_{n,n}$ allows general vector space theorems and techniques to be used to study complex numbers, polynomials, and matrices. These are powerful methods and yield new information in all three cases.

We know that every linear transformation preserves linear combinations of vectors; the isomorphisms are the ones preserving bases.

THEOREM 2   If V and W are finite dimensional vector spaces, the following are equivalent for a linear transformation $T : V \to W$:

(1) T is an isomorphism.
(2) If $\{\mathbf{b}_1, \mathbf{b}_2, \cdots, \mathbf{b}_n\}$ is any basis of V, then $\{T(\mathbf{b}_1), T(\mathbf{b}_2), \cdots, T(\mathbf{b}_n)\}$ is a basis of W.
(3) There exists a basis $\{\mathbf{b}_1, \mathbf{b}_2, \cdots, \mathbf{b}_n\}$ of V such that $\{T(\mathbf{b}_1), T(\mathbf{b}_2), \cdots, T(\mathbf{b}_n)\}$ is a basis of W.

PROOF $(1) \Rightarrow (2)$. If $\{\mathbf{b}_1, \mathbf{b}_2, \cdots, \mathbf{b}_n\}$ is any basis of V, then $\{T(\mathbf{b}_1), T(\mathbf{b}_2), \cdots, T(\mathbf{b}_n)\}$ is independent because T is one-to-one, and it spans W because T is onto. The verifications are left to the reader.

$(2) \Rightarrow (3)$. This follows because V has a finite basis (being finite dimensional).

$(3) \Rightarrow (1)$. Given a basis $\{\mathbf{b}_1, \mathbf{b}_2, \cdots, \mathbf{b}_n\}$ as in (3), T is one-to-one because $\{T(\mathbf{b}_1), T(\mathbf{b}_2), \cdots, T(\mathbf{b}_n)\}$ is independent and T is onto because it spans W, so T is an isomorphism. Again the details are left to the reader.

Condition (3) in Theorem 2 is a useful test for when a linear transformation is actually an isomorphism, and it can be used to *construct* isomorphisms. The next example provides an illustration.

Example 4   If V is the space of all 2×2 symmetric matrices, find an isomorphism $T : \mathbb{P}_2 \to V$ such that $T(x) = I$.

SOLUTION   Write $\mathbf{d}_1 = I = \begin{bmatrix} 1 & 0 \\ 0 & 1 \end{bmatrix}$, $\mathbf{d}_2 = \begin{bmatrix} 1 & 0 \\ 0 & 0 \end{bmatrix}$ and $\mathbf{d}_3 = \begin{bmatrix} 0 & 1 \\ 1 & 0 \end{bmatrix}$. Then $\mathcal{B} = \{1, x, x^2\}$ and $\mathcal{D} = \{\mathbf{d}_1, \mathbf{d}_2, \mathbf{d}_3\}$ are bases of $\mathbb{P}_2$ and V respectively. By Theorem 3 §5.3 there is a linear transformation $T : \mathbb{P}_2 \to V$ such that $T(1) = \mathbf{d}_2$, $T(x) = \mathbf{d}_1 = I$, and $T(x^2) = \mathbf{d}_3$. Since T clearly takes the basis $\mathcal{B}$ to the basis $\mathcal{D}$, it is an isomorphism by Theorem 2.[14]

THEOREM 3   Let V and W denote finite dimensional vector spaces.

(1) $V \cong W$ if and only if $dim\,V = dim\,W$.
(2) If $dim\,V = dim\,W$, a linear transformation $T : V \to W$ is an isomorphism if and only if it is either one-to-one or onto.

---

[14] Of course, we can extend T linearly to get the formula $T(a + bx + cx^2) = a\mathbf{d}_1 + b\mathbf{d}_2 + c\mathbf{d}_3 = \begin{bmatrix} a+b & c \\ c & a \end{bmatrix}$. However, such detail is usually unnecessary and it is customary to simply specify T on a basis.

(3)$\Rightarrow$(1). Given (3), $M_\mathcal{B}(T)$ is a diagonalizable matrix, so let $\{X_1,\ X_2,\ \cdots,\ X_n\}$ be a basis of $\mathbb{R}^n$ consisting of eigenvectors of $M_\mathcal{B}(T)$. If $X_j = C_\mathcal{B}(\mathbf{b}_j)$ for each j, then $\mathcal{D} = \{\mathbf{b}_1,\ \mathbf{b}_2,\ \cdots,\ \mathbf{b}_n\}$ is a basis of V (because $C_\mathcal{B}^{-1}$ is an isomorphism and $\mathbf{b}_j = C_\mathcal{B}^{-1}(X_j)$ for each j). Since $\mathcal{D}$ consists of eigenvectors of T by Lemma 2, this proves (1).

Finally, the last sentence follows from Lemma 2.

Example 10 Let $T : \mathbb{M}_{2,2} \to \mathbb{M}_{2,2}$ be defined by $T(A) = A^T$ for each matrix A in $\mathbb{M}_{2,2}$. Determine if T is diagonalizable and, if so, find a basis of $\mathbb{M}_{2,2}$ consisting of eigenvectors of T.

SOLUTION Consider the standard basis $\mathcal{B} = \{E_{11},\ E_{12},\ E_{21},\ E_{22}\}$ of $\mathbb{M}_{2,2}$ where E_{ij} is the matrix unit with 1 in the (i, j)-position and zeros elsewhere. Then

$$T(E_{11}) = E_{11},\ T(E_{12}) = E_{21},\ T(E_{21}) = E_{12},\ \text{and}\ T(E_{22}) = E_{22}$$

as is easily verified. Hence

$$M_\mathcal{B}(T) = \begin{bmatrix} 1 & 0 & 0 & 0 \\ 0 & 0 & 1 & 0 \\ 0 & 1 & 0 & 0 \\ 0 & 0 & 0 & 1 \end{bmatrix}$$

so the characteristic polynomial of T is $c_T(x) = c_{M_\mathcal{B}(T)}(x) = (x-1)^3(x+1)$. Thus $M_\mathcal{B}(T)$ (and hence T) has eigenvalues $\lambda_1 = 1$ of multiplicity 3 and $\lambda_2 = -1$ of multiplicity 1. Moreover, corresponding eigenvectors of $M_\mathcal{B}(T)$ are

$$X_1 = \begin{bmatrix} 1 \\ 0 \\ 0 \\ 0 \end{bmatrix},\ Y_1 = \begin{bmatrix} 0 \\ 1 \\ 1 \\ 0 \end{bmatrix},\ \text{and}\ Z_1 = \begin{bmatrix} 0 \\ 0 \\ 0 \\ 1 \end{bmatrix}\ \text{for}\ \lambda_1,\ \text{and}\ X_2 = \begin{bmatrix} 0 \\ -1 \\ 1 \\ 0 \end{bmatrix}\ \text{for}\ \lambda_2.$$

Hence $M_\mathcal{B}(T)$ is diagonalizable by Theorem 10 §4.7, so T is diagonalizable by Theorem 5. In addition, we have

$$X_1 = C_\mathcal{B}\begin{bmatrix} 1 & 0 \\ 0 & 0 \end{bmatrix},\ Y_1 = C_\mathcal{B}\begin{bmatrix} 0 & 1 \\ 1 & 0 \end{bmatrix},\ Z_1 = C_\mathcal{B}\begin{bmatrix} 0 & 0 \\ 0 & 1 \end{bmatrix},\ X_2 = C_\mathcal{B}\begin{bmatrix} 0 & -1 \\ 1 & 0 \end{bmatrix}.$$

Hence Lemma 2 shows that $\mathcal{D} = \left\{ \begin{bmatrix} 1 & 0 \\ 0 & 0 \end{bmatrix}, \begin{bmatrix} 0 & 1 \\ 1 & 0 \end{bmatrix}, \begin{bmatrix} 0 & 0 \\ 0 & 1 \end{bmatrix}, \begin{bmatrix} 0 & -1 \\ 1 & 0 \end{bmatrix} \right\}$ is a basis of eigenvectors of T (showing again that T is diagonalizable).

If $T : \mathbb{M}_{2,2} \to \mathbb{M}_{2,2}$ is the transposition operator in Example 10, observe further that the eigenspaces of T are

$$E_{\lambda_1}(T) = \{A \mid A^T = A\} \quad \text{and} \quad E_{\lambda_2}(T) = \{A \mid A^T = -A\},$$

and so consist of all symmetric and all skew-symmetric matrices, respectively. Furthermore, if we separate out the vectors in $\mathcal{D}$ corresponding to different eigenvalues, we obtain bases for the eigenspaces:

$$E_{\lambda_1}(T) = span\left\{ \begin{bmatrix} 1 & 0 \\ 0 & 0 \end{bmatrix}, \begin{bmatrix} 0 & 1 \\ 1 & 0 \end{bmatrix}, \begin{bmatrix} 0 & 0 \\ 0 & 1 \end{bmatrix} \right\}$$

$$= \left\{ \begin{bmatrix} a & b \\ b & c \end{bmatrix} \mid a,\ b,\ \text{and}\ c\ \text{in}\ \mathbb{R} \right\},$$

$$E_{\lambda_2}(T) = span\left\{ \begin{bmatrix} 0 & -1 \\ 1 & 0 \end{bmatrix} \right\}$$

$$= \left\{ \begin{bmatrix} 0 & -d \\ d & 0 \end{bmatrix} \mid d\ \text{in}\ \mathbb{R} \right\}.$$

This phenomenon holds more generally, and depends only upon the fact that $T^2 = 1_{\mathbb{M}_{2,2}}$. To see this, we need the techniques developed in the next section (this result is Exercise 26 §5.6).

Exercises 5.5

1. In each case either show that the statement is true or give an example showing that it is false. Throughout, A and B denote $n \times n$ matrices and S and T are operators $V \to V$.

   a) If $det A = det B$, then A and B are similar.

   b) If A is similar to B, then kA is similar to kB for any scalar k.

   c) If $T = R^{-1} \circ S \circ R$ for some isomorphism $R : V \to V$, then S and T have the same eigenvalues.

   d) If A is diagonalizable and $A = M_\mathcal{B}(T)$ for some basis $\mathcal{B}$, then V has a basis of T-eigenvectors.

   e) If $\mathbf{v}$ and $\mathbf{w}$ are distinct eigenvectors of T, then $\{\mathbf{v}, \mathbf{w}\}$ is independent.

   f) If $A = M_\mathcal{B}(T)$ and $B = M_\mathcal{B}(S)$ for some basis $\mathcal{B}$, then A and B are similar.

   g) If $\mathbf{v}$ is an eigenvector of T, the same is true of $k\mathbf{v}$ for all scalars $k \neq 0$.

   h) If $\mathbf{v}$ is an eigenvector of T and $\mathbf{w}$ is in $ker T$, then $\mathbf{v} + \mathbf{w}$ is an eigenvector of T.

2. Let $T : \mathbb{P}_2 \to \mathbb{P}_2$ be given by
   $T(a + bx + cx^2) = (2a - b) + (a + b + c)x + (c - a)x^2$.

   a) Find $M_\mathcal{B}(T)$ where $\mathcal{B} = \{1, x, x^2\}$.

   b) Is T invertible? Defend your answer.

3. Let $T : \mathbb{M}_{2,2} \to \mathbb{M}_{2,2}$ be given by
   $$T\begin{bmatrix} a & b \\ c & d \end{bmatrix} = \begin{bmatrix} a+b+c & 2c-a \\ b+d & c-d \end{bmatrix}.$$

   a) Find $M_\mathcal{B}(T)$ where $\mathcal{B} = \{E_{11}, E_{12}, E_{21}, E_{22}\}$ is the standard basis of matrix units.

   b) Is T invertible? Defend your answer.

4. If $T : \mathbb{P}_1 \to \mathbb{P}_1$ has matrix $M_\mathcal{B}(T) = \begin{bmatrix} 1 & -2 \\ -2 & 3 \end{bmatrix}$ where $\mathcal{B} = \{1, x\}$, find $T^{-1}(2x - 3)$.

5. If $T : \mathbb{M}_{2,2} \to \mathbb{M}_{2,2}$ has matrix
   $$M_\mathcal{B}(T) = \begin{bmatrix} 1 & 0 & 1 & 1 \\ 3 & 1 & -1 & 0 \\ 0 & 0 & -1 & 0 \\ 2 & 0 & 0 & 1 \end{bmatrix}$$ where $\mathcal{B} = \{E_{11}, E_{12}, E_{21}, E_{22}\}$
   is the standard basis of matrix units, find $T^{-1}\begin{bmatrix} 2 & 3 \\ -1 & 1 \end{bmatrix}$.

6. If B is a fixed 2×2 matrix, define $T : \mathbb{M}_{2,2} \to \mathbb{M}_{2,2}$ by $T(A) = BA$ for all A in $\mathbb{M}_{2,2}$. If $B = \begin{bmatrix} a & b \\ c & d \end{bmatrix}$, find a basis $\mathcal{B}$ of $\mathbb{M}_{2,2}$ such that $M_\mathcal{B}(T) = \begin{bmatrix} aI_2 & bI_2 \\ cI_2 & dI_2 \end{bmatrix}$.

7. a) Find the eigenvalues and eigenvectors of the matrix $A = \begin{bmatrix} 1 & 2 \\ 3 & 2 \end{bmatrix}$.

   b) If $T : \mathbb{R}^2 \to \mathbb{R}^2$ is defined by $T(X) = AX$ for all X in $\mathbb{R}^2$, use a) to find a basis of eigenvectors of T.

   c) If $T : \mathbb{P}_1 \to \mathbb{P}_1$ is defined by $T(a + bx) = (a + 2b) + (3a + 2b)x$, use a) to find a basis of eigenvectors of T.

8. Let $D : \mathbb{P}_3 \to \mathbb{P}_3$ be the differentiation operator given by $D(p(x)) = p'(x)$.

   a) Find the matrix of D with respect to the basis $\mathcal{B} = \{1, x, x^2, x^3\}$.

   b) Is D an isomorphism? Justify your answer.

   c) Show that $D^4 = 0$ is the zero operator.

9. Let $\mathcal{B} = \{\mathbf{b}_1, \mathbf{b}_2, \mathbf{b}_3\}$ be a basis of V, and let
   $\mathbf{d}_1 = 2\mathbf{b}_1 - \mathbf{b}_2$, $\mathbf{d}_2 = \mathbf{b}_2 - \mathbf{b}_3$, and $\mathbf{d}_3 = \mathbf{b}_1 + \mathbf{b}_2 + \mathbf{b}_3$.

   a) Show that $\mathcal{D} = \{\mathbf{d}_1, \mathbf{d}_2, \mathbf{d}_3\}$ is a basis of V.

   b) Find the change matrix $P_{\mathcal{B} \leftarrow \mathcal{D}}$.

10. Let $\mathcal{B} = \{\mathbf{b}_1, \mathbf{b}_2, \mathbf{b}_3\}$ be a basis of V. If $T : V \to V$ is an operator satisfying $T(\mathbf{b}_1) = \mathbf{b}_1 + \mathbf{b}_2$, $T(\mathbf{b}_2) = \mathbf{b}_2 + \mathbf{b}_3$, and $T(\mathbf{b}_3) = \mathbf{b}_1$, find:

    a) $M_\mathcal{B}(T)$.   b) $T^{-1}(\mathbf{b}_2)$.

11. Let $\mathcal{B} = \{\mathbf{b}_1, \mathbf{b}_2, \mathbf{b}_3\}$ be a basis of V. If $T : V \to V$ is an operator with matrix $M_\mathcal{B}(T) = \begin{bmatrix} 1 & 0 & 3 \\ -2 & 1 & 4 \\ 0 & -1 & 1 \end{bmatrix}$, find $T(2\mathbf{b}_2 - 5\mathbf{b}_3)$.

12. Let $\mathcal{B}$ be a basis of V where $dim V = n$. If A is $n \times n$, show that $A = M_\mathcal{B}(T)$ for some operator $T : V \to V$.

13. Describe the operator $T : V \to V$ if it has the property that $V = E_\lambda(T)$ for some real number λ.

14. Let $\mathcal{B} = \{\mathbf{v}, \mathbf{w}\}$ be a basis of V, and let $T : V \to V$ be defined by $T(\mathbf{v}) = \mathbf{v}$ and $T(\mathbf{w}) = \mathbf{v} - \mathbf{w}$.

    a) Find a basis of eigenvectors of T.

    b) Find the matrix $M_\mathcal{B}(T)$ and diagonalize it.

15. Let $T : \mathbb{P}_n \to \mathbb{P}_n$ be defined by $T(p(x)) = p(x) + x\,p'(x)$ where p' indicates the derivative. Show that T is an isomorphism by considering $M_\mathcal{B}(T)$ where $\mathcal{B} = \{1, x, x^2, \cdots, x^n\}$.

16. If k is any number, define $T : \mathbb{M}_{2,2} \to \mathbb{M}_{2,2}$ by $T(A) = A + kA^T$. Show that T is an isomorphism if $k \neq \pm 1$ by considering $M_\mathcal{B}(T)$ where
    $$\mathcal{B} = \left\{\begin{bmatrix} 1 & 0 \\ 0 & 0 \end{bmatrix}, \begin{bmatrix} 0 & 0 \\ 0 & 1 \end{bmatrix}, \begin{bmatrix} 0 & 1 \\ 1 & 0 \end{bmatrix}, \begin{bmatrix} 0 & -1 \\ 1 & 0 \end{bmatrix}\right\}.$$

17. Let $Q : \mathbb{R}^2 \to \mathbb{R}^2$ denote reflection in some line L through the origin.

    a) Show geometrically that any direction vector $\vec{d}$ for L is an eigenvector of Q.

    b) Use a geometrical argument to find eigenvectors independent of $\vec{d}$.

    c) Show that Q is diagonalizable.

18. Let S and T be linear operators $V \to V$ where $dim V$ is finite. Show that $det(S \circ T) = det S \, det T$.

19. Let S and T be linear operators $V \to V$ where $dim V$ is finite. Show that $tr(S \circ T) = tr(T \circ S)$. [Hint: Lemma 3 §4.7.]

20. Let S and T be two operators on a vector space V of dimension n.

a) If $T = R \circ S$ for some isomorphism $R : V \to V$, show that $ker S = ker T$.

b) If $ker S = ker T$ show that $T = R \circ S$ for some isomorphism $R : V \to V$. [Hint: Let $\mathcal{B} = \{\mathbf{b}_1, \cdots, \mathbf{b}_r, \mathbf{b}_{r+1}, \cdots, \mathbf{b}_n\}$ be a basis of V such that $\{\mathbf{b}_{r+1}, \cdots, \mathbf{b}_n\}$ is a basis of $ker S = ker T$. Then show that there exist bases of V of the form $\mathcal{D} = \{S(\mathbf{b}_1), \cdots, S(\mathbf{b}_r), \mathbf{d}_{r+1}, \cdots, \mathbf{d}_n\}$ and $\mathcal{F} = \{T(\mathbf{b}_1), \cdots, T(\mathbf{b}_r), \mathbf{f}_{r+1}, \cdots, \mathbf{f}_n\}$. Define R on the basis $\mathcal{D}$ by taking $R[S(\mathbf{b}_i)] = T(\mathbf{b}_i)$ for $1 \le i \le r$ and $R(\mathbf{d}_j) = \mathbf{f}_j$ for $r < j \le n$.]

c) If A and B are $n \times n$ matrices, show that $null A = null B$ if and only if $B = C A$ for some invertible matrix C. [Hint: See Example 2 §5.3.]

21. Show that $M_{\mathcal{D}'\mathcal{B}'}(T)P_{\mathcal{B}' \leftarrow \mathcal{B}} = P_{\mathcal{D}' \leftarrow \mathcal{D}}M_{\mathcal{D}\mathcal{B}}(T)$ where $T : V \to W$ is a linear transformation, $\mathcal{B}$ and $\mathcal{B}'$ are bases of V, and $\mathcal{D}$ and $\mathcal{D}'$ and are bases of W. [Hint: Right multiply by $C_{\mathcal{B}}(\mathbf{v})$ for arbitrary $\mathbf{v}$ in V, and use Lemma 1 and Theorems 1 and 2.]

5.6 INVARIANT SUBSPACES

As noted earlier, the central problem in linear algebra is to find a way to discover the "simplest" matrix for a linear operator $T : V \to V$. Often the way to do this is to regard T as an operator on subspaces of V of smaller dimension, and then find a way to build up the matrix of T on V from smaller matrices. The notion of a T-invariant subspace of V is a basic tool in this endeavour.

5.6.1 Invariant Subspaces

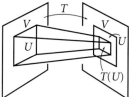

Suppose $T : V \to V$ is a linear operator. A subspace U of V is called T-**invariant** if
$$T(\mathbf{u}) \text{ is in } U \text{ for every vector u in } U.$$
If we write $T(U) = \{T(\mathbf{u}) \mid \mathbf{u} \text{ in } U\}$, this condition can be compactly expressed as
$$T(U) \subseteq U.$$
This is shown in the diagram.

Example 1 $\{\mathbf{0}\}$ and V are T-invariant subspaces of V for every operator $T : V \to V$.

Example 2 If λ is an eigenvalue of the operator $T : V \to V$, show that the eigenspace $E_\lambda(T)$ is a T-invariant subspace of V.

SOLUTION If $\mathbf{u}$ is in $E_\lambda(T)$, then $T(\mathbf{u}) = \lambda\mathbf{u}$ is again in $E_\lambda(T)$ because $E_\lambda(T)$ is a subspace.

Example 3 Let V be a 2-dimensional vector space with basis $\{\mathbf{v}, \mathbf{w}\}$, and define $T : V \to V$ by taking $T(\mathbf{v}) = -\mathbf{w}$ and $T(\mathbf{w}) = \mathbf{v}$. Show that V has no T-invariant subspace other than $\{\mathbf{0}\}$ and V.

SOLUTION Suppose that a T-invariant subspace U exists other than $\{\mathbf{0}\}$ or V; we show that this leads to a contradiction. Since $dim V = 2$, we have $dim U = 1$, so $U = \mathbb{R}\mathbf{u}$ for some vector $\mathbf{u} \neq \mathbf{0}$ in V. Since $T(\mathbf{u})$ is in U, we have $T(\mathbf{u}) = \lambda\mathbf{u}$ for some real number λ. On the other hand, $\mathbf{u}$ is in $V = span\{\mathbf{v}, \mathbf{w}\}$, so we can write $\mathbf{u} = a\mathbf{v} + b\mathbf{w}$ where a and b are in $\mathbb{R}$. Hence the equation $\lambda\mathbf{u} = T(\mathbf{u})$ becomes
$$\lambda a\mathbf{v} + \lambda b\mathbf{w} = \lambda\mathbf{u} = T(\mathbf{u}) = T(a\mathbf{v} + b\mathbf{w}) = aT(\mathbf{v}) + bT(\mathbf{w}) = -a\mathbf{w} + b\mathbf{v}.$$
Since $\{\mathbf{v}, \mathbf{w}\}$ is independent, it follows that $\lambda a = b$ and $\lambda b = -a$. But then $\lambda^2 a = \lambda(\lambda a) = \lambda b = -a$, so that $(\lambda^2 + 1)a = 0$. Hence $a = 0$ because λ is real. Similarly $\lambda^2 b = -b$, so $b = 0$, and we obtain $\mathbf{u} = a\mathbf{v} + b\mathbf{w} = \mathbf{0}$, a contradiction.

We now give a useful test for when a subspace U is T-invariant: Simply check that T carries every vector in some (usually finite) spanning set for U back into U.

LEMMA 1   If $T : V \to V$ is a linear operator and $U = span\{\mathbf{u}_1, \mathbf{u}_2, \cdots, \mathbf{u}_m\}$ is a subspace of V, then U is T-invariant if and only if $T(\mathbf{u}_i)$ is in U for each $i = 1, 2, \cdots, m$.

PROOF   If U is T-invariant, then certainly $T(\mathbf{u}_i)$ is in U for each i. Conversely, assume that each $T(\mathbf{u}_i)$ is in U, and let $\mathbf{u}$ be any vector in U. Then $\mathbf{u} = r_1\mathbf{u}_1 + r_2\mathbf{u}_2 + \cdots + r_m\mathbf{u}_m$ for some r_i in $\mathbb{R}$, so $T(\mathbf{u}) = r_1T(\mathbf{u}_1) + r_2T(\mathbf{u}_2) + \cdots + r_mT(\mathbf{u}_m)$ is also in U because U is a subspace. Thus U is T-invariant.

Example 4   Write $B = \begin{bmatrix} 1 & -1 \\ 1 & 0 \end{bmatrix}$, define $T : \mathbb{M}_{2,2} \to \mathbb{M}_{2,2}$ by $T(A) = BA$ for all A in $\mathbb{M}_{2,2}$, and consider the subspace $U = span\{I, B\}$ of $\mathbb{M}_{2,2}$. Show that U is a T-invariant subspace of $\mathbb{M}_{2,2}$ which is not an eigenspace of T.

SOLUTION   We have $T(I) = B$ is in U, and $T(B) = B^2$, so it is enough (by Lemma 1) to show that B^2 is in U. This follows from the fact that $B^2 = B - I$ (verify). [This can be seen as follows: The characteristic polynomial of B is $c_B(x) = x^2 - x + 1$, and the Cayley-Hamilton theorem (Theorem 7 below) asserts that $c_B(B) = 0$.] To see that U is not an eigenspace of T, simply observe that $T(B) = B^2 = B - I \neq \lambda B$ for any number λ (otherwise $(1 - \lambda)B = I$, a contradiction).

We now come to the principal reason for the importance of T-invariant subspaces. If $T : V \to V$ is an operator and U is a T-invariant subspace of V, the fact that $T(\mathbf{u})$ is in U for each vector $\mathbf{u}$ in U means that

$$T : U \to U \text{ is an operator } \textit{on the vector space } U,$$

called the **restriction** of T to U. This is very important for two reasons: First, the dimension of U will in general be smaller than the dimension of V so it will be easier to find a "simple" matrix for $T : U \to U$ (possibly by induction on the dimension). Second, if a basis of U is extended to a basis of V, the corresponding matrix of $T : V \to V$ takes a simplified, block upper triangular form. This is the content of the following theorem.

THEOREM 1   Let $T : V \to V$ be a linear operator where $dim V = n$, and let U be a T-invariant subspace of V. If $\mathcal{B}_0 = \{\mathbf{u}_1, \mathbf{u}_2, \cdots, \mathbf{u}_m\}$ is any basis of U, extend it to a basis

$$\mathcal{B} = \{\mathbf{u}_1, \mathbf{u}_2, \cdots, \mathbf{u}_m, \mathbf{v}_{m+1}, \cdots, \mathbf{v}_n\}$$

of V in any way at all. Then

$$M_\mathcal{B}(T) = \begin{bmatrix} M_{\mathcal{B}_0}(T) & Y \\ 0 & A \end{bmatrix}$$

in block triangular form, where $M_{\mathcal{B}_0}(T)$ is the $\mathcal{B}_0$-matrix of the restriction of T to U.

PROOF   First write the $n \times n$ matrix $M_\mathcal{B}(T)$ in terms of its columns:

$$M_\mathcal{B}(T) = [C_\mathcal{B}(T(\mathbf{u}_1)) \quad C_\mathcal{B}(T(\mathbf{u}_2)) \quad \cdots \quad C_\mathcal{B}(T(\mathbf{u}_m)) \quad C_\mathcal{B}(T(\mathbf{v}_{m+1})) \quad \cdots \quad C_\mathcal{B}(T(\mathbf{v}_n))].$$

Since $\mathbf{u}_i$ is in U for each $i = 1, 2, \cdots, m$, the fact that U is T-invariant means $T(\mathbf{u}_i)$ is in U. Hence the $\mathcal{B}$-expansion of $T(\mathbf{u}_i)$ has the form

$$T(\mathbf{u}_i) = r_1\mathbf{u}_1 + r_2\mathbf{u}_2 + \cdots + r_m\mathbf{u}_m + 0\mathbf{v}_{m+1} \cdots + 0\mathbf{v}_n$$

where $r_1, r_2, \cdots, r_m$ are real numbers. It follows that

$$C_\mathcal{B}(T(\mathbf{u}_i)) = [r_1 \quad r_2 \quad \cdots \quad r_m \quad 0 \quad 0 \quad \cdots \quad 0]^T \quad \text{and} \quad C_{\mathcal{B}_0}(T(\mathbf{u}_i)) = [r_1 \quad r_2 \quad \cdots \quad r_m]^T.$$

This means that, for each i, the column $C_{\mathcal{B}}(T(\mathbf{u}_i))$ in $M_{\mathcal{B}}(T)$ consists of the column $C_{\mathcal{B}_0}(T(\mathbf{u}_i))$ on top and zeros below. Since our hypotheses give us no information about the remaining columns $C_{\mathcal{B}}(T(\mathbf{v}_k))$ in $M_{\mathcal{B}}(T)$, this shows that $M_{\mathcal{B}}(T)$ has the triangular form given in the Theorem.

Example 5

In Example 4 we considered the operator $T : \mathbb{M}_{2,2} \to \mathbb{M}_{2,2}$ defined by $T(A) = BA$ for all A in $\mathbb{M}_{2,2}$, where $B = \begin{bmatrix} 1 & -1 \\ 1 & 0 \end{bmatrix}$, and we showed that $U = span\{I,\ B\}$ is a T-invariant subspace of $\mathbb{M}_{2,2}$. Complete $\mathcal{B}_o = \{I,\ B\}$ to a basis $\mathcal{B}$ of $\mathbb{M}_{2,2}$, and so illustrate Theorem 1.

SOLUTION

$\mathcal{B}_o$ is independent because $B \neq kI$ for any real number k. One possible completion (verify) of $\mathcal{B}_o$ to a basis of $\mathbb{M}_{2,2}$ is $\mathcal{B} = \{I,\ B,\ E_{11},\ E_{12}\}$ where $E_{11} = \begin{bmatrix} 1 & 0 \\ 0 & 0 \end{bmatrix}$ and $E_{12} = \begin{bmatrix} 0 & 1 \\ 0 & 0 \end{bmatrix}$. Since $B^2 = B - I$ (see Example 4), we see that

$$
\begin{aligned}
T(I) &= BI = B & &\text{so} & C_{\mathcal{B}}(T(I)) &= [0\ 1\ 0\ 0]^T, \\
T(B) &= B^2 = B - I & &\text{so} & C_{\mathcal{B}}(T(B)) &= [-1\ 1\ 0\ 0]^T, \\
T(E_{11}) &= BE_{11} = B + E_{12} & &\text{so} & C_{\mathcal{B}}(T(E_{11})) &= [0\ 1\ 0\ 1]^T, \\
T(E_{12}) &= BE_{12} = I - E_{11} + E_{12} & &\text{so} & C_{\mathcal{B}}(T(E_{12})) &= [1\ 0\ -1\ 1]^T.
\end{aligned}
$$

Hence the $\mathcal{B}$-matrix of T is

$$
\begin{aligned}
M_{\mathcal{B}}(T) &= [C_{\mathcal{B}}(T(I))\ \ C_{\mathcal{B}}(T(B))\ \ C_{\mathcal{B}}(T(E_{11}))\ \ C_{\mathcal{B}}(T(E_{12}))] \\
&= \begin{bmatrix} 0 & -1 & 0 & 1 \\ 1 & 1 & 1 & 0 \\ 0 & 0 & 0 & -1 \\ 0 & 0 & 1 & 1 \end{bmatrix}.
\end{aligned}
$$

This has the block upper triangular form expected from Theorem 1.

Theorem 1 has an important consequence that will be used later.

THEOREM 2

Let $T : V \to V$ be an operator where $dim V = n$, let U be a T-invariant subspace of V, and let $q(x)$ denote the characteristic polynomial of the restriction of T to U. Then

$$c_T(x) = p(x)\,q(x) \quad \text{for some polynomial } p(x).$$

PROOF

Let $dim U = m$. Choose a basis $\mathcal{B}_0$ of U, so that $q(x) = det[xI_m - M_{\mathcal{B}_0}(T)]$. Extend $\mathcal{B}_0$ to a basis $\mathcal{B}$ of V. Then $M_{\mathcal{B}}(T)$ has the block form $M_{\mathcal{B}}(T) = \begin{bmatrix} M_{\mathcal{B}_0}(T) & Y \\ 0 & A \end{bmatrix}$ by Theorem 1 for some $(n-m) \times (n-m)$ matrix A. Now a routine matrix computation (using Theorem 3 §2.2) gives

$$
\begin{aligned}
c_T(x) &= c_{M_{\mathcal{B}}(T)}(x) \\
&= det[xI_n - M_{\mathcal{B}}(T)] \\
&= det \begin{bmatrix} xI_m - M_{\mathcal{B}_0}(T) & -Y \\ 0 & xI_{n-m} - A \end{bmatrix} \\
&= det[xI_m - M_{\mathcal{B}_0}(T)]\ det[xI_{n-m} - A] \\
&= q(x)\,c_A(x).
\end{aligned}
$$

Theorem 2 follows with $p(x) = c_A(x)$.

If $T : V \rightarrow V$ is a linear operator, the triangular matrix

$$M_{\mathcal{B}}(T) = \begin{bmatrix} M_{\mathcal{B}_0}(T) & Y \\ 0 & A \end{bmatrix}$$

in Theorem 1 results from choosing the basis $\mathcal{B}$ so that the first few vectors are a basis $\mathcal{B}_0$ of some T-invariant subspace of V. If we can choose the remaining vectors in $\mathcal{B}$ so that they also span a T-invariant subspace, we can make $Y = 0$ and so get a block diagonal matrix for T. Describing how and when this can be done requires the idea of a direct sum decomposition of V, and we digress slightly to discuss this concept.

5.6.2   Direct Sums

Let V be any vector space. If U and W are subspaces of V, define their **sum** $U + W$ and **intersection** $U \cap W$ as follows:

$$U + W = \{\mathbf{u} + \mathbf{w} \mid \mathbf{u} \text{ in } U \text{ and } \mathbf{w} \text{ in } W\}$$

and

$$U \cap W = \{\mathbf{v} \text{ in } V \mid \mathbf{v} \text{ is in both } U \text{ and } W\}.$$

Thus $U + W$ consists of all sums of a vector in U and a vector in W, while $U \cap W$ consists of all vectors in both U and W. The routine proof of the following lemma is left to the reader.

LEMMA 2   If U and W are subspaces of V, then $U + W$ and $U \cap W$ are both subspaces of V.

The most important pairs of subspaces U and W of a vector space V turn out to be those for which

$$U + W = V \quad \text{and} \quad U \cap W = \{\mathbf{0}\}.$$

When this is the case we say that V is the **direct sum** of U and W and we indicate this by writing

$$V = U \oplus W.$$

In this case we call each of U and W a **complement** of the other in V. A subspace U can have more than one complement.

Example 6   If $U = \mathbb{R}[1 \ \ 0]$ in $V = \mathbb{M}_{1,2}$, show that each of $W_1 = \mathbb{R}[0 \ \ 1]$, $W_2 = \mathbb{R}[1 \ \ 1]$, and $W_3 = \mathbb{R}[1 \ \ -1]$ are complements of U in $\mathbb{M}_{1,\,2}$.

SOLUTION   We show that $V = U \oplus W_2$, and leave the other two cases to the reader. To see that $V = U + W_2$, observe that

$$[x \ \ y] = (x - y)[1 \ \ 0] + y[1 \ \ 1] \text{ is in } U + W_2 \text{ for all } x \text{ and } y.$$

Now suppose that $[x \ \ y]$ is in both $U = \mathbb{R}[1 \ \ 0]$ and $W_2 = \mathbb{R}[1 \ \ 1]$. Then $[x \ \ y] = r[1 \ \ 0] = s[1 \ \ 1]$ for some r and s in $\mathbb{R}$, so comparing second entries gives $0 = s$. Thus $[x \ \ y] = s[1 \ \ 1] = 0$, and we have proved that $U \cap W_2 = 0$. Hence $V = U \oplus W_2$.

Direct sum decompositions occur frequently as the following examples show.

Example 7   Consider the subspaces $U = \{A \text{ in } \mathbb{M}_{n,n} \mid A^T = A\}$ and $W = \{A \text{ in } \mathbb{M}_{n,n} \mid A^T = -A\}$ of $\mathbb{M}_{n,n}$ consisting of all symmetric and all skew-symmetric matrices, respectively. Show that $\mathbb{M}_{n,n} = U \oplus W$.

SOLUTION | Here the fact that $U \cap W = \{0\}$ is the observation that only the zero matrix is both symmetric and skew-symmetric (verify). To see that $U + W = \mathbb{M}_{n,n}$, let A be any matrix in $\mathbb{M}_{n,n}$ and consider the decomposition $A = \frac{1}{2}(A + A^T) + \frac{1}{2}(A - A^T)$. It is a routine exercise to verify that $\frac{1}{2}(A + A^T)$ is symmetric (and so is in U) and $\frac{1}{2}(A - A^T)$ is skew-symmetric (and so is in W). Hence $\mathbb{M}_{n,n} = U + W$.

Example 8 | Consider the space $\mathbb{F}[a, b]$ of all real valued functions defined on the interval $[a, b]$. A function f in $\mathbb{F}[a, b]$ is called **even** if $f(-x) = f(x)$ for all x in $[a, b]$, and f is called **odd** if $f(-x) = -f(x)$ for all x in $[a, b]$. If U consists of all even functions and W consists of all odd functions, show that $\mathbb{F}[a, b] = U \oplus W$.

SOLUTION | We leave to the reader the verification that U and W are both subspaces of $\mathbb{F}[a, b]$. If f is in $U \cap W$, then f is both even and odd, so $f(-x) = f(x)$ and $f(-x) = -f(x)$ both hold for all x in $[a, b]$. It follows that $f(x) = 0$ for all x; in other words, $f = f_0$ is the zero vector in $\mathbb{F}[a, b]$ (see Example 5 §5.1). Hence $U \cap W = \{f_0\}$ is the zero subspace of $\mathbb{F}[a, b]$.

Next, if f is any function in $\mathbb{F}[a, b]$, define $g : [a, b] \to \mathbb{R}$ and $h : [a, b] \to \mathbb{R}$ by

$$g(x) = \tfrac{1}{2}\{f(x) + f(-x)\} \quad \text{and} \quad h(x) = \tfrac{1}{2}\{f(x) - f(-x)\}$$

for all x in $[a, b]$. Then g and h both lie in $\mathbb{F}[a, b]$, and the reader can verify that g is even and h is odd. Moreover $g(x) + h(x) = f(x)$ holds for all x in $[a, b]$, which means that $f = g + h$. Hence $\mathbb{F}[a, b] = U + W$.

Example 9 | If U denotes any subspace of $\mathbb{R}^n$, show that

$$\mathbb{R}^n = U \oplus U^\perp$$

where $U^\perp = \{X \text{ in } \mathbb{R}^n \mid X \cdot Y = 0 \text{ for all } Y \text{ in } U\}$ is the orthogonal complement of U.

SOLUTION | If X is in both U and $U^\perp$, then $0 = X \cdot X = \|X\|^2$, so $X = 0$. Hence $U \cap U^\perp = \{0\}$. To see that $\mathbb{R}^n = U + U^\perp$, let X be any vector in $\mathbb{R}^n$ and write $P = proj_U(X)$. Then $X = P + (X - P)$, and the Projection theorem (Theorem 2 §4.6) asserts that P is in U and $(X - P)$ is in $U^\perp$. It follows that $\mathbb{R}^n = U + U^\perp$.

Clearly, $V = U + W$ if and only if every vector $\mathbf{v}$ in V has the form $\mathbf{v} = \mathbf{u} + \mathbf{w}$ for some $\mathbf{u}$ in U and $\mathbf{w}$ in W. We are interested in the situation where this representation is *unique*, that is where condition (1) in the following lemma holds.

LEMMA 3 | The following conditions are equivalent for subspaces U and W of a vector space V:
(1) If $\mathbf{u} + \mathbf{w} = \mathbf{u}_1 + \mathbf{w}_1$ where $\mathbf{u}$, $\mathbf{u}_1$ in U, and $\mathbf{w}$, $\mathbf{w}_1$ in W, then $\mathbf{u} = \mathbf{u}_1$ and $\mathbf{w} = \mathbf{w}_1$.
(2) If $\mathbf{u} + \mathbf{w} = \mathbf{0}$ where $\mathbf{u}$ is in U and $\mathbf{w}$ is in W, then $\mathbf{u} = \mathbf{0}$ and $\mathbf{w} = \mathbf{0}$.
(3) $U \cap W = \{\mathbf{0}\}$.

PROOF | (1)$\Rightarrow$(2). If $\mathbf{u} + \mathbf{w} = \mathbf{0}$, (2) follows by taking $\mathbf{u}_1 = \mathbf{0}$ and $\mathbf{w}_1 = \mathbf{0}$ in (1).

(2)$\Rightarrow$(3). If $\mathbf{v}$ is in $U \cap W$, then $\mathbf{v} + (-\mathbf{v}) = \mathbf{0}$ so $\mathbf{v} = \mathbf{0}$ by (2) because $\mathbf{v}$ is in U and $-\mathbf{v}$ is in W.

(3)$\Rightarrow$(1). Suppose that $\mathbf{u} + \mathbf{w} = \mathbf{u}_1 + \mathbf{w}_1$ as in (1). Then $\mathbf{u} - \mathbf{u}_1 = \mathbf{w}_1 - \mathbf{w}$, and this vector is in both U (left side) and W (right side). Hence $\mathbf{u} - \mathbf{u}_1 = \mathbf{0}$ and $\mathbf{w}_1 - \mathbf{w} = \mathbf{0}$ by (3), proving (1).

We can now give some important characterizations of direct sum decompositions.

THEOREM 3   If U and W are subspaces of V where $dim V$ is finite, the following are equivalent:

(1) $V = U \oplus W$.

(2) Every vector $\mathbf{v}$ in V has a unique representation in the form $\mathbf{v} = \mathbf{u} + \mathbf{w}$ with $\mathbf{u}$ in U and $\mathbf{w}$ in W.

(3) If $\mathcal{B}_1 = \{\mathbf{u}_1, \mathbf{u}_2, \cdots, \mathbf{u}_m\}$ and $\mathcal{B}_2 = \{\mathbf{w}_1, \mathbf{w}_2, \cdots, \mathbf{w}_k\}$ are any bases of U and W respectively, then $\mathcal{B} = \{\mathbf{u}_1, \mathbf{u}_2, \cdots, \mathbf{u}_m, \mathbf{w}_1, \mathbf{w}_2, \cdots, \mathbf{w}_k\}$ is a basis of V.

(4) There exist bases $\mathcal{B}_1 = \{\mathbf{u}_1, \mathbf{u}_2, \cdots, \mathbf{u}_m\}$ and $\mathcal{B}_2 = \{\mathbf{w}_1, \mathbf{w}_2, \cdots, \mathbf{w}_k\}$ of U and W respectively such that $\mathcal{B} = \{\mathbf{u}_1, \mathbf{u}_2, \cdots, \mathbf{u}_m, \mathbf{w}_1, \mathbf{w}_2, \cdots, \mathbf{w}_k\}$ is a basis of V.

PROOF $(1) \Rightarrow (2)$. Since $V = U + W$, every vector $\mathbf{v}$ in V has the form $\mathbf{v} = \mathbf{u} + \mathbf{w}$ for some vectors $\mathbf{u}$ in U and $\mathbf{w}$ in W. This representation is unique by Lemma 3 because $U \cap W = \{\mathbf{0}\}$.

$(2) \Rightarrow (3)$. If $\mathbf{v}$ is in V, use (2) to write $\mathbf{v} = \mathbf{u} + \mathbf{w}$ where $\mathbf{u}$ is in U and $\mathbf{w}$ is in W. Since $\mathbf{u}$ and $\mathbf{w}$ are in $span\{\mathcal{B}_1\}$ and $span\{\mathcal{B}_2\}$ respectively, it follows that $\mathbf{v} = \mathbf{u} + \mathbf{w}$ is in $span\{\mathcal{B}\}$. Hence $V = span\{\mathcal{B}\}$.

To see that $\mathcal{B}$ is independent, suppose numbers s_i and t_j exist such that

$$s_1\mathbf{u}_1 + s_2\mathbf{u}_2 + \cdots + s_m\mathbf{u}_m + t_1\mathbf{w}_1 + t_2\mathbf{w}_2 + \cdots + t_k\mathbf{w}_k = \mathbf{0}.$$

If we write $\mathbf{u} = s_1\mathbf{u}_1 + s_2\mathbf{u}_2 + \cdots + s_m\mathbf{u}_m$ and $\mathbf{w} = t_1\mathbf{w}_1 + t_2\mathbf{w}_2 + \cdots + t_k\mathbf{w}_k$, we have $\mathbf{u} + \mathbf{w} = \mathbf{0}$ with $\mathbf{u}$ in U and $\mathbf{w}$ in W. The uniqueness in (2) implies that $\mathbf{u} = \mathbf{0}$ and $\mathbf{w} = \mathbf{0}$, and then the independence of $\mathcal{B}_1$ and $\mathcal{B}_2$ forces $s_i = 0$ for each i and $t_j = 0$ for each j. Hence $\mathcal{B}$ is independent.

$(3) \Rightarrow (4)$. This is is clear since U and W *have* bases.

$(4) \Rightarrow (1)$. Given (4), every vector $\mathbf{v}$ in V is in $span\{\mathcal{B}\}$, and so there exist s_i and t_j in $\mathbb{R}$ such that

$$\mathbf{v} = s_1\mathbf{u}_1 + s_2\mathbf{u}_2 + \cdots + s_m\mathbf{u}_m + t_1\mathbf{w}_1 + t_2\mathbf{w}_2 + \cdots + t_k\mathbf{w}_k.$$

Hence $\mathbf{v} = \mathbf{u} + \mathbf{w}$ where $\mathbf{u} = s_1\mathbf{u}_1 + s_2\mathbf{u}_2 + \cdots + s_m\mathbf{u}_m$ is in U and $\mathbf{w} = t_1\mathbf{w}_1 + t_2\mathbf{w}_2 + \cdots + t_k\mathbf{w}_k$ is in W. It follows that $V = U + W$. If $\mathbf{v}$ is in $U \cap W$, (4) gives $\mathbf{v} = s_1\mathbf{u}_1 + s_2\mathbf{u}_2 + \cdots + s_m\mathbf{u}_m$ and $\mathbf{v} = t_1\mathbf{w}_1 + t_2\mathbf{w}_2 + \cdots + t_k\mathbf{w}_k$ with s_i and t_j in $\mathbb{R}$. Then the independence of $\mathcal{B}$ implies that $s_i = 0 = t_j$ for all i and j, so $\mathbf{v} = \mathbf{0}$. This proves that $U \cap W = \{\mathbf{0}\}$, and so proves (1).

If $\mathcal{B} = \{\mathbf{u}_1, \mathbf{u}_2, \cdots, \mathbf{u}_m, \mathbf{w}_1, \mathbf{w}_2, \cdots, \mathbf{w}_k\}$ is any basis of a vector space V, then condition (4) of Theorem 3 shows that $V = U \oplus W$ where $U = span\{\mathbf{u}_1, \mathbf{u}_2, \cdots, \mathbf{u}_m\}$ and $W = span\{\mathbf{w}_1, \mathbf{w}_2, \cdots, \mathbf{w}_k\}$. Moreover, every direct sum decomposition of V arises in this way by partitioning some basis $\mathcal{B}$ of V into two parts.

The following useful result is an immediate consequence of Condition (4) in Theorem 3.

THEOREM 4   If V is a finite dimensional vector space and $V = U \oplus W$ where U and W are subspaces of V, then $dim V = dim U + dim W$.

5.6.3   Reducible Operators

Returning to T-invariant subspaces, we can now prove the promised refinement of Theorem 1 wherein we outline how to find a basis such that the matrix of the operator T is block diagonal.

THEOREM 5   Let $T : V \rightarrow V$ be a linear operator where $dim V = n$, let
$$V = U \oplus W \text{ where both } U \text{ and } W \text{ are } T\text{-invariant,}$$
and let $\mathcal{B}_1 = \{\mathbf{u}_1, \mathbf{u}_2, \cdots, \mathbf{u}_m\}$ and $\mathcal{B}_2 = \{\mathbf{w}_1, \mathbf{w}_2, \cdots, \mathbf{w}_k\}$ be bases of U and W respectively. Then $\mathcal{B} = \{\mathbf{u}_1, \mathbf{u}_2, \cdots, \mathbf{u}_m, \mathbf{w}_1, \mathbf{w}_2, \cdots, \mathbf{w}_k\}$ is a basis of V and $M_{\mathcal{B}}(T)$ has the block diagonal form

$$M_{\mathcal{B}}(T) = \begin{bmatrix} M_{\mathcal{B}_1}(T) & 0 \\ 0 & M_{\mathcal{B}_2}(T) \end{bmatrix}$$

where $M_{\mathcal{B}_1}(T)$ and $M_{\mathcal{B}_2}(T)$ are the matrices of the restrictions of T to U and W respectively.

PROOF   Theorem 4 shows that $\mathcal{B}$ is a basis of V, and Theorem 1 shows that the columns in $M_{\mathcal{B}}(T)$ corresponding to $\mathcal{B}_1$ have the required form because U is T-invariant. Since W is also T-invariant, a similar argument works for the remaining columns of $M_{\mathcal{B}}(T)$.

An operator $T : V \rightarrow V$ is called **reducible** if a direct sum decomposition $V = U \oplus W$ can be found such that both U and W are T-invariant.

Example 10   In Example 4 we considered the operator $T : \mathbb{M}_{2,2} \rightarrow \mathbb{M}_{2,2}$ defined by $T(A) = BA$ for all A in $\mathbb{M}_{2,2}$, where $B = \begin{bmatrix} 1 & -1 \\ 1 & 0 \end{bmatrix}$. Show that T is reducible.

SOLUTION   In Example 4 we showed that $U = span\{I, B\}$ is a T-invariant subspace of $\mathbb{M}_{2,2}$ with basis $\mathcal{B}_1 = \{I, B\}$. In Example 5 we completed $\mathcal{B}_1$ to a basis $\{I, B, E_{11}, E_{12}\}$ and found that $\mathbb{M}_{2,2} = U \oplus W_1$ where $W_1 = span\{E_{11}, E_{12}\}$. The problem is that W_1 is *not* T-invariant.

However a different completion of the basis $\mathcal{B}_1$ *does* produce a T-invariant complement of U. If we write $\mathcal{B}_2 = \{E_{11}, E_{21}\}$, we find that $W = span\{\mathcal{B}_2\}$ is T-invariant by Lemma 1 because $T(E_{11}) = E_{11} + E_{21}$ and $T(E_{21}) = -E_{11}$. Moreover, $\mathcal{B} = \{I, B, E_{11}, E_{21}\}$ is a basis of V (verify) so $V = U \oplus W$. Hence T is reducible. In fact,

$$M_{\mathcal{B}}(T) = \begin{bmatrix} M_{\mathcal{B}_1}(T) & 0 \\ 0 & M_{\mathcal{B}_2}(T) \end{bmatrix}$$

where $M_{\mathcal{B}_1}(T) = \begin{bmatrix} 0 & -1 \\ 1 & 1 \end{bmatrix}$ because $T(I) = B$ and $T(B) = B - I$, and $M_{\mathcal{B}_2}(T) = \begin{bmatrix} 1 & -1 \\ 1 & 0 \end{bmatrix}$ because $T(E_{11}) = E_{11} + E_{21}$ and $T(E_{21}) = -E_{11}$.

The operator T in Example 10 has a natural T-invariant subspace U, but the first complement W_1 of U we considered was not T-invariant. However we succeeded in finding a T-invariant complement W of U, so T is in fact reducible. Sometimes, however, an operator can fail to be reducible even though it has an invariant subspace; the problem is that *no* invariant complement exists. Here is an example.

Example 11   Let $\{\mathbf{u}, \mathbf{v}\}$ be a basis of V and define $T : V \rightarrow V$ by $T(\mathbf{u}) = \mathbf{u}$ and $T(\mathbf{v}) = \mathbf{u} + \mathbf{v}$. Show that $U = \mathbb{R}\mathbf{u}$ is T-invariant but has no T-invariant complement in V.

SOLUTION U is T-invariant by Lemma 1 because $T(\mathbf{u}) = \mathbf{u}$. Suppose that $V = U \oplus W$ where W is also T-invariant. Then $dim W = 1$ by Theorem 4 (because $dim V = 2$), say $W = \mathbb{R}\mathbf{w}$. Write $\mathbf{w} = a\mathbf{u} + b\mathbf{v}$ where a and b are in $\mathbb{R}$. Then $b \neq 0$ because otherwise $\mathbf{w} = a\mathbf{u}$ is in $U \cap W = \{\mathbf{0}\}$. Since W is T-invariant, there is a real number λ such that $T(\mathbf{w}) = \lambda\mathbf{w}$.

Since $\mathbf{w} = a\mathbf{u} + b\mathbf{v}$, the fact that T is linear gives

$$\lambda a\mathbf{u} + \lambda b\mathbf{v} = \lambda\mathbf{w} = T(\mathbf{w}) = aT(\mathbf{u}) + bT(\mathbf{v}) = a\mathbf{u} + b(\mathbf{u} + \mathbf{v}) = (a + b)\mathbf{u} + b\mathbf{v}.$$

Since $\{\mathbf{u}, \mathbf{v}\}$ is independent, this gives $\lambda a = a + b$ and $\lambda b = b$. Hence $\lambda = 1$ (because $b \neq 0$) so that $a + b = \lambda a = a$. This gives $b = 0$, a contradiction.

Sometimes, a direct sum decomposition can be found into two eigenspaces of an operator. This not only shows that the operator is reducible, but diagonalizable as well. The next example is an illustration.

Example 12   An operator $T : V \to V$ is called an **idempotent** if $T^2 = T$.

(1) If T is an idempotent, show that T is diagonalizable by showing that V is the direct sum of its eigenspaces.

(2) If $A = A^2$ is any idempotent matrix, show that A is similar to $\begin{bmatrix} 0 & 0 \\ 0 & I_m \end{bmatrix}$ for some integer m (so A is diagonalizable).

SOLUTION   (1) If λ is an eigenvalue of T, we first show that either $\lambda = 0$ or $\lambda = 1$. Indeed, if $T(\mathbf{v}) = \lambda\mathbf{v}$ where $\mathbf{v} \neq \mathbf{0}$, then

$$\lambda\mathbf{v} = T(\mathbf{v}) = T^2(\mathbf{v}) = T(T(\mathbf{v})) = T(\lambda\mathbf{v}) = \lambda T(\mathbf{v}) = \lambda^2\mathbf{v}.$$

Hence $\lambda = \lambda^2$ because $\mathbf{v} \neq \mathbf{0}$, so $\lambda = 0$ or $\lambda = 1$. Hence there are two eigenspaces:

$$E_0(T) = \{\mathbf{u} \text{ in } V \mid T(\mathbf{u}) = \mathbf{0}\} \quad \text{and} \quad E_1(T) = \{\mathbf{w} \text{ in } V \mid T(\mathbf{w}) = \mathbf{w}\}.$$

We claim that $V = E_0(T) \oplus E_1(T)$. It is clear that $E_0(T) \cap E_1(T) = \{\mathbf{0}\}$. Moreover $V = E_0(T) + E_1(T)$ because any vector $\mathbf{v}$ in V can be written in the form $\mathbf{v} = (\mathbf{v} - T(\mathbf{v})) + T(\mathbf{v})$ and (since $T^2 = T$) it is easy to verify that $\mathbf{v} - T(\mathbf{v})$ is in $E_0(T)$ and that $T(\mathbf{v})$ is in $E_1(T)$. Hence

$$V = E_0(T) \oplus E_1(T)$$

and both $E_0(T)$ and $E_1(T)$ are T-invariant (by Example 2). Moreover, if $\mathcal{B}_0$ and $\mathcal{B}_1$ are bases of $E_0(T)$ and $E_1(T)$ respectively, the matrices of the restriction of T to $E_0(T)$ and $E_1(T)$ are $M_{\mathcal{B}_0}(T) = 0$ and $M_{\mathcal{B}_1}(T) = I_m$ where $m = dim(E_1(T))$. Thus Theorem 5 provides a basis $\mathcal{B}$ of V such that

$$M_{\mathcal{B}}(T) = \begin{bmatrix} M_{\mathcal{B}_0}(T) & 0 \\ 0 & M_{\mathcal{B}_1}(T) \end{bmatrix} = \begin{bmatrix} 0 & 0 \\ 0 & I_m \end{bmatrix}.$$

In particular, T is diagonalizable.

(2) If A is $n \times n$ and $A^2 = A$, define $T_A : \mathbb{R}^n \to \mathbb{R}^n$ by $T_A(X) = AX$ for all X in $\mathbb{R}^n$. Then $T_A^2 = T_A$ (verify) so, by part (1), there exists a basis $\mathcal{B}$ of $\mathbb{R}^n$ such that

$$M_{\mathcal{B}}(T_A) = \begin{bmatrix} 0 & 0 \\ 0 & I_m \end{bmatrix} \text{ where } m = dim(E_1(A)).$$

Since $A = M_{\mathcal{E}}(T_A)$ where $\mathcal{E}$ is the standard basis of $\mathbb{R}^n$, we have $A \sim M_{\mathcal{B}}(T_A)$ by Theorem 3 §5.5, as required.

A subspace U of a vector space V is called a **proper subspace** if $U \neq \{\mathbf{0}\}$ and $U \neq V$. Hence a one-dimensional subspace has no proper subspaces. Our interest here is in how this relates to direct sum decompositions. The vector space V always has the trivial direct decomposition

$$V = \{\mathbf{0}\} \oplus V.$$

We call all other direct decompositions $V = U \oplus W$ **proper**. Thus $V = U \oplus W$ is proper if U is a proper subspace of V (equivalently, if W is a proper subspace of V).

If $T : V \to V$ is an operator, the vector space V is called T-**irreducible** if no proper direct decomposition $V = U \oplus W$ can be found where both U and W are T-invariant. This certainly happens if V has *no* T-invariant subspaces except $\{0\}$ and V, and such a space is called T-**simple**.[18] If $dim V = 1$, then V is T-simple for every operator $T : V \to V$ (verify), and Example 3 describes a 2-dimensional, T-simple space. However, even though every T-simple space is T-irreducible, it is possible to have a T-irreducible space that is not T-simple.

Example 13

As in Example 11, let $\mathcal{B} = \{\mathbf{u}, \mathbf{v}\}$ be a basis of V and define $T : V \to V$ by $T(\mathbf{u}) = \mathbf{u}$ and $T(\mathbf{v}) = \mathbf{u} + \mathbf{v}$. Show that V is a T-irreducible space that is not T-simple.

PROOF

The subspace $\mathbb{R}\mathbf{u}$ is T-invariant by Lemma 1, so V is not T-simple because $dim V = 2$. In Example 11 we showed that $\mathbb{R}\mathbf{u}$ has no T-complement in V; we now show that V is in fact irreducible. Suppose on the contrary that T is reducible, say $V = Z \oplus W$, where Z and W are proper, T-invariant subspaces of V. Since $dim V = 2$, the fact that Z and W are proper means that $dim Z = 1$ and $dim W = 1$, say $Z = \mathbb{R}\mathbf{z}$ and $W = \mathbb{R}\mathbf{w}$ where $\mathbf{z} \neq \mathbf{0}$ and $\mathbf{w} \neq \mathbf{0}$. Moreover, since Z and W are T-invariant, it follows that $\mathbf{z}$ and $\mathbf{w}$ are both eigenvectors of T (verify). But $\{\mathbf{z}, \mathbf{w}\}$ is independent because $\mathbb{R}\mathbf{z} \cap \mathbb{R}\mathbf{w} = \{\mathbf{0}\}$, and so is a basis of eigenvectors of T. This means that T is diagonalizable, and hence that $M_{\mathcal{B}}(T) = \begin{bmatrix} 1 & 1 \\ 0 & 1 \end{bmatrix}$ is a diagonalizable matrix, a contradiction by Example 7 §2.3. So T is irreducible.

5.6.4 The Cayley-Hamilton Theorem

We conclude this section by using invariant subspaces to prove a classical theorem of linear algebra, the Cayley-Hamilton theorem, which asserts that every matrix satisfies its characteristic polynomial. The following example provides an illustration.

Example 14

If $A = \begin{bmatrix} 1 & -1 \\ 2 & 3 \end{bmatrix}$, then the characteristic polynomial is $c_A(x) = det(xI - A) = x^2 - 4x + 5$. If we substitute A for x in $c_A(x)$ the result is $c_A(A) = A^2 - 4A + 5I$.[19] The Cayley-Hamilton theorem asserts that in fact $c_A(A) = 0$; indeed

$$c_A(A) = A^2 - 4A + 5I = \begin{bmatrix} -1 & -4 \\ 8 & 7 \end{bmatrix} - \begin{bmatrix} 4 & -4 \\ 8 & 12 \end{bmatrix} + \begin{bmatrix} 5 & 0 \\ 0 & 5 \end{bmatrix} = \begin{bmatrix} 0 & 0 \\ 0 & 0 \end{bmatrix},$$

as expected.

Our approach to the Cayley-Hamilton theorem is to prove it first for operators by showing that every operator $T : V \to V$ satisfies its characteristic polynomial. This clearly entails defining what is meant by $p(T)$ where $p(x)$ is any polynomial. This, in turn, means that we must define sums and scalar multiples of operators.

Suppose that $S : V \to V$ and $T : V \to V$ are operators and that a is a scalar. We define new operators $S + T : V \to V$ and $aT : V \to V$ as follows:

$$(S + T)(\mathbf{v}) = S(\mathbf{v}) + T(\mathbf{v}) \quad \text{for all } \mathbf{v} \text{ in } V$$

and

$$(aT)(\mathbf{v}) = a\, T(\mathbf{v}) \quad \text{for all } \mathbf{v} \text{ in } V.$$

---

[18] T-simple spaces are sometimes call **completely T-irreducible**, especially in older books, but we prefer the term T-simple.

[19] Note that we are thinking of 5 in $c_A(x)$ as $5x^0$, and then taking $5A^0 = 5I$ in $c_A(A)$.

It is a routine matter to verify that $S + T$ and aT are both linear; they are called the **sum** of S and T, and the **scalar product** of T by a, respectively. If we recall that the power T^k means the composition of T with itself k times, we can define $p(T)$ for every polynomial $p(x)$. Indeed, if

$$p(x) = a_0 + a_1 x + a_2 x^2 + a_3 x^3 + \cdots + a_m x^m \text{ where each } a_i \text{ is in } \mathbb{R},$$

we define the operator $p(T) : V \to V$ by

$$p(T) = a_0 + a_1 T + a_2 T^2 + a_3 T^3 + \cdots + a_m T^m.$$

Thus, for example, if $p(x) = 3 - 5x + 7x^3$, the action of $p(T)$ on a vector $\mathbf{v}$ is

$$p(T)(\mathbf{v}) = (3 - 5T + 7T^3)(\mathbf{v}) = 3\mathbf{v} - 5T(\mathbf{v}) + 7T^3(\mathbf{v}) \text{ for all } \mathbf{v} \text{ in } V.$$

Of course, $T^3(\mathbf{v})$ means $T(T(T(\mathbf{v})))$ for each vector $\mathbf{v}$.

Now suppose that $\mathbf{v}$ is any nonzero vector in V where $dim V$ is finite, and consider the subsets

$$\{\mathbf{v}\},\ \{\mathbf{v},\ T(\mathbf{v})\},\ \{\mathbf{v},\ T(\mathbf{v}),\ T^2(\mathbf{v})\},\ \cdots.$$

The first of these sets is independent because $\mathbf{v} \neq \mathbf{0}$. But they cannot all be independent because $dim V$ is finite, so one of them is dependent. Let $m \geq 1$ be the smallest integer such that $\{\mathbf{v},\ T(\mathbf{v}),\ T^2(\mathbf{v}),\ \cdots,\ T^m(\mathbf{v})\}$ is dependent. Then

$$\mathcal{B}_0 = \{\mathbf{v},\ T(\mathbf{v}),\ T^2(\mathbf{v}),\ \cdots,\ T^{m-1}(\mathbf{v})\}$$

is independent. (If $m = 1$, this is taken to mean that $\mathcal{B}_0 = \{\mathbf{v}\}$.)[20] Having found $\mathcal{B}_0$, write

$$U = span\mathcal{B}_0 = span\{\mathbf{v},\ T(\mathbf{v}),\ T^2(\mathbf{v}),\ \cdots,\ T^{m-1}(\mathbf{v})\} \tag{$*$}$$

so that $dim(U) = m$ and $\mathcal{B}_0$ is a basis of U.

Since $\{\mathbf{v},\ T(\mathbf{v}),\ T^2(\mathbf{v}),\ \cdots,\ T^{m-1}(\mathbf{v}),\ T^m(\mathbf{v})\}$ is dependent, Lemma 2 §5.2 implies that $T^m(\mathbf{v})$ is in U. This has two consequences: First we can write

$$T^m(\mathbf{v}) = -r_0\mathbf{v} - r_1 T(\mathbf{v}) - r_2 T^2(\mathbf{v}) - \cdots - r_{m-1}T^{m-1}(\mathbf{v}) \tag{$**$}$$

where each r_i is in $\mathbb{R}$. (The reason for the minus signs will be apparent shortly.) The second consequence of the fact that $T^m(\mathbf{v})$ is in U is that it shows (using Lemma 1) that U is a T-invariant subspace of V, called the T-**cyclic subspace** generated by $\mathbf{v}$. Hence $T : U \to U$ is an operator on U, and ($*$) and ($**$) show that the $\mathcal{B}_0$-matrix of T is

$$M_{\mathcal{B}_0}(T) = \begin{bmatrix} 0 & 0 & \cdots & 0 & -r_0 \\ 1 & 0 & \cdots & 0 & -r_1 \\ 0 & 1 & \cdots & 0 & -r_2 \\ \vdots & \vdots & & \vdots & \vdots \\ 0 & 0 & \cdots & 1 & -r_{m-1} \end{bmatrix}. \tag{$***$}$$

If we let $q(x)$ denote the characteristic polynomial of the restriction of T to U, we have

$$q(x) = c_{M_{\mathcal{B}_0}(T)}(x) = det[xI - M_{\mathcal{B}_0}(T)] \tag{$****$}$$

$$= r_0 + r_1 x + r_2 x^2 + \cdots + r_{m-1} x^{m-1} + x^m$$

as the reader can verify.[21] For this reason, the matrix in ($***$) is called the **companion matrix** of the polynomial $q(x) = r_0 + r_1 x + r_2 x^2 + \cdots + r_{m-1} x^{m-1} + x^m$.

We can now prove the operator version of the Cayley-Hamilton theorem.

THEOREM 6   If $T : V \to V$ is a linear operator where $dim V = n$, then T satisfies its characteristic polynomial, that is

$$c_T(T) = 0.$$

---

[20] Note that $\{\mathbf{v},\ T(\mathbf{v})\}$ is dependent if and only if $\mathbf{v}$ is an eigenvector of T (verify).

[21] This is the reason for the negative signs in ($**$).

PROOF   We are to prove that $c_T(T)(\mathbf{v}) = \mathbf{0}$ for every vector $\mathbf{v}$ in This is clear if $\mathbf{v} = \mathbf{0}$ because $c_T(T)$ is linear. If $\mathbf{v} \neq \mathbf{0}$, we use it to construct U, $\mathcal{B}_0$, and $q(x)$ as above. If we complete $\mathcal{B}_0$ to a basis of V in any way at all, then Theorem 2 asserts that

$$c_T(x) = p(x)\, q(x) \quad \text{for some polynomial } p(x).$$

Hence $c_T(T)(\mathbf{v}) = p(T)\, [q(T)(\mathbf{v})]$ so it suffices to show that $q(T)(\mathbf{v}) = \mathbf{0}$. But (****) and (**) give

$$q(T)(\mathbf{v}) = r_0\mathbf{v} + r_1T(\mathbf{v}) + r_2T^2(\mathbf{v}) + \cdots + r_{m-1}T^{m-1}(\mathbf{v}) + T^m(\mathbf{v}) = \mathbf{0}.$$

This completes the proof.

The Cayley-Hamilton theorem is the matrix version of Theorem 6. We need one more observation about matrices of operators: If $S : V \to V$ and $T : V \to V$ are operators on a vector space V and $\mathcal{B}$ is any basis of V, then

$$M_\mathcal{B}(S + T) = M_\mathcal{B}(S) + M_\mathcal{B}(T)$$

$$M_\mathcal{B}(aT) = a\, M_\mathcal{B}(T) \text{ for any scalar } a$$

$$M_\mathcal{B}(S \circ T) = M_\mathcal{B}(S)M_\mathcal{B}(T)$$

The last of these is part of Theorem 1 §5.5, and the routine verifications of the first two are left as an exercise.

THEOREM 7   **Cayley-Hamilton Theorem.**[22] Every square matrix A satisfies its characteristic polynomial, that is

$$c_A(A) = 0.$$

PROOF   Define $T_A : \mathbb{R}^n \to \mathbb{R}^n$ by $T_A(X) = AX$ for all X in $\mathbb{R}^n$. Then $c_{T_A}(T_A) = 0$ by Theorem 6. If $\mathcal{E}$ is the standard basis of $\mathbb{R}^n$, then

$$M_\mathcal{E}(T_A) = A \quad \text{and} \quad c_{T_A}(x) = c_{M_\mathcal{E}(T_A)}(x) = c_A(x).$$

Now write $c_A(x) = r_0 + r_1x + r_2x^2 + \cdots + r_nx^n$, and compute

$$
\begin{aligned}
c_A(A) &= r_0I + r_1A + r_2A^2 + \cdots + r_nA^n \\
&= r_0M_\mathcal{E}(1_{\mathbb{R}^n}) + r_1M_\mathcal{E}(T_A) + r_2M_\mathcal{E}(T_A)^2 + \cdots + r_nM_\mathcal{E}(T_A)^n \\
&= M_\mathcal{E}(r_01_{\mathbb{R}^n} + r_1T_A + r_2T_A^2 + \cdots + r_nT_A^n) \\
&= M_\mathcal{E}(c_{T_A}(T_A)) \\
&= M_\mathcal{E}(0) \\
&= 0.
\end{aligned}
$$

This is what we wanted.

Exercises 5.6

Throughout these exercises let V denote a vector space and let U and W denote subspaces of V.

1. In each case either show that the statement is true or give an example showing that it is false. Throughout, let $T : V \to V$ denote an operator.
   a) $\ker T$ is T-invariant.
   b) $\operatorname{im} T$ is T-invariant.
   c) It can happen that V has no T-invariant subspace.
   d) $U + W$ contains both U and W, and is contained in every such subspace.
   e) $U \cap W$ is contained in both U and W, and contains every such subspace.
   f) If T is an isomorphism, the only T-invariant subspaces are V and $\{\mathbf{0}\}$.
   g) If $\mathbf{v}$ is an eigenvector of T, then $\mathbb{R}\mathbf{v}$ is T-invariant.
   h) If $\mathbb{R}\mathbf{v}$ is T-invariant where $\mathbf{v} \neq \mathbf{0}$, then $\mathbf{v}$ is an eigenvector of T.

[22] This theorem is named after the English mathematician Arthur Cayley (1821–1895), one of the pioneers in matrix theory, and William Rowan Hamilton (1805–1865), an Irish mathematician famous for his work on physical dynamics. The theorem was established for a special class of matrices by Hamilton in 1853, and Cayley announced the general version five years later.

2. Let V have basis $\mathcal{B} = \{\mathbf{b}_1, \mathbf{b}_2, \mathbf{b}_3, \mathbf{b}_4\}$, and define $T : V \rightarrow V$ by $T(\mathbf{b}_1) = \mathbf{b}_1$, $T(\mathbf{b}_2) = \mathbf{b}_2 + 2\mathbf{b}_4$, $T(\mathbf{b}_3) = \mathbf{b}_1$, $T(\mathbf{b}_4) = \mathbf{0}$. Show that $T^2 = T$, find a basis $\mathcal{B}_o$ of $E_1(T)$, extend it to a basis of V, and illustrate Theorem 1.

3. Let $T : \mathbb{P}_2 \rightarrow \mathbb{P}_2$ be defined by
$T(a + bx + cx^2) = (a - 2b - c) - (a + 3b + c)x - (a + 4b)x^2$.
  a) Show that $U = span\{1, \; x + x^2\}$ is T-invariant.
  b) Use **a)** to find a basis $\mathcal{B}$ of such that $M(T)$ is block upper triangular.
  c) Use **b)** to compute $c_T(x)$.

4. a) Show that every subspace of $E_\lambda(T)$ is T-invariant.
  b) Describe the action of the restriction of T to $E_\lambda(T)$.

5. If $T : V \rightarrow V$ is an operator and U is a subspace of V, show that $T(U)$ is a subspace of V, T-invariant if U is T-invariant.

6. In each case show that $V = U \oplus W$.
  a) $V = \mathbb{M}_{2,2}$, $U = \left\{ \begin{bmatrix} a & b \\ a & b \end{bmatrix} \mid a, b \text{ in } \mathbb{R} \right\}$, and
  $W = \left\{ \begin{bmatrix} c & c \\ d & -d \end{bmatrix} \mid c, d \text{ in } \mathbb{R} \right\}$.
  b) $V = \mathbb{P}_3$, $U = \{a + b(x - x^2) \mid a, \; b \text{ in } \mathbb{R}\}$ and $W = \{c(1 + x) + dx^3 \mid c, \; d \text{ in } \mathbb{R}\}$.
  c) $V = \mathbb{R}^4$, $U = \{[a \; -b \; b \; a]^T \mid a, \; b \text{ in } \mathbb{R}\}$ and $W = \{[c \; d \; c \; d]^T \mid c, \; d \text{ in } \mathbb{R}\}$.

7. Define $T : \mathbb{P}_3 \rightarrow \mathbb{P}_3$ by $T(a + bx + cx^2 + dx^3)$
$= (2a + b) + (-5a - 2b)x + (c + 2d)x^2 - (c + d)x^3$
for all a, b, c, and d. Show that $\mathbb{P}_3$ has two 2-dimensional T-invariant subspaces U and W such that $\mathbb{P}_3 = U \oplus W$, but that T has no real eigenvalue. [Hint: First find $M_\mathcal{B}(T)$ where $\mathcal{B} = \{1, \; x, \; x^2, \; x^3\}$.]

8. Let $T : V \rightarrow V$ be an operator.
  a) Show that every subspace of V is T-invariant if and only every nonzero vector $\mathbf{v}$ in V is an eigenvector of T.
  b) If **a)** holds, show that there is a constant λ such that $T(\mathbf{v}) = \lambda\mathbf{v}$ for every vector $\mathbf{v}$ in V.

9. Let V be a finite dimensional vector space. Show that V and $\{\mathbf{0}\}$ are the only subspaces of V that are T-invariant for every operator $T : V \rightarrow V$. [Hint: Theorem 3 §5.3.]

10. Let $V = U \oplus W$ and $V = U \oplus W_1$.
  a) If $dimV$ is finite, show that $dimW = dim(W_1)$.
  b) If $W_1 \subseteq W$, show that $W_1 = W$.
  c) If $V = U_1 \oplus W_1$ where $U_1 \subseteq U$ and $W_1 \subseteq W$, show that $U_1 = U$ and $W_1 = W$.

11. Show that $U \cap W = \{\mathbf{0}\}$ if and only if $\{\mathbf{u}, \; \mathbf{w}\}$ is independent for all nonzero vectors $\mathbf{u}$ in U and $\mathbf{w}$ in W.

12. If $U \cap W = \{\mathbf{0}\}$ and $dimU + dimW = dimV$, show that $V = U \oplus W$.

13. Suppose that $V = U \oplus W$ where both U and W are T-invariant. If the restrictions of T to U and W are both diagonalizable, show that T is diagonalizable.

14. Let $T : V \rightarrow V$ be a linear operator where $dimV = n$.
  a) Show that $E_\lambda(T) \cap E_\mu(T) = \{\mathbf{0}\}$ if $\lambda \neq \mu$.
  b) If $\lambda \neq \mu$ are the only eigenvalues of an operator T, and if $dim(E_\lambda(T)) + dim(E_\mu(T)) = n$, show that T is diagonalizable.
  c) If $\lambda \neq \mu$ are the only eigenvalues of T and $dimV = 2$, show that T is diagonalizable.
  d) Give an example where T has exactly two distinct eigenvalues but is not diagonalizable.

15. Let $T : V \rightarrow V$ be an operator. If V is T-simple and $T \neq 0$, show that T is an isomorphism. (**Schur's Lemma.**) [Hint: Consider $kerT$ and imT.]

16. Let S and T be linear operators $V \rightarrow V$, and assume that $S \circ T = T \circ S$.
  a) If λ is an eigenvalue of S, show that $E_\lambda(S)$ is T-invariant.
  b) Show that imS and $kerS$ are both T-invariant.
  c) If U is a T-invariant subspace of V, show that $S(U)$ is also T-invariant.

17. Let $T : V \rightarrow V$ be an operator, and let U be the T-cyclic subspace generated by $\mathbf{v} \neq \mathbf{0}$ in V (see the discussion preceding Theorem 6). If W is any T-invariant subspace that contains $\mathbf{v}$, show that $U \subseteq W$. [Thus U is the "smallest" T-invariant subspace containing $\mathbf{v}$.]

18. Determine if the following are true or false. Justify your answer.
  a) If $dimV = 3$, and $V = U \oplus W$ where both U and W are T-invariant, then T is diagonalizable.
  b) If $dimV = 2$, and $V = U \oplus W$ where both U and W are T-invariant, then T is diagonalizable.

19. If $T : V \rightarrow V$ is an operator and $dimV = 1$, show that V is T-simple.

20. Let $T : V \rightarrow V$ be an operator. If $U = \mathbb{R}\mathbf{u}$ is a 1-dimensional subspace of V, show that U is T-invariant if and only if $\mathbf{u}$ is an eigenvector of T.

21. a) If $dimV > 1$ and V is T-simple, show that T has no real eigenvalue.
  b) Let $A = \begin{bmatrix} B & 0 \\ 0 & C \end{bmatrix}$ where $B = \begin{bmatrix} 2 & 1 \\ -5 & -2 \end{bmatrix}$ and $C = \begin{bmatrix} -1 & 1 \\ -2 & 1 \end{bmatrix}$. Show the converse of **a)** is false as follows: Consider the operator $T_A : \mathbb{R}^4 \rightarrow \mathbb{R}^4$ such that $T_A(X) = AX$ for all X in $\mathbb{R}^4$. Show that T_A has no real eigenvalue, but that $\mathbb{R}^4 = U \oplus W$ where U and W are both 2-dimensional and T_A-invariant.

22. Let $T : V \rightarrow V$ be an operator where $dimV = 2$. Show that V is T-reducible if and only if T is diagonalizable.

23. Let $T : V \to V$ be an operator with real eigenvalue λ. If $\mathcal{B}_0$ is any basis of $E_\lambda(T)$, show that $M_{\mathcal{B}_0}(T) = \lambda I$.

24. If $T : V \to V$ is an operator and U and W are T-invariant subspaces of V, show that $U \cap W$ and $U + W$ are also T-invariant.

25. a) If $V = U \oplus W$, define $T : V \to V$ as follows: Given $\mathbf{v}$ in V, write it as $\mathbf{v} = \mathbf{u} + \mathbf{w}$ with $\mathbf{u}$ in U and $\mathbf{w}$ in W, and take $T(\mathbf{v}) = \mathbf{u}$. Show that T is an operator, $T^2 = T$, $imT = U$, and $kerT = W$.
b) Show that every operator $T : V \to V$ that satisfies $T^2 = T$ arises as in **a)** for some direct decomposition $V = U \oplus W$. [Hint : Try $U = imT$ and $W = kerT$.]

26. a) An operator $T : V \to V$ is called an **involution** if $T^2 = 1_V$. (Examples: conjugation on $\mathbb{C}$; transposition on $\mathbb{M}_{n,n}$; $T(p(x)) = p(1 - x)$ on $\mathbb{P}_n$.) If T is an involution, show that T is diagonalizable by showing that V is the direct sum of the eigenspaces of T. [Hint: Example 12.]
b) If $A^2 = I$ where A is a square matrix, show that A is similar to a block matrix of the form $\begin{bmatrix} I_m & 0 \\ 0 & -I_k \end{bmatrix}$. [Hint: Example 12.]

27. Let $S : V \to V$ and $T : V \to V$ be operators, let $\mathcal{B}$ be a basis of V, and let a be a scalar.
a) Show that $S + T$ and aT are operators.
b) Show that $M_{\mathcal{B}}(S + T) = M_{\mathcal{B}}(S) + M_{\mathcal{B}}(T)$ and $M_{\mathcal{B}}(aT) = aM_{\mathcal{B}}(T)$.

5.7 GENERAL INNER PRODUCTS

The importance of the dot product in $\mathbb{R}^n$ would be difficult to exaggerate. It leads to the idea of an orthogonal basis and hence to a number of results of both theoretical and practical interest, including the Projection theorem, approximation and least squares, the Principal Axis theorem, and the Principal Value Decomposition. In this section we generalize the dot product to the idea of an inner product on an arbitrary vector space, and so see that the techniques we developed for $\mathbb{R}^n$ in Chapter 4 using the dot product will generalize to a much wider context.

5.7.1 Inner Products

An **inner product** $\langle \ , \ \rangle$ on a vector space V is a function that assigns a real number $\langle \mathbf{v}, \mathbf{w} \rangle$ to every pair of vectors $\mathbf{v}$ and $\mathbf{w}$ in V in such a way that the following axioms are satisfied for all vectors $\mathbf{u}, \mathbf{v}$, and $\mathbf{w}$ in V and all scalars r:

P1. $\langle \mathbf{v}, \mathbf{w} \rangle = \langle \mathbf{w}, \mathbf{v} \rangle$.
P2. $\langle \mathbf{u}, \mathbf{v} + \mathbf{w} \rangle = \langle \mathbf{u}, \mathbf{v} \rangle + \langle \mathbf{u}, \mathbf{w} \rangle$.
P3. $\langle r\mathbf{v}, \mathbf{w} \rangle = r \langle \mathbf{v}, \mathbf{w} \rangle$.
P4. $\langle \mathbf{v}, \mathbf{v} \rangle > 0$ whenever $\mathbf{v} \neq \mathbf{0}$.

A vector space endowed with an inner product is called an **inner product space**. Note that $\langle \mathbf{v}, r\mathbf{w} \rangle = r \langle \mathbf{v}, \mathbf{w} \rangle$ is an immediate consequence of Axioms P1 and P3, and that $\langle \mathbf{v} + \mathbf{w}, \mathbf{u} \rangle = \langle \mathbf{v}, \mathbf{u} \rangle + \langle \mathbf{w}, \mathbf{u} \rangle$ follows from Axioms P1 and P2.

Before giving examples, we clarify Axiom P4. Axiom P2 gives $\langle \mathbf{v}, \mathbf{0} \rangle = \langle \mathbf{v}, \mathbf{0} + \mathbf{0} \rangle = \langle \mathbf{v}, \mathbf{0} \rangle + \langle \mathbf{v}, \mathbf{0} \rangle$, so
$$\langle \mathbf{v}, \mathbf{0} \rangle = 0 \text{ for every vector } \mathbf{v} \text{ in } V.$$

With Axiom P1, this proves the first part of the following theorem and gives some useful refinements of Axiom P4 (parts (2) and (3) in the theorem).

THEOREM 1 If $\mathbf{v}$ is any vector in an inner product space, then:
(1) $\langle \mathbf{0}, \mathbf{v} \rangle = \mathbf{0} = \langle \mathbf{v}, \mathbf{0} \rangle$.
(2) $\langle \mathbf{v}, \mathbf{v} \rangle \geq 0$ for all vectors $\mathbf{v}$.
(3) $\langle \mathbf{v}, \mathbf{v} \rangle = 0$ if and only if $\mathbf{v} = \mathbf{0}$.

Example 1   The dot product $\langle X, Y \rangle = X \cdot Y$ is an inner product on $\mathbb{R}^n$ (see Theorem 1 §4.5).

Example 2   Define $\langle\ ,\ \rangle$ on $\mathbb{M}_{n,n}$ by $\langle A, B \rangle = tr(AB^T)$, where trA denotes the trace of the square matrix A. Then Axioms P1, P2, and P3 follow from the fact that $tr(\ )$ is a linear transformation which satisfies $tr(A^T) = trA$ for all A. If $R_1, \cdots, R_n$ are the rows of A, then the (i, j)-entry of AA^T is $R_i \cdot R_j$ (verify), so

$$\langle A, A \rangle = tr(AA^T) = R_1 \cdot R_1 + R_2 \cdot R_2 + \cdots + R_n \cdot R_n$$
$$= \|R_1\|^2 + \|R_2\|^2 + \cdots + \|R_n\|^2.$$

Hence if $A \neq 0$, then some $R_i \neq 0$, so $\|R_i\|^2 > 0$ and $\langle A, A \rangle > 0$. This is Axiom P4. We note in passing that $\langle A, A \rangle$ is the sum of the squares of all n^2 entries of the $n \times n$ matrix A.

Example 3   Any $n + 1$ distinct real numbers $a_0, a_1, a_2, \cdots, a_n$ determine an inner product $\langle\ ,\ \rangle$ on $\mathbb{P}_n$ as follows: Define

$$\langle p(x), q(x) \rangle = p(a_0)q(a_0) + \cdots + p(a_n)q(a_n)$$

for all polynomials $p(x)$ and $q(x)$ in $\mathbb{P}_n$. Axioms P1, P2, and P3 are routine verifications. If $p(x) \neq 0$, then $p(a_i) \neq 0$ for some i because nonzero polynomials of degree at most n can have at most n distinct roots (see Appendix A.3). But then $\langle p(x), p(x) \rangle = p(a_0)^2 + p(a_1)^2 + \cdots + p(a_n)^2 > 0$, proving Axiom P4.

The next example involves calculus.

Example 4   The set $\mathbf{C}[a, b]$ of all continuous real valued functions on the interval $[a, b]$ is a subspace of $\mathbb{F}[a, b]$. Define $\langle\ ,\ \rangle$ on $\mathbf{C}[a, b]$ by

$$\langle f, g \rangle = \int_a^b f(x)g(x)dx.$$

Again, all the axioms except P4 are routine properties of integrals. But if $\langle f, f \rangle = 0$, then $\int_a^b f(x)^2 dx = 0$. Since $f(x)^2$ is continuous and $f(x)^2 \geq 0$ for all x in $[a, b]$, it is a theorem of calculus (see the diagram) that $f(x)^2 = 0$ for all x. Hence $f = 0$ is the zero function, proving that Axiom P4 holds.

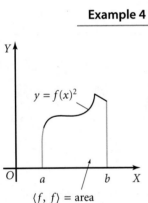

$\langle f, f \rangle$ = area

Because of axioms P2 and P3, every inner product is linear in the first variable, that is

$$\langle r_1\mathbf{v}_1 + r_2\mathbf{v}_2 + \cdots + r_m\mathbf{v}_m, \mathbf{w} \rangle = r_1\langle \mathbf{v}_1, \mathbf{w} \rangle + r_2\langle \mathbf{v}_2, \mathbf{w} \rangle + \cdots + r_m\langle \mathbf{v}_m, \mathbf{w} \rangle$$

for all vectors $\mathbf{v}_i$ and $\mathbf{w}$. Of course, linearity in the second variable now follows from Axiom P1. Hence computations with an inner product are carried out much as for the dot product in $\mathbb{R}^n$.

In fact, the linearity enables us to easily describe *all* inner products $\langle\ ,\ \rangle$ on $\mathbb{R}^n$. Let $\mathcal{E} = \{E_1, E_2, \cdots, E_n\}$ denote the standard basis of $\mathbb{R}^n$, and consider the $n \times n$ matrix $P = [p_{ij}]$ where

$$p_{ij} = \langle E_i, E_j \rangle \quad \text{for all } i \text{ and } j.$$

If $X = [x_1 x_2 \cdots x_n]^T$ and $Y = [y_1 y_2 \cdots y_n]^T$ are any two vectors in $\mathbb{R}^n$, then $X = \Sigma_i x_i E_i$ and $Y = \Sigma_j y_j E_j$, so the linearity of $\langle\ ,\ \rangle$ gives $\langle X, Y \rangle$ as a matrix product:

$$\langle X, Y \rangle = \langle \Sigma_i x_i E_i, \Sigma_j y_j E_j \rangle = \Sigma_{i,j} x_i y_j \langle E_i, E_j \rangle = \Sigma_{i,j} x_i p_{ij} y_j = X^T PY.$$

In particular $X^T PX = \langle X, X \rangle > 0$ whenever $X \neq 0$ by P4. Since P is symmetric (by Axiom P1), this shows that P is a positive definite matrix (see Section 4.8). On the other hand, if P is any positive definite matrix and we define $\langle X, Y \rangle = X^T PY$ for all X and Y in $\mathbb{R}^n$, it is a routine matter to verify that $\langle\ ,\ \rangle$ is an inner product on $\mathbb{R}^n$. Hence we have

THEOREM 2

Every positive definite matrix P gives rise to an inner product $\langle \ , \ \rangle$ on $\mathbb{R}^n$ given by
$$\langle X, \ Y \rangle = X^T P Y \quad \text{for all } X \text{ and } Y \text{ in } \mathbb{R}^n.$$

Moreover, every inner product on $\mathbb{R}^n$ arises in this way from some positive definite matrix P.

Note that the dot product on $\mathbb{R}^n$ corresponds to $P = I$ in Theorem 2.

Theorem 2 can be stated also in the language of quadratic forms in Section 4.8: If $\langle \ , \ \rangle$ is an inner product on $\mathbb{R}^n$, then $q(X) = \langle X, \ X \rangle$ is a positive definite quadratic form in n variables, and every such quadratic form arises in this way from an inner product.

Example 5

Define $\langle \ , \ \rangle$ on $\mathbb{R}^2$ by
$$\big\langle [x_1, \ x_2]^T, \ [y_1, \ y_2]^T \big\rangle = x_1 y_1 - 2 x_1 y_2 - 2 x_2 y_1 + 5 x_2 y_2 .$$

Hence $P = \begin{bmatrix} 1 & -2 \\ -2 & 5 \end{bmatrix}$ in Theorem 2. Since P is a positive definite matrix by Theorem 4 §4.8, it follows that $\langle \ , \ \rangle$ is an inner product. Note that Axioms P1, P2, and P3 hold for *any* symmetric matrix P; Axiom P4 also can be seen directly in this case because
$$\big\langle [x_1, \ x_2]^T, \ [x_1, \ x_2]^T \big\rangle = x_1^2 - 4 x_1 x_2 + 5 x_2^2 = (x_1 - 2 x_2)^2 + x_2^2 .$$

5.7.2 Norms and Orthogonality

We showed in Theorem 1 that $\langle \mathbf{v}, \ \mathbf{v} \rangle \geq 0$ holds for all vectors $\mathbf{v}$ in any inner product space V. Hence, as in $\mathbb{R}^n$, we can define the **norm**[23] of $\mathbf{v}$ by
$$\|\mathbf{v}\| = \sqrt{\langle \mathbf{v}, \ \mathbf{v} \rangle} .$$

A vector of norm 1 is called a **unit vector**.

Example 6

Compute $\|p(x)\|$ if $p(x) = 2 - x - x^2$ where $\mathbb{P}_2$ has the norm in Example 3 determined by the numbers -1, 1, and 2.

SOLUTION

$\|p(x)\|^2 = \big\langle p(x), \ p(x) \big\rangle = p(-1)^2 + p(1)^2 + p(2)^2 = 2^2 + 0^2 + (-4)^2 = 20$, so $\|p(x)\| = 2\sqrt{5}$.

The proof of Theorem 2 §4.5 and its Corollary goes through as written to prove the following fundamental inequalities about norms.

THEOREM 3

Let V be an inner product space.

(1) **Cauchy-Schwarz Inequality.** $|\langle \mathbf{v}, \ \mathbf{w} \rangle| \leq \|\mathbf{v}\| \ \|\mathbf{w}\|$ for all $\mathbf{v}$ and $\mathbf{w}$ in V.

(2) **Triangle Inequality.** $\|\mathbf{v} + \mathbf{w}\| \leq \|\mathbf{v}\| + \|\mathbf{w}\|$ for all $\mathbf{v}$ and $\mathbf{w}$ in V.

Again motivated by the situation in $\mathbb{R}^n$, we say that two vectors $\mathbf{v}$ and $\mathbf{w}$ are **orthogonal** if
$$\langle \mathbf{v}, \ \mathbf{w} \rangle = 0$$

---

[23] The term *length* is used for $\mathbb{R}^n$, reflecting the geometric interpretation of $\mathbb{R}^2$ and $\mathbb{R}^3$, but *norm* is used more commonly for spaces of polynomials or functions.

and we say that a set $\{\mathbf{e}_0, \mathbf{e}_1, \cdots, \mathbf{e}_m\}$ of vectors is an **orthogonal set**[24] if

$$\mathbf{e}_i \neq \mathbf{0} \text{ for each } i, \text{ and} \langle \mathbf{e}_i, \mathbf{e}_j \rangle = 0 \text{ for all } i \neq j.$$

An orthogonal set consisting of unit vectors is called an **orthonormal** set. If $\{\mathbf{e}_0, \mathbf{e}_1, \cdots, \mathbf{e}_m\}$ is an orthogonal set of vectors, we can **normalize** it to obtain the orthonormal set $\left\{ \frac{1}{\|\mathbf{e}_0\|}\mathbf{e}_0, \frac{1}{\|\mathbf{e}_1\|}\mathbf{e}_1, \cdots, \frac{1}{\|\mathbf{e}_m\|}\mathbf{e}_m \right\}$.

Example 7 Show that $\{\sin x, \cos x\}$ is orthogonal in the space $\mathbf{C}[-\pi, \pi]$ of all continuous real valued functions on the interval $[-\pi, \pi]$.

SOLUTION We have $\langle \sin x, \cos x \rangle = \int_{-\pi}^{\pi} \sin x \, \cos x \, dx = -\frac{1}{4}[\cos(2x)]_{-\pi}^{\pi} = 0$.

The following theorem includes Theorems 4 and 5 in Section 4.5 in the case of the dot product in $\mathbb{R}^n$, and the same proofs go through.

THEOREM 4 Let $\{\mathbf{e}_0, \mathbf{e}_1, \cdots, \mathbf{e}_m\}$ be an orthogonal set in an inner product space V.

(1) $\{\mathbf{e}_0, \mathbf{e}_1, \cdots, \mathbf{e}_m\}$ is independent.
(2) **Pythagoras' Theorem.** $\|\mathbf{e}_0 + \mathbf{e}_1 + \cdots + \mathbf{e}_m\|^2 = \|\mathbf{e}_0\|^2 + \|\mathbf{e}_1\|^2 + \cdots + \|\mathbf{e}_m\|^2$.

Part (1) in Theorem 4 suggests the concept of an orthogonal basis for an arbitrary inner product space V, and the general version of the Expansion theorem (Theorem 6 in Section 4.5) remains valid.

THEOREM 5 **Expansion Theorem.** Let $\{\mathbf{e}_1, \mathbf{e}_2, \cdots, \mathbf{e}_n\}$ be an orthogonal basis of an inner product space V. Then

$$\mathbf{v} = \frac{\langle \mathbf{v}, \mathbf{e}_0 \rangle}{\|\mathbf{e}_0\|^2}\mathbf{e}_0 + \frac{\langle \mathbf{v}, \mathbf{e}_1 \rangle}{\|\mathbf{e}_1\|^2}\mathbf{e}_1 + \cdots + \frac{\langle \mathbf{v}, \mathbf{e}_n \rangle}{\|\mathbf{e}_n\|^2}\mathbf{e}_n \quad \text{for every vector } \mathbf{v} \text{ in } V.$$

We are going to make use of this general version of the Expansion theorem in several situations. The first application requires an important orthogonal basis of $\mathbb{P}_n$.

Example 8 **Lagrange polynomials.**[25] Consider the inner product on $\mathbb{P}_n$ determined (see Example 3) by $n + 1$ distinct real numbers, $a_0, a_1, a_2, \cdots, a_n$:

$$\langle p(x), q(x) \rangle = p(a_0)q(a_0) + p(a_1)q(a_1) + \cdots + p(a_n)q(a_n).$$

Define the **Lagrange polynomials** $\delta_0(x), \delta_1(x), \delta_2(x), \cdots, \delta_n(x)$ by

$$\delta_k(x) = \frac{\Pi_{i \neq k}(x - a_i)}{\Pi_{i \neq k}(a_k - a_i)}$$

where $\Pi_{i \neq k}(x - a_i)$ means the product of all the terms $(x - a_i)$ with $(x - a_k)$ omitted. Note that the denominator of $\delta_k(x)$ is nonzero because the a_i are distinct. Clearly each $\delta_k(x)$ has degree n, and we have

$$\delta_k(a_k) = 1 \quad \text{and} \quad \delta_k(a_i) = 0 \quad \text{if } i \neq k. \tag{$*$}$$

---

[24] We are labelling from 0 here in anticipation of the main application to infinite orthogonal sets, where this is customary.

[25] Joseph Louis Lagrange (1736–1813) was one of the great mathematicians. He made important contributions to many parts of mathematics. He is also remembered for his skill at exposition, and his *Méchanique Analytique* was described by Hamilton as a "scientific poem".

If $p(x)$ is any polynomial in $\mathbb{P}_n$, this shows that

$$\langle p(x),\ \delta_k(x)\rangle = p(a_k) \quad \text{for each } k.$$

In particular, if we take $p(x) = \delta_i(x)$ it follows that

$$\mathcal{D} = \{\delta_0(x),\ \delta_1(x),\ \delta_2(x),\ \cdots,\ \delta_n(x)\}$$

is an orthonormal basis of $\mathbb{P}_n$. Hence the Expansion theorem gives the following simple formula for the expansion of any polynomial $p(x)$ in terms of the basis $\mathcal{D}$:

$$p(x) = p(a_0)\,\delta_0(x) + p(a_1)\,\delta_1(x) + \cdots + p(a_n)\,\delta_n(x).$$

More generally, let f be any function in $\mathbb{F}[a,\ b]$, where $[a,\ b]$ is an interval containing all the a_i. Then ($*$) shows that the polynomial

$$p_f(x) = f(a_0)\,\delta_0(x) + f(a_1)\,\delta_1(x) + \cdots + f(a_n)\,\delta_n(x) \qquad (**)$$

agrees with f on the $n + 1$ numbers a_i; that is,

$$f(a_i) = p_f(a_i) \quad \text{holds for each } i = 1,\ 2,\ \cdots,\ n.$$

The polynomial $p_f(x)$ is called the **Lagrange interpolation polynomial** for f, and is the unique polynomial in $\mathbb{P}_n$ that coincides with f at each a_i.

The Lagrange polynomials have many applications, one of which we explore in the following example.

Example 9 **Numerical integration.** Suppose that we want to approximate $\int_a^b f(x)dx$. The idea is to choose $n + 1$ distinct numbers $a_0,\ a_1,\ a_2,\ \cdots,\ a_n$ in the interval $[a,\ b]$, let $\delta_0(x),\ \delta_1(x),\ \delta_2(x),\ \cdots,\ \delta_n(x)$ be the corresponding Lagrange polynomials, and approximate f by the Lagrange interpolation polynomial p_f given in ($**$). Then we obtain the approximation (called a **Gaussian quadrature formula**)

$$\int_a^b f(x)dx \approx \int_a^b p_f(x)dx = f(a_0)\,d_0 + f(a_1)\,d_1 + \cdots + f(a_n)\,d_n$$

where $\approx$ means "approximately equal", and $d_i = \int_a^b \delta_i(x)dx$ for each i. This approximation is exact by Example 8 if f is a polynomial of degree at most n and, with careful choice of the a_i, is an important tool in numerical analysis.

The techniques for finding orthogonal sets in an arbitrary inner product space V are entirely analogous to those in $\mathbb{R}^n$. The following lemma shows how to enlarge any orthogonal set; the proof of Lemma 1 §4.5 goes through as written.

LEMMA 1 **Orthogonal Lemma.** Let $\{\mathbf{e}_0,\ \mathbf{e}_1,\ \cdots,\ \mathbf{e}_m\}$ be an orthogonal set in an inner product space V. Given $\mathbf{v}$ in V, write

$$\mathbf{e}_{m+1} = \mathbf{v} - \left(\frac{\langle \mathbf{v},\ \mathbf{e}_0\rangle}{\|\mathbf{e}_0\|^2}\mathbf{e}_0 + \frac{\langle \mathbf{v},\ \mathbf{e}_1\rangle}{\|\mathbf{e}_1\|^2}\mathbf{e}_1 + \cdots + \frac{\langle \mathbf{v},\ \mathbf{e}_m\rangle}{\|\mathbf{e}_m\|^2}\mathbf{e}_m \right).$$

Then $\langle \mathbf{e}_{m+1},\ \mathbf{e}_i\rangle = 0$ for each $i = 1,\ 2,\ \cdots,\ m$, and if $\mathbf{v}$ is not in $span\{\mathbf{e}_0,\ \mathbf{e}_1,\ \cdots,\ \mathbf{e}_m\}$ then $\{\mathbf{e}_0,\ \mathbf{e}_1,\ \cdots,\ \mathbf{e}_m,\ \mathbf{e}_{m+1}\}$ is an orthogonal set.

As in $\mathbb{R}^n$, the Orthogonal lemma leads to the general version of the Gram-Schmidt algorithm for obtaining an orthogonal basis of a subspace from any convenient basis. Again the proof of Theorem 8 §4.5 goes through.

THEOREM 6   **Gram-Schmidt Algorithm.** If $\{\mathbf{b}_0, \mathbf{b}_1, \cdots, \mathbf{b}_m\}$ is any basis of a subspace U of an inner product space V, construct $\mathbf{e}_0, \mathbf{e}_1, \cdots, \mathbf{e}_m$, in U successively as follows:

$$\mathbf{e}_0 = \mathbf{b}_0$$

$$\mathbf{e}_1 = \mathbf{b}_1 - \frac{\langle \mathbf{b}_1, \mathbf{e}_0 \rangle}{\|\mathbf{e}_0\|^2} \mathbf{e}_0$$

$$\mathbf{e}_2 = \mathbf{b}_2 - \frac{\langle \mathbf{b}_2, \mathbf{e}_0 \rangle}{\|\mathbf{e}_0\|^2} \mathbf{e}_0 - \frac{\langle \mathbf{b}_2, \mathbf{e}_1 \rangle}{\|\mathbf{e}_1\|^2} \mathbf{e}_1$$

$$\vdots$$

$$\mathbf{e}_k = \mathbf{b}_k - \frac{\langle \mathbf{b}_k, \mathbf{e}_0 \rangle}{\|\mathbf{e}_0\|^2} \mathbf{e}_0 - \frac{\langle \mathbf{b}_k, \mathbf{e}_1 \rangle}{\|\mathbf{e}_1\|^2} \mathbf{e}_1 - \cdots - \frac{\langle \mathbf{b}_k, \mathbf{e}_{k-1} \rangle}{\|\mathbf{e}_{k-1}\|^2} \mathbf{e}_{k-1}$$

$$\vdots$$

for each $k = 1, 2, 3, \cdots, m$. Then:

(1) $\{\mathbf{e}_0, \mathbf{e}_1, \cdots, \mathbf{e}_m\}$ is an orthogonal basis of U.

(2) $span\{\mathbf{e}_0, \mathbf{e}_1, \cdots, \mathbf{e}_k\} = span\{\mathbf{b}_0, \mathbf{b}_1, \cdots, \mathbf{b}_k\}$ for each $k = 0, 1, \cdots, m$.

Example 10   If $V = \mathbb{P}_3$ with the inner product $\langle p, q \rangle = \int_{-1}^{1} p(x)q(x)dx$, apply the Gram-Schmidt algorithm to the basis $\{1, x, x^2, x^3\}$ of $\mathbb{P}_3$ to obtain the orthogonal basis $\left\{1, x, \frac{1}{3}(3x^2 - 1), \frac{1}{5}(5x^3 - 3x)\right\}$.

SOLUTION   By the Gram-Schmidt algorithm, we obtain polynomials $q_0, q_1, \cdots$ one after the other.[26] To begin with, we have $q_0(x) = 1$. The algorithm continues:

$$q_1(x) = x - \frac{\langle x, q_0 \rangle}{\|q_0\|^2} q_0 = x - \frac{0}{2} q_1 = x,$$

$$q_2(x) = x^2 - \frac{\langle x^2, q_0 \rangle}{\|q_0\|^2} q_0 - \frac{\langle x^2, q_1 \rangle}{\|q_1\|^2} q_1$$

$$= x^2 - \frac{2/3}{2} q_0 - 0 q_1 = x^2 - \frac{1}{3} = \frac{1}{3}(3x^2 - 1),$$

$$q_3(x) = x^3 - \frac{\langle x^3, q_0 \rangle}{\|q_0\|^2} q_0 - \frac{\langle x^3, q_1 \rangle}{\|q_1\|^2} q_1 - \frac{\langle x^3, q_2 \rangle}{\|q_2\|^2} q_2$$

$$= x^3 - 0 q_0 - \frac{2/5}{2/3} q_1 - 0 q_2$$

$$= x^3 - \frac{3}{5}x = \frac{1}{5}(5x^3 - 3x).$$

The polynomials in Example 10 all have leading coefficient 1. In applications (for example differential equations) it is customary to take scalar multiples $p(x)$ of these polynomials such that $p(1) = 1$. The result is the orthogonal basis

$$\left\{1, x, \tfrac{1}{2}(3x^2 - 1), \tfrac{1}{2}(5x^3 - 3x)\right\} \quad \text{of } \mathbb{P}_3.$$

These are the first four **Legendre polynomials**, and we will return to them below.

Let U be a subspace of an arbitrary inner product space V. As in $\mathbb{R}^n$, define the **orthogonal complement** $U^\perp$ of U in V by

$$U^\perp = \{\mathbf{v} \text{ in } V \mid \langle \mathbf{u}, \mathbf{v} \rangle = \mathbf{0} \text{ for all } \mathbf{u} \text{ in } U\}.$$

This is a subspace of V even if V is not finite dimensional, and we have

THEOREM 7   If U is a finite dimensional subspace of an arbitrary inner product space V, then $V = U \oplus U^\perp$.

---

[26] For simplicity of notation, we occasionally write a polynomial $q(x)$ simply as q. This amounts to thinking of q as a function in $\mathbb{F}[\mathbb{R}]$.

PROOF   If $\mathbf{v}$ is in $U \cap U^\perp$, then $\|\mathbf{v}\|^2 = \langle \mathbf{v}, \ \mathbf{v} \rangle = 0$, so $\mathbf{v} = \mathbf{0}$. Hence $U \cap U^\perp = \{\mathbf{0}\}$. Now choose an orthogonal basis $\{\mathbf{e}_0, \ \mathbf{e}_1, \ \cdots, \ \mathbf{e}_m\}$ of U. If $\mathbf{v}$ is any vector in V, the Orthogonal lemma shows that $\mathbf{v} - (r_0\mathbf{e}_0 + r_1\mathbf{e}_1 + \cdots + r_m\mathbf{e}_m)$ is in $U^\perp$ for certain real numbers r_i. It follows that $V = U + U^\perp$.

If U is a subspace of $\mathbb{R}^n$, we showed that $U^{\perp\perp} = U$ (Theorem 3 §4.6). However, lest the reader get the idea that *all* properties of orthogonal complements in $\mathbb{R}^n$ extend to the general case, we now give an example where $U^{\perp\perp} \neq U$.

Example 11   Consider $\mathbb{P}$ with the inner product $\langle p, \ q \rangle = \int_0^1 p(x)q(x)dx$, and let U denote the subspace of all polynomials with zero constant term. Show that $U^\perp = \{0\}$, so $U^{\perp\perp} = \mathbb{P} \neq U$.

SOLUTION   Observe first that $U = \{x \, q(x) \mid q(x) \text{ in } \mathbb{P}\}$. Suppose that $p(x)$ is in $U^\perp$. Then $\langle p(x), \ x \, q(x) \rangle = 0$ for all $q(x)$ in $\mathbb{P}$, so

$$\langle x \, p(x), \ q(x) \rangle = \int_0^1 x \, p(x)q(x)dx = \int_0^1 p(x)(x \, q(x))dx = \langle p(x), \ x \, q(x) \rangle = 0$$

for all $q(x)$ in $\mathbb{P}$. Taking $q(x) = x \, p(x)$ gives $\|x \, p(x)\|^2 = 0$, whence $x \, p(x) = 0$. This implies that $p(x) = 0$, and hence that $U^\perp = \{0\}$, as asserted. Note also that $U \oplus U^\perp \neq \mathbb{P}$.

It is no coincidence that the subspace U is infinite dimensional in Example 11; we show below (Theorem 9) that $U^{\perp\perp} = U$ holds for all finite dimensional subspaces of any inner product space.

5.7.3   Projections and Approximation

Let $\mathbf{v}$ be a vector in an inner product space V, and let U be a finite dimensional subspace of V with orthogonal basis $\{\mathbf{e}_0, \mathbf{e}_1, \cdots, \mathbf{e}_m\}$. As in Section 4.6, define the **projection** of $\mathbf{v}$ on U by

$$proj_U(\mathbf{v}) = \frac{\langle \mathbf{v}, \mathbf{e}_0 \rangle}{\|\mathbf{e}_0\|^2}\mathbf{e}_0 + \frac{\langle \mathbf{v}, \mathbf{e}_1 \rangle}{\|\mathbf{e}_1\|^2}\mathbf{e}_1 + \cdots + \frac{\langle \mathbf{v}, \mathbf{e}_m \rangle}{\|\mathbf{e}_m\|^2}\mathbf{e}_m. \qquad (*\!*\!*)$$

As the notation implies, $proj_U(\mathbf{v})$ depends on U and $\mathbf{v}$ only, and not on the choice of orthogonal basis $\{\mathbf{e}_0, \mathbf{e}_1, \cdots, \mathbf{e}_m\}$ of U (the proof of Lemma 1 §4.6 goes through). The basic properties of projections are given in the following result which extends the Projection theorem for $\mathbb{R}^n$ (Theorem 2 §4.6) to the case where V is an arbitrary inner product which need not be finite dimensional.

THEOREM 8   **Projection Theorem**. Let U be a finite dimensional subspace of an arbitrary inner product space V. Then:

(1) $proj_U(\mathbf{v})$ is in U and $\mathbf{v} - proj_U(\mathbf{v})$ is in $U^\perp$ for every vector $\mathbf{v}$ in V.

(2) $proj_U : V \to V$ is a linear transformation with image U and kernel $U^\perp$.

PROOF   (1) That $proj_U(\mathbf{v})$ is in U for every vector $\mathbf{v}$ follows from $(*\!*\!*)$ because each $\mathbf{e}_i$ is in U, and $\mathbf{v} - proj_U(\mathbf{v})$ is in $U^\perp$ because it is orthogonal to each $\mathbf{e}_i$ by the Orthogonal lemma.

(2) The linearity of $proj_U : V \to V$ follows from Axioms P2 and P3 (verify). We have $im(proj_U) \subseteq U$ by (1); and $U \subseteq im(proj_U)$ because $\mathbf{u} = proj_U(\mathbf{u})$ by the Expansion theorem for every $\mathbf{u}$ in U. Hence $U = im(proj_U)$. Turning to the kernel, if $\mathbf{v}$ is in $ker(proj_U)$, then $\mathbf{v} = \mathbf{v} - proj_U(\mathbf{v})$ is in $U^\perp$ by the Projection theorem. Thus $ker(proj_U) \subseteq U^\perp$. On the other hand, if $\mathbf{v}$ is in $U^\perp$, then $(*\!*\!*)$ shows that $proj_U(\mathbf{v}) = \mathbf{0}$, so $U^\perp \subseteq ker(proj_U)$. Hence $U^\perp = ker(proj_U)$.

The projection theorem has an important consequence which we record in the following theorem.

THEOREM 9

If U is a finite dimensional subspace in an arbitrary inner product space V, then
$$V = U \oplus U^{\perp} \text{ and } U^{\perp\perp} = U.$$

PROOF

The fact that $V = U \oplus U^{\perp}$ restates the projection theorem, and the inclusion $U \subseteq U^{\perp\perp}$ always holds (verify). If $\mathbf{v}$ is in $U^{\perp\perp}$, write $\mathbf{p} = proj_U(\mathbf{v})$. Then $\mathbf{p}$ is in U by the Projection theorem so $\mathbf{p}$ is in $U^{\perp\perp}$. Hence $\mathbf{v} - \mathbf{p}$ is in $U^{\perp\perp}$. But $\mathbf{v} - \mathbf{p}$ is in $U^{\perp}$ by the Projection theorem, and it follows that $\mathbf{v} = \mathbf{p}$. Thus $\mathbf{v}$ is in U, proving that $U^{\perp\perp} \subseteq U$. This is what we wanted.

Here is an example outlining how the Projection theorem can be applied to time series analysis in statistics.

Example 12

Statistical Trend Analysis. Let f be a function of time t, say some measure of stock market value or the degree of global warming, and assume that f is known only at times $t_0, t_1, \cdots, t_m$. One constantly arising question is whether the data values $f(t_0), f(t_1), \cdots, f(t_m)$ exhibit a "linear trend", in which case we might use the least squares line $f(t) = a_0 + a_1 t$ to estimate other values of $f(t)$. If there is a "quadratic trend" we would fit a quadratic $f(t) = a_0 + a_1 t + a_2 t^2$, and so on for a "cubic trend", etc. The difficulty in deciding which trend is appropriate is that, when a polynomial is fitted to the data, the coefficients may not be "statistically independent".

To remedy this, one procedure is to use the inner product on $\mathbb{P}_m$ (from Example 3) given by
$$\langle p, q \rangle = p(t_0)q(t_0) + p(t_1)q(t_1) + \cdots + p(t_m)q(t_m),$$

and apply the Gram-Schmidt algorithm to the basis $\{1, x, x^2, \cdots, x^m\}$ of $\mathbb{P}_m$ to obtain an orthogonal basis $\{q_0, q_1, \cdots, q_m\}$. Let p_f be the Lagrange interpolation polynomial for f in Example 8 (that is, the unique polynomial in $\mathbb{P}_m$ such that $p_f(t_i) = f(t_i)$ for each i). Assuming (as is usually the case) that we are only interested in trends of degree no more than 4, we compute the projection of p_f onto $\mathbb{P}_4$:
$$proj_{\mathbb{P}_4}(p_f) = b_0 q_0 + b_1 q_1 + b_2 q_2 + b_3 q_3 + b_4 q_4.$$

The coefficients $b_i = \frac{\langle p_f, q_i \rangle}{\|q_i\|^2}$ are called the **trend coefficients** for f. They are easily computed, statistically independent (for most data), and b_1 measures the linear trend, b_2 measures the quadratic trend, etc. More information on this can be found in books on linear models in statistics.[27]

We now turn to an extension of the Approximation theorem for $\mathbb{R}^n$ (Section 4.6) which is valid for inner product spaces that may not be finite dimensional.

THEOREM 10

Approximation Theorem. Let U be a finite dimensional subspace of an arbitrary inner product space V. If $\mathbf{v}$ is any vector in V, then $proj_U(\mathbf{v})$ is the vector in U that is closest to $\mathbf{v}$ in the sense that
$$\|\mathbf{v} - proj_U(\mathbf{v})\| < \|\mathbf{v} - \mathbf{u}\| \quad \text{for all } \mathbf{u} \text{ in } U, \ \mathbf{u} \neq proj_U(\mathbf{v}).$$

PROOF

For convenience write $\mathbf{p} = proj_U(\mathbf{v})$. Given $\mathbf{u}$ in U, we can write $\mathbf{v} - \mathbf{u} = (\mathbf{v} - \mathbf{p}) + (\mathbf{p} - \mathbf{u})$ where $\mathbf{v} - \mathbf{p}$ is in $U^{\perp}$ and $\mathbf{p} - \mathbf{u}$ is in U. Hence Pythagoras' theorem gives $\|\mathbf{v} - \mathbf{u}\|^2 = \|\mathbf{v} - \mathbf{p}\|^2 + \|\mathbf{p} - \mathbf{u}\|^2$. This does it because $\|\mathbf{p} - \mathbf{u}\| > 0$ if $\mathbf{u} \neq \mathbf{p}$.

---

[27] For example, I. Guttman, *Linear Models, An Introduction*, Wiley, 1982.

In Chapter 4 we used the $\mathbb{R}^n$-version of the Approximation theorem to find all best approximations to a solution of an inconsistent system of linear equations and to find least squares approximating polynomials for finite sets of data pairs. Both these applications required the finite dimensionality of the underlying vector space $\mathbb{R}^n$. However, much can be said when the underlying space is infinite dimensional.

An infinite set $\{\mathbf{e}_0,\ \mathbf{e}_1,\ \mathbf{e}_2,\ \cdots,\ \mathbf{e}_n,\ \cdots\}$ in an inner product space V is called **orthogonal** if

$$\mathbf{e}_i \neq 0 \text{ for each } i \quad \text{and} \quad \langle \mathbf{e}_i,\ \mathbf{e}_j \rangle = 0 \text{ whenever } i \neq j.$$

Such orthogonal sets can be found by an extension of the Gram-Schmidt algorithm.

We need the following idea. An infinite set $\{\mathbf{b}_0,\ \mathbf{b}_1,\ \mathbf{b}_2,\ \cdots,\ \mathbf{b}_m,\ \cdots\}$ of vectors in an inner product space is called (linearly) **independent** if $\{\mathbf{b}_0,\ \mathbf{b}_1,\ \mathbf{b}_2,\ \cdots,\ \mathbf{b}_m\}$ is independent for each m. One example is $\{1,\ x,\ x^2,\ \cdots,\ x^n,\ \cdots\}$ in $\mathbb{P}$.

Example 13   Suppose that $\{\mathbf{b}_0,\ \mathbf{b}_1,\ \mathbf{b}_2,\ \cdots,\ \mathbf{b}_m,\ \cdots\}$ is an infinite independent set of vectors in an inner product space. Apply the Gram-Schmidt process to the vectors $\mathbf{b}_i$ as follows: Take

$$\mathbf{e}_0 = \mathbf{b}_0$$

and, having determined $\mathbf{e}_0,\ \mathbf{e}_1,\ \mathbf{e}_2,\ \cdots,\ \mathbf{e}_{m-1}$ for some $m \geq 1$, take

$$\mathbf{e}_m = b_m - \frac{\langle \mathbf{b}_m,\ \mathbf{e}_0 \rangle}{\|\mathbf{e}_0\|^2}\mathbf{e}_0 - \frac{\langle \mathbf{b}_m,\ \mathbf{e}_1 \rangle}{\|\mathbf{e}_1\|^2}\mathbf{e}_1 - \cdots - \frac{\langle \mathbf{b}_{m-1},\ \mathbf{e}_{m-1} \rangle}{\|\mathbf{e}_{m-1}\|^2}\mathbf{e}_{m-1}.$$

This produces an infinite orthogonal set $\{\mathbf{e}_0,\ \mathbf{e}_1,\ \mathbf{e}_2,\ \cdots,\ \mathbf{e}_m,\ \cdots\}$ by Theorem 6. In fact we have $span\{\mathbf{e}_0,\ \mathbf{e}_1,\ \mathbf{e}_2,\ \cdots,\ \mathbf{e}_m\} = span\{\mathbf{b}_0,\ \mathbf{b}_1,\ \mathbf{b}_2,\ \cdots,\ \mathbf{b}_m\}$ for each m.

Now assume that an infinite orthogonal set

$$\mathcal{E} = \{\mathbf{e}_0,\ \mathbf{e}_1,\ \mathbf{e}_2,\ \cdots,\ \mathbf{e}_n,\ \cdots\}$$

is given in an inner product space V. We use it to define subspaces U_m as follows:

$$U_m = span\{\mathbf{e}_0,\ \mathbf{e}_1,\ \mathbf{e}_2,\ \cdots,\ \mathbf{e}_m\} \quad \text{for each } m \geq 1.$$

Clearly $U_0 \subseteq U_1 \subseteq U_2 \subseteq \cdots \subseteq U_m \subseteq \cdots$, and $dim(U_m) = m + 1$ for each m because $\{\mathbf{e}_0,\ \mathbf{e}_1,\ \mathbf{e}_2,\ \cdots,\ \mathbf{e}_m\}$ is an (orthogonal) basis of U_m. Given $\mathbf{v}$ in V and $m \geq 1$, define

$$\mathbf{v}_m = proj_{U_m}(\mathbf{v}) = \frac{\langle \mathbf{v},\ \mathbf{e}_0 \rangle}{\|\mathbf{e}_0\|^2}\mathbf{e}_0 + \frac{\langle \mathbf{v},\ \mathbf{e}_1 \rangle}{\|\mathbf{e}_1\|^2}\mathbf{e}_1 + \cdots + \frac{\langle \mathbf{v},\ \mathbf{e}_m \rangle}{\|\mathbf{e}_m\|^2}\mathbf{e}_m. \qquad (****)$$

The vector $\mathbf{v}_m$ is in U_m for each m, and is called the mth $\mathcal{E}$-**approximation** of $\mathbf{v}$. The reason for the name will be apparent soon.

Recall that Theorem 10 with $U = U_{m+1}$ gives $\|\mathbf{v} - \mathbf{v}_{m+1}\| \leq \|\mathbf{v} - \mathbf{u}\|$ for each vector $\mathbf{u}$ in U_{m+1}. But $\mathbf{v}_m$ is in U_{m+1} because $U_m \subseteq U_{m+1}$, so we have

$$\|\mathbf{v} - \mathbf{v}_{m+1}\| \leq \|\mathbf{v} - \mathbf{v}_m\| \quad \text{for each } m = 0, 1, 2, \cdots.$$

Using this we obtain

$$\|\mathbf{v} - \mathbf{v}_0\| \geq \|\mathbf{v} - \mathbf{v}_1\| \geq \|\mathbf{v} - \mathbf{v}_2\| \geq \cdots \geq \|\mathbf{v} - \mathbf{v}_m\| \geq \cdots.$$

Thus the vectors $\mathbf{v}_0,\ \mathbf{v}_1,\ \mathbf{v}_2,\ \cdots$ are better and better approximations to $\mathbf{v}$ (this is the reason for calling these $\mathbf{v}_i$ the $\mathcal{E}$-approximations of $\mathbf{v}$). Furthermore, each vector $\mathbf{v}_m$ is easily computable from $\mathbf{v}$ and the $\mathbf{e}_i$ because of $(****)$.

Hence the following is a general method in approximation theory: Given a vector $\mathbf{v}$ in an inner product space V, find an orthogonal set $\{\mathbf{e}_0,\ \mathbf{e}_1,\ \mathbf{e}_2,\ \cdots,\ \mathbf{e}_n,\ \cdots\}$ in V such that the vectors $\mathbf{v}_m$ approach $\mathbf{v}$, that is

$$\lim_{m \to \infty} \|\mathbf{v} - \mathbf{v}_m\| = 0.$$

Then $\mathbf{v}_m$ is a suitable approximation to $\mathbf{v}$ if m is large enough.[28]

---

[28] We say that a sequence of numbers $a_1,\ a_2,\ a_3,\ \cdots$ approaches a number a, and write $\lim_{n \to \infty} a_n = a$, if the numbers a_i become and remain very close to a as n increases. More precisely: We ask that for any small number $\varepsilon > 0$ there should exist an integer N such that $|a_n - a| < \varepsilon$ for all $n \geq N$. This notion is fundamental in calculus.

14. In each case we have two transformations $\mathbb{R}^2 \overset{T}{\to} \mathbb{R}^2 \overset{S}{\to} \mathbb{R}^2$ and we identify the composite $S \circ T$ by first finding its matrix and then using Theorems 1 and 3.

b) T is rotation through π with matrix $A = \begin{bmatrix} -1 & 0 \\ 0 & -1 \end{bmatrix}$,

S is reflection in the X-axis with matrix $B = \begin{bmatrix} 1 & 0 \\ 0 & -1 \end{bmatrix}$, so

$S \circ T$ has matrix $BA = \begin{bmatrix} -1 & 0 \\ 0 & 1 \end{bmatrix}$. Hence $S \circ T$ is reflection in the Y-axis.

d) T is reflection in the X-axis with matrix $A = \begin{bmatrix} 1 & 0 \\ 0 & -1 \end{bmatrix}$,

S is rotation through $\frac{\pi}{2}$ with matrix $B = \begin{bmatrix} 0 & -1 \\ 1 & 0 \end{bmatrix}$, so

$S \circ T$ has matrix $BA = \begin{bmatrix} 0 & 1 \\ 1 & 0 \end{bmatrix}$. Hence $S \circ T$ is reflection in the line $y = x$.

16. In each case we are given two transformations $\mathbb{R}^2 \overset{T}{\to} \mathbb{R}^2 \overset{S}{\to} \mathbb{R}^2$, we find $S \circ T$ by finding the matrices A and B of S and T respectively, and using Theorems 1 and 3.

b) $A = \begin{bmatrix} 0 & 1 \\ 1 & 0 \end{bmatrix}$, $B = \begin{bmatrix} 0 & -1 \\ -1 & 0 \end{bmatrix}$, so $BA = \begin{bmatrix} -1 & 0 \\ 0 & -1 \end{bmatrix}$ and $(S \circ T)(\vec{v}) = -\vec{v}$ for all $\vec{v}$ in $\mathbb{R}^2$.

d) $A = \begin{bmatrix} 1 & 0 \\ 0 & 2 \end{bmatrix}$, $B = \begin{bmatrix} 0 & -1 \\ 1 & 0 \end{bmatrix}$, $BA = \begin{bmatrix} 0 & -2 \\ 1 & 0 \end{bmatrix}$, so $(S \circ T)\begin{bmatrix} x \\ y \end{bmatrix} = \begin{bmatrix} -2y \\ x \end{bmatrix}$.

18. See the solution of Exercise 20.

20. Let T be reflection in a line L through the origin.

a) If X is any point in the plane, write $Y = T(X)$. Then Y and X are reflections of each other in the line L and, in particular, $X = T(Y)$. Eliminating Y gives $T(T(X)) = X$, that is $(T \circ T)(X) = X$. Now think of this as $(T \circ T)(X) = 1_{\mathbb{R}^2}(X)$ so, as this holds for every X in $\mathbb{R}^2$, we have $T \circ T = 1_{\mathbb{R}^2}$. Hence $T = T^{-1}$ by Theorem 6, as required.

b) Assume first that L has a slope m (that is, L is not vertical). Then $T = Q_m$ has matrix $A = \frac{1}{1+m^2}\begin{bmatrix} 1-m^2 & 2m \\ 2m & m^2-1 \end{bmatrix}$ and we compute

$$A^2 = \left(\frac{1}{1+m^2}\right)^2 \begin{bmatrix} 1-m^2 & 2m \\ 2m & m^2-1 \end{bmatrix}^2$$

$$= \left(\frac{1}{1+m^2}\right)^2 \begin{bmatrix} (1+m^2)^2 & 0 \\ 0 & (1+m^2)^2 \end{bmatrix} = \begin{bmatrix} 1 & 0 \\ 0 & 1 \end{bmatrix} = I.$$

Hence $A^{-1} = A$, so $T^{-1} = T$. Finally, if L is the Y-axis, then $A = \begin{bmatrix} -1 & 0 \\ 0 & 1 \end{bmatrix}$ and it is easy to see that $A^2 = I$ in this case too.

22. Let $S : \mathbb{R}^2 \to \mathbb{R}^2$ denote reflection in the X-axis. If $T : \mathbb{R}^2 \to \mathbb{R}^2$ is any reflection, write $T \circ S = R$. Then R is a rotation by the preceding exercise and, composing on the right by S^{-1}, we see that $T = R \circ S^{-1}$. But $S^{-1} = S$ by Exercise 20, so this gives $T = R \circ S$. Hence T is S followed by R, as required.

24. b) Suppose that $A^{-1} = A^T$, so that $A^T A = I$. Then given any $\vec{v}$ in $\mathbb{R}^2$ we have $\|A\vec{v}\|^2 = (A\vec{v})^T(A\vec{v}) = \vec{v}^T A^T A \vec{v} = \vec{v}^T I \vec{v} = \vec{v}^T \vec{v} = \|\vec{v}\|^2$. It follows that $\|A\vec{v}\| = \|\vec{v}\|$ for every $\vec{v}$ in $\mathbb{R}^2$. Replacing $\vec{v}$ by $\vec{v} - \vec{w}$ gives $\|A\vec{v} - A\vec{w}\| = \|\vec{v} - \vec{w}\|$, that is $\|T(\vec{v}) - T(\vec{w})\| = \|\vec{v} - \vec{w}\|$. This shows that the matrix transformation T induced by A is an isometry.

25. b) $\begin{bmatrix} 0 & -1 & 1 \\ 1 & 0 & 1 \\ 0 & 0 & 1 \end{bmatrix}$.   **d)** $\frac{1}{2}\begin{bmatrix} 1 & -\sqrt{3} & 1-2\sqrt{3} \\ \sqrt{3} & 1 & 2+\sqrt{3} \\ 0 & 0 & 2 \end{bmatrix}$.

26. b) $\frac{1}{1+m^2}\begin{bmatrix} 1 & m & -mb \\ m & m^2 & b \\ 0 & 0 & 1+m^2 \end{bmatrix}$.

3.5   THE CROSS PRODUCT: OPTIONAL

1. b) $\frac{7}{2}\sqrt{2}$.

3. b) 7.

4. b) True. If $\vec{v} \times \vec{w} = \vec{w} \times \vec{v}$ then, since $\vec{w} \times \vec{v} = -(\vec{v} \times \vec{w})$, we obtain $2(\vec{v} \times \vec{w}) = \vec{0}$, whence $\vec{v} \times \vec{w} = \vec{0}$. By Theorem 5, $\vec{v}$ and $\vec{w}$ are parallel.

d) True by Theorem 1 because
$det[\vec{u} \ \ \vec{v} \ \ \vec{w}]^T$
$= -det[\vec{u} \ \ \vec{w} \ \ \vec{v}]^T$
$= det[\vec{w} \ \ \vec{u} \ \ \vec{v}]^T$.

6. $\vec{u} \times \vec{v} = \vec{u} \times (-\vec{u} - \vec{w})$
$\quad = -[\vec{u} \times (\vec{u} + \vec{w})]$
$\quad = -[(\vec{u} \times \vec{u}) + (\vec{u} \times \vec{w})]$
$\quad = -(\vec{u} \times \vec{w}) = \vec{w} \times \vec{u}.$
Similarly, $\vec{u} \times \vec{v} = \vec{v} \times \vec{w}$.

8. A, B, and C are colinear if and only if the parallelogram determined by $\overrightarrow{AB}$ and $\overrightarrow{AC}$ has zero area; if and only if $\|\overrightarrow{AB} \times \overrightarrow{AC}\| = 0$; if and only if $\overrightarrow{AB} \times \overrightarrow{AC} = \vec{0}$.

10. Theorem 1 gives $|\vec{u} \cdot (\vec{v} \times \vec{w})| = |det[\vec{u} \ \ \vec{v} \ \ \vec{w}]|$. Rearranging columns in a determinant merely changes the sign of the determinant.

12. If h is the shortest distance, the parallelogram determined by $\overrightarrow{P_0 P}$ and $\vec{d}$ has area $\|\overrightarrow{P_0 P} \times \vec{d}\|$ by Theorem 5, so $\|\overrightarrow{P_0 P} \times \vec{d}\| = \|\vec{d}\| \cdot h$. The desired formula follows.

CHAPTER **4**

The Vector Space $\mathbb{R}^n$

4.1   SUBSPACES AND SPANNING

2. b) $\mathbb{R}^6$.   **d)** $\mathbb{R}^1 = \mathbb{R}$.

3. b) Not equal.   **d)** Equal.

4. b) $nullA = \mathbb{R}^4$, and $imA = \{0\}$.

d) $nullA = span\left\{ \begin{bmatrix} -1 \\ 0 \\ 0 \\ 5 \end{bmatrix} \right\}$, and

$imA = span\left\{ \begin{bmatrix} 0 \\ 1 \\ 0 \\ 0 \end{bmatrix}, \begin{bmatrix} -7 \\ 4 \\ 1 \\ 0 \end{bmatrix}, \begin{bmatrix} 1 \\ 0 \\ 0 \\ 1 \end{bmatrix} \right\}$.

5. b) Subspace. $U = span\{[0 \; 1 \; 0]^T\}$.
   d) Not a subspace. $\vec{0}$ is not in U.
   f) Subspace. $U = span\{[1 \; 1 \; 0]^T, [0 \; 0 \; 1]^T\}$.

6. b) X is not in $span\{Y, Z\}$: $[1 \; 2 \; 15 \; 11]^T = s[2 \; -1 \; 0 \; 2]^T + t[1 \; -1 \; -3 \; 1]^T$ has no solution.
   d) $X = 3Y + 4Z$.

7. b) The vectors span $\mathbb{R}^4$. One way to see this is to observe that the matrix A with these vectors as columns is invertible (the determinant is -42), so each $E_i = AX$ for some column in $\mathbb{R}^n$. Hence E_i is in the span of these vectors by Example 12.

8. b) False. Let X be any vector in $\mathbb{R}^n$ that is not in U. If $r = 0$, then $rX = 0X = 0 \in U$.
   d) True. Use axiom S3 with $r = -1$.
   f) False. 0 is not in this set.

10. Clearly $aX \in span\{X\}$ so $span\{aX\} \subseteq span\{X\}$ by Theorem 1. Since $a \neq 0$, $X = a^{-1}(aX) \in span\{aX\}$, so $span\{X\} \subseteq span\{aX\}$, again by Theorem 1. Hence $span\{X\} = span\{aX\}$.

12. No. For example, $[0 \; 0 \; 0]^T$ is not in $\mathbb{R}^2$.

14. Let Y be in U, say $Y = a_1X_1 + a_2X_2 + \cdots + a_kX_k, a_i$ in $\mathbb{R}$. If $AX_i = 0$ for each i, then
$AY = a_1AX_1 + a_2AX_2 + \cdots + a_kAX_k$
$= a_10 + a_20 + \cdots + a_k0 = 0.$

15. b) Always $im(AV) \subseteq imA$ because any vector in $im(AV)$ has the form $(AV)X = A(VX)$ and so is in imA. Conversely, let $Y \in imA$, say $Y = AX$ where X is in $\mathbb{R}^n$. Since V is invertible, we can write $Y = AX = A(VV^{-1})X = AV(V^{-1}X)$. Hence Y is in $im(AV)$ because $V^{-1}X$ is in $\mathbb{R}^n$. It follows that $imA \subseteq im(AV)$. Thus we have $im(AV) = imA$.

16. b) By axiom S2, $-X = (-1)X \in U$. Then we can write $Y = (X + Y) + (-X)$ which is in U by axiom S3.

18. S1. The zero matrix 0 is in U because $A0 = 0 = B0$.
   S2. If X, Y are in U, then $A(X + Y) = AX + AY = BX + BY = B(X + Y)$; thus $X + Y$ is in U.
   S3. If X is in U and r is in $\mathbb{R}$, then $A(rX) = r(AX) = r(BX) = B(rX)$; thus rX is in U.

20. The fact that the zero vector is in U forces $B = 0$.

22. We have $span\{V\} = \{aV \mid a$ in $\mathbb{R}\}$. If $U \neq \{0\}$ is a subspace, say $0 \neq aV \in U$, then $V = a^{-1}(aV) \in U$. Hence $span\{V\} \subseteq U$, and it follows that $U = span\{V\}$.

24. b) S2. Given X, Y in $U + W$, write $X = X_1 + X_2$ and $Y = Y_1 + Y_2$, where X_1, Y_1 are in U and X_2, Y_2 are in W. Then $X + Y = (X_1 + Y_1) + (X_2 + Y_2)$ is in $U + W$ because $X_1 + Y_1$ is in U and $X_2 + Y_2$ is in W.

4.2   LINEAR INDEPENDENCE

1. b) If $r[1 \; 1 \; 1]^T + s[2 \; 1 \; 0]^T = [0 \; 0 \; 0]^T$, then $r + 2s = 0, r + s = 0$, and $r = 0$. This implies that $r = s = 0$, so the vectors are independent by the Independence test.

d) If $r[1 \; 0 \; 1 \; 0]^T + s[0 \; 1 \; 0 \; 1]^T + t[3 \; -1 \; 2 \; -1]^T = [0 \; 0 \; 0 \; 0]^T$, equating coefficients gives the equations $r + 3t = 0, s - t = 0, r + 2t = 0$, and $s - t = 0$. This implies that $r = s = t = 0$, and so the vectors are independent by the Independence test.

2. b) Dependent. $[2 \; -6]^T + 2[-1 \; 3]^T = 0$.
   d) Independent.   **f)** Independent.

3. b) Invertible. The columns are independent.
   d) Not invertible. If C_1, C_2, C_3, C_4, and C_5 denote the columns of A, then $C_1 - 2C_2 - C_3 + C_4 + 0C_5 = 0$.

4. b) Independent. $det \begin{bmatrix} 1 & 1 & 0 \\ 1 & -1 & 0 \\ -1 & 1 & 1 \end{bmatrix} = -2 \neq 0.$

d) Independent. $det \begin{bmatrix} 1 & 4 & 0 & 1 \\ 0 & 4 & 1 & 3 \\ -2 & -3 & 0 & 3 \\ 5 & 2 & -3 & 1 \end{bmatrix} = -55 \neq 0.$

5. b) Does not span $\mathbb{R}^3$. $det \begin{bmatrix} 0 & 8 & -9 \\ -6 & -3 & 7 \\ -6 & 5 & -2 \end{bmatrix} = 0.$

d) Does not span $\mathbb{R}^4$. $det \begin{bmatrix} 2 & 3 & 4 & -5 \\ 1 & 5 & -4 & 0 \\ 7 & 4 & -3 & 6 \\ -2 & 5 & -3 & -4 \end{bmatrix} = 0.$

6. The sets where the given vectors would form a square matrix.

7. b) True. If $rX + sY = 0$, then $rX + sY + 0Z = 0$, whence $r = s = 0$ by the independence of $\{X, Y, Z\}$.

d) False. One of the X_i could be a linear combination of the other vectors.

f) False. We could take $a = b = c = 0$ for *any* set $\{X, Y, Z\}$ of vectors.

h) True. This is the negation of the definition of independence.

9. b) Independent. If $a(X + Y) + b(Y + Z) + c(Z + X) = 0$, then $(a + c)X + (a + b)Y + (b + c)Z = 0$. Since $\{X, Y, Z, W\}$ is independent, $\{X, Y, Z\}$ is also independent which forces $a + c = 0$, $a + b = 0$, and $b + c = 0$. The only solution is $a = b = c = 0$.

d) Dependent. $(X + Y) - (Y + Z) + (Z + W) - (W + X) = 0$.

10. Use Theorems 2 and 3 on the columns of A.

12. Set a linear combination equal to zero and obtain a set of equations in the coefficients that has only the trivial solution.

14. Suppose $rY + r_1X_1 + r_2X_2 + \cdots + r_kX_k = 0$. If $r \neq 0$, show that Y is in $span\{X_1, X_2, \cdots, X_k\}$, contrary to assumption. So $r = 0$ and the independence of $\{X_1, X_2, \cdots, X_k\}$ can be applied.

16. b) Since $\mathcal{X}$ is dependent, some nontrivial linear combination $r_1X_1 + r_2X_2 + \cdots + r_mX_m = 0$, where each X_i is in $\mathcal{X}$. But each X_i is also in $\mathcal{Y}$ (because $\mathcal{X} \subseteq \mathcal{Y}$) so this is a nontrivial linear combination of vectors in $\mathcal{Y}$ that vanishes. Hence $\mathcal{Y}$ is dependent too.

4.3 DIMENSION

1. b) 3   **d)** 3

2. b) Independent (and so span $\mathbb{R}^3$ by Theorem 4) because

$det \begin{bmatrix} -1 & 1 & 1 \\ 1 & -1 & 1 \\ 1 & 1 & -1 \end{bmatrix} = 4 \neq 0.$

d) Independent (and so span $\mathbb{R}^4$ by Theorem 4) because

$det \begin{bmatrix} 1 & 1 & 0 & 0 \\ 1 & 0 & 1 & 1 \\ 0 & 0 & 1 & 0 \\ 0 & 1 & 0 & 1 \end{bmatrix} = -2 \neq 0.$

3. b) The first four vectors are independent by Theorem 2 §4.2 because $det \begin{bmatrix} 2 & 6 & 3 & 1 \\ 3 & 1 & 6 & 0 \\ 5 & -4 & 3 & 0 \\ -4 & -7 & 2 & 0 \end{bmatrix} = 289 \neq 0$, and so these vectors form a basis of $\mathbb{R}^4$ by Theorem 4. The given set has too many vectors to be a basis for $\mathbb{R}^4$ by the Corollary to Theorem 1.

d) These vectors are independent by Theorem 2 §4.2, since

$det \begin{bmatrix} 1 & 5 & 3 & 2 \\ -6 & 1 & 9 & 0 \\ 3 & 5 & 0 & 3 \\ -7 & 9 & 2 & 0 \end{bmatrix} = 441$, and so form a basis of $\mathbb{R}^4$ by Theorem 4.

4. b) False. Both sets are independent, so the subspaces they span are of dimension 3 and 2, respectively, and so cannot be equal.

d) False. Both sets are independent, so the subspaces they span have dimensions 2 and 4, respectively, and so cannot be equal.

5. b) $\left\{ \begin{bmatrix} 1 \\ 0 \\ 0 \end{bmatrix}, \begin{bmatrix} 0 \\ 1 \\ 0 \end{bmatrix}, \begin{bmatrix} 0 \\ 0 \\ 1 \end{bmatrix} \right\}$ **d)** $\{1\}$

6. In each case we find a basis inside the given spanning set (as guaranteed by Theorem 3).

b) $\{[2 \; 1 \; 0 \; -1]^T, [-1 \; 1 \; 1 \; 2]^T\}$; dimension is 2. In fact, $[2 \; 7 \; 4 \; 5]^T = 3[2 \; 1 \; 0 \; -1]^T + 4[-1 \; 1 \; 1 \; 2]^T$.

d) $\{[-2 \; 0 \; 3 \; 1]^T, [1 \; 2 \; -1 \; 0]^T, [1 \; 2 \; 2 \; 1]^T\}$; dimension is 3. In fact, $[-2 \; 8 \; 5 \; 3]^T = 3[-2 \; 0 \; 3 \; 1]^T + 4[1 \; 2 \; -1 \; 0]^T$.

7. b) $\{[1 \; 1 \; 0 \; 1]^T, [1 \; -1 \; 1 \; 0]^T\}$. Dimension is 2.

d) $\{[1 \; 0 \; 1 \; 0]^T, [-1 \; 1 \; 0 \; 1]^T, [0 \; 1 \; 0 \; 1]^T\}$. Dimension is 3.

8. b) $\{[-2 \; 4 \; 1 \; 0 \; 0]^T, [7 \; -11 \; 0 \; 2 \; 1]^T\}$. $dim(nullA) = 2$.

9. b) The condition can be written as $A^TX = 0$. The solution is $[-2s - 2t \; -2s + t \; s \; t]^T$, so the corresponding basis of U is $\{[-2 \; -2 \; 1 \; 0]^T, [-2 \; 1 \; 0 \; 1]^T\}$ and $dimU = 2$.

d) Rearrange the condition $X^TA = (BX)^T$ to give $(A^T - B)X = 0$. As in part **b)**, a basis of U is $\{[1 \; 1 \; 1 \; 0 \;]^T, [1 \; -4 \; 0 \; 2]^T\}$ and $dimU = 2$.

10. b) False. Take the standard basis of $\mathbb{R}^3$ as a counterexample.

d) False. $\left\{ \begin{bmatrix} 1 \\ 0 \\ 0 \\ 0 \\ 1 \end{bmatrix}, \begin{bmatrix} 0 \\ 1 \\ 0 \\ 0 \\ 1 \end{bmatrix}, \begin{bmatrix} 0 \\ 0 \\ 1 \\ 0 \\ 1 \end{bmatrix}, \begin{bmatrix} 0 \\ 0 \\ 0 \\ 1 \\ 1 \end{bmatrix}, \begin{bmatrix} 0 \\ 0 \\ 0 \\ -1 \\ 1 \end{bmatrix} \right\}$ is a basis of $\mathbb{R}^5$.

f) False. Take $Y_i = -X_i$ for $1 \le i \le 4$. Then $\{X_1 + Y_1, X_2 + Y_2, X_3 + Y_3, X_4 + Y_4\} = \{0, 0, 0, 0\} = \{0\}$ which is not a basis of $\mathbb{R}^4$.

12. Let X be a vector in $\mathbb{R}^n$ such that $X \ne 0$. Then the set $\{X\}$ is linearly independent, and so by Theorem 3 can be enlarged to a basis of $\mathbb{R}^n$.

14. The condition is that $\{X, Y, Z, W\}$ must span $\mathbb{R}^3$. In this case the set $\{X, Y, Z, W\}$ contains a basis of $\mathbb{R}^3$ by Theorem 3. Conversely, if $\{X, Y, Z, W\}$ contains a basis of $\mathbb{R}^3$, then the three vectors of that basis will span $\mathbb{R}^3$. Hence $\{X, Y, Z, W\}$ spans $\mathbb{R}^3$ by Theorem 1 §4.1.

16. b) If $t_1(X + W) + t_2(Y + W) + t_3(Z + W) + t_4 W = 0$, collecting coefficients gives $t_1 = t_2 = t_3 = 0$ and $t_1 + t_2 + t_3 + t_4 = 0$. Hence $t_1 = t_2 = t_3 = t_4 = 0$.

17. b) Assume that $\{aX + bY, cX + dY\}$ is independent. To show that A is invertible, let $AX = 0$; we must show that $X = 0$. If we write $X = \begin{bmatrix} r \\ s \end{bmatrix}$, the condition $AX = 0$ implies that $ra + sc = 0$ and $rb + sd = 0$, and hence that $r(aX + bY) + s(cX + dY) = (ra + sc)X + (rb + sd)Y = 0$. This yields $r = s = 0$ by the independence of $\{X, Y\}$, as required.

18. b) $\{E_1, E_2, \cdots, E_n\}$ is not contained in $span\{X_1, \cdots, X_k\}$ since $dim[span\{X_1, \cdots, X_k\}] \le k < n$. So some $E_{l_{k+1}}$ is not in $span\{X_1, \cdots, X_k\}$, whence $\{X_1, \cdots, X_k, E_{l_{k+1}}\}$ is independent by the Independent lemma. If $\{X_1, \cdots, X_k, E_{l_{k+1}}\}$ spans $\mathbb{R}^n$, we are done. Otherwise, $\{E_1, E_2, \cdots, E_n\}$ is not contained in $span\{X_1, \cdots, X_k, E_{l_{k+1}}\}$ so some $E_{l_{k+2}}$ is not in $span\{X_1, \cdots, X_k, E_{l_{k+1}}\}$. Hence $\{X_1, \cdots, X_k, E_{l_{k+1}}, E_{l_{k+2}}\}$ is independent. Continuing, we eventually reach a basis of $\mathbb{R}^n$.

20. Since $dimU \le dimW$ and $dimW = 1$, either $dimU = 0$ or $dimU = 1$. If $dimU = 0$, then $U = \{0\}$; if $dimU = 1$, then $U = W$ by part (2) of Theorem 4.

22. $U \cap W$ is a subspace of U, so $dim(U \cap W) \le dimU = 2$. Thus $dim(U \cap W) = 0, 1,$ or 2. If $dim(U \cap W) = 2$, then $U \cap W = U$ by Theorem 4; in particular $U \subseteq W$.

23. b) Let $\{Y_1, \cdots, Y_k\}$ be a basis of $im(UA)$, say $Y_i = (UA)X_i$ for some X_i in $\mathbb{R}^n$. It follows that $U^{-1}Y_i = AX_i$ is in imA, and it suffices to show that $\mathcal{D} = \{U^{-1}Y_1, \cdots, U^{-1}Y_k\}$ is a basis of imA. If $t_1(U^{-1}Y_1) + \cdots + t_k(U^{-1}Y_k) = 0$, then $t_1Y_1 + \cdots + t_kY_k = 0$, so each $t_i = 0$ by the independence of the Y_i, proving that $\mathcal{D}$ is independent. Finally, given Y in imA, write $Y = AX$ where X is in $\mathbb{R}^n$, so $UY = UAX$ is in $im(UA)$. Hence write $UY = s_1Y_1 + \cdots + s_kY_k$, s_i in

$\mathbb{R}$, so that $Y = s_1U^{-1}Y_1 + \cdots + s_kU^{-1}Y_k$. This shows that $\mathcal{D}$ spans imA.

24. We show that $span\{X_1, X_2, \cdots, X_n\} = U$. If not, choose Y in U which is not in $span\{X_1, X_2, \cdots, X_n\}$. Then by Lemma 1, $\{Y, X_1, X_2, \cdots, X_n\}$ is linearly independent, contrary to the maximality of $\{X_1, X_2, \cdots, X_n\}$. So $span\{X_1, X_2, \cdots, X_n\} = U$ after all.

26. b) Let $AX_i = \lambda_iX_i$ for each $i = 1, 2, \cdots, n + m$. It follows that $BY_i = \lambda_iY_i$ and $CZ_i = \lambda_iZ_i$ for each i. Moreover, if Y and Z are arbitrary columns in $\mathbb{R}^n$ and $\mathbb{R}^m$ respectively, then $\begin{bmatrix} Y \\ Z \end{bmatrix}$ is a linear combination of the $X_i = \begin{bmatrix} Y_i \\ Z_i \end{bmatrix}$. It follows that Y is the same linear combination of the Y_i, and hence that $\mathbb{R}^n = span\{Y_1, \cdots, Y_{n+m}\}$. Thus $\{Y_1, \cdots, Y_{n+m}\}$ contains a basis of $\mathbb{R}^n$ consisting of eigenvectors of B (by Theorem 3); that is, B is diagonalizable by Theorem 3 §2.3. Similarly, C is diagonalizable.

4.4   RANK

1. b) $rowA = span\{[-5 \ -4], [8 \ 0]\}$.
$colA = span\{[-5 \ 8 \ -1]^T, [-4 \ 0 \ -3]^T\}$.

d) $rowA = span\{[9 \ -5 \ 1 \ -1], [8 \ -5 \ -3 \ 1], [0 \ 4 \ 7 \ 6], [0 \ 2 \ -7 \ 7]\}$.
$colA = span\{[9 \ 8 \ 0 \ 0]^T, [-5 \ -5 \ 4 \ 2]^T, [1 \ -3 \ 7 \ -7]^T, [-1 \ 1 \ 6 \ 7]^T\}$.

2. (c) and (b) share the same column space since the columns of matrix (b) can be obtained by adding columns 1 and 2 of (a) to column 3, and adding column 1 to column 4 and then subtracting column 2 from column 4. However, the two matrices do not share the same row space. For matrix (c), $rowA = span\{[1 \ 0 \ 1 \ 1], [0 \ 1 \ 1 \ -1]\}$, whereas for matrix (b), $rowA = span\{[1 \ 0 \ 0 \ 0], [0 \ 1 \ 0 \ 0]\}$.

3. b) $rankA = dim(rowA) = 2$. Indeed: $[4 \ -13 \ 5 \ 6]^T = -2[1 \ 2 \ -1 \ 3]^T + 3[2 \ -3 \ 1 \ 4]^T$.

4. b) $\{[1 \ 2 \ -1 \ 0 \ 4]^T, [-3 \ 1 \ 0 \ 2 \ 5]^T, [-7 \ 7 \ -2 \ 6 \ 13]^T\}$.

$$\begin{bmatrix} 1 & -3 & -7 & -2 \\ 2 & 1 & 7 & 3 \\ -1 & 0 & -2 & -1 \\ 0 & 2 & 6 & 2 \\ 4 & 5 & 13 & 9 \end{bmatrix} \rightarrow \begin{bmatrix} 1 & 0 & 0 & 1 \\ 0 & 1 & 0 & 1 \\ 0 & 0 & 1 & 0 \\ 0 & 0 & 0 & 0 \\ 0 & 0 & 0 & 0 \end{bmatrix}.$$

5. b) $rowA : \{[1 \ 2 \ 0 \ 5 \ 7 \ 1], [2 \ 1 \ 1 \ -1 \ 0 \ 3], [0 \ 0 \ 0 \ 0 \ 0 \ 1]\}$; $colA : \{[1 \ 2 \ -5 \ 1]^T, [2 \ 1 \ 2 \ -1]^T, [1 \ 3 \ 9 \ 2]^T\}$; $rankA = 3$;

$$A \rightarrow \begin{bmatrix} 1 & 2 & 0 & 5 & 7 & 1 \\ 0 & 1 & -\frac{1}{3} & \frac{11}{3} & \frac{14}{3} & 0 \\ 0 & 0 & 0 & 0 & 0 & 1 \\ 0 & 0 & 0 & 0 & 0 & 0 \end{bmatrix}$$

6. b) $nullA = span\{[6 \ 0 \ -4 \ 1 \ 0]^T, [5 \ 0 \ -3 \ 0 \ 1]^T\}$;

$$A \to \begin{bmatrix} 1 & 0 & 0 & -6 & -5 \\ 0 & 1 & 0 & 0 & 0 \\ 0 & 0 & 1 & 4 & 3 \\ 0 & 0 & 0 & 0 & 0 \end{bmatrix} \text{ so } rankA = 3;$$

$dim(nullA) = n - rankA = 5 - 3 = 2$.

7. b) False. Consider $A = \begin{bmatrix} 1 & 0 & 0 \\ 0 & 1 & 0 \end{bmatrix}$.

Here, $rowA = span\{[1 \ 0 \ 0]^T, [0 \ 1 \ 0]^T\} \neq \mathbb{R}^n$.

d) False. $\begin{bmatrix} 1 & 0 & 0 \\ 0 & 0 & 0 \end{bmatrix}$ has rank 1.

f) False. Let $A = \begin{bmatrix} 1 & 0 \\ 0 & 1 \end{bmatrix}$ and $B = \begin{bmatrix} -1 & 0 \\ 0 & -1 \end{bmatrix}$. Then

$rankA = 2 = rankB$ but $rank(A + B) = rank\begin{bmatrix} 0 & 0 \\ 0 & 0 \end{bmatrix} = 0$.

8. The rows could be independent, so $rankA = dim(rowA) = 3$, But A can have at most 3 independent columns ($rankA \leq 3$ — the number of rows). So the 4 columns of A cannot be independent.

10. No, the rank cannot be equal to both the number of rows and the number of columns.

12. If A is $m \times n$ and both the rows and columns are independent, then $m = rankA = n$, a contradiction.

14. b) It follows from **a)** that $col(AB) \subseteq colA$. Taking dimensions gives $rank(AB) \leq rankA$.

16. b) Write $A = [C_1 \ C_2 \ \cdots \ C_n]$ where C_j is column j of A. We have $colA = span\{C_1, C_2, \cdots, C_n\}$ and $col([A \ B]) = span\{C_1, C_2, \cdots, C_n, B\}$. By **a)**, the system $AX = B$ has a solution if and only if B is in $colA$; that is, if and only if $colA = col([A \ B])$. But $colA \subseteq col([A \ B])$, so $colA = col([A \ B])$ if and only if $dim[colA] = dim\{col([A \ B])\}$; that is, if and only if $rankA = rank[A \ B]$.

18. b) If $AB = I_m$, then $rankA \geq rank(AB) = m$ using Exercise 14. But $rankA \leq m$ because A is $m \times n$.

20. b) If $rankA = m$, then AA^T is invertible by Theorem 4. The rest is routine.

4.5 ORTHOGONALITY

1. b) As in Example 2: $\|3X - 4Y\| = \sqrt{76} = 2\sqrt{19}$.

d) $(3X + 4Y) \cdot (X - 5Y) = 1$.

2. b) Verify that the dot product of each pair of vectors is zero.

3. b) $\{\frac{1}{\sqrt{14}}[-3 \ 1 \ 2]^T, \frac{1}{\sqrt{3}}[1 \ 1 \ 1]^T, \frac{1}{\sqrt{42}}[1 \ -5 \ 4]^T\}$.

5. b) Setting the dot products of the three vectors with $[a \ b \ c \ d]^T$ equal to zero produces a homogeneous system of linear equations.
Solution: $[a \ b \ c \ d]^T = [-5s \ 4s \ 2s \ 5s]^T$.

6. b) $[a \ b \ c]^T = \frac{-4a+b+5c}{42}[-4 \ 1 \ 5]^T +$
$\frac{-a+b-c}{3}[-1 \ 1 \ -1]^T + \frac{2a+3b+c}{14}[2 \ 3 \ 1]^T$.

7. b) $F_1 = [2 \ 1]^T, F_2 = [-1 \ 2]^T$.

d) $F_1 = [0 \ 1 \ 1]^T, F_2 = [1 \ 0 \ 0]^T, F_3 = [0 \ -1 \ 1]^T$.

8. b) $Q = \frac{\sqrt{5}}{5}\begin{bmatrix} 2 & 1 \\ 1 & -2 \end{bmatrix}, R = \frac{\sqrt{5}}{5}\begin{bmatrix} 5 & 3 \\ 0 & 1 \end{bmatrix}$.

d) $Q = \frac{\sqrt{3}}{3}\begin{bmatrix} 1 & 1 & 0 \\ -1 & 0 & 1 \\ 0 & 1 & 1 \\ 1 & -1 & 1 \end{bmatrix}, R = \frac{\sqrt{3}}{3}\begin{bmatrix} 3 & 0 & -1 \\ 0 & 3 & 1 \\ 0 & 0 & 2 \end{bmatrix}$.

9. b) False. Consider $\{X, \ Y\} = \{[1 \ 0]^T, [0 \ 1]^T\}$. Then $\{X, \ X + Y\} = \{[1 \ 0]^T, [1 \ 1]^T\}$, so $X \cdot (X + Y) = [1 \ 0]^T \cdot [1 \ 1]^T = 1 + 0 = 1 \neq 0$. Thus $\{X, \ X + Y\}$ is not orthogonal.

d) True. In order for $\{X_1, \ X_2, \ Y_1, \ Y_2, \ Y_3\}$ to be orthogonal, $X_1 \cdot X_2 = 0$, $Y_i \cdot Y_j = 0$, and $X_i \cdot Y_j = 0$ for all i and j. This is the case here since $\{X_1, \ X_2\}$ and $\{Y_1, \ Y_2, \ Y_3\}$ are orthogonal, and since we are assuming that $X_i \cdot Y_j = 0$ for all i and j.

f) False. $E = [1 \ 0]^T$ and $X = [2 \ 1]^T$.

h) True. If Q has columns C_i, then the $(i, \ j)$-entry of Q^TQ is $C_i \cdot C_j$.

10. Each $a_iX_i \neq 0$ as $a_i \neq 0$ and $X_i \neq 0$; and $(a_iX_i) \cdot (a_jX_j) = a_ia_j(X_i \cdot X_j) = a_ia_j(0) = 0$ if $i \neq j$.

12. b) We have $X + Y + Z = [2 \ 1 \ 1]^T$, so $\|X + Y + Z\|^2 = 6$, while $\|X\|^2 = \|Y\|^2 = \|Z\|^2 = 2$. However, $X \cdot Z = 1 + 1 + 0 = 2$ so X and Z are not orthogonal.

14. Show that $\|AX\|^2 = \lambda\|X\|^2$.

16. If $X = a_1F_1 + \cdots + a_mF_m$, then $\|X\|^2 = a_1(X \cdot F_1) + \cdots + a_m(X \cdot F_m) = 0$. So $\|X\| = 0$, $X = 0$.

18. b) If $\{F_1, \ \cdots, \ F_{m-1}, \ H\}$ is another orthonormal basis of U, expand H in terms of the orthonormal basis $\{F_1, \ \cdots, \ F_{m-1}, \ G\}$ using the Expansion theorem, and conclude that $H = aG$ where $a = H \cdot G$ is a real number. Show that $a = \pm 1$ because H and G are unit vectors.

20. Let A be the matrix with the X_i^T as its rows, and let $B = [Y_1 \ Y_2 \ \cdots \ Y_n]$ be the matrix with the Y_j as its columns. Show that $AB = I_n$ and so B is invertible by Theorem 5 §1.5. Hence B has independent columns by Theorem 2 §4.2.

22. By Theorem 1 §1.6, it is enough to show that $A \to B$ by row operations, where B is row-echelon with orthogonal rows. We know that $A \to R$ where R is row-echelon. Apply the Gram-Schmidt process to the nonzero rows of R, starting at the bottom. The algorithm replaces each of these rows by itself minus a linear combination of the rows below it, and so preserves the row-echelon character of the matrix. Since this is done using row operations, and since the resulting rows are orthogonal, we can get to a matrix B of the desired form.

4.6 PROJECTIONS AND APPROXIMATION

1. b) $X = \frac{1}{21}\begin{bmatrix} 23 \\ 10 \\ 64 \end{bmatrix} + \frac{1}{21}\begin{bmatrix} -2 \\ 11 \\ -1 \end{bmatrix}$. **d)** $X = \frac{1}{3}\begin{bmatrix} 6 \\ -5 \\ 8 \\ -2 \end{bmatrix} + \frac{4}{3}\begin{bmatrix} 0 \\ 2 \\ 1 \\ -1 \end{bmatrix}$.

f) $X = \frac{1}{12}\begin{bmatrix} 5a - 5b + c - 3d \\ -5a + 5b - c + 3d \\ a - b + 11c + 3d \\ -3a + 3b + 3c + 3d \end{bmatrix} + \frac{1}{12}\begin{bmatrix} 7a + 5b - c + 3d \\ 5a + 7b + c - 3d \\ -a + b + c - 3d \\ 3a - 3b - 3c + 9d \end{bmatrix}$.

2. b) First note that $\begin{bmatrix} 1 \\ 3 \\ -1 \\ -2 \end{bmatrix} = -\begin{bmatrix} 1 \\ -1 \\ 0 \\ 2 \end{bmatrix} + \begin{bmatrix} 2 \\ 2 \\ -1 \\ 0 \end{bmatrix}$ and

$\begin{bmatrix} 7 \\ 1 \\ -2 \\ 6 \end{bmatrix} = 3\begin{bmatrix} 1 \\ -1 \\ 0 \\ 2 \end{bmatrix} + 2\begin{bmatrix} 2 \\ 2 \\ -1 \\ 0 \end{bmatrix}$, so the new vectors are indeed in U, and so form a basis (as $dim\, U = 2$). Using this basis:

$$proj_U(X) = \frac{4}{15}\begin{bmatrix} 1 \\ 3 \\ -1 \\ 2 \end{bmatrix} + \frac{8}{90}\begin{bmatrix} 7 \\ 1 \\ -2 \\ 6 \end{bmatrix} = \frac{4}{9}\begin{bmatrix} 2 \\ 2 \\ -1 \\ 0 \end{bmatrix}.$$

3. b) By Gram-Schmidt, use the orthogonal basis $\{[1\ \ -1\ \ 0]^T, [1\ \ 1\ \ -2]^T\}$. Then the closest vector to X is

$proj_U(X) = \frac{1}{2}\begin{bmatrix} 1 \\ -1 \\ 0 \end{bmatrix} + \frac{-3}{6}\begin{bmatrix} 1 \\ 1 \\ -2 \end{bmatrix} = \begin{bmatrix} 0 \\ -1 \\ 1 \end{bmatrix}.$

d) By Gram-Schmidt, use the orthogonal basis $\{[1\ \ -1\ \ 1\ \ 0]^T, [1\ \ 1\ \ 0\ \ 0]^T, [0\ \ 0\ \ 0\ \ 1]^T\}$. Then the closest vector to $X = [3\ \ 0\ \ 5\ \ -1]^T$ is

$proj_U(X) = \frac{8}{3}\begin{bmatrix} 1 \\ -1 \\ 1 \\ 0 \end{bmatrix} + \frac{3}{2}\begin{bmatrix} 1 \\ 1 \\ 0 \\ 0 \end{bmatrix} + \frac{-1}{1}\begin{bmatrix} 0 \\ 0 \\ 0 \\ 1 \end{bmatrix} = \frac{1}{6}\begin{bmatrix} 25 \\ -7 \\ 16 \\ -6 \end{bmatrix}.$

4. b) $A^TA = \begin{bmatrix} 6 & 6 \\ 6 & 27 \end{bmatrix}$, $A^TB = \begin{bmatrix} 7 \\ 14 \end{bmatrix}$; $(A^TA)Z = A^TB$ has solution $Z = \begin{bmatrix} \frac{5}{6} \\ \frac{1}{3} \end{bmatrix}$.

d) $A^TA = \begin{bmatrix} 23 & 16 & -13 \\ 16 & 19 & -20 \\ -13 & -20 & 30 \end{bmatrix}$, $A^TB = \begin{bmatrix} 6 \\ 6 \\ -14 \end{bmatrix}$; $(A^TA)Z = A^TB$

has solution $Z = \begin{bmatrix} \frac{722}{1339} \\ -\frac{1722}{1339} \\ -\frac{1460}{1339} \end{bmatrix}$.

5. b) $M^TM = \begin{bmatrix} 4 & 3 & 11 \\ 3 & 11 & 27 \\ 11 & 27 & 83 \end{bmatrix}$, $M^TY = \begin{bmatrix} 2 \\ -2 \\ -8 \end{bmatrix}$, so $Z = \begin{bmatrix} \frac{74}{55} \\ \frac{137}{220} \\ -\frac{21}{44} \end{bmatrix}$.

Hence $y = \frac{74}{55} + \frac{137}{220}x - \frac{21}{44}x^2$.

6. b) $M^TM = \begin{bmatrix} 5 & 6 & 30 & 84 \\ 6 & 30 & 84 & 354 \\ 30 & 84 & 354 & 1236 \\ 84 & 354 & 1236 & 4890 \end{bmatrix}$, $M^TY = \begin{bmatrix} 5 \\ 3 \\ 9 \\ 39 \end{bmatrix}$,

$Z = \begin{bmatrix} \frac{429}{133} \\ -\frac{743}{798} \\ -\frac{219}{266} \\ \frac{13}{57} \end{bmatrix}$, $y = \frac{429}{133} - \frac{743}{798}x - \frac{219}{266}x^2 + \frac{13}{57}x^3$.

8. b) $U^\perp = span\{[5\ \ 3\ \ 1\ \ 0], [-5\ \ -2\ \ 0\ \ 1]\}$.

9. Throughout this exercise, write $proj_U(X) = P$.
  b) True. If P is in $U^\perp$, then P is in $U \cap U^\perp = \{0\}$, so $P = 0$. Hence $X = X - P$ is in $U^\perp$ by the Projection theorem.
  d) True. If $P = 0$, then $X = X - P$ is in $U^\perp$ by the Projection theorem.
  f) False. $0 \subseteq \mathbb{R}^n$ but $0^\perp = \mathbb{R}^n \nsubseteq 0 = (\mathbb{R}^n)^\perp$.

10. $P = proj_U(X)$ is in U for any choice of X, so if $X = P$, then X is in U. Conversely, if X is in U, then $P - X$ is in U so, since $P - X$ is always in $U^\perp$, it follows that $P - X = 0$. Hence $P = X$, as required.

12. If X is in $W^\perp$, then $X \cdot Y = 0$ for every Y in W. Since $U \subseteq W$, this means that $X \cdot Y = 0$ for every Y in U, that is X is in $U^\perp$.

14. b) If $U = \mathbb{R}^n$, then any vector in $U^\perp$ is orthogonal to every vector in $U = \mathbb{R}^n$, in particular to itself. So $U^\perp = \{0\}$. Conversely, if $U^\perp = \{0\}$ and X is in $\mathbb{R}^n$, let $P = proj_U(X)$. Then the Projection theorem shows that $X - P$ is in $U^\perp = \{0\}$, so $X = P$. Hence X is in U.

16. b) Let $\{F_1, \cdots, F_m\}$ be an orthogonal basis of U, so that $proj_U(X) = \sum_{i=1}^{m} \frac{X \cdot F_i}{\|F_i\|^2}F_i$ for every X in $\mathbb{R}^n$. Then

$proj_U(aX) = \sum_{i=1}^{m} \frac{(aX) \cdot F_i}{\|F_i\|^2}F_i = \sum_{i=1}^{m} a(\frac{X \cdot F_i}{\|F_i\|^2})F_i = a\sum_{i=1}^{m} \frac{X \cdot F_i}{\|F_i\|^2}F_i$
$\qquad\qquad = a\, proj_U(X).$

18. Let $\{F_1, \cdots, F_k\}$ be an orthogonal basis of U, and extend it to an orthogonal basis $\{F_1, \cdots, F_k, F_{k+1}, \cdots, F_n\}$ of $\mathbb{R}^n$. By the preceding exercise we have $U^\perp = span\{F_{k+1}, \cdots, F_n\}$.

Thinking of the F_i as columns, consider the $n \times n$ matrix A with $F_{k+1}^T, \cdots, F_n^T$ as its first $n-k$ rows, and the rest of the rows zero. Then $AX = 0$ if and only if $F_i^T X = 0$ for $k+1 \le i \le n$, if and only if $F_i \cdot X = 0$ for $k+1 \le i \le n$, if and only if X is in $(U^\perp)^\perp = U$. Hence $U = \{X \mid AX = 0\}$, as required.

20. b) $(I - E)^2 = I - 2E + E^2 = I - 2E + E = I - E$, and $(I - E)^T = I^T - E^T = I - E$.

4.7 ORTHOGONAL DIAGONALIZATION

1. b) False. Consider the matrix $\begin{bmatrix} \frac{1}{2} & -1 \\ \frac{1}{2} & 1 \end{bmatrix}$.

d) False. Consider the matrix $\frac{1}{\sqrt{2}}\begin{bmatrix} 1 & 1 \\ -1 & 1 \end{bmatrix}$.

f) True. $(P^T A P)^T = P^T A^T P^{TT} = P^T A^T P = P^T A P$ because $A^T = A$.

2. b) $\frac{1}{5}\begin{bmatrix} 3 & 4 \\ -4 & 3 \end{bmatrix}$ **d)** $\frac{1}{\sqrt{6}}\begin{bmatrix} \sqrt{2} & 0 & 2 \\ -\sqrt{2} & \sqrt{3} & 1 \\ \sqrt{2} & \sqrt{3} & -1 \end{bmatrix}$

f) $\frac{1}{7}\begin{bmatrix} 2 & 3 & -6 \\ 6 & 2 & 3 \\ -3 & 6 & 2 \end{bmatrix}$

4. The expansion is $Y = (Y \cdot X_1)X_1 + (Y \cdot X_2)X_2 + \cdots + (Y \cdot X_n)X_n$, so $Y = (Y \cdot X_1)X_1$ because Y is orthogonal to $X_2, \cdots, X_n$. Since $\|Y\| = 1 = \|X_1\|$, this implies that $|Y \cdot X_1| = 1$, so $Y \cdot X_1 = \pm 1$. Hence $Y = \pm X_1$.

5. b) $P = \frac{1}{\sqrt{2}}\begin{bmatrix} -1 & 1 & 0 \\ 0 & 0 & \sqrt{2} \\ 1 & 1 & 0 \end{bmatrix}$; $P^T A P = diag(-4, 10, 5)$.

d) $P = \frac{1}{\sqrt{182}}\begin{bmatrix} 2\sqrt{14} & 3\sqrt{13} & 3 \\ 0 & -\sqrt{13} & 13 \\ -3\sqrt{14} & 2\sqrt{13} & 2 \end{bmatrix}$; $P^T A P = diag(1, 0, 14)$.

f) $P = \frac{1}{2}\begin{bmatrix} 1 & -1 & 0 & \sqrt{2} \\ -1 & 1 & 0 & \sqrt{2} \\ -1 & -1 & \sqrt{2} & 0 \\ 1 & 1 & \sqrt{2} & 0 \end{bmatrix}$; $P^T A P = diag(0, -4, 8, 8)$.

6. If cP is orthogonal then $(cP)^{-1} = (cP)^T$, so $I = (cP)(cP)^T = c^2 PP^T = c^2 I$. Hence $c^2 = 1$, and $c = \pm 1$. Conversely, $-P$ is orthogonal because $(-P)^T(-P) = P^T P = I$.

8. b) Each row of P contains exactly one 1 because no two columns of I_n have a 1 in the same row. It follows that the rows of P are the rows of I_n in some order.

10. The (i, j)-entry of $A^T A$ equals $C_i^T C_j = C_i \cdot C_j$.

12. (ii) $\Rightarrow$ (iii). If $A^2 = I$, let λ be an eigenvalue of A, say $AX = \lambda X$ for some column $X \ne 0$. Then $X = IX = A^2 X = A(\lambda X) = \lambda(AX) = \lambda(\lambda X) = \lambda^2 X$. Since $X \ne 0$ this means that $\lambda^2 = 1$, so $\lambda = \pm 1$.

14. If $\lambda \ge 0$ for every eigenvalue λ of A, let $P^T A P = D = diag(\lambda_1, \lambda_2, \cdots, \lambda_n)$ where the λ_i are the eigenvalues of A. Since the λ_i are nonnegative by

hypothesis, write $D_1 = diag(\sqrt{\lambda_1}, \sqrt{\lambda_2}, \cdots, \sqrt{\lambda_n})$, so that $D_1^2 = D$. Now use the Hint.

16. b) If $A \overset{\circ}{\sim} B$, say $B = P^T A P$ where P is orthogonal, then $B^T = P^T A^T P$; that is, $A^T \overset{\circ}{\sim} B^T$.

d) If $A \overset{\circ}{\sim} B$, say $B = P^T A P$ where P is orthogonal, then A and B are similar (because $P^T = P^{-1}$) and so have the same eigenvalues by Theorem 6 §2.3.

18. b) If P is orthogonal and symmetric, then $P^{-1} = P^T = P$. If $E = \frac{1}{2}(I - P)$, then $E^2 = \frac{1}{4}(I - 2P + P^2) = \frac{1}{4}(I - 2P + I) = E$, and $E^T = \frac{1}{2}(I^T - P^T) = \frac{1}{2}(I - P) = E$.

20. b) If $A^m = 0$, let $AX = \lambda X$, $X \ne 0$. Then $A^2 X = A(\lambda X) = \lambda(AX) = \lambda^2 X$. Continue to get $A^k X = \lambda^k X$ for every $k \ge 1$. Then $\lambda^m X = A^m X = 0$, so $\lambda^m = 0$, $\lambda = 0$. Hence, by Theorem 7, let $P^T A P = U$ be upper triangular where P is orthogonal. Then $U^m = P^T A^m P = 0$. Because U is triangular, it follows that every element a on the main diagonal of U also satisfies $a^m = 0$, so $a = 0$. Hence U has zeros on the main diagonal.

22. Apply Theorem 7 to A^T, then transpose.

4.8 QUADRATIC FORMS

1. b) False. $\begin{bmatrix} 1 & 1 \\ 0 & 2 \end{bmatrix}$.

d) True. See the discussion following Theorem 3.

f) False. $\begin{bmatrix} 1 & 2 \\ 0 & 2 \end{bmatrix}$.

2. b) $\begin{bmatrix} 2 & 3 & 3 \\ 3 & 1 & -1 \\ 3 & -1 & 5 \end{bmatrix}$.

3. b) $y_1 = \frac{1}{\sqrt{5}}(x_1 - 2x_2)$, $y_2 = \frac{1}{\sqrt{5}}(2x_1 + x_2)$, $q = -2y_1^2 + 3y_2^2$.

d) $y_1 = \frac{1}{\sqrt{4+2\sqrt{2}}}[x_1 + (1 + \sqrt{2})x_2]$,
$y_2 = \frac{1}{\sqrt{4-2\sqrt{2}}}[x_1 + (1 - \sqrt{2})x_2]$,
$q = (1 + 2\sqrt{2})y_1^2 + (1 - 2\sqrt{2})y_2^2$.

f) $y_1 = \frac{1}{3}(2x_1 + x_2 + 2x_3)$, $y_2 = \frac{1}{\sqrt{5}}(x_1 - 2x_2)$,
$y_3 = \frac{1}{\sqrt{5}}(-2x_2 + x_3)$, $q = 9y_2^2 + 9y_3^2$.

4. b) Ellipse. $y_1 = \frac{1}{\sqrt{5}}(-2x_1 + x_2)$, $y_1 = \frac{1}{\sqrt{5}}(x_1 + 2x_2)$.

5. b) Maximum $\frac{1}{2}(-1 + 5\sqrt{2})$, Minimum $-\frac{1}{2}(1 + 5\sqrt{2})$.
d) Maximum $-1 + 2\sqrt{3}$, Minimum $-1 - 2\sqrt{3}$.

6. b) $U = \frac{\sqrt{3}}{3}\begin{bmatrix} 3 & -2 \\ 0 & \sqrt{2} \end{bmatrix}$. **d)** $U = \frac{\sqrt{5}}{5}\begin{bmatrix} 5 & 3 & -2 \\ 0 & 1 & 1 \\ 0 & 0 & \sqrt{15} \end{bmatrix}$.

8. b) $A = \begin{bmatrix} 3 & 2 \\ 2 & 1 \end{bmatrix}$ is not positive definite because $det A = -1$ is not positive (Theorem 4). However, $A^2 = \begin{bmatrix} 13 & 8 \\ 8 & 5 \end{bmatrix}$ is positive definite by Theorem 4 because $det A = 1 > 0$.

d) If $k \geq 3$ is odd and A^k is positive definite, we show that A^{k-2} is also positive definite. If $X \neq 0$ in $\mathbb{R}^n$, let $Y = A^{-1}X$ so that $Y \neq 0$ and $X = AY$. As before, the fact that A is symmetric gives
$X^T A^{k-2} X = (AY)^T A^{k-2}(AY) = Y^T A^k Y > 0$ because A^k is positive definite and $Y \neq 0$. Hence A^{k-2} is positive definite.

10. Let A and B be positive definite $n \times n$ matrices. If $X \neq 0$ in $\mathbb{R}^n$, then $X^T(A + B)X = X^T AX + X^T BX > 0$ because both $X^T AX > 0$ and $X^T BX > 0$. Hence $A + B$ is positive definite.

12. b) If $(A^T A)X = \lambda X$ where $X \neq 0$, then
$\|AX\|^2 = (AX)^T(AX) = X^T(A^T AX) = X^T(\lambda X) = \lambda \|X\|^2$.
Since $\|X\| \neq 0$, this gives $\lambda = \frac{\|AX\|^2}{\|X\|^2} \geq 0$.

14. Follow the Hint, and take $B = PD_0 P^T$.

16. b) Suppose A is positive definite with Cholesky factorization $A = U^T U$. Let D be the diagonal matrix with the same (positive) diagonal entries as U, and write $U_1 = D^{-1}U$. Since the diagonal entries of D^{-1} are the reciprocals of those of U, it follows that U_1 is unit upper triangular. But then $A = U^T U = (DU_1)^T(DU_1) = U_1^T D^2 U_1$ is a factorization of the desired type.

Conversely, suppose $A = U^T DU$ is such a factorization. If $X \neq 0$ in $\mathbb{R}^n$, then $X^T AX = (UX)^T D(UX) > 0$ because $UX \neq 0$ (as U is invertible) and D is positive definite (by Theorem 4). Hence A is positive definite. [Note that this shows that $U^T PU$ is positive definite whenever P is positive definite and U is invertible.]

18. b) We have $X = UY$, so
$q = X^T AX = (UY)^T A(UY) = Y^T(U^T AU)Y = Y^T BY$
where $B = U^T AU$.

4.9   LINEAR TRANSFORMATIONS

1. b) True. By Theorem 4.
   d) False. Consider the transformation in **b)** with $X = \vec{e}_1$ and $Y = \vec{e}_2$.
   f) True. If S and T have invertible standard matrices A and B, respectively, then $S \circ T$ has matrix AB, which is invertible.

2. If $X = (1 - f)Y + fZ$ where $0 \leq f \leq 1$, then
$T(X) = (1 - f)T(Y) + fT(Z)$.

4. The standard matrix is $A = \begin{bmatrix} I_m & 0 \end{bmatrix}_{m \times n}$ in block form.

6. b) Standard matrix $\begin{bmatrix} 4 & -2 & 0 & \frac{3}{2} \\ -4 & 3 & -1 & -\frac{3}{2} \end{bmatrix}$.

7. b) $T\begin{bmatrix} x_1 \\ x_2 \\ x_3 \end{bmatrix} = \frac{1}{9}\begin{bmatrix} 53x_1 - 47x_2 + 25x_3 \\ -29x_1 + 23x_2 + 41x_3 \\ -20x_1 - 4x_2 + 23x_3 \end{bmatrix}$

8. Since $X \neq 0$, the set $\{X\}$ is independent and so is part of a basis $\{X, X_2, \cdots, X_n\}$ of $\mathbb{R}^n$ by Theorem 3 §4.3. Now use Theorem 4.

10. Write $X = r_1 Y_1 + \cdots + r_k Y_k$ where each r_i is in $\mathbb{R}$. Hence $T(X) = r_1 T(Y_1) + \cdots + r_k T(Y_k) = r_1 0 + \cdots + r_k 0 = 0$ for every X in $\mathbb{R}^n$.

12. b) If X is in $kerT$, then
$X = 1_{\mathbb{R}^n}(X) = (S \circ T)(X) = S(T(X)) = S(0) = 0$.

14. b) Let $Y = T(X)$, X in $\mathbb{R}^n$.
By hypothesis, $X = r_1 X_1 + \cdots + r_k X_k$ for r_i in $\mathbb{R}$, so
$Y = T(X) = r_1 T(X_1) + \cdots + r_k T(X_k)$.
Hence $imT \subseteq span\{T(X_1), \cdots, T(X_k)\}$; the other inclusion follows from Theoreom 1 §4.1.

16. Using the notation of Theorem 9, show that
$[T(X + Y) - T(X) - T(Y)] \bullet T(F_i) = 0$ for each i.
Since $\{T(F_1), T(F_2), \cdots, T(F_n)\}$ is a basis of $\mathbb{R}^n$, we have $T(X + Y) = T(X) + T(Y)$.

18. b) If A and B are the (invertible) matrices of S and T, respectively, then the matrix of $S \circ T$ is AB which is invertible. Use Theorem 5.

20. $(T \circ T)(X) = T(T(X)) = A(AX) = A^2 X = AX = T(X)$ for all X in $\mathbb{R}^n$. So $T \circ T = T$.

22. $(T \circ Q_Y)(X) = T[Q_Y(X)] = T[X + Y] = T(X) + T(Y) = Q_{T(Y)}[T(X)] = (Q_{T(Y)} \circ T)(X)$ for all X.

24. Choose a unit vector $\vec{n}$ normal to the plane, and choose two orthogonal unit vectors $\vec{u}$ and $\vec{v}$ in the plane. Then $\mathcal{B} = \{\vec{n}, \vec{u}, \vec{v}\}$ is a basis of $\mathbb{R}^3$ (it is orthonormal),
$M_\mathcal{B}(T) = \begin{bmatrix} -1 & 0 & 0 \\ 0 & 1 & 0 \\ 0 & 0 & 1 \end{bmatrix}$ because $T(\vec{n}) = -\vec{n}, T(\vec{u}) = \vec{u}$,
$T(\vec{v}) = \vec{v}$, and $M_\mathcal{B}(T)$ is similar to the standard matrix of T.

26. By Lemma 4, $C_\mathcal{F}(X) = P^{-1}X$, so $AC_\mathcal{F}(X) = BC_\mathcal{F}(X)$ becomes $AP^{-1}X = BP^{-1}X$ for all X. Hence $AP^{-1} = BP^{-1}$ by Lemma 1, so $A = B$.

28. b) $\|(aT)(X)\|^2 = a^2 \|T(X)\|^2$ for all X in $\mathbb{R}^n$, so $\|T(X)\|^2 = \|X\|^2$ for all X if and only if $a^2 = 1$; that is, if and only if $a = \pm 1$.

30. 2) Given X in $\mathbb{R}^n$, write $X = T(Y)$ where Y is in $\mathbb{R}^n$. Then $T^{-1}(X) = T^{-1}[T(Y)] = Y$ by the preceding exercise. But then, $\|T^{-1}(X)\| = \|Y\| = \|T(Y)\| = \|X\|$, where $\|T(Y)\| = \|Y\|$ because T is an isometry. This shows that T^{-1} is an isometry.

32. Theorem 7 states that $C_\mathcal{F}[T(X)] = M_\mathcal{F}(T)C_\mathcal{F}(X)$ for all X in $\mathbb{R}^n$, and Theorem 6 states that $P_{\mathcal{G} \leftarrow \mathcal{F}}C_\mathcal{F}(X) = C_\mathcal{G}(X)$ for all X. By the Hint, we are to show that $P_{\mathcal{G} \leftarrow \mathcal{F}}M_\mathcal{F}(T) = M_\mathcal{G}(T)P_{\mathcal{G} \leftarrow \mathcal{F}}$. If X is arbitrary in $\mathbb{R}^n$, multiply the left side by $C_\mathcal{F}(X)$ to get:
$$P_{\mathcal{G} \leftarrow \mathcal{F}}M_\mathcal{F}(T)C_\mathcal{F}(X) = P_{\mathcal{G} \leftarrow \mathcal{F}}C_\mathcal{F}[T(X)] = C_\mathcal{G}[T(X)]$$
$$= M_\mathcal{G}(T)C_\mathcal{G}(X) = M_\mathcal{G}(T)P_{\mathcal{G} \leftarrow \mathcal{F}}C_\mathcal{F}(X).$$
Hence $[P_{\mathcal{G} \leftarrow \mathcal{F}}M_\mathcal{F}(T)]C_\mathcal{F}(X) = [M_\mathcal{G}(T)P_{\mathcal{G} \leftarrow \mathcal{F}}]C_\mathcal{F}(X)$ for all X in $\mathbb{R}^n$. Since we may "cancel" $C_\mathcal{F}(X)$ from both sides (by Exercise 26), the result follows.

4.10 COMPLEX MATRICES

1. b) False. $\frac{1}{\sqrt{2}}\begin{bmatrix} 1 & -1 \\ 1 & 1 \end{bmatrix}$ is unitary but not Hermitian.

d) True. This is part of Theorem 4.

f) True. If U and V are unitary, then
$(UV)^* = V^*U^* = V^{-1}U^{-1} = (UV)^{-1}$.

2. b) $\|Z\| = \sqrt{5+9+2} = 4$, $\|W\| = \sqrt{4+5+1} = \sqrt{10}$,
$\langle Z, W \rangle = 2 + 7i$, so not orthogonal.

d) $\|Z\| = \sqrt{5+25+5+4} = \sqrt{39}$,
$\|W\| = \sqrt{5+2+9+10} = \sqrt{26}$,
$\langle Z, W \rangle = 0$, so orthogonal.

3. b) Hermitian (and normal), not unitary.

d) Unitary (and normal), not Hermitian.

4. b) $U = \frac{1}{\sqrt{14}}\begin{bmatrix} -2 & 3-i \\ 3+i & 2 \end{bmatrix}$, $U^*ZU = \begin{bmatrix} -1 & 0 \\ 0 & 6 \end{bmatrix}$

d) $U = \frac{1}{\sqrt{3}}\begin{bmatrix} \sqrt{3} & 0 & 0 \\ 0 & 1+i & 1 \\ 0 & -1 & 1-i \end{bmatrix}$, $U^*ZU = \begin{bmatrix} 1 & 0 & 0 \\ 0 & 0 & 0 \\ 0 & 0 & 3 \end{bmatrix}$

6. Write $U = \begin{bmatrix} a & b \\ c & d \end{bmatrix}$ and suppose that $U^{-1}AU = T = \begin{bmatrix} p & z \\ 0 & q \end{bmatrix}$.
We have $AU = UT$ and comparing entries gives $-c = ap$
and $a = cp$. Hence $a(1 + p^2) = 0 = c(1 + p^2)$, so $a = 0 = c$
if p is real; contradiction. But p is indeed real because both
a and c are real and they are not both zero (U is invertible).

8. b) If H is Hermitian, then $H^* = H$, so it is clear that
$HH^* = H^*H$. Hence H is normal.

9. b) $U = diag(u_1, \cdots, u_n)$ is unitary if and only if $|u_i| = 1$
for each i.

10. b) If $ZZ^* = I$ and $H = Z^*Z$, then
$H^2 = Z^*ZZ^*Z = Z^*IZ = Z^*Z = H$.

12. Observe that $\langle X, Y \rangle = X^T \overline{Y}$ for all columns X and Y
in $\mathbb{C}^n$. We have $\langle X, Z^*Y \rangle = X^T \overline{(Z^*Y)} = X^T \overline{Z^*}\, \overline{Y}$.
But $\overline{Z^*} = \overline{\left[\overline{Z^T}\right]} = Z^T$, so we get
$\langle X, Z^*Y \rangle = X^T Z^T \overline{Y} = (ZX)^T \overline{Y} = \langle ZX, Y \rangle$.

14. Using Theorem 3: $Z^*(Z^{-1})^* = (Z^{-1}Z)^* = I^* = I$.

16. If G is both Hermitian and unitary, then $G^{-1} = G^* = G$,
so $G^2 = I$. Hence if $GX = \lambda X$ for some $X \neq 0$, then
$X = G^2X = G(\lambda X) = \lambda^2 X$. It follows that $\lambda^2 = 1$, so
$\lambda = \pm 1$.

18. Since $NN^* = N^*N$, Theorem 3 gives
$(zN)(zN)^* = z\bar{z}NN^* = \bar{z}zN^*N = \bar{z}N^*(zN) = (zN)^*(zN)$.

20. b) If $A = [a_{jk}]$ and $B = [b_{jk}]$, then $A + iB = 0$ becomes
$[a_{jk} + ib_{jk}] = 0$, whence $a_{jk} + ib_{jk} = 0$ for all j and k.
This forces $a_{jk} = 0 = b_{jk}$ for all j and k, and hence
$A = 0 = B$.

22. b) Let Z be nilpotent, say $Z^k = 0$ for some $k \geq 1$. The
polynomial $c_Z(x)$ has only the eigenvalues of Z as its
roots, and so its only root is 0. Hence $c_Z(x) = x^n$.

24. b) First $detZ = \lambda_1\lambda_2 \cdots \lambda_n$ by the Corollary to Schur's
theorem, and so $detZ$ is real by Theorem 4 (because
Z is Hermitian). Hence $det(Z^*) = det[(\overline{Z})^T] = det(\overline{Z}) = detZ$.

4.11 SINGULAR VALUE DECOMPOSITION

2. If $\sigma_1 \geq \cdots \geq \sigma_r$ are the nonzero singular values of A, write
$D = diag(\sigma_1, \cdots, \sigma_r)$. If A is $m \times n$, let $A = P\begin{bmatrix} D & 0 \\ 0 & 0 \end{bmatrix}_{m \times n} Q^T$
be a singular value decomposition of A. Then
$A^T = Q\begin{bmatrix} D^T & 0 \\ 0 & 0 \end{bmatrix}_{n \times m} P^T = Q\begin{bmatrix} D & 0 \\ 0 & 0 \end{bmatrix}_{n \times m} P^T$. It follows by
Theorem 2 that the entries of D are the singular values of A^T.

4. If $A = P\Sigma Q^T$ is a singular value decomposition of A then,
since the determinant of any orthogonal matrix is ± 1, we
have $detA = (\pm 1)\, det\Sigma$. Hence $|detA| = det\Sigma$ is the product of the singular values of A.

6. By Theorem 3 §4.4, $rankA = n$ if and only if A^TA is
invertible. But A^TA is invertible if and only if all its
eigenvalues are nonzero, and this holds if and only if the
singular values of A are all nonzero.

8. Let $\lambda_1, \cdots, \lambda_n$ be the eigenvalues of the symmetric
matrix A^TA, and observe that each $\lambda_i > 0$ by Example 2
and the fact that A is invertible. Since A^TA is symmetric,
let $Q^T(A^TA)Q = diag(\lambda_1, \cdots, \lambda_n)$ where Q is orthogonal
and (by changing the order of the columns of Q)
$\lambda_1 \geq \cdots \geq \lambda_n$. Hence $D = diag(\sqrt{\lambda_1}, \cdots, \sqrt{\lambda_n})$ has
positive entries and, writing $P = AQD^{-1}$, we have
$PDQ^T = (AQ)Q^T = A$. One verifies that $P^TP = I$.

10. If A is symmetric with (real) eigenvalues $\lambda_1, \cdots, \lambda_n$,
we show more generally that the singular values of A
are $|\lambda_1|, \cdots, |\lambda_n|$. If $AX = \lambda_iX$ where $X \neq 0$, then
$(A^TA)X = A^2X = A(\lambda_iX) = \lambda_i(AX) = \lambda_i^2X$. This shows
that $|\lambda_i| = \sqrt{\lambda_i^2}$ is a singular value of A. Conversely,
observe that $x^2I - A^2 = -(xI - A)(-xI - A)$, so that
$c_{A^2}(x^2) = (-1)^n c_A(x)c_A(-x)$. Now suppose that σ is a
singular value of A, that is σ is an eigenvalue of $A^TA = A^2$.
Hence $0 = c_{A^2}(\sigma^2) = (-1)^n c_A(\sigma)c_A(-\sigma)$, so either
$c_A(\sigma) = 0$ or $c_A(-\sigma) = 0$. In other words, either $\sigma = \lambda_i$
or $-\sigma = \lambda_i$ for some i; that is, $\sigma = |\lambda_i|$ for some i.

12. Let λ be an eigenvalue of G. Then $|\lambda| = 1$ because G is
orthogonal (by Theorem 3 §4.7), so $\lambda = 1$ because $\lambda \geq 0$
(G is positive definite). Since G is diagonalizable (being
symmetric), let $P^{-1}GP = D$ where D is diagonal. But
$D = I$ because the entries of D are eigenvalues of G, so
$G = PDP^{-1} = I$.

14. If λ is an eigenvalue of kG, then $(kG)X = \lambda X$ for some $X \neq 0$. Hence $GX = \frac{\lambda}{k}X$, so $\frac{\lambda}{k}$ is an eigenvalue of G. Hence $\frac{\lambda}{k} \geq 0$ because G is positive semidefinite, so $\lambda \geq 0$ because $k > 0$. Since kG is symmetric (because G is symmetric), we are done.

16. $GP = \begin{bmatrix} 0 & \sqrt{2} \\ 0 & \sqrt{2} \end{bmatrix} = GQ$, P and Q are orthogonal, and G is positive semidefinite (eigenvalues are 0 and 2).

18. b) Let $\{Q_1, \cdots, Q_n\}$ be an orthonormal basis of $\mathbb{R}^n$. Given $X = r_1Q_1 + \cdots + r_nQ_n$, r_i in $\mathbb{R}$, then $\|X\|^2 = \Sigma_i r_i^2$. Since $BX = \Sigma_i r_i BQ_i = \Sigma_i r_i \lambda_i Q_i$, a similar computation gives $X^TBX = \Sigma_i r_i^2 \lambda_i$. Hence the fact that $\lambda_i \geq \lambda_n$ for each i gives $X^TBX \geq \lambda_n\|X\|^2$. It follows that $R(X) \geq \lambda_n$. Similarly, $R(X) \leq \lambda_1$.

CHAPTER 5

Vector Spaces

5.1 EXAMPLES AND BASIC PROPERTIES

1. b) True. Every multiple of any nonzero vector.
d) True. $1 = \sin^2 x + \cos^2 x$ for all real x.
f) False. $\frac{1}{2} \cdot 3$ not in this set.
h) False. $\mathbb{R}$ has no proper subspaces.

2. b) Not a vector space. Axiom S5 fails (and no others).
d) Not a vector space. Axioms S4 and S5 fail (and no others).
f) Not a vector space. Axioms S4 and S5 fail (and no others).

3. b) This is a vector space. The axioms are rules of complex arithmetic.
d) Not a vector space. Axioms A1, A4, A5, and S1 all fail.
f) Not a vector space. Axiom S3 fails (and no others).
h) Not a vector space. Axioms S2 and S3 fail (and no others).

4. The zero vector is $[0 \ -1]$, the negative of $[x \ y]$ is $[-x \ -2-y]$.

6. b) Not a subspace. **d)** Subspace.
f) Subspace.

7. b) Subspace. **d)** Subspace.
f) Not a subspace.

8. b) Subspace. **d)** Not a subspace.
f) Subspace. **h)** Subspace.

9. Write $U = span\{u, w\}$.
b) v_1 is in U; v_2 is not in U.
d) v_1 is not in U; v_2 is in U.
f) v_1 is in U; v_2 is not in U.

10. b) No. 1 is not in the span of these vectors.

11. b) $x = 2t$, $y = 0$, $z = t$, t arbitrary.

12. b) If $Y_0 = [y_1 \ \cdots \ y_n]$ and $y_k \neq 0$, and if $\{E_1, \cdots, E_n\}$ is the standard basis of $\mathbb{R}^m$, then $E_j = AY_0$ where A has (i, j)-entry y_k^{-1} and all other entries zero. So $E_j \in U$, whence $\mathbb{R}^m \subseteq U$.

14. b) If $v + v' = 0$ then $-v + (v + v') = -v + 0$, so $(-v + v) + v' = -v$. Thus $0 + v' = -v$, that is $v' = -v$.

16. $a(-v) = a[(-1)v] = [a(-1)]v = (-a)v$.

18. Let $U \neq 0$ be a subspace of V. If $0 \neq u \in U$, then $u = av$, $a \in \mathbb{R}$, so $v = a^{-1}u \in \mathbb{R}u$. Hence $\mathbb{R}v \subseteq U$, so $\mathbb{R}v = U$.

20. b) $f_a = af_1$ is in $\mathbb{R}f_1$ for all a, so $U \subseteq \mathbb{R}f_1$. Clearly $\mathbb{R}f_1 \subseteq U$.

22. b) If $a \neq 0$, then $v - w = 0$, so $v = w$.

24. b) Write $U = span\{1 + x^3, x + x^2, 1 + x + x^2, 2x - x^3\}$. Then $1 = (1 + x + x^2) - (x + x^2)$ is in U; so $x^3 = (1 + x^3) - 1$ is in U, whence $x = \frac{1}{2}\{(2x - x^3) + x^3\}$ is in U, and finally $x^2 = (x + x^2) - x$ is in U. Hence $\mathbb{P}_3 = span\{1, x, x^2, x^3\} \subseteq U$. Clearly $U \subseteq \mathbb{P}_3$.

26. Since $Y \neq 0$, let $AY \neq 0$ with $A \in \mathbb{M}_{m,n}$ (if entry j of Y is nonzero, let the $(1, j)$-entry of A be 1 and let the other entries be 0). Now suppose that $\mathbb{M}_{m,n} = span\{A_1, \cdots, A_k\}$, so that $A = r_1A_1 + \cdots + r_kA_k$, $r_i \in \mathbb{R}$. Then $AY = r_1A_1Y + \cdots + r_kA_kY = 0$ by hypothesis, a contradiction. Hence $\mathbb{M}_{m,n} \neq span\{A_1, \cdots, A_k\}$.

28. If $\mathcal{F}$ is a finite set of polynomials, let n be the maximum of the degrees of the polynomials in $\mathcal{F}$. Then each of these polynomials is in $\mathbb{P}_n$, so $span\{\mathcal{F}\} \subseteq \mathbb{P}_n$. Hence $span\{\mathcal{F}\}$ cannot equal $\mathbb{P}$.

30. Compute $(1 + 1)(v + w)$ twice, first using Axiom S2 first, and then using Axiom S3 first.

5.2 INDEPENDENCE AND DIMENSION

1. b) True.   **d)** False.   **f)** False.
    h) False.   **j)** True.   **l)** False.

2. b) Independent.   **d)** Not independent.
    f) Independent.   **h)** Independent.

3. b) Dimension 2.   **d)** Dimension 3. **f)** Dimension 2.
    h) Dimension 3.   **j)** Dimension 2. **l)** Dimension 3.

4. b) If $\mathbb{P}_n = span\{p_1(x), \cdots, p_k(x)\}$ where the coefficients of each $p_i(x)$ sum to zero, then $p_i(1) = 0$ for all i. But then $p(1) = 0$ for every polynomial $p(x)$ in $span\{p_1(x), \cdots, p_k(x)\} = \mathbb{P}_n$, a contradiction.

6. b) Let $z = a + bi$ where $a \neq 0$ and $b \neq 0$ by hypothesis. If $rz + s\bar{z} = 0$, r, s in $\mathbb{R}$, then equating real and imaginary parts gives $(r + s)a = 0$ and $(r - s)b = 0$. Thus $r + s = 0 = r - s$, which implies that $r = s = 0$. Thus $\{z, \bar{z}\}$ is independent, and so is a basis of $\mathbb{C}$ because $dim(\mathbb{C}) = 2$.

8. As V is finite dimensional, let $V = span\{v_1, \cdots, v_m\}$. Then each v_i is a linear combination of a finite set $\mathcal{S}_i$ of vectors in $\mathcal{S}$. Hence $\mathcal{S}_1 \cup \mathcal{S}_2 \cup \cdots \cup \mathcal{S}_m$ is a finite spanning set of V, and so contains a basis of V by Theorem 3.

10. If $rA + sB = 0$, r, s in $\mathbb{R}$, transpose to get $rA - sB = 0$. Adding these equations gives $2rA = 0$, whence $r = 0$ because $A \neq 0$. Then $sB = 0$ from the first equation, so $s = 0$ because $B \neq 0$.

12. b) Given C in $\mathbb{M}_{m,n}$, the matrix $P^{-1}CQ^{-1}$ is also in $\mathbb{M}_{m,n}$, so write $P^{-1}CQ^{-1} = s_1 A_1 + \cdots + s_k A_k$. Then $C = s_1 P A_1 Q + \cdots + s_k P A_k Q$, $s_i \in \mathbb{R}$, and it follows that $span\{PA_1 Q, \cdots, PA_k Q\} = \mathbb{M}_{m,n}$.

14. Let $p(x)$ and $q(x)$ have, respectively, degrees n and m, and leading coefficients $a_n \neq 0$ and $b_m \neq 0$. If $rp(x) + sq(x) + tp(x)q(x) = 0$, r, s, t in $\mathbb{R}$, the highest power of x on the left is x^{m+n}, and so its coefficient $ta_n b_m = 0$. Hence $t = 0$, so $rp(x) + sq(x) = 0$. Now $r = s = 0$ by hypothesis.

16. b) If $r(a + bx) + s(a_1 + b_1 x) = 0$, then $ra + sa_1 = 0 = rb + sb_1$, so $r[a \ \ b]^T + s[a_1 \ \ b_1]^T = 0$. Hence $r = s = 0$ because $\{[a \ \ b]^T, [a_1 \ \ b_1]^T\}$ is independent. This proves that $\{a + bx, a_1 + b_1 x\}$ is independent, and so is a basis of $\mathbb{P}_1$, by Theorem 4 because $dim(\mathbb{P}_1) = 2$.

18. $\left\{ \begin{bmatrix} 1 & 0 \\ 0 & 0 \end{bmatrix}, \begin{bmatrix} 0 & 0 \\ 0 & 1 \end{bmatrix}, \begin{bmatrix} 1 & 1 \\ 0 & 0 \end{bmatrix}, \begin{bmatrix} 1 & 0 \\ 1 & 0 \end{bmatrix} \right\}$.

20. b) Show that $O_n = span\{x, x^3, x^5, \cdots\}$ by comparing coefficients in $p(x) = -p(-x)$. If $n = 2k$ is even, then $O_n = span\{x, x^3, x^5, \cdots, x^{2k-1}\}$ so $dim(O_n) = k = \frac{n}{2}$. If $n = 2k + 1$ is odd, then $O_n = span\{x, x^3, x^5, \cdots, x^{2k+1}\}$, so $dim(O_n) = k + 1 = \frac{n+1}{2}$.

22. If $U \neq 0$ and $U \neq V$, then $dim U = 1$. So $U = \mathbb{R}v$ where $\{v\}$ is any basis of U. If $V = \mathbb{R}^2$, this says that the proper subspaces U are lines $U = \mathbb{R}v$ (with direction vector v).

24. b) Yes. If $r(u + v) + s(v + w) + t(w + u) = 0$, then $0 = r + t = r + s = s + t$, so $r = s = t = 0$.
    d) Yes. If $r(u + v) + s(v + w) + t(w + u) + x(z + u) = 0$, then $r + t + x = 0$, $r + s = 0$, $s + t = 0$ and $x = 0$, whence $r = s = t = x = 0$.

26. $\{v\}$ is independent because $v \neq 0$, so Theorem 3 applies.

28. If $r_1(w + v_1) + r_2(w + v_2) + \cdots + r_k(w + v_k) = 0$, $(r_1 + r_2 + \cdots + r_k)w + r_1 v_1 + r_2 v_2 + \cdots + r_k v_k = 0$. Hence each $r_i = 0$ by Lemma 1.

30. Let $U = span\{v_1, v_2, \cdots, v_k\}$. If $U \neq V$, choose $v \in V$ such that $v \notin U$. Then $\{v, v_1, v_2, \cdots, v_k\}$ is independent by Lemma 1, contrary to the maximality of the independent set $\{v_1, v_2, \cdots, v_k\}$.

32. Let $\{v_1, v_2, \cdots, v_k\}$ be a basis of U, and extend it to a basis $\{v_1, v_2, \cdots, v_k, v_{k+1}, \cdots, v_m\}$ of W by Theorem 3. Take $X = span\{v_1, v_2, \cdots, v_k, v_{k+1}, \cdots, v_l\}$.

34. b) We prove that $x_k = x_0 e_k + x_1 f_k$ for all $k \geq 0$ by induction on k. It holds for $k = 0$ and for $k = 1$ by the choice of $e_0, e_1, f_0,$ and f_1. If it holds for k and $k + 1$, then one verifies that $x_{k+2} = ax_k + bx_{k+1} = x_0 e_{k+1} + x_1 f_{k+1}$, so the result holds for $k + 1$, and the induction goes through.

5.3 LINEAR TRANSFORMATIONS

1. b) False.   **d)** True.   **f)** False.
    h) True.   **j)** True.   **l)** False.

2. b) False.   **d)** True.
    f) False.   **h)** False.

3. b) $T(A + B) = P(A + B)Q = PAQ + PBQ = T(A) + T(B)$, and $T(rA) = P(rA)Q = rPAQ = rT(A)$.
    d) $T(X + X_1) = Y \bullet (X + X_1) = Y \bullet X + Y \bullet X_1 = T(X) + T(X_1)$, and $T(rX) = Y \bullet (rX) = r(Y \bullet X) = rT(X)$.
    f) Adding two linear combinations adds the coefficients of e_1; and multiplying a linear combination by r multiplies the coefficient of e_1 by r.
    h) Adding two matrices adds their second columns; and multiplying a matrix by r multiplies its second column by r.

4. b) Not linear. $rank(A + B)$ need not equal $rankA + rankB$. For example $A = \begin{bmatrix} 1 & 0 \\ 0 & 1 \end{bmatrix}$ and $B = \begin{bmatrix} 0 & 1 \\ 1 & 0 \end{bmatrix}$. Note that $rank(rA) = r \cdot rankA$ always holds.

5. b) $T(v) = \begin{bmatrix} a + c \\ 2a + b \end{bmatrix}$.

6. $T(3e + f) = 18e - 3f$ and $T(f) = 3e$.

8. $T(\mathbf{v} - \mathbf{v}_1) = T[\mathbf{v} + (-1)\mathbf{v}_1]$ Definition of subtraction
$= T(\mathbf{v}) + T[(-1)\mathbf{v}_1]$ Axiom T1
$= T(\mathbf{v}) + (-1)T(\mathbf{v}_1)$ Axiom T2
$= T(\mathbf{v}) - T(\mathbf{v}_1).$ Definition of subtraction

10. b) T is clearly a transformation $\mathbb{F}[0, 1] \to \mathbb{R}$; it is linear by properties of the integral.

12. (b)$\Rightarrow$(c). Given any vector $\mathbf{v}$ in V, $T(\mathbf{v})$ is in $imT = \{\mathbf{0}\}$, so $T(\mathbf{v}) = \mathbf{0}$. Thus $T = 0$.

14. b) $imT = \{T(X) \mid X \text{ in } \mathbb{R}^n\} = \{r_1\mathbf{v}_1 + \cdots + r_n\mathbf{v}_n \mid r_i \text{ in } \mathbb{R}\}$
$= span\{\mathbf{v}_1, \cdots, \mathbf{v}_n\}$. So T is onto if and only if $imT = V$, if and only if $\{\mathbf{v}_1, \cdots, \mathbf{v}_n\}$ spans V.

15. b) Let $\{\mathbf{b}_1, \cdots, \mathbf{b}_k\}$ be a basis of U, and extend it to a basis $\{\mathbf{b}_1, \cdots, \mathbf{b}_k, \mathbf{c}_1, \cdots, \mathbf{c}_m\}$ of V. Define $S : V \to V$ by $S(\mathbf{b}_i) = \mathbf{b}_i$ for each i and $S(\mathbf{c}_j) = \mathbf{0}$ for all j.
If $\mathbf{v} = r_1\mathbf{b}_1 + \cdots + r_k\mathbf{b}_k + s_1\mathbf{c}_1 + \cdots + s_m\mathbf{c}_m$,
then $S(\mathbf{v}) = r_1\mathbf{b}_1 + \cdots + r_k\mathbf{b}_k$ is in U. Thus $imS \subseteq U$. But each $\mathbf{b}_i = S(\mathbf{b}_i)$ is in imS, so $U \subseteq imS$ because $U = span\{\mathbf{b}_1, \cdots, \mathbf{b}_k\}$.

16. T is onto because, given r in $\mathbb{R}$, $r = tr(A)$ where A has $(1, 1)$-entry r and all other entries 0. So the Dimension theorem gives $dim(\mathbb{M}_{n, n}) = dim(kerT) + dim(imT)$, that is $n^2 = dim(kerT) + 1$.

18. If the system is $AX = 0$ where A is $m \times n$, define $T : \mathbb{R}^n \to \mathbb{R}^m$ by $T(X) = AX$. Then T is linear and $kerT$ is the space of all solutions. The Dimension theorem gives $n = dim(\mathbb{R}^n) = dim(kerT) + dim(imT) \leq dim(kerT) + m$ because $imT \subseteq \mathbb{R}^m$. Hence $dim(kerT) \geq n - m > 0$ by hypothesis, so $kerT \neq 0$. This means that there are non-trivial solutions to $AX = 0$.

20. Define $T : \mathbb{M}_{n,n} \to \mathbb{M}_{n,n}$ by $T(A) = A - A^T$. By Example 11, $kerT = U$ and $imT = W$. Thus the Dimension theorem gives $n^2 = dim(\mathbb{M}_{n,n}) = dimU + dimW$.

22. Define $T : \mathbb{M}_{n,n} \to \mathbb{M}_{n,n}$ by $T(B) = B^T - 3B$. Then T is linear (verify) and we claim that T is one-to-one. For if $T(B) = 0$ then $B^T = 3B$, whence $B = (B^T)^T = (3B)^T = 3B^T = 9B$, so $B = 0$. Hence T is onto (Corollary to the Dimension theorem) so every matrix A in $\mathbb{M}_{n,n}$ has the form $A = T(B) = B^T - 3B$ for some $B \in \mathbb{M}_{n,n}$.

24. If $D : \mathbb{P}_n \to \mathbb{P}_{n-1}$ denotes differentiation, then $T(x^k) = kx^{k-1} = D(x^k)$ for each $k = 0, 1, 2, \cdots n$. [If $k = 0$, this is $T(1) = 0 = D(1)$.] Hence $T = D$ by Theorem 2.

26. b) Suppose that $T : \mathbb{P}_n \to \mathbb{R}$ is linear and satisfies $T(x^k) = a^k$ for each $k \geq 0$. If we define $a = T(x)$, then $T(x^k) = a^k = E_a(x^k)$ for all $k \geq 1$. Moreover, $T(1) = T(x^0) = a^0 = 1 = E_a(1)$. Hence T and E_a agree on the basis $\{1, x, x^2, \cdots, x^n\}$, and so $T = E_a$ by Theorem 2.

28. b) If $T : V \to W$ is onto, then $dimV = dim(kerT) + dim(imT) = dim(kerT) + dim(W) \geq dimW$. Conversely, if $m = dimW \leq dimV = n$, let $\{\mathbf{w}_1, \cdots, \mathbf{w}_m\}$ be a basis of W, and let $\{\mathbf{v}_1, \cdots, \mathbf{v}_m, \mathbf{v}_{m+1}, \cdots, \mathbf{v}_n\}$ be a basis of V. Define $T : V \to W$ by $T(\mathbf{v}_i) = \mathbf{w}_i$ for $1 \leq i \leq m$ and $T(\mathbf{v}_j) = \mathbf{0}$ for $m < j \leq n$. Then T is onto (if $\mathbf{w}$ is in W, then $\mathbf{w} = r_1\mathbf{w}_1 + \cdots + r_m\mathbf{w}_m = r_1T(\mathbf{v}_1) + \cdots + r_mT(\mathbf{v}_m) = T(r_1\mathbf{v}_1 + \cdots + r_m\mathbf{v}_m) \in imT$. Since $\mathbf{w}$ was arbitrary in W, it follows that $imT = W$.

5.4 ISOMORPHISMS AND MATRICES

1. b) True. **d)** False. **f)** True. **h)** False.

2. b) $T^{-1}(z) = \bar{z}$ **d)** $T^{-1}\{[r \ \ s]^T\} = r + (s - r)x$
f) $T^{-1}(\mathbf{v}) = \frac{1}{k}\mathbf{v}$
h) $T^{-1}[x \ \ y]^T = [ky - x \ \ y]^T$. Here $T^2 = 1_{\mathbb{R}^2}$ so $T^{-1} = T$.

4. $T(x) = 2^x$.

6. b) $C_{\mathcal{B}}(\mathbf{v}) = [1 \ \ 0 \ \ 1 \ \ -2]^T$.

7. b) $\begin{bmatrix} 1 & 0 & 0 & 0 \\ 0 & 0 & 1 & 0 \\ 0 & 1 & 0 & 0 \\ 0 & 0 & 0 & 1 \end{bmatrix}$

8. b) $T\begin{bmatrix} x \\ y \\ z \end{bmatrix} = \begin{bmatrix} x & -x + 2y + z \\ y + 2z & x \end{bmatrix}$

10. $M_{\mathcal{E}\mathcal{B}}(T) = [C_{\mathcal{E}}[T(\mathbf{b}_1)] \quad C_{\mathcal{E}}[T(\mathbf{b}_2)] \quad \cdots \quad C_{\mathcal{E}}[T(\mathbf{b}_n)]]$
$= [T(\mathbf{b}_1) \quad T(\mathbf{b}_2) \quad \cdots \quad T(\mathbf{b}_n)]$.

12. $M_{\mathcal{E}\mathcal{D}}(1_{\mathbb{R}^n}) = [C_{\mathcal{E}}(\mathbf{b}_1) \quad C_{\mathcal{E}}(\mathbf{b}_2) \quad \cdots \quad C_{\mathcal{E}}(\mathbf{b}_n)]$
$= [\mathbf{b}_1 \quad \mathbf{b}_2 \quad \cdots \quad \mathbf{b}_n] = U.$

14. b) Given $\mathbf{v}$ in V, we have $(S \circ T)(\mathbf{v}) = (S \circ T_1)(\mathbf{v})$, that is $S[T(\mathbf{v})] = S[T_1(\mathbf{v})]$. Since S is one-to-one, this gives $T(\mathbf{v}) = T_1(\mathbf{v})$, proving that $T = T_1$.

16. If $S \circ T = 1_V$, then $S \circ T$ is one-to-one and onto, so (Exercise 15) T is one-to-one and S is onto. But then S and T are both isomorphisms by Theorem 3. Thus $S \circ T = 1_V$ gives $S \circ T \circ T^{-1} = 1_V \circ T^{-1}$; so $S \circ 1_W = T^{-1}$, that is $S = T^{-1}$. But then $T \circ S = T \circ T^{-1} = 1_W$.

18. If $T : V \to W$ is one-to-one and $\mathcal{B} = \{\mathbf{b}_1, \cdots, \mathbf{b}_n\}$ is a basis of V, Then $\{T(\mathbf{b}_1), \cdots, T(\mathbf{b}_n)\}$ is independent (verify), so extend it to a basis $\mathcal{D} = \{T(\mathbf{b}_1), \cdots, T(\mathbf{b}_n), \mathbf{d}_1, \cdots, \mathbf{d}_m\}$ of W. Now define $S : W \to V$ by $S[T(\mathbf{b}_i)] = \mathbf{b}_i$ for $1 \leq i \leq n$ and $S(\mathbf{d}_j) = \mathbf{0}$ for $1 \leq j \leq m$. Show that $S \circ T$ and 1_V agree on the basis $\mathcal{B}$, so $S \circ T = 1_V$.

20. b) If U^{-1} exists, then $(S_U)^{-1} = S_{U^{-1}}$.

22. Equate columns in $M_{\mathcal{D}\mathcal{B}}(T) = M_{\mathcal{D}\mathcal{B}}(T_1)$ to get $C_{\mathcal{D}}[T(\mathbf{b}_j)] = C_{\mathcal{D}}[T_1(\mathbf{b}_j)]$ for each j. Use the fact that $C_{\mathcal{D}}$ is one-to-one.

24. Use the Hint.

25. **b)** If $A \to B$ by row operations, then $B = UA$ where $U = E_k \cdots E_2 E_1$. Conversely, if $B = UA$ where U is invertible, then $U \to I_m$ so $U = E_k \cdots E_2 E_1$ by Theorem 1 §1.6. But then $B = E_k \cdots E_2 E_1 A$ so $B \to A$.

5.5 LINEAR OPERATORS AND SIMILARITY

1. **b)** True. **d)** True. **f)** False. **h)** False.

2. **b)** Invertible because $M_{\mathcal{B}}(T)$ is invertible (determinant 4).

4. $T^{-1}(2x - 3) = 5 + 4x$.

6. $\mathcal{B} = \{E_{11}, E_{12}, E_{21}, E_{22}\}$.

8. **b)** No because $M_{\mathcal{B}}(D)$ is not invertible. Alternatively, $D(1) = 0$ so $1 \in \ker D$.

10. **b)** $T^{-1}(\mathbf{b}_2) = \mathbf{b}_1 - \mathbf{b}_3$.

12. Define T so that $T(\mathbf{b}_j)$ has column j of A as its $\mathcal{B}$-coordinate vector.

14. $M_{\mathcal{B}}(T) = \begin{bmatrix} 1 & 1 \\ 0 & -1 \end{bmatrix}$.

16. $M_{\mathcal{B}}(T) = \begin{bmatrix} k+1 & 0 & 0 & 0 \\ 0 & k+1 & 0 & 0 \\ 0 & 0 & k+1 & 0 \\ 0 & 0 & 0 & 1-k \end{bmatrix}$.

18. If $\mathcal{B}$ is any basis of V, then $\det T = \det[M_{\mathcal{B}}(T)]$ for any operator $T : V \to V$. Hence Theorem 1 gives $\det(S \circ T) = \det[M_{\mathcal{B}}(S \circ T)] = \det[M_{\mathcal{B}}(S) M_{\mathcal{B}}(T)] = \det[M_{\mathcal{B}}(S)] \det[M_{\mathcal{B}}(T)] = \det S \det T$.

20. **b)** Assume that $\ker S = \ker T$, and let $\mathcal{B} = \{\mathbf{b}_1, \cdots, \mathbf{b}_m, \mathbf{b}_{m+1}, \cdots, \mathbf{b}_n\}$ be a basis of V such that $\{\mathbf{b}_{m+1}, \cdots, \mathbf{b}_n\}$ is a basis of $\ker S = \ker T$. Then $\{S(\mathbf{b}_1), \cdots, S(\mathbf{b}_m)\}$ is independent (verify), so we enlarge it to a basis $\mathcal{D} = \{S(\mathbf{b}_1), \cdots, S(\mathbf{b}_m), \mathbf{d}_{m+1}, \cdots, \mathbf{d}_n\}$ of V. Similarly construct a basis $\mathcal{F} = \{T(\mathbf{b}_1), \cdots, T(\mathbf{b}_m), \mathbf{f}_{m+1}, \cdots, \mathbf{f}_n\}$ of V, and define R on the basis $\mathcal{D}$ by setting $R[S(\mathbf{b}_i)] = T(\mathbf{b}_i)$ for $1 \leq i \leq m$, and $R(\mathbf{d}_j) = \mathbf{f}_j$ for $m < j \leq n$. Then R is an isomorphism because it carries the basis $\mathcal{D}$ to the basis $\mathcal{F}$, and $R \circ S = T$ because they agree on the basis $\mathcal{B}$ (verify).

5.6 INVARIANT SUBSPACES

1. **b)** True. If $\mathbf{w}$ is in $\mathrm{im}\,T$, say $\mathbf{w} = T(\mathbf{v})$, then $T(\mathbf{w}) = T[T(\mathbf{v})]$ is also in $\mathrm{im}\,T$.

d) True. If $\mathbf{u} \in U$, then $\mathbf{u} = \mathbf{u} + \mathbf{0}$ is in $U + W$, so $U \subseteq U + W$. Similarly $W \subseteq U + W$. On the other hand, if $U \subseteq Y$ and $W \subseteq Y$ where Y is a subspace, then $\mathbf{u} + \mathbf{w}$ is in Y for all $\mathbf{u} \in U$ and $\mathbf{w} \in W$, that is $U + W \subseteq Y$.

f) False. If $T : \mathbb{M}_{2,2} \to \mathbb{M}_{2,2}$ is defined by $T(A) = A^T$, then T is an isomorphism (in fact $T^{-1} = T$) but $U = \{A \mid A^T = A\}$ is a T-invariant subspace for which $U \neq 0$ and $U \neq \mathbb{M}_{2,2}$.

h) True. If $\mathbb{R}\mathbf{v}$ is T-invariant, then $T(\mathbf{v})$ is in $\mathbb{R}\mathbf{v}$, so $T(\mathbf{v}) = \lambda\mathbf{v}$ for some λ in $\mathbb{R}$.

2. Since $\mathcal{B}$ is a basis of V, show that $T^2 = T$ by showing that $T^2(\mathbf{b}_i) = T(\mathbf{b}_i)$ for every $\mathbf{b}_i$ in $\mathcal{B}$. We have $E_1(T) = \mathrm{span}\{\mathbf{b}_1, \mathbf{b}_2 + 2\mathbf{b}_4\}$; extend $\{\mathbf{b}_1, \mathbf{b}_2 + 2\mathbf{b}_4\}$ to a basis $\mathcal{C}$ of V, say $\mathcal{C} = \{\mathbf{b}_1, \mathbf{b}_2 + 2\mathbf{b}_4, \mathbf{b}_3, \mathbf{b}_4\}$ (verify that $\mathcal{C}$ is independent, hence a basis because $\dim V = 4$). Then

$$M_{\mathcal{C}}(T) = \begin{bmatrix} 1 & 0 & 1 & 0 \\ 0 & 1 & 0 & 0 \\ 0 & 0 & 0 & 0 \\ 0 & 0 & 0 & 0 \end{bmatrix}.$$

4. **b)** The restriction of T to the T-invariant subspace $E_\lambda(T)$ is the scalar operator λ.

6. **b)** $\{1, x - x^2\}$ is a basis of U and $\{1 + x, x^3\}$ is a basis of W, and one verifies that $\{1, x - x^2, 1 + x, x^3\}$ is a basis of $\mathbb{P}_3$ — verifying independence is easiest. So Theorem 3 applies.

8. **b)** Let $\{\mathbf{v}_1, \mathbf{v}_2, \cdots, \mathbf{v}_n\}$ be a basis of V and, by hypothesis, let $T(\mathbf{v}_1) = \lambda\mathbf{v}_1$ and, given $i > 1$, let $T(\mathbf{v}_i) = \mu\mathbf{v}_i$. Then $T(\mathbf{v}_1 + \mathbf{v}_i) = \gamma(\mathbf{v}_1 + \mathbf{v}_i)$ for some $\gamma \in \mathbb{R}$, so $\lambda\mathbf{v}_1 + \mu\mathbf{v}_i = T(\mathbf{v}_1) + T(\mathbf{v}_i) = T(\mathbf{v}_1 + \mathbf{v}_i) = \gamma(\mathbf{v}_1 + \mathbf{v}_i) = \gamma\mathbf{v}_1 + \gamma\mathbf{v}_i$. The fact that $\{\mathbf{v}_1, \mathbf{v}_i\}$ is independent shows that $\lambda = \gamma$ and $\mu = \gamma$, whence $\lambda = \mu$. But then $T(\mathbf{v}_i) = \lambda\mathbf{v}_i$ holds for every i. Now show that $T(\mathbf{v}) = \lambda\mathbf{v}$ holds for every vector $\mathbf{v}$ in V.

10. **b)** We are assuming that $W_1 \subseteq W$. If w is in W then, since $V = U + W_1$, write $w = u + w_1$, u in U and w_1 in W_1. Then $w - w_1 = u$ is in U (right side) and in W (left side as $W_1 \subseteq W$), so $w - w_1$ is in $U \cap W = (\mathbf{0})$. Hence $w = w_1$ is in W_1, and it follows that $W \subseteq W_1$. Since $W_1 \subseteq W$, this shows that $W = W_1$.

12. Consider $U + W = U \oplus W$, a subspace of V. Then Theorem 4 gives $\dim(U \oplus W) = \dim U + \dim W = \dim V$ by hypothesis, so $U \oplus W = V$.

14. **b)** By a), $E_\lambda(T) \cap E_\mu(T) = \{\mathbf{0}\}$. If $\dim\{E_\lambda(T)\} + \dim\{E_\mu(T)\} = n$, then $V = E_\lambda(T) \oplus E_\mu(T)$ by Exercise 12. If $\mathcal{C} = \{\mathbf{c}_1, \mathbf{c}_2, \cdots, \mathbf{c}_k\}$ and $\mathcal{D} = \{\mathbf{d}_{k+1}, \mathbf{d}_{k+2}, \cdots, \mathbf{d}_n\}$ are bases of $E_\lambda(T)$ and $E_\mu(T)$ respectively, then $M_{\mathcal{C}}(T) = \lambda I_k$ and $M_{\mathcal{D}}(T) = \mu I_{n-k}$. Moreover, $\mathcal{B} = \{\mathbf{c}_1, \mathbf{c}_2, \cdots, \mathbf{c}_k, \mathbf{d}_{k+1}, \mathbf{d}_{k+2}, \cdots, \mathbf{d}_n\}$ is a basis of V and $M_{\mathcal{B}}(T) = \begin{bmatrix} M_{\mathcal{C}}(T) & 0 \\ 0 & M_{\mathcal{D}}(T) \end{bmatrix} = \begin{bmatrix} \lambda I_k & 0 \\ 0 & \mu I_{n-k} \end{bmatrix}$ is diagonal.

d) Write $B = \begin{bmatrix} 1 & 1 & 0 \\ 0 & 1 & 0 \\ 0 & 0 & 1 \end{bmatrix}$, $U = \left\{ \begin{bmatrix} r \\ s \\ 0 \end{bmatrix} \mid r,\ s \text{ in } \mathbb{R} \right\}$ and

$W = \left\{ \begin{bmatrix} 0 \\ 0 \\ t \end{bmatrix} \mid t \text{ in } \mathbb{R} \right\}$. Define $T : \mathbb{R}^3 \to \mathbb{R}^3$

by $T(X) = BX$. Then U and W are T-invariant, $U \oplus W = \mathbb{R}^3$, but T is not diagonalizable because its standard matrix B is not diagonalizable.

16. b) If $\mathbf{v}$ is in imS, say $\mathbf{v} = S(\mathbf{w})$, then
$T(\mathbf{v}) = T[S(\mathbf{w})] = (T \circ S)(\mathbf{w}) = (S \circ T)(\mathbf{w}) = S[T(\mathbf{w})]$
is also in imS. Hence imS is T-invariant. If $\mathbf{v}$ is in $kerS$, then
$S[T(\mathbf{v})] = (S \circ T)(\mathbf{v}) = (T \circ S)(\mathbf{v}) = T[S(\mathbf{v})] = T(\mathbf{0}) = \mathbf{0}$.
Hence $T(\mathbf{v})$ is in $kerS$, proving that $kerS$ is T-invariant.

18. b) True. We have $dimU = 1 = dimW$, and the matrix of T restricted to either of them is diagonal (it is 1×1). So T is diagonalizable by Theorem 5.

20. If $U = \mathbb{R}\mathbf{u}$ is T-invariant, $\mathbf{u} \neq \mathbf{0}$, then $T(\mathbf{u})$ is in U, that is $T(\mathbf{u}) = \lambda\mathbf{u}$ for some λ in $\mathbb{R}$. Conversely, if $T(\mathbf{u}) = \lambda\mathbf{u}$, then $T(r\mathbf{u}) = rT(\mathbf{u}) = r\lambda\mathbf{u}$ is in $\mathbb{R}\mathbf{u}$; that is, $\mathbb{R}\mathbf{u} = U$ is T-invariant.

22. Let $T : V \to V$ be an operator where $dimV = 2$. If V is T-reducible, let $V = U \oplus W$ where U and W are both T-invariant. Then $dimU = 1 = dimW$, say $U = \mathbb{R}\mathbf{u}$ and $W = \mathbb{R}\mathbf{w}$. Then $\mathcal{B} = \{\mathbf{u},\ \mathbf{w}\}$ is a basis of eigenvectors of V, so T is diagonalizable by Theorem 4 §5.5.

Conversely, if T is diagonalizable, let $\mathcal{B} = \{\mathbf{u},\ \mathbf{w}\}$ be a basis of eigenvectors. Then both $\mathbb{R}\mathbf{u}$ and $\mathbb{R}\mathbf{w}$ are T-invariant, and $V = \mathbb{R}\mathbf{u} \oplus \mathbb{R}\mathbf{w}$, so V is T-reducible.

24. If $\mathbf{v}$ is in $U \cap W$, then $T(\mathbf{v})$ is in U because U is T-invariant and $\mathbf{v}$ is in U. Similarly $T(\mathbf{v})$ is in W, so $T(\mathbf{v})$ is in $U \cap W$. This shows that $U \cap W$ is T-invariant. Similarly, $U + W$ is T-invariant.

26. b) If A is an $n \times n$ matrix such that $A^2 = I$, define $T : \mathbb{R}^n \to \mathbb{R}^n$ by $T(X) = AX$. Show that $T^2 = 1_{\mathbb{R}^n}$ so, by **a)**, there is a basis $\mathcal{B}$ of $\mathbb{R}^n$ such that $M_\mathcal{B}(T) = \begin{bmatrix} I_m & 0 \\ 0 & -I_k \end{bmatrix}$. Then $A = M_\mathcal{E}(T)$ is the standard matrix of T, and so $A \sim M_\mathcal{B}(T)$ by Theorem 2 §5.3.

5.7 GENERAL INNER PRODUCTS

1.

	b)	d)	f)
P1	True	True	True
P2	True	True	True
P3	True	True	True
P4	False	False	False

2. $\langle \mathbf{v},\ \mathbf{0} \rangle = \langle \mathbf{0},\ \mathbf{v} \rangle = \langle 0\mathbf{v},\ \mathbf{v} \rangle = 0\langle \mathbf{v},\ \mathbf{v} \rangle = 0$.

4. b) If $\langle \_,\ \_ \rangle$ and $\langle \_,\ \_ \rangle_1$ are two inner products, the norm functions are $\|\mathbf{v}\| = \sqrt{\langle \mathbf{v},\ \mathbf{v} \rangle}$ and $\|\mathbf{v}\|_1 = \sqrt{\langle \mathbf{v},\ \mathbf{v} \rangle_1}$. Thus, $\|\mathbf{v}\| = \|\mathbf{v}\|_1$ for every vector $\mathbf{v}$ in V if and only if $\langle \mathbf{v},\ \mathbf{v} \rangle = \langle \mathbf{v},\ \mathbf{v} \rangle_1$ for all $\mathbf{v}$.

6. b) $\langle \delta_k,\ \delta_m \rangle = \Sigma_{i=1}^n \delta_k(i)\delta_m(i)$. If $k \neq m$, then $\delta_k(i)\delta_m(i) = 0$ for every i because one of the factors is zero. If $k = m$, then $\langle \delta_k,\ \delta_k \rangle = \Sigma_{i=1}^n \delta_k(i)^2 = 1$ because exactly one term equals 1, and the rest equal 0.

8. Define $\langle \mathbf{v},\ \mathbf{w} \rangle = C_\mathcal{B}(\mathbf{v}) \cdot C_\mathcal{B}(\mathbf{w})$ for all $\mathbf{v}$ and $\mathbf{w}$ in V. Then $\langle \mathbf{v},\ \mathbf{w} \rangle = \langle \mathbf{w},\ \mathbf{v} \rangle$ because $X \cdot Y = Y \cdot X$ for all X and Y in $\mathbb{R}^n$. Since C is linear, we obtain
$\langle r\mathbf{v},\ \mathbf{w} \rangle = C_\mathcal{B}(r\mathbf{v}) \cdot C_\mathcal{B}(\mathbf{w}) = r[C_\mathcal{B}(\mathbf{v}) \cdot C_\mathcal{B}(\mathbf{w})] = r\langle \mathbf{v},\ \mathbf{w} \rangle$,
and $\langle \mathbf{u},\ \mathbf{v} + \mathbf{w} \rangle = C_\mathcal{B}(\mathbf{u}) \cdot C_\mathcal{B}(\mathbf{v} + \mathbf{w})$
$\qquad = C_\mathcal{B}(\mathbf{u}) \cdot C_\mathcal{B}(\mathbf{v}) + C_\mathcal{B}(\mathbf{u}) \cdot C_\mathcal{B}(\mathbf{w})$
$\qquad = \langle \mathbf{u},\ \mathbf{v} \rangle + \langle \mathbf{u},\ \mathbf{w} \rangle$.
Finally, $\langle \mathbf{v},\ \mathbf{v} \rangle = C_\mathcal{B}(\mathbf{v}) \cdot C_\mathcal{B}(\mathbf{v}) = \|C_\mathcal{B}(\mathbf{v})\|^2 > 0$ if $\mathbf{v} \neq \mathbf{0}$ because $C_\mathcal{B}(\mathbf{v}) \neq \mathbf{0}$ ($C_\mathcal{B}$ is one-to-one).

10. b) Write $b_0 = b_0(x) = 1$, $b_1 = b_1(x) = x$, and $b_2 = b_2(x) = x^2$, and construct the orthogonal basis $e_0 = e_0(x)$, $e_1 = e_1(x)$, and $e_2 = e_2(x)$ using the Gram-Schmidt algorithm. First $e_0 = b_0 = 1$; then
$e_1 = b_1 - \frac{\langle b_1,\ e_0 \rangle}{\|e_0\|^2}e_0 = x - \frac{1/2}{1}1 = x - \frac{1}{2}$;
$e_2 = b_2 - \frac{\langle b_2,\ e_0 \rangle}{\|e_0\|^2}e_0 - \frac{\langle b_2,\ e_1 \rangle}{\|e_1\|^2}e_1$
$\quad = x^2 - \frac{1/3}{1}1 - \frac{1/12}{1/12}(x - \frac{1}{2})$
$\quad = x^2 - x + \frac{1}{6}$.

12. Write $\mathbf{v} = \Sigma_{i=1}^n r_i\mathbf{b}_i$ and $\mathbf{w} = \Sigma_{j=1}^n s_j\mathbf{b}_j$, so that $C_\mathcal{B}(\mathbf{v}) = [r_1 \ r_2 \ \cdots \ r_n]^T$ and $C_\mathcal{B}(\mathbf{w}) = [s_1 \ s_2 \ \cdots \ s_n]^T$. Hence $\langle \mathbf{v},\ \mathbf{w} \rangle = \left\langle \Sigma_{i=1}^n r_i\mathbf{b}_i,\ \Sigma_{j=1}^n s_j\mathbf{b}_j \right\rangle = \Sigma_{i,j} r_i s_j \langle \mathbf{b}_i,\ \mathbf{b}_j \rangle$. But $\langle \mathbf{b}_i,\ \mathbf{b}_j \rangle = 0$ or 1 according as $i \neq j$ or $i = j$, so $\langle \mathbf{v},\ \mathbf{w} \rangle = \Sigma_{i=1}^n r_i s_i = C_\mathcal{B}(\mathbf{v}) \cdot C_\mathcal{B}(\mathbf{w})$.

14. Using the notation in the exercise,
$\langle \mathbf{v},\ \mathbf{v} \rangle = \left\langle \Sigma_{i=1}^n r_i\mathbf{b}_i, \Sigma_{j=1}^n r_j\mathbf{b}_j \right\rangle = \Sigma_{i,j} r_i r_j \langle \mathbf{b}_i,\ \mathbf{b}_j \rangle = \Sigma_{i=1}^n r_i^2$
because $\langle \mathbf{b}_i,\ \mathbf{b}_j \rangle = 0$ or 1 according as $i \neq j$ or $i = j$.

16. If $\mathbf{v}$ is in $(U + W)^\perp$, then $\langle \mathbf{v},\ \mathbf{z} \rangle = 0$ for all $\mathbf{z}$ in $U + W$. Since $U \subseteq U + W$, this shows that $\mathbf{v}$ is in $U^\perp$; similarly $\mathbf{v}$ is in $W^\perp$, so $\mathbf{v}$ is in $U^\perp \cap W^\perp$. Thus $(U + W)^\perp \subseteq U^\perp \cap W^\perp$. On the other hand, if $\mathbf{v}$ is in $U^\perp \cap W^\perp$, then $\mathbf{v}$ is in $U^\perp$ so $\langle \mathbf{v},\ \mathbf{u} \rangle = 0$ for all $\mathbf{u}$ in U. Similarly $\langle \mathbf{v},\ \mathbf{w} \rangle = 0$ for all $\mathbf{w}$ in W, so $\langle \mathbf{v},\ \mathbf{u} + \mathbf{w} \rangle = \langle \mathbf{v},\ \mathbf{u} \rangle + \langle \mathbf{v},\ \mathbf{w} \rangle = 0 + 0 = 0$ for all $\mathbf{u} + \mathbf{w}$ in $U + W$. Thus $\mathbf{v}$ is in $(U + W)^\perp$, which proves that $U^\perp \cap W^\perp \subseteq (U + W)^\perp$. This completes the proof.

18. By Theorem 10, $\|\mathbf{v} - proj_{U_2}(\mathbf{v})\| \leq \|\mathbf{v} - \mathbf{u}\|$ for all $\mathbf{u}$ in U_2. If we take $\mathbf{u} = proj_{U_1}(\mathbf{v})$, then $\mathbf{u}$ is in U_1 and $U_1 \subseteq U_2$, so $\mathbf{u}$ is in U_2. The result follows.

19. We must show that $\{\mathbf{b}_1, \cdots, \mathbf{b}_n\}$ is independent for each $n \geq 1$, and we do it by induction on n. If $n = 1$, it is because $\mathbf{b}_1 \neq \mathbf{0}$. If $\{\mathbf{b}_1, \cdots, \mathbf{b}_n\}$ is independent, observe that $\{\mathbf{b}_1, \cdots, \mathbf{b}_n\} \subseteq W_n$ because $\mathbf{b}_i \in W_i \subseteq W_n$ for each $i \leq n$. Since $\mathbf{b}_{n+1} \notin W_n$, it follows that $\{\mathbf{b}_1, \cdots, \mathbf{b}_n, \mathbf{b}_{n+1}\}$ is independent by the Independent lemma (Lemma 1 §5.2). This completes the induction.

20.
$$\langle fh, \ g \rangle = \int_a^b (fh)(x)\, g(x)\, dx$$
$$= \int_a^b [f(x)h(x)] g(x)\, dx$$
$$= \int_a^b f(x)[h(x)g(x)]\, dx$$
$$= \int_a^b f(x)[(hg)(x)]\, dx$$
$$= \langle f, \ hg \rangle.$$

22. a) $\|\mathbf{v}\| = \sqrt{\langle \mathbf{v}, \ \mathbf{v} \rangle} \geq 0$ for all $\mathbf{v}$ because $\langle \mathbf{v}, \ \mathbf{v} \rangle \geq 0$ by P4 and Theorem 1, and $\sqrt{\ }$ denotes the positive square root. This is (1). Next (2) is (3) of Theorem 1, and (4) is the triangle inequality (Theorem 3). Finally, $\|r\mathbf{v}\| = \sqrt{\langle r\mathbf{v}, \ r\mathbf{v} \rangle} = \sqrt{r^2 \langle \mathbf{v}, \ \mathbf{v} \rangle} = \sqrt{r^2}\sqrt{\langle \mathbf{v}, \mathbf{v} \rangle} = |r|\,\|\mathbf{v}\|$. This is (3).

b) Here, (1) is clear because $|x| \geq 0$ for all x; (2) is because $|x| = 0$ if and only if $x = 0$; (3) is because $|rx| = |r|\,|x|$ for all r and x; and (4) is because $|x + y| \leq |x| + |y|$ for all real numbers x and y. Hence this is a norm on $\mathbb{R}^2$.

Suppose that $\|\_\|$ arises from an inner product $\langle \_, \ \_ \rangle$ on $\mathbb{R}^2$. Then Theorem 2 shows that there is a positive definite matrix $P = \begin{bmatrix} a & b \\ b & c \end{bmatrix}$ such that

$\langle X, \ Y \rangle = X^T P Y$ for all X, Y in $\mathbb{R}^2$. Writing $X = [x \ \ y]^T$, this means that

$$(|x| + |y|)^2 = [x \ \ y]\, P \begin{bmatrix} x \\ y \end{bmatrix} = ax^2 + 2bxy + cy^2 \text{ for all } x \text{ and } y \text{ in } \mathbb{R}.$$

Taking $[x \ \ y]^T = [1 \ \ 0]^T$, $[0 \ \ 1]^T$, and $[1 \ \ 1]^T$ gives respectively, $a = 1$, $c = 1$, and $b = 1$. But then $(|x| + |y|)^2 = x^2 + 2xy + y^2 = (x + y)^2$ for all x and y, a contradiction (take $x = 1$ and $y = -1$).

24. Taking $m = 5$ in Theorem 12 gives
$$p_6 = \tfrac{11}{6}p_5 - \tfrac{5}{6}p_4$$
$$= \tfrac{11}{6}x \cdot \tfrac{1}{8}(63x^5 - 70x^3 + 15x) - \tfrac{5}{6} \cdot \tfrac{1}{8}(35x^4 - 30x^2 + 3)$$
$$= \tfrac{1}{48}(693x^6 - 945x^4 + 315x^2 - 15)$$
$$= \tfrac{1}{16}(231x^6 - 315x^4 + 105x^2 - 5).$$

Then taking $m = 6$ gives
$$p_7 = \tfrac{1}{16}(429x^7 - 693x^5 + 315x^3 - 35x).$$

26. We prove that $p_m(-1) = (-1)^m$ by induction on $m \geq 0$. It holds for $m = 0$ because $p_0 = 1 = (-1)^0$ and $p_1(-1) = -1 = (-1)^1$. If it holds for $m - 1$ and m, Theorem 12 (with $x = -1$) gives

$$p_{m+1}(-1) = \tfrac{1}{m+1}\left\{ (2m+1)(-1)p_m(-1) - mp_{m-1}(-1) \right\}$$
$$= \tfrac{1}{m+1}\left\{ (2m+1)(-1)^{m+1} - m(-1)^{m-1} \right\}$$
$$= \tfrac{(-1)^{m+1}}{m+1}\left\{ (2m+1) - m \right\} = (-1)^{m+1}$$

where we used the fact that $(-1)^{m-1} = (-1)^{m+1}$ for every integer m.